RN

N

APPLIED NONLINEAR PROGRAMMING

Applied Nonlinear Programming

David M. Himmelblau

The University of Texas, Austin, Texas

McGRAW-HILL BOOK COMPANY

New York St. Louis San Francisco Düsseldorf Johannesburg Kuala Lumpur
London Mexico Montreal New Delhi Panama
Rio de Janeiro Singapore Sydney Toronto

Applied Nonlinear Programming

Library of Congress Catalog Card Number 76-148127
07-028921-2

567890DODO798

This book was set in Times New Roman, and was printed and bound by R. R. Donnelley & Sons Company. The designer was Paula Tuerk. The editors were B. J. Clark and Madelaine Eichberg. John A. Sabella supervised production.

Contents

Preface

The purpose of this book is to describe as simply as possible and evaluate several of the more effective methods of nonlinear programming. Even though quite a number of algorithms have been proposed for the solution of the general nonlinear programming problem, only a few have been demonstrated to be effective when applied to large-scale problems. None of the algorithms has proved to be so superior that it can be classified as a universal panacea for nonlinear programming problems.

This book aims to describe current techniques as they are used rather than to provide mathematical proofs that the nonlinear programming algorithms converge under certain types of problem formulations. Although these proofs are important, they apply only to severely restricted categories of problems, and hence serve best as background information for the user of an algorithm. In contrast to linear programming, even if a particular strategy does not readily yield a convergence proof, the strategy may be effective. The reverse is also true, namely, that a guarantee of convergence for an algorithm for special cases may offer little insight as regards satisfactory strategies for more complex problems.

Only nonlinear programming algorithms that have been demonstrated in practice to be somewhat effective are described extensively. Some algorithms are much better than others, in senses to be defined in more detail in the text, and an evaluation of the respective codes is carried out in as much detail as feasible. Among the criteria used in comparing the codes are:

1. Reliability (success in achieving a solution)
2. Speed of solution
3. Preparation time by the user
4. Accuracy of the solution
5. Degree of satisfaction of the constraints

The techniques considered are designed to optimize a nonlinear function subject to nonlinear equality and/or inequality constraints all of which are functions of a large number of variables. All the variables are deterministic in contrast to random or stochastic variables. The subject treated does not include integer or fractional programming nor the optimization of dynamic problems, i.e., those in which time is a parameter. All the methods to be covered are operational only with the aid of large-sized high-speed digital or hybrid computers; the use of analog computers is not considered.

No attempt has been made to cover the individual optimization techniques in great depth, but sufficient details have been provided to enable the reader to follow the essential steps in each method. However, it has often been observed that subtle details in the coding of an algorithm, especially in the frequently used steps, have a significant influence on the performance of the algorithm. Detailed worked examples following each section illustrate the computation aspects of the algorithms, and a large number of information flow charts are given to illustrate the logic. Appendix B contains several computer codes for the better algorithms not readily available in the open literature or from commercial organizations. Because a uniform notation has been employed for all the algorithms, much more insight is obtained into their structural relationships to one another and their common features than can be obtained from a review of the pertinent literature.

Like Gaul, this book is divided into three parts. Part One comprises the first two chapters. Chapter 1 is a brief introduction, and Chapter 2 describes the general nonlinear programming problem, its formulation, its relation to other types of programming, and the necessary and sufficient conditions for an optimal solution to exist.

Part Two treats unconstrained nonlinear programming algorithms. Chapter 3 describes the gradient, second derivative, and related strategies using derivatives, and Chapter 4 covers search strategies. Chapter 5 evaluates the various unconstrained algorithms.

Part Three describes algorithms for constrained optimization. Chapter 6 treats linearization methods, and Chapter 7 treats penalty function methods. Chapter 8 describes the flexible tolerance technique. The constrained algorithms are evaluated in Chapter 9. Appendix A contains a number of test problems, together with their solutions. Each of the chapters (except for the first) contains additional problems for the reader to solve.

The background necessary to understand the algorithms is a knowledge of calculus, some passing familiarity with matrix and vector notation and manipulations, and a brief acquaintance with the methods of solution of linear programming problems. For those unfamiliar with matrix notation, Appendix C summarizes the essential features used in this book. Some familiarity with Fortran programming is necessary to read the computer codes, but instructions are provided so that they can be applied routinely by a user who merely knows how to punch cards. Such application has proved successful, but of course can lead to pitfalls for the unwary.

Finally, I would like to acknowledge the help of Dr. A. R. Colville, J. Abadie, and M. R. Anderberg; the fine assistance of Dr. Darcy A. Paviani, from whose dissertation Chapter 8 was prepared; and the extensive computational analyses of David C. Stocker and Desmond Bond. All of their efforts made it possible to carry out the evaluation of many of the constrained and unconstrained algorithms.

David M. Himmelblau

APPLIED NONLINEAR PROGRAMMING

Part One

Background information

In Part One the nonlinear programming problem is outlined, its relation to a real physical problem explained, and some of the terminology associated with nonlinear programming defined. In addition, methods of telling whether or not a supposedly optimal solution is indeed optimal are described.

1

Introduction

Throughout history men have employed elaborate rituals to help them reach a decision. They have poured libations, sacrificed animals, read the stars, and watched the flight of birds. They have put their faith in proverbs and rules of thumb devised to take some of the guesswork out of living. Today's management of decision making employs a new and perhaps more scientific ritual, the use of the computer. Unaided, the human mind still cannot possibly weigh the manifold complexities involved in the operation of a business enterprise, the design of a missile, or the routing of traffic. A voluminous bundle of mathematical optimization techniques has evolved to take advantage of the prolific capabilities of digital and hybrid computers. Among these techniques is mathematical programming, of which nonlinear programming is a special case.

Mathematical programming is a term coined by Robert Dorfman about 1950, and now is a generic term encompassing linear programming, integer programming, convex programming, nonlinear programming, network flow theory, dynamic programming, and programming under uncertainty. Nonlinear programming deals with the optimization of nonlinear linear functions subject to linear and/or nonlinear constraints. Typical areas of application are forecasting, production scheduling, inventory control, quality control, maintenance and repairs, process design, accounting procedures, and capital budgeting. No general method exists to solve nonlinear problems in the sense that the simplex algorithm exists to solve optimization problems in which all the functions are linear. Thus, to some extent, nonlinear programming exists as an experimental field of research. It has advanced to date through the proposal and programming of particular algorithms, examination of the results of the application of the algorithms to problems of interest, and the construction of better algorithms based on the experience gained.

The bulk of thc research in the last twenty years in the field of mathematical programming has been concentrated in the area of linear programming. The contributions have been of such a magnitude as to leave the state of the art in excellent shape to resolve most linear programming problems.

On the other hand, many strategies have been suggested to solve nonlinear programming problems, but far more algorithms have been proposed than have been successfully applied. The range of applicability of existing nonlinear programming algorithms is limited. With future improvements in computers and the growing need to represent more accurately the problems of the real world, there is a definite need for more widely applicable methods of solving nonlinear programming problems.

Most real-world problems have several solutions, and some may have an infinite number of solutions. The purpose of optimization is to find the best possible solution among the many potential solutions for a given problem in terms of some effectiveness or performance criterion. A problem which admits of only one solution does not have to be optimized. Optimization can be accomplished by many strategies ranging from quite sophisticated analytical and numerical mathematical procedures to the intelligent application of simple arithmetic. Assuming that the problem to be optimized is defined in some way (it does not have to be in a mathematical form), the various general methods of optimization can be conveniently classified as follows:

1. *Analytical methods* which make use of the classical techniques of differential calculus and the calculus of variations. These methods seek the extremum of a function $f(\mathbf{x})$ by finding the values of $\mathbf{x}$ that cause the derivatives of $f(\mathbf{x})$ with respect to $\mathbf{x}$ to vanish. When the extremum of $f(\mathbf{x})$ is sought in the presence of constraints, techniques such as Lagrange multipliers and constrained variation are used. For the application of analytical methods, the problem to be optimized must be described in mathematical terms, so that the functions and vari-

ables can be manipulated by known rules. For large, highly nonlinear problems, analytical methods prove unsatisfactory, and will not be discussed in this text.

2. *Numerical methods* which use past information to generate better solutions to the optimization problem by means of iterative procedures. Numerical methods can be used to solve problems that cannot be solved analytically, and because practical problems prove tractable to numerical techniques, numerical methods of nonlinear programming are the ones described in this text.

Other general methods that can be effectively employed in optimization but will not be described are:

3. *Graphical methods*, i.e., preparation of a plot of the function to be maximized or minimized as a function of one or more variables. The extremum of the function is obtained directly from the graph by inspection. These methods have the advantage of being elementary and of revealing at once whether or not a solution exists. On the other hand, they are restricted to criteria with only one, or at the most two, independent variables.
4. *Experimental methods*. The extremum of a function may be achieved by direct experimentation on the actual process variables rather than by manipulation of a mathematical description of the process. The results of one experiment are used to decide where to locate the next experiment so as to achieve improved operating results.
5. *Case study methods*. These methods involve evaluating a number of representative solutions for the same problem to determine the best possible solution. Thus the "best" solution obtained by using case studies is likely to be suboptimal.

In the optimization of mathematical representations of real processes, a number of related difficulties are encountered that, for the purposes of discussion, can be placed into two categories. One category concerns the formulation of the mathematical model of the process, and the other, the numerical techniques of solution. We can only mention these difficulties here and indicate, where appropriate in connection with a particular algorithm, how they are resolved.

The mathematical model contains the functions to be treated in the optimization. It goes without further comment that the model should reasonably represent the significant features of the real process if the extremum sought is to be meaningful. Even when this qualification is met, typical difficulties encountered with the model are:

1. The criterion to be optimized may be *insensitive* to changes in the independent (decision) variables, so that no clear-cut extremum can be located.
2. The criterion to be optimized or one or more of the constraints may become *unbounded* in the range of the search for the extremum, or the partial derivatives of the functions in the model may become unbounded. Models with polynomials in the denominator are particularly subject to this hazard, as for example,

$$y = \frac{b_0 + b_1 x_1}{b_2 x_1 + b_3 x_2}$$

in which the function and the first partial derivative of y with respect to x_1,

$$\frac{\partial y}{\partial x_1} = -\frac{-b_0 b_2 + b_1 b_2 - b_1 b_2 x_2 + b_1 b_3 x_2}{(b_2 x_1 + b_3 x_2)^2}$$

become unbounded when $b_2 x_1 = -b_3 x_2$. The way to overcome this difficulty is to suitably restrict the range of the independent variables by adding constraints to the problem or to reformulate the mathematical model.
3. There may be poor *scaling* among the variables. Scaling difficulties can occur, for instance, when one of the terms in the criterion is of a much different order of magnitude than another in view of the significant figures in each term. Then the criterion is insensitive to changes in the values of the variables in the small term. For example, the value of an objective function

$$y = 100x_1^2 - 0.010x_2^2$$

would be unaffected by changes in x_2 unless x_2, because of its physical units, were much greater than x_1. If x_2 were of the same magnitude as x_1, one or both variables could be multiplied by scaling factors which converted the two terms on the right-hand side of the equation to roughly equal magnitude. Let

$$\tilde{x}_1 = 10x_1 \qquad x_1^2 = 10^{-2}\tilde{x}_1^2$$

$$\tilde{x}_2 = 10^{-1}x_2 \qquad x_2^2 = 10^2\tilde{x}_2^2$$

Then the terms in the objective function become of the same order of magnitude. After the extremum was found for

$$y = \tilde{x}_1^2 - \tilde{x}_2^2$$

the values of x_1 and x_2 could be determined from the values of $\tilde{x}_1$ and $\tilde{x}_2$. Of course, it is not always so easy to rescale the functions in a mathematical model as just illustrated.

4. There may be *interaction* among the variables in a poorly designed mathematical model. Parameter interaction can be illustrated by examining an extremely simple criterion in which two parameters are multiplied by each other:

$$y = 2x_1x_2 + 10$$

The individual values of x_1 and x_2 can range over any series of values for a given value of the product x_1x_2. Scaling is more difficult if interaction exists. Quadratic functions can be transformed to canonical form so that the interaction term is removed.* New coordinate axes are defined, termed *principal axes*, about which the quadratic surface is symmetric. For example, the surface

$$y = 7x_1^2 + 6x_2^2 + 5x_3^2 - 4x_1x_2 - 4x_2x_3 - 6x_1 - 24x_2 + 18x_3 + 18$$

can be transformed to

$$y - 18 = 3\tilde{x}_1^2 + 6\tilde{x}_2^2 + 9\tilde{x}_3^2$$

by a translation of origin and rotation of axes. In the new coordinate system, the scaling of each term is decidely clearer than in the original coordinate system. Nonlinear functions become quadratic functions only if the model is modified by some suitable transformation or approximated by expansion in a truncated Taylor series. A more subtle example, but one just as vulnerable to interaction among the variables, involves a model such as

$$y = x_1e^{b_1x_2}$$

in which x_1 multiplies $e^{b_1x_2}$.

5. The *null effect* may exist in the mathematical model. The null effect can be illustrated by using the following criterion:

$$y = x_1^2 + 2x_1x_2 + x_2^2 + 2$$
$$= (x_1 + x_2)^2 + 2$$

After the transformation $x_1 + x_2 = \tilde{x}_1$ is made, we find

$$y = \tilde{x}_1^2 + 2$$

Observe that only one variable is left, $\tilde{x}_1$, that need be varied to find the extremum of y.

The second category of difficulties is related to the numerical techniques of solution of the optimization problem.

1. How can suitable initial guesses for the independent variables be obtained? Because the problem contains nonlinear functions, more than one extremum may exist, a feature absent from linear analysis. Consequently, if the initial guesses for the variables are too far away from the extremum, the optimization may not terminate at the global (best) extremum, but at some other extremum. Often approximate optimal values of the independent variables will be known from earlier studies or from physical reasoning. The ultimate resort is to try several starting vectors in the feasible range and ascertain whether or not they all yield the same value of the criterion at the extremum, but there are hazards in this approach, as can be seen from the comments made in connection with the difficulties in forming a suitable model.
2. How can the stochastic (random) nature of real variables be handled? We ignore in this text the very real possibility that the coefficients and variables in the mathematical model may be random variables.
3. How can the numerical computational errors be reduced? Errors in truncating functions reduce the effectiveness of many algorithms. Stability is concerned with whether the solution of approximating nonlinear programming problems converges in the limit to the solution of the original problem. Roundoff error also can play a troublesome role in optimization, particularly when derivatives are approximated by difference schemes.

Like all mathematical tools, nonlinear programming techniques cannot be blindly applied to a given problem without some forethought. Like all artisans' tools, the use of nonlinear programming requires some skill on the part of the user. There is no avoidance of the requirements that the mathematical model be carefully designed, and that appropriate numerical procedures be employed.

The remaining chapters in this book are, essentially, divided into three parts. First, the nonlinear programming problem and its evolution is described. Next, techniques of unconstrained nonlinear programming are described and compared. Finally, practical algorithms for constrained nonlinear programming are presented and evaluated. The appendixes contain a number of test problems and their solutions, as well as some of the computer codes for nonlinear programming algorithms not available commercially.

2

The nonlinear programming problem and its optimal solution

In engineering, economics, and the physical sciences, as well as in other fields, the analyst is frequently faced with the problem of optimizing complex arrangements of equipment, operations, circuits, or processes. He wishes to minimize or maximize some function, termed the *objective function*, representing cost, weight, throughput, or the like, subject to certain constraints. When formulated as mathematical statements, a broad class of these optimization problems can be grouped together into a category termed the *nonlinear programming problem*; methods of solving such problems are called nonlinear programming. In this chapter we first describe somewhat formally the general nonlinear programming problem and certain special subproblems. Then the relationship between the goal of optimization of a real process and the mathematical representation of the optimization is characterized by means of an example. Next, certain definitions and terminology are briefly outlined, and finally, the conditions for optimality are described.

2.1 THE LINEAR PROGRAMMING PROBLEM

A linear programming problem is one in which a *linear* function is the criterion to be minimized or maximized, a criterion subject to constraints that are also *linear* functions. A combination of scalars or vectors denoted in general by X_i is said to be *linear* if the scalars or vectors can be assembled in the form

$$c_1X_1 + c_2X_2 + \cdots + c_nX_n \tag{2.1-1}$$

where the c's are constants. For example, the following function is linear in the variables x_1, x_2, and x_3:

$$4x_1 + 3x_2 + 5x_3 + 2$$

whereas the following function is nonlinear in the same variables:

$$2x_1^2 + x_1x_2 + 3e^{x_3}$$

The X's are said to be *linearly dependent* if, for some set of c_i's (assuming the c_i's are not all zero), the following is true:

$$c_1X_1 + c_2X_2 + \cdots + c_nX_n = \sum_{i=1}^{n} c_iX_i = 0 \tag{2.1-2}$$

On the other hand, if $\sum_{i=1}^{n} c_iX_i = 0$ only if the c_i's are all zero, the X's are said to be *linearly independent*.

Linear programming has flourished since World War II, drawing the attention of many mathematicians, economists, and engineers because of its widespread practical applications as well as its mathematical elegance. Fruitful applications have been demonstrated in the areas of:

1. Optimal routing for air transport
2. Time-phased distribution of supply from factories and depots to bases
3. Allocation of electronic equipment to naval vessels
4. Production scheduling
5. Contract awards
6. Communications system design and message routing
7. Personnel assignment
8. Maximal flows in transportation networks
9. Gasoline blending

To some extent the publicity attracted to linear programming has distorted its significance, for it is applicable only when the underlying hypotheses are

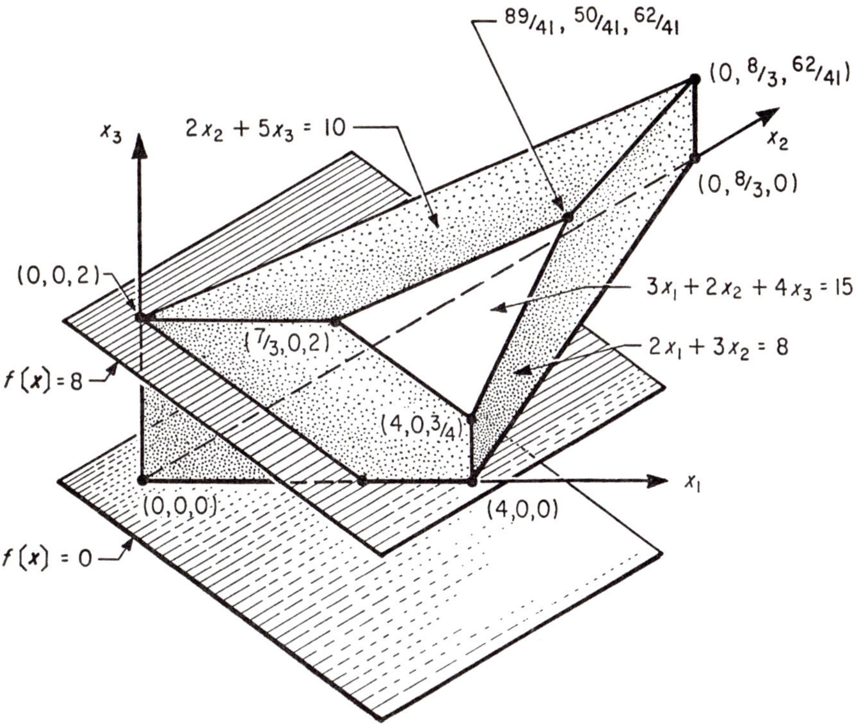

Fig. 2.1-1 Geometric representation of the functions in a linear programming problem.

satisfied, and these are predicated on a linear mathematical representation of the real world. Nonlinear programming avoids such drastic simplifications.

Although the linear programming problem can be stated in many related forms, we will write it as follows:[1]

$$\text{Minimize:} \quad y = \sum_{i=1}^{n} c_i x_i \tag{2.1-3a}$$

$$\text{Subject to:} \quad \sum_{i=1}^{n} a_{ij} x_i - b_j \geq 0 \qquad j = 1, \ldots, m \tag{2.1-3b}$$

$$x_i \geq 0 \qquad i = 1, \ldots, n \tag{2.1-3c}$$

where the a's, b's, and c's are constants, and the x's are the variables whose values are sought. Various methods have been proposed to solve the problem posed by Eqs. (2.1-3), references for which can be found at the end of

[1] G. B. Dantzig, "Linear Programming and Extension," Princeton University Press, Princeton, N.J., 1963; D. J. Wilde and C. S. Beightler, "Foundations of Optimization," Prentice-Hall, Inc., Englewood Cliffs, N.J., 1967.

this chapter. It is assumed that the reader is familiar with the revised simplex method of solution. Figure 2.1–1 is a geometric representation of the bounding planes for a typical linear programming problem, specifically:

$$\begin{aligned}
\text{Maximize:}\quad & y = 3x_1 + 5x_2 + 4x_3 \\
\text{Subject to:}\quad & 2x_1 + 3x_2 \leq 8 \\
& 2x_2 + 5x_3 \leq 10 \\
& 3x_1 + 2x_2 + 4x_3 \leq 15
\end{aligned}$$

for nonnegative values of x_1, x_2, and x_3. The objective function is illustrated by two plane surfaces of increasing value. In the form of expressions (2.1–3) the problem can be restated as

$$\begin{aligned}
\text{Minimize:}\quad & -y = -(3x_1 + 5x_2 + 4x_3) \\
\text{Subject to:}\quad & -(2x_1 + 3x_2) + 8 \geq 0 \\
& -(2x_2 + 5x_3) + 10 \geq 0 \\
& -(3x_1 + 2x_2 + 4x_3) + 15 \geq 0 \\
& x_1 \geq 0 \qquad x_2 \geq 0 \qquad x_3 \geq 0
\end{aligned}$$

An example will illustrate how the mathematical statements in the linear programming problem are prepared from the available information.

Example 2.1–1 Formulation of a linear programming problem

This example illustrates the relation between Eqs. (2.1–3) and a real problem. A truckline has borrowed \$600,000 to spend on new equipment and is contemplating three kinds of trucks. Truck *A* costs \$10,000, truck *B* \$20,000, and truck *C* \$23,000. How many trucks of each kind should be ordered to obtain the greatest capacity in ton-miles per day based on the following data?

Truck *A* requires one driver per shift, a maximum of three shifts per day, and produces 2100 ton-miles per shift.

Truck *B* requires two drivers per shift, a maximum of three shifts per day, and produces 3600 ton-miles per shift.

Truck *C* requires two drivers per shift, a maximum of three shifts per day, and produces 3780 ton-miles per shift.

There is a limit of 30 trucks and 145 drivers.

The problem can be formulated as a linear programming problem as follows. Because there are three possible shifts for each truck, we will represent the shifts by the subscripts 1, 2, and 3, and the number of trucks of each type by the capital letters *A*, *B*, and *C*. First the criterion for optimization is selected; in this example the criterion is the profit function corresponding to function (2.1–3*a*).

$$
\begin{aligned}
y = {} & 2100A_1 + 4200A_2 + 6300A_3 \\
& + 3600B_1 + 7200B_2 + 10{,}800B_3 \\
& + 3780C_1 + 7560C_2 + 11{,}340C_3
\end{aligned}
$$

where y is the number of ton-miles. Second, the constraints are written. There are three types of constraints—one the limiting total cost of \$600,000, one the maximum number of trucks, 30, and the third the maximum number of drivers, 145:

$$
\begin{aligned}
&\textit{Cost:} && 10{,}000\,(A_1 + A_2 + A_3) + 20{,}000\,(B_1 + B_2 + B_3) \\
& && \quad + 23{,}000\,(C_1 + C_2 + C_3) \leq 600{,}000 \\
&\textit{Trucks:} && A_1 + A_2 + A_3 + B_1 + B_2 + B_3 + C_1 + C_2 + C_3 \leq 30 \\
&\textit{Drivers:} && A_1 + 2A_2 + 3A_3 + 2B_1 + 4B_2 + 6B_3 + 2C_1 + 4C_2 + 6C_3 \leq 145
\end{aligned}
$$

In addition, since trucks are physical objects and cannot be negative, the inequalities corresponding to (2.1–3c) are

$$
\begin{aligned}
A_i &\geq 0 \\
B_i &\geq 0 \qquad i = 1, 2, 3 \\
C_i &\geq 0
\end{aligned}
$$

The problem as posed may be solved by a suitable linear programming technique to find the numbers of trucks of types A, B, and C that maximize y, the ton-miles. The answer is 12 of type A, 0 of type B, and 18 of type C.

Matrix notation provides a compact way of stating mathematical programming problems and describing algorithms for their solution. Appendix C summarizes some of the background information relative to matrices for the reader who has not previously encountered this type of notation. We will let $\mathbf{x}$ and $\mathbf{c}$ be $n \times 1$ column vectors in E^n (e.g., in the n-dimensional euclidean space composed of the variables), $\mathbf{a}$ be an $n \times m$ matrix of constants, and $\mathbf{b}$ be an $m \times 1$ column vector.

$$
\mathbf{x} = \begin{bmatrix} x_1 \\ x_2 \\ \cdot \\ \cdot \\ \cdot \\ x_n \end{bmatrix}
\qquad
\mathbf{a} = \begin{bmatrix} a_{11} & a_{12} & \cdots & a_{1m} \\ a_{21} & a_{22} & \cdots & a_{2m} \\ \cdots & \cdots & \cdots & \cdots \\ a_{n1} & a_{n2} & \cdots & a_{nm} \end{bmatrix}
\qquad
\mathbf{b} = \begin{bmatrix} b_1 \\ b_2 \\ \cdot \\ \cdot \\ \cdot \\ b_m \end{bmatrix}
\qquad
\mathbf{c} = \begin{bmatrix} c_1 \\ c_2 \\ \cdot \\ \cdot \\ \cdot \\ c_n \end{bmatrix}
$$

Then the equivalent of Eqs. (2.1–3) in matrix notation is

$$
\begin{aligned}
&\text{Minimize:} && y \equiv f(\mathbf{x}) = \mathbf{c}^T\mathbf{x} && \text{(2.1–4}a\text{)} \\
&\text{Subject to:} && \mathbf{a}^T\mathbf{x} \geq \mathbf{b} && \text{(2.1–4}b\text{)} \\
& && \mathbf{x} \geq \mathbf{0} && \text{(2.1–4}c\text{)}
\end{aligned}
$$

where the superscript T denotes transpose. A vector $\mathbf{x}^*$ satisfying expressions (2.1–4) is the desired solution.

2.2 THE GENERAL NONLINEAR PROGRAMMING PROBLEM

In the broadest sense, the general nonlinear problem is to find an extremum of an objective function subject to equality and/or inequality constraints. The constraints may be linear and/or nonlinear. However, it is customary to be somewhat more restrictive in talking about the general nonlinear programming problem, and to exclude specifically from consideration the following special cases:

1. The variables are restricted to integer values (nonlinear integer programming).
2. The constraints involve the parameter time in the form of differential equations (optimal control; dynamic optimization).

We will let the continuous functions $f(\mathbf{x})$ denote the objective function, $h_1(\mathbf{x}), \ldots, h_m(\mathbf{x})$ denote the equality constraints, and $g_{m+1}(\mathbf{x}), \ldots, g_p(\mathbf{x})$ denote the inequality constraints, where $\mathbf{x} = [x_1, \ldots, x_n]^T$ is a column vector of components $x_1, \ldots, x_n$, in the n-dimensional euclidean space.

As in linear programming, the variables $x_1, x_2, \ldots, x_n$ may be design parameters, controller adjustments, instrument readings, etc., while the objective function may represent cost, weight, revenue, and so forth, and the constraints represent the technical requirements, operating conditions, flow capacities, or safety factors inherent in the process.

The nonlinear programming problem can be formally stated as

$$\text{Minimize:} \quad f(\mathbf{x}) \qquad \mathbf{x} \in E^n \tag{2.2-1}$$

subject to m linear and/or nonlinear equality constraints

$$h_j(\mathbf{x}) = 0 \qquad j = 1, \ldots, m \tag{2.2-2}$$

and $(p - m)$ linear and/or nonlinear inequality constraints

$$g_j(\mathbf{x}) \geq 0 \qquad j = m + 1, \ldots, p \tag{2.2-3}$$

Although in some special cases the equality constraints can be explicitly solved for selected variables and those variables eliminated from the problem as independent variables, reducing the problem to one with inequality constraints only, most often the equality constraints can be solved only implicitly and must be retained.

An alternative representation of expressions (2.2–1) through (2.2–3) sometimes encountered is

$$\text{Minimize:} \quad \{f(\mathbf{x}) \mid \mathbf{x} \in R\} \tag{2.2–4}$$

where R is the domain of $\mathbf{x}$ for which conditions (2.2–2) and (2.2–3) are satisfied, e.g.,

$$R = \{\mathbf{x} \mid h_j(\mathbf{x}) = 0; \, g_j(\mathbf{x}) \geq 0 \qquad \text{for all } j\} \tag{2.2–5}$$

The inequality sign in $g_j(\mathbf{x}) \geq 0$ can be reversed by multiplying through by -1 without changing the mathematical statement of the problem.

As a simple example of a nonlinear programming problem that can be illustrated graphically, we can write

$$\begin{aligned} \text{Minimize:} \quad & f(\mathbf{x}) = x_1^2 + x_2^2 + 2x_2 \\ \text{Subject to:} \quad & h_1(\mathbf{x}) = x_1^2 + x_2^2 - 1 \quad = 0 \\ & g_2(\mathbf{x}) = x_1 + 2x_2 - 0.5 \geq 0 \\ & g_3(\mathbf{x}) = x_1 \geq 0 \qquad g_4(\mathbf{x}) = x_2 \geq 0 \end{aligned}$$

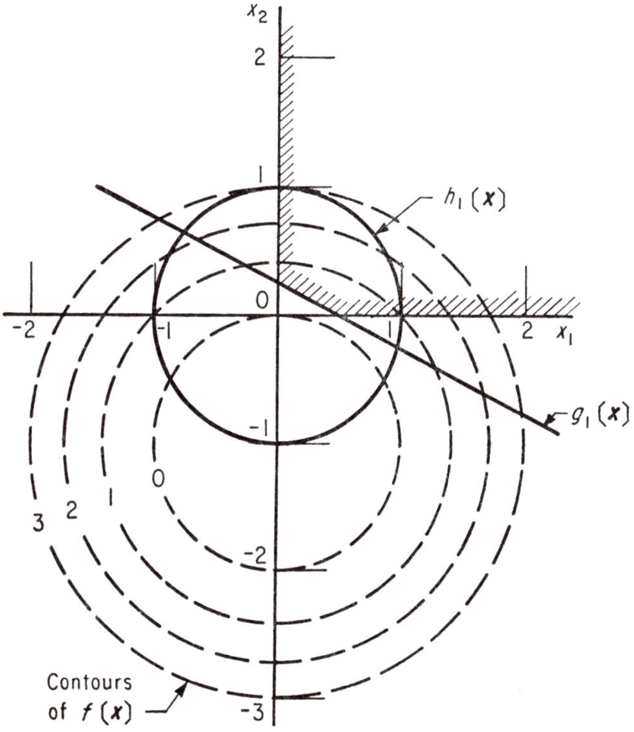

Fig. 2.2–1 Geometric representation of the functions in a nonlinear programming problem.

In Fig. 2.2–1, the objective function is depicted by dashed lines, the equality constraint by a solid heavy line, and the boundary of the region formed by the inequality constraints designated by the shaded lines (with the shading in the interior of the region).

For each point $\mathbf{x}$ of the n-dimensional space of variables $x_1, x_2, \ldots, x_n$ the function $f(\mathbf{x})$ has a particular value, and as a consequence, the n-dimensional space is a scalar field for the optimality criterion. A family of contours (equipotential hypersurfaces) can be drawn in the space corresponding to specific values of $f(\mathbf{x})$ as indicated in Fig. 2.2–1. The space of variables $x_1, x_2, \ldots, x_n$ is also a scalar field for the constraint functions and equations, and equipotential hypersurfaces for these bounding functions can also be drawn. In general, it is not possible to ascertain beforehand by classical calculus the location of the vector $\mathbf{x}^*$ that yields the minimum (or maximum) value of $f(\mathbf{x})$, for $\mathbf{x}^*$ may be located on the intersection of the constraint surfaces or within it.

The linear and the *quadratic programming* problems can be considered to be two special cases of the general nonlinear programming problem. When the function (2.2–1) and the equalities (2.2–2) and inequalities (2.2–3) are all linear, one obtains a linear programming problem. If the objective function is quadratic and the constraints are linear, one obtains the quadratic programming problem

$$\text{Minimize:} \quad f(\mathbf{x}) = a_0 + \mathbf{c}^T\mathbf{x} + \mathbf{x}^T\mathbf{Q}\mathbf{x} \tag{2.2–6a}$$

$$\text{Subject to:} \quad \mathbf{a}^T\mathbf{x} \geq \mathbf{b} \tag{2.2–6b}$$

$$\mathbf{x} \geq \mathbf{0} \tag{2.2–6c}$$

where $\mathbf{Q}$ is a positive definite or semidefinite symmetric square matrix, and $\mathbf{a}$ and $\mathbf{b}$ are coefficient matrices previously defined in connection with Eq. (2.1–4). Positive definite matrices are defined in Appendix C. Sometimes linear equality constraints are included as part of the quadratic programming problem

$$\acute{\mathbf{a}}^T\mathbf{x} = \acute{\mathbf{b}} \tag{2.2–6d}$$

An example of a quadratic programming problem is

$$\begin{aligned}
\text{Minimize:} \quad & f(\mathbf{x}) = 0.5x_1^2 + 0.5x_2^2 - x_1 - 2x_2 \\
\text{Subject to:} \quad & g_1(\mathbf{x}):\ 6 - 2x_1 - 3x_2 \geq 0 \\
& g_2(\mathbf{x}):\ 5 - x_1 - 4x_2 \geq 0 \\
& g_3(\mathbf{x}):\ x_1 \geq 0 \\
& g_4(\mathbf{x}):\ x_2 \geq 0
\end{aligned}$$

In all three classes of problems—nonlinear, linear, and quadratic—one wants to find the vector $\mathbf{x}^* = [x_1^*, \ldots, x_n^*]^T$ that minimizes (or alternatively, maximizes) $f(\mathbf{x})$ under conditions such that $h_j(\mathbf{x}) = 0, j = 1, \ldots, m$, and $g_j(\mathbf{x}) \geq 0, j = m + 1, \ldots, p$.

2.3 RELATION OF THE NONLINEAR PROGRAMMING PROBLEM TO A REAL PROCESS

In certain optimization problems, such as least squares ("minimize the sum of the squares of the deviations between the observed and predicted response") or the minimization of an integral generated from a variational problem, the nonlinear programming problem statement is easily connected with the physical problem to be solved. But in other cases this is not so. A simple examination of the mathematical statement of a nonlinear programming problem cannot by itself bring out all the factors involved in the optimization of a real process. In this section we briefly review the interaction between the physical problem and its mathematical representation.

In the optimization of a real process the parameters and/or the variables are connected by physical laws, such as the conservation of mass or energy, that must be incorporated in the nonlinear programming problem as equality constraints even if they are only inferred. Thus one group of constraints consists of functional relations that must be taken into account if the optimization is to be physically realizable. A second group of constraints incorporates existing limits on variables or parameters that ensure their physical realizability or compatibility with the process; this second group comprises the inequality constraints. In addition, empirical relations, normally equalities, may be substituted for or added to the constraints. Finally, definitions are often made to simplify the process-model statements, and these comprise additional equality constraints when they cannot be explicitly solved for the defined variable. Figure 2.3–1 illustrates the relationships among the parts of the nonlinear programming problem and nonlinear programming itself.

Each equality constraint absorbs one degree of freedom in the process model and results in one dependent variable being generated. It is usually assumed that the analyst prepares the process-model statements carefully enough so that the equalities are independent, for if by omission or error he includes two redundant or otherwise dependent equations, then the apparent number of degrees of freedom will be different from the actual number. The true residual number of degrees of freedom should correspond to the number of *independent variables* (often termed *decision variables*) in the nonlinear

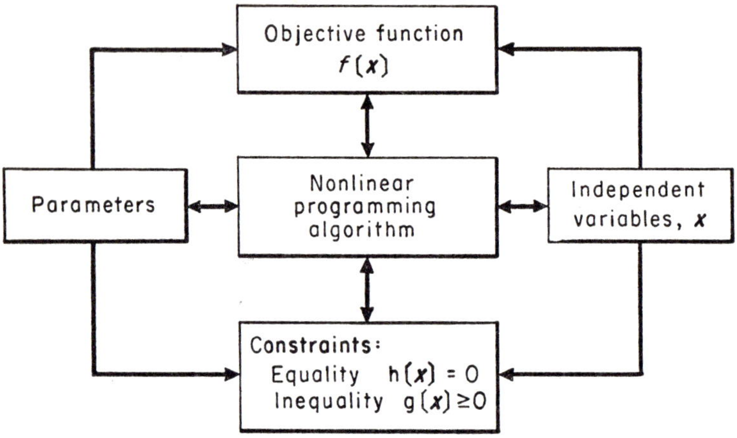

Fig. 2.3–1 Relationships in the nonlinear programming problem and in nonlinear programming.

programming problem. The number of residual degrees of freedom is an important concept in any type of optimization subject to equality constraints, because if the number of variables equals the number of independent equality constraints, no optimization need take place—the values of all the variables can be determined directly from the simultaneous solution of the system of equality constraints, $h_j(\mathbf{x}) = 0, j = 1, \ldots, n$. If the number of variables exceeds the number of independent equality constraints, m, the only type of solution that can be obtained for a process model is to adjust the $(n - m)$ decision variables until an objective function attains its optimum value. If the number of independent equality constraints exceeds the number of variables, optimization is also required, except that in this case the objective function must consist of some type of statistical criterion, such as the one used in least squares.

Because in nonlinear programming problems derived from physical processes it may not be convenient to substitute nonlinear equalities into the objective function and thus eliminate the dependent variables, one or more of the dependent variables in the problem may be treated as a decision variable along with the true independent variables. For example, in the problem

$$\text{Minimize:} \quad f(\mathbf{x}) = x_1^2 - 3x_2^2 + x_1x_2 + x_1x_3 + x_3 + 6$$

$$\text{Subject to:} \quad h_1(\mathbf{x}) = (x_1 - x_2 + 2)^3 - (\sqrt{x_2} + x_3 + 2)^2 = 0$$

$$h_2(\mathbf{x}) = x_1 + x_2 + x_3 + 3 = 0$$

it is quite easy to solve constraint $h_2(\mathbf{x})$ for x_3, eliminate x_3 from $f(\mathbf{x})$ and $h_1(\mathbf{x})$, and eliminate constraint $h_2(\mathbf{x})$, but to solve $h_1(\mathbf{x})$ for either x_1 or x_2

so that one of these variables can be eliminated from the objective function is much more complicated. It usually proves easier, especially if the problem contains several nonlinear equality constraints, to retain $h_1(\mathbf{x})$ as an equality constraint and treat $\mathbf{x}$ as a vector containing two variables for numerical calculations. Nevertheless, the true residual degree of freedom is only one. Some algorithms do take advantage of the reduced number of degrees of freedom, taking into account the equality constraints and active inequality constraints by searching for the optimum in a reduced space.

On eliminating one variable in the objective function by substitution, it is necessary to be careful not inadvertently to change the domain of a variable. For example, if $f(\mathbf{x}) = -x_1^2 + x_2$ and $h(\mathbf{x}) = -x_1^2 - x_2^2 + 1 = 0$, x_2 must be limited to $-1 \leq x_2 \leq 1$, because smaller or larger values of x_2 will yield imaginary values of x_1. Elimination of x_1 by substituting $x_1^2 = 1 - x_2^2$ gives $f(x_2) = f(\mathbf{x}) = x_2 + x_2^2 - 1$, and apparently x_2 is unbounded, whereas in fact the constraints $-1 \leq x_2 \leq 1$ must be added to $f(x_2)$ to render the problem unchanged.

As an illustration of the residual degrees of freedom for $n > m$, consider the problem of finding the volume and dimensions of the largest box when length and girth combined cannot exceed 72 in. (The answer is $V = 24 \times 12 \times 12 = 3456$ in.^{3}.) The problem can be formulated as a maximization problem in which the performance criterion is the volume of the box.

$$\text{Maximize:} \quad f(\mathbf{x}) = x_1 x_2 x_3 \qquad \mathbf{x} \in E^3$$

subject to the conditions imposed on the dimensions *plus the implicit* nonnegativity conditions on the dimensions

$$g_1(\mathbf{x}): \quad 72 - x_1 - 2x_2 - 2x_3 \geq 0$$

$$g_{j+1}(\mathbf{x}): \quad x_j \geq 0 \qquad j = 1, \ldots, 3$$

If one forgets to include the implicit constraints in a problem, a valid mathematical solution may be obtained that bears no correspondence to reality.

Since there are no equality constraints involved, the problem has three residual degrees of freedom, which means that all three variables can be varied independently as long as the inequality constraints are not violated. If an equality constraint is incorporated into the problem, such as to require that the height and width of the box be equal, that is, $h_1(\mathbf{x}) = x_2 - x_3 = 0$, then the problem will have only two residual degrees of freedom. Clearly, in this simple case, one variable, either x_2 or x_3, may be eliminated from the objective function, and the problem becomes one of maximizing the volume by adjusting two independent variables only. However, in more realistic problems, elimination of one variable by substitution into the objective function may not prove feasible. Which specific variables become decision variables and which become dependent variables is somewhat arbitrary, but an analyst will have in mind certain natural decision variables associated with any process model, either the controllable variables or certain mathematically convenient variables.

Example 2.3–1 below formulates portions of a nonlinear programming problem to illustrate how the real world is related to its mathematical representation. Note that the variables are the mechanism through which *information* flows between the objective function and the constraints. Both dependent and decision variables can appear in the objective function.

Example 2.3–1 Modeling and optimization of a blast furnace

The operation of a blast furnace is a familiar and important operation in every large-scale steel mill. In several respects it can be considered typical of a process of industrial significance. There are a relatively large number of important process variables (several of which cannot be measured) that interact in a highly complex manner; there are numerous constraints which must be respected; and the nature of the plant is such that the optimum operating point varies appreciably from time to time. Consequently, a detailed examination of the problem of optimizing the operation of a blast furnace proves instructive in revealing the type and magnitude of the difficulties to be encountered in representing mathematically a typical process.

PROCESS DESCRIPTION

The operation of a blast furnace is semicontinuous. The raw materials are iron ore containing, roughly, 20 to 60 percent iron as oxides and a variety of other metallic and nonmetallic oxides, plus coke, which burns to blast-furnace gas. Apart from the gas, which may serve as a heating medium in other processes, the output of the furnace consists of molten iron, still containing some impurities (notably carbon and phosphorus) that must be removed in the steelmaking process, and slag, containing most of the impurities, which is of little value. The costs of the iron ore and the coke fuel are approximately the same. Operation of the blast furnace calls for selection of the ores, a production rate, and a mode of operation which will maximize the "profit" of the works or minimize the cost of producing the required quantity and quality of molten iron. Figure E2.3–1 shows schematically the flow of materials in the blast furnace, which itself is part of a much larger mill.

Improvement in the performance of this or any process by computational rather than experimental techniques can be accomplished by the following steps:

1. Analysis of the process, in which the important variables and specific characteristics of the problem are defined.

Process	Process Analysis	Mathematical Representation
	Variables and Parameters Route the External Information and Process Information	Decision Variables, Dependent Variables, and Coefficients

Between the Process and Its Mathematical Representation — Between the Objective Function and Process Model

Process diagram inputs: Coke B, Coke A, Ore 1, Ore 2, Ore 3, Cast Iron Scrap; Limestone, Gas Output; Slag, Pig Iron.

Input-Output Variables / Associated Costs and Revenues:

Ore 1: x_1 — Marginal production costs: c_1
Ore 2: x_2 — c_2
etc.

Cast Iron Scrap: x_6 — Market price

Coke A: x_7 — Market price: c_7
Coke B: x_8 — c_8

Pig Iron: F — Market price: c_F

Gas: G — Allocated price: c_G

Objective Function: $f(x)$

$$\text{Minimize: } f[x] = c_1 x_1 + c_2 x_2 + \ldots + c_7 x_7 + c_8 x_8$$

$$+ \cdots + c_{11}\left(\frac{P}{S}\right) + \cdots + c_{12}\left(\frac{Si + Al}{Ca + Mg}\right) + \cdots$$

$$- c_F (F + F^{1.2}) + \cdots - c_G G + \cdots$$

Process Model

Material and Energy Balances:

Metal balance
Slag balance
Gas balance
Energy balance
Elemental balances (O, H, S, Si, etc.)

Equality Constraints: $h_j[x] = 0$ $j = 1, \ldots, m$

$$a_1 x_1 + a_2 x_2 + \ldots + a_3 \frac{Ca + Mg}{Al} + \cdots = 0$$

$$[a_{10} C + a_{11}(H - \tfrac{o}{8}) + a_{12} S] (x_7 + x_8) T_1$$

$$+ a_{13} FT_2 + \cdots \quad = 0 \quad \text{etc.}$$

Process Limits:

Coke quantities
Hot metal production rate
Ore availability
Elements in slag
Elements in metal
"Basicity"
Sales limits

Inequality Constraints: $g_j[x] \leq 0$ $j = m+1, \ldots, p$

$$x_7 \leq a_{30}$$

$$[x_2/(x_1 + x_2 + \ldots)] \leq 0.2$$

$$a_{42} \leq (Ca + Mg)/(Si + Al)$$

etc.

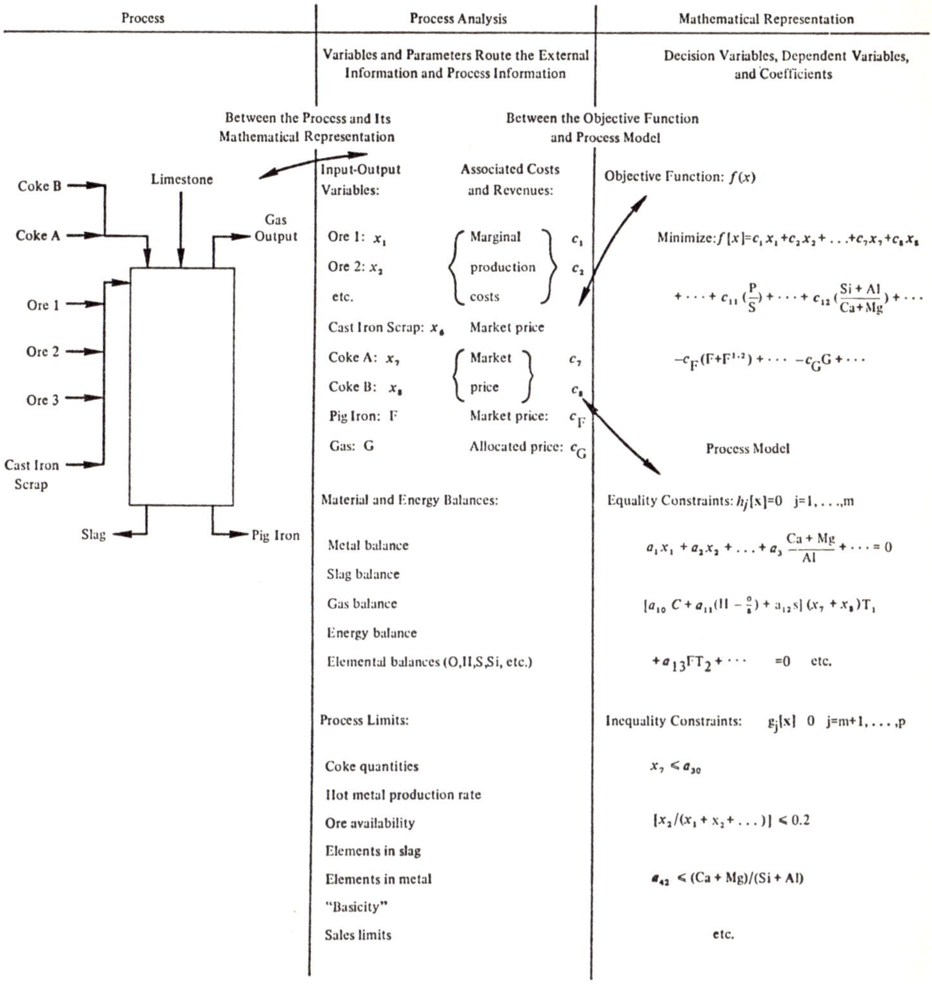

Fig. E2.3-1   Relation between the process and its mathematical representation.

2. Definition of an objective function or performance criterion (profit, operating cost, volume, etc.) and expression of the criterion as a *mathematical function*.
3. Development of a mathematical process *model* that relates the input-output variables and lists the constraints.
4. Application of an optimization procedure to the mathematical formulation of the problem.

Steps 1 through 4 are represented schematically in Fig. E2.3-1. Some of the rationale underlying the equations is as follows.

THE OBJECTIVE FUNCTION

To formulate a cost function as a criterion, two categories of costs have to be considered:

1. Costs associated with the material flows (the input and output variables), such as purchased materials costs less revenue from the sale of by-products
2. Costs associated with process operations, and related to the process variables by analysis or empirical curves

A typical objective function is shown in Fig. E2.3–1.

MATHEMATICAL MODEL

The next step in formulating the problem is to construct a mathematical model of the process by considering the fundamental chemical and physical phenomena which govern it. For the case of the blast furnace, typical considerations are:

1. *Iron ore.* Ores of different grades are available in restricted quantities. Different ores have different percentages of iron and different types and amount of impurities. The proportion of each ore that finds its way into the hot metal is assumed to have a fixed value.
2. *Coke.* The amount of coke that may be burnt in any furnace is effectively limited by the furnace design. The coke-consumption rate can be based on empirical relationships developed through multiple regression.
3. *Ore quality.* A limit has to be placed upon the amount of "hard" ores used. Similarly, a limit must be placed on the amount of fine ore, an excess of which disrupts the flow of gas through the furnace and limits production.
4. *Phosphorus.* All phosphorus in the raw material finds its way into the molten metal. There is an upper limit on the phosphorus permitted, although precise quantities are sometimes prescribed. In general, it is cheaper to produce higher-phosphorus iron, but it is more expensive to refine it.
5. *Other elements.* Calcium, silicon, magnesium, and aluminum oxides become the slag. Two-thirds of all the manganese goes into the hot metal, and there are limits to the permissible quantity. The sulfur in the loading must not exceed 1.6 percent of the total slag weight; otherwise too much sulfur finds its way into the molten metal.
6. *Slag.* For technical reasons, the level of impurities in the slag must be controlled. These take the form of an upper limit on the percentage of magnesium, upper and lower limits on the percentage of silicon and aluminum, and close limits on the "basicity" ratio $(CaO + MgO)/(SiO_2 + Al_2O_3)$.

From these and other factors it is possible to prepare:

1. A set of input and output variables
2. A set of steady-state input-output material and energy balances
3. A set of restrictions on the input and output variables expressing the operating and market limitations

Typical relations are shown in Fig. E2.3–1.

As might be expected, the major shortcomings in forming the nonlinear programming problem are the lack of valid values for the parameters in the material and energy balances; the assumption of steady-state conditions when, in practice, changes in the process take place; the stochastic rather than the deterministic nature of the process variables and parameters; and so forth. However, these are deficiencies in the model-building phase of the analysis rather than in the optimization phase of the analysis, which is the primary concern of this book.

2.4 NOTATION AND TERMINOLOGY

To outline certain aspects of the terminology to be used, a few preliminary remarks are made in this section concerning some of the terms which occur rather frequently in the literature of optimization as well as in this book.

2.4-1 Optimal Solutions

The volumn vector $\mathbf{x}^* = [x_1^*, \ldots, x_n^*]^T$, which satisfies the expressions (2.2–1), (2.2–2), and (2.2–3), is called the *optimal point*, and the corresponding value of $f(\mathbf{x}^*)$ is termed the *optimal value* of the objective function. The pair $\mathbf{x}^*$ and $f(\mathbf{x}^*)$ constitutes an *optimal solution.* Various categories of optimal solutions can exist if the objective function is not *unimodal*, i.e., has one extremum, as illustrated by the multimodal function in Fig. 2.4–1. A global optimal solution represents the smallest value of $f(\mathbf{x})$, whereas a *local*

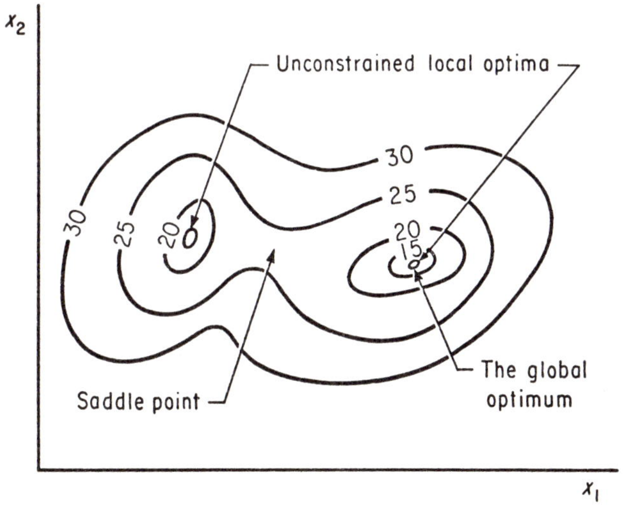

Fig. 2.4–1 Classification of optimal solutions.

(or relative) optimal solution represents the smallest value of $f(\mathbf{x})$ in the vicinity of some $\mathbf{x}$ vector. For both the global and local minimum

$$f(\mathbf{x}^*) \leq f(\mathbf{x})$$

but the global optimal solution refers to all $\mathbf{x}$ in E^n, whereas the local optimal solution refers only to a small region ζ, where $\|\mathbf{x} - \mathbf{x}^*\| < \zeta$. If the precision of the optimal solution is to be taken into account, a more exact condition for the optimal solution is

$$f(\mathbf{x}^*) \leq f(\mathbf{x}) - \gamma$$

where γ is some small number.

All the algorithms to be described in subsequent chapters will yield only locally optimal solutions inasmuch as they depend primarily upon local properties of the objective function and the constraints in converging to $\mathbf{x}^*$. Some of the algorithms, such as the one in Chap. 8, are less likely to terminate at a nonglobal optimum because a wide dispersion of $\mathbf{x}$'s is used in the search, but convergence to a global optimum cannot be guaranteed without advance information about the nature of the objective function and constraints. In practice, the prospect of a local extremum being the global extremum can be tested by using a number of starting vectors, but even if only one local solution is found, it cannot be demonstrated in general that the solution is assuredly the global optimum. Fortunately, for problems based on real processes, the objective function usually is a well-behaved function with a single extremum. Therefore, for most practical purposes, the use of numerical procedures that provide a local solution to the programming problem is not a great disadvantage.

2.4-2 Concavity and Convexity

The concepts of concavity and convexity assist in determining under what conditions a local optimal solution is also the global optimal solution, a matter of some concern in view of what has been said above concerning multiple optima.

A function $\phi(\mathbf{x})$ is called *convex* over the domain of R if for *any* two vectors, $\mathbf{x}_1$ and $\mathbf{x}_2 \in R$,

$$\phi(\theta\mathbf{x}_1 + (1 - \theta)\mathbf{x}_2) \leq \theta\phi(\mathbf{x}_1) + (1 - \theta)\phi(\mathbf{x}_2) \qquad (2.4\text{–}1)$$

where θ is a scalar with the range $0 \leq \theta \leq 1$. The function $\phi(\mathbf{x})$ is *strictly convex* if, for $\mathbf{x}_1 \neq \mathbf{x}_2$, the sign of (2.4–1) may be replaced with the inequality ($<$) sign. (A vector inequality $\mathbf{x} \geq \mathbf{y}$ means $x_i \geq y_i$ for each element; for

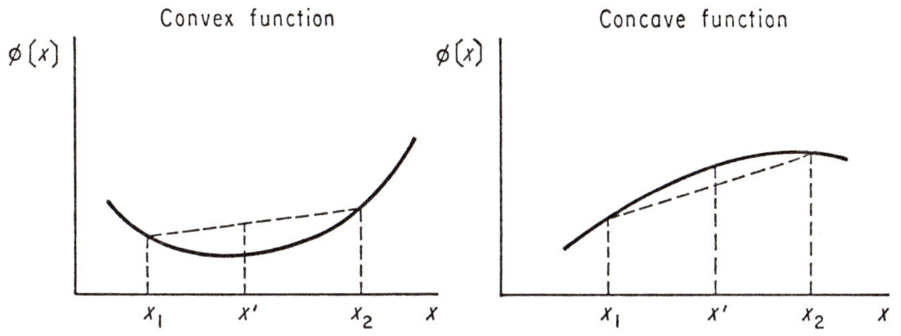

Fig. 2.4-2 Convex and concave functions (in a given range of x).

$\mathbf{x} > \mathbf{y}, x_i > y_i$, for all i.) Other types of convexity are described by Ponstein.[1] The reverse inequalities are analogous. Figure 2.4-2 illustrates geometrically a strictly convex function of one independent variable; a convex function cannot have any value larger than the values of the function obtained by linear interpolation between $\phi(\mathbf{x}_1)$ and $\phi(\mathbf{x}_2)$. If the reverse inequality of (2.4-1) holds, the function is said to be *concave*. Thus a function $\phi(\mathbf{x})$ is *concave* (strictly concave) if $-\phi(\mathbf{x})$ is convex (strictly convex). Linear functions are both convex and concave. A differentiable convex function has the following properties:

(2.4-2)

(*a*) $\phi(\mathbf{x}_2) - \phi(\mathbf{x}_1) \geq \nabla^T\phi(\mathbf{x}_1)(\mathbf{x}_2 - \mathbf{x}_1) \qquad \text{for all } \mathbf{x}_1, \mathbf{x}_2$

(*b*) The matrix of the second partial derivatives of $\phi(\mathbf{x})$ with respect to $\mathbf{x}$ (the hessian matrix) is positive definite (or positive semidefinite) for all $\mathbf{x}$ if $\phi(\mathbf{x})$ is strictly convex (or convex).

(*c*) Over the domain of R, $\phi(\mathbf{x})$ has only one extremum.

The requirement that a function be unimodal is much weaker than the requirement that it be convex or concave, for as Fig. 2.4-3*a* indicates, unimodality demands neither continuity nor the existence of a unique derivative.

A set of points (or region) is defined as a *convex set* in *n*-dimensional space if, for all pairs of two points $\mathbf{x}_1$ and $\mathbf{x}_2$ in the set, the straight-line segment joining them is also entirely in the set. Thus every point $\mathbf{x}$, where

$$\mathbf{x} = \theta\mathbf{x}_1 + (1 - \theta)\mathbf{x}_2 \qquad 0 \leq \theta \leq 1$$

is also in the set. Figure 2.4-4 illustrates a convex and nonconvex set in the

[1] J. Ponstein, *J. SIAM Rev.*, **9**:115 (1967).

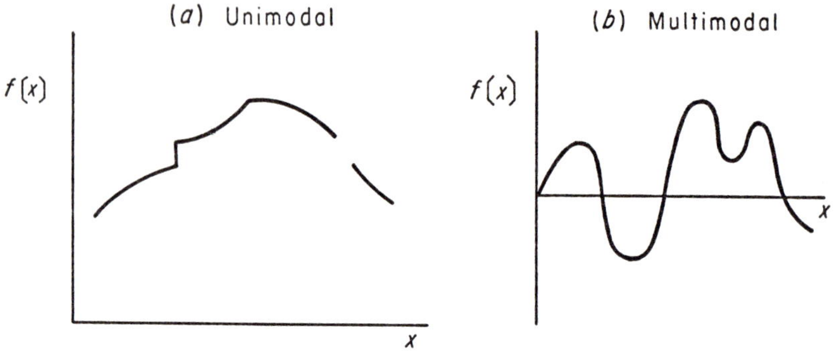

Fig. 2.4–3 Unimodal and multimodal functions.

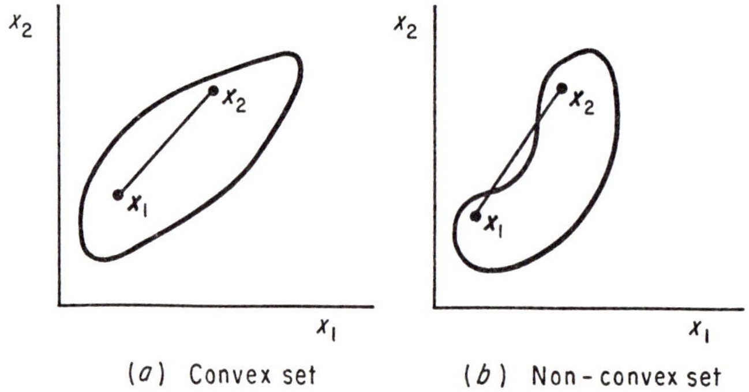

Fig. 2.4–4 Convex and nonconvex sets.

two-dimensional space. As an example, the following general set of expressions form a convex region (possibly empty or unbounded):

$$g_j(\mathbf{x}) \leq b_j$$
$$\mathbf{a}_j^T\mathbf{x} = b_j$$

if the $g_j(\mathbf{x})$ are all convex, as illustrated in Fig. 2.4–5.

An important result in mathematical programming[1] evolves from the concepts of convexity. For the nonlinear programming problem known as the *convex programming problem*,[2]

Minimize: $f(\mathbf{x})$

Subject to: $g_j(\mathbf{x}) \geq 0 \qquad j = 1, \ldots, p$

$$\mathbf{x} \geq \mathbf{0}$$

[1] H. W. Kuhn and A. W. Tucker, Nonlinear Programming, *Proc. 2d Berkeley Symp. on Mathematical Statistics and Programming*, University of California Press, Berkeley, 1951, pp. 481–493.

[2] Sometimes equality constraints $h_j(\mathbf{x}) = 0$ are added to the inequality constraints in the convex programming problem, in which case the $h_j(\mathbf{x})$ must be linear.

in which (1) $f(\mathbf{x})$ is a convex function and (2) each inequality constraint is a concave function (the constraints form a convex set), the following property can be shown to be true: *The local minimum is also the global minimum.* Analogously, a local maximum is the global maximum if the objective function is concave and the constraints form a convex set.

Consider the following problem, the functions for which are illustrated in Fig. 2.4–5.

$$\begin{aligned} \text{Minimize:} \quad & f(\mathbf{x}) = x_1^2 + x_2^2 - 4x_1 + 4 \\ \text{Subject to:} \quad & g_1(\mathbf{x}): \ x_1 - x_2 + 2 \geq 0 \\ & g_2(\mathbf{x}): \ x_1^2 + x_2 - 1 \geq 0 \\ & g_3(\mathbf{x}): \ x_1 \geq 0 \\ & g_4(\mathbf{x}): \ x_2 \geq 0 \end{aligned}$$

By inspection (or analytical means) it can be seen that the constraints form a convex region (shaded in the feasible portion) because constraints $g_1(\mathbf{x})$

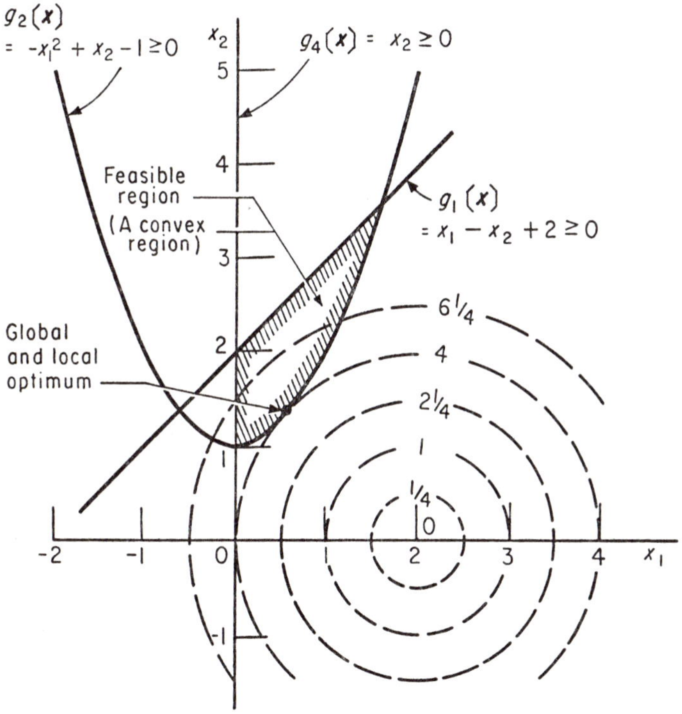

Fig. 2.4–5 A convex programming problem illustrating the feasible region (comprising a convex set) and the global optimum.

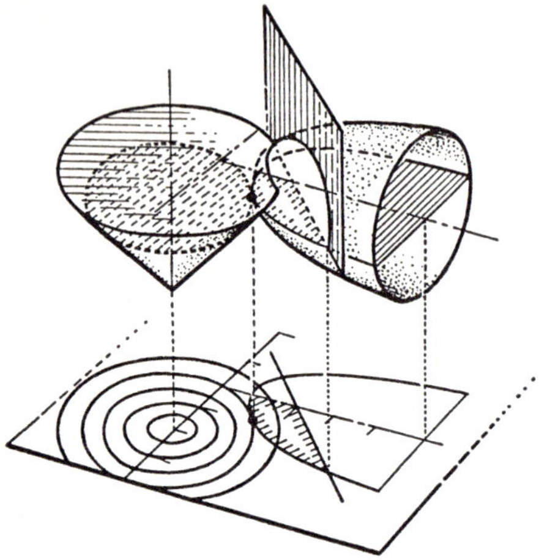

Fig. 2.4-5 *continued*

and $g_3(\mathbf{x})$ (and $g_4(\mathbf{x})$) are linear and hence concave (as well as convex), and constraint $g_2(\mathbf{x})$ is strictly concave. Concavity of $g_2(\mathbf{x})$ can be shown by noting that the hessian matrix of $-g_2(\mathbf{x})$ is positive semidefinite.

$$-\begin{bmatrix} \dfrac{\partial^2 g_2(\mathbf{x})}{\partial x_1^2} & \dfrac{\partial^2 g_2(\mathbf{x})}{\partial x_1\,\partial x_2} \\ \dfrac{\partial^2 g_2(\mathbf{x})}{\partial x_2\,\partial x_1} & \dfrac{\partial^2 g_2(\mathbf{x})}{\partial x_2^2} \end{bmatrix} = -\begin{bmatrix} -2 & 0 \\ 0 & 0 \end{bmatrix} \geq \mathbf{0}$$

The objective function of $f(\mathbf{x})$ is strictly convex, and the local optimum, consequently known to be also the global optimum, is at $\mathbf{x}^* = [0.58 \quad 1.34]^T$, where $f(\mathbf{x}) = 3.80$.

In a linear programming problem having an optimal solution, the objective function is always convex, and the constraints form a convex set, so that the local optimum is always a global optimum. As for the quadratic programming problem, the constraints are the same as for the linear programming problem, and the objective function is convex if $\mathbf{x}^T\mathbf{Q}\mathbf{x}$ is positive semidefinite; hence $\mathbf{Q}$ must be positive semidefinite. However, only in special circumstances can it be shown that the general nonlinear function $f(\mathbf{x})$ is a convex function and the constraints form a convex set. For example, one major difficulty is that nonlinear *equalities* cannot be part of a convex region larger than a single point because the straight line joining any two nonadjacent points satisfying the equality cannot also lie on the other points along the equality as required for convexity. However, in the special case in which only inequality constraints comprise the constraint set and the constraints are all concave functions, so that the points for which $g_j(\mathbf{x}) \geq 0$ form a convex set, then the nonlinear programming problem may be a convex programming problem.

2.4-3 Feasibility

Any vector $\mathbf{x}$ that satisfies both the equality and inequality constraints is called a *feasible point* or vector. The set of all points which satisfy the constraints constitutes the *feasible domain* of $f(\mathbf{x})$ and will be represented by R; any point not in R is termed *nonfeasible.* A *constrained optimum* is one in which the local optimum lies on the boundary of the feasible region. If the constraints consist only of equalities, a feasible $\mathbf{x}$ vector must be on the intersection of all the hypersurfaces corresponding to $h_j(\mathbf{x}) = 0$. In relation to just the inequality constraints, a point $\mathbf{x}$ may be classified either as an *interior point* (a feasible point), a *boundary point* (a feasible point), or an *exterior point* (a nonfeasible point). An interior point is one for which all the $g_j(\mathbf{x}) > 0$; a boundary point satisfies at least one $g_j(\mathbf{x}) = 0$; and an exterior point causes at least one $g_j(\mathbf{x}) < 0$. The set of points for which the $g_j(\mathbf{x}) = 0, j = 1, \ldots, p$, defines the *boundary surfaces* of the inequality constraint set. An *active* or *binding* inequality constraint is one for which $g_j(\mathbf{x}) = 0$. The region of admissible values of the variables may be simply connected as in Fig. 2.4-6*a* or nonsimply connected as in Fig. 2.4-6*b*, in which case the nonlinear programming algorithm is likely to miss searching more than one or two feasible regions unless a large number of starting vectors are employed. Fortunately, most nonlinear programming problems based on real processes are formulated so that only a simply connected feasible region exists. Section 6.2 describes the most common way to obtain a feasible point, or an interior point, from a nonfeasible point.

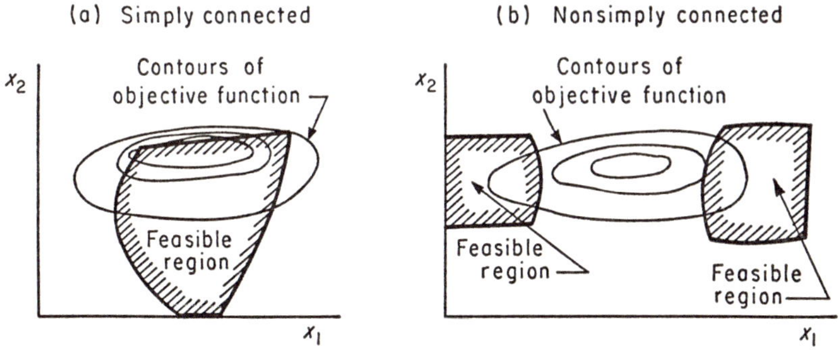

Fig. 2.4-6 Examples of simply connected and nonsimply connected feasible regions (as pertaining to inequality constraints).

2.4-4 The Gradient

The set of points for which the objective function has a constant value is called a *contour* of $f(\mathbf{x})$. A few such contours are illustrated in Fig. 2.4-7. If the objective function is continuous and differentiable, the *gradient* of $f(\mathbf{x})$ exists and is defined as the *column vector* of the first partial derivatives of $f(\mathbf{x})$ with respect to $\mathbf{x}$ evaluated at some point $\mathbf{x}$. A superscript k, $k = 0, 1, \ldots,$ will be used to denote the point in E^n at which the gradient is evaluated, so that the gradient at $\mathbf{x}^{(k)}$ is

$$\nabla f(\mathbf{x}^{(k)}) = \begin{bmatrix} \dfrac{\partial f(\mathbf{x}^{(k)})}{\partial x_1} \\ \cdot \\ \cdot \\ \cdot \\ \dfrac{\partial f(\mathbf{x}^{(k)})}{\partial x_n} \end{bmatrix} \tag{2.4-3}$$

The expression $\nabla^T f(\mathbf{x}^{(k)})$ will denote a row vector. Most books on vectors and matrices explain how the gradient of a scalar function points in the direc-

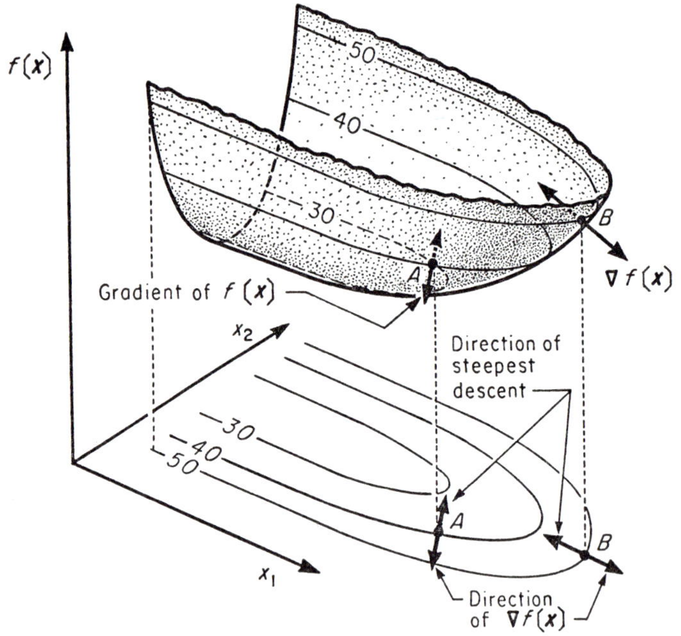

Fig. 2.4-7 The gradient (direction of steepest ascent) and the direction of steepest descent at two points.

tion of the greatest increase in the value of the function, that is, in the direction of *steepest ascent*, and is orthogonal to that contour of $f(\mathbf{x})$ that passes through $\mathbf{x}^{(k)}$. The negative of the gradient is in the direction of *steepest descent*. Any vector $\mathbf{v}$ orthogonal to $\nabla f(\mathbf{x}^{(k)})$, such as the tangent surface to $f(\mathbf{x}^{(k)})$ at $\mathbf{x}^{(k)}$, can be denoted by $\mathbf{v}^T \nabla f(\mathbf{x}^k) = 0$.

One should note that the gradient is not the direction of greatest increase in $f(\mathbf{x})$ if some other metric besides the euclidean metric is chosen. For example, if instead of letting the length of the vector $\mathbf{x}$ be $\|\mathbf{x}\| = (\mathbf{x}^T\mathbf{x})^{\frac{1}{2}}$, if we let $\|\mathbf{x}\| = \sum_j \|x_j\|$, then the direction of greatest increase in $f(\mathbf{x}^{(k)})$ is obtained by finding that component of $\nabla f(\mathbf{x}^{(k)})$ having the largest absolute value and setting the component of $\mathbf{x}$ at either $+1$ or -1 (according to the sign of the component), and the other components at zero, as in the simplex method for linear programming.

2.4-5 Approximation of Functions

Some of the mathematical programming procedures to be discussed later on require linear or quadratic approximations of $f(\mathbf{x})$, $g_j(\mathbf{x})$, and $h_j(\mathbf{x})$. A linear, or first-order, approximation of the objective function, $f(\mathbf{x})$, for example, can be made by a truncated Taylor series about $\mathbf{x}^{(k)}$.

$$f(\mathbf{x}) \approx f(\mathbf{x}^{(k)}) + \nabla^T f(\mathbf{x}^{(k)})(\mathbf{x} - \mathbf{x}^{(k)}) \tag{2.4-4}$$

A quadratic approximation of $f(\mathbf{x})$ can be made by neglecting the third- and higher-order terms in the Taylor series

$$f(\mathbf{x}) \approx f(\mathbf{x}^{(k)}) + \nabla^T f(\mathbf{x}^{(k)})(\mathbf{x} - \mathbf{x}^{(k)}) + \tfrac{1}{2}(\mathbf{x} - \mathbf{x}^{(k)})^T \nabla^2 f(\mathbf{x}^{(k)})(\mathbf{x} - \mathbf{x}^{(k)}) \tag{2.4-5}$$

where $\nabla^2 f(\mathbf{x}^{(k)})$ is the *hessian matrix* of $f(\mathbf{x})$, $\mathbf{H}(\mathbf{x})$, that is, the square matrix of the second partial derivatives of $f(\mathbf{x})$ evaluated at $\mathbf{x}^{(k)}$.

$$\nabla^2 f(\mathbf{x}^{(k)}) = \mathbf{H}(\mathbf{x}^{(k)}) = \begin{bmatrix} \dfrac{\partial^2 f(\mathbf{x}^{(k)})}{\partial x_1^2} & \cdots & \dfrac{\partial^2 f(\mathbf{x}^{(k)})}{\partial x_1\, \partial x_n} \\ \cdots & \cdots & \cdots \\ \dfrac{\partial^2 f(\mathbf{x}^{(k)})}{\partial x_n\, \partial x_1} & \cdots & \dfrac{\partial^2 f(\mathbf{x}^{(k)})}{\partial x_n^2} \end{bmatrix} \tag{2.4-6}$$

2.5 THE NECESSARY AND SUFFICIENT CONDITIONS FOR A SOLUTION TO BE AN OPTIMAL SOLUTION

Considerable effort has been devoted in the study of nonlinear programming to delimiting the necessary and sufficient conditions for an $\mathbf{x}$ vector to be a local extremum. Optimality criteria for certain special cases of the general nonlinear programming problem listed in expressions (2.2–1) through (2.2–3) have been formulated, but the structure of the nonlinear programming problem when general functions are involved is such that completely comprehensive optimality criteria have yet to be devised. Consequently, we can only describe certain special cases in this section, but they are of quite common occurrence and of practical importance. The conditions that determine whether or not an **x** vector solves a nonlinear programming problem will be stated in the form of theorems without the associated proofs (which are beyond our scope here), but references are given for the interested reader.

2.5–1 Nonlinear Programming without Constraints

The problem is

$$\text{Minimize:} \quad f(\mathbf{x}) \qquad \text{for } \mathbf{x} \in E^n \tag{2.5–1}$$

For an unconstrained nonlinear programming problem the *necessary conditions* for $\mathbf{x}^*$ to be a local minimum of problem (2.5–1) are that

1. $f(\mathbf{x})$ be differentiable at $\mathbf{x}^*$.
2. $\nabla f(\mathbf{x}^*) = \mathbf{0}$; i.e., a stationary point exists at $\mathbf{x}^*$.

The *sufficient conditions* for $\mathbf{x}^*$ to be a local minimum of problem (2.5–1) are, in addition to conditions 1 and 2 above,

3. $\nabla^2 f(\mathbf{x}^*) > \mathbf{0}$; i.e., the hessian matrix is positive definite.

(The corresponding conditions for a maximum are the same, except that the hessian matrix of $f(\mathbf{x}^*)$ must be negative definite.)

Figure 2.5–1 indicates how a minimum can exist that does not satisfy the necessary and sufficient conditions. However, when the sufficient conditions are satisfied, $\mathbf{x}^*$ is guaranteed to be a minimum.

2.5–2 Nonlinear Programming with Both Equality and Inequality Constraints

The problem is

$$\begin{aligned} &\text{Minimize:} && f(\mathbf{x}) && \mathbf{x} \in E^n \\ &\text{Subject to:} && h_j(\mathbf{x}) = 0 && j = 1, \ldots, m \\ & && g_j(\mathbf{x}) \geq 0 && j = m + 1, \ldots, p \end{aligned} \tag{2.5–2}$$

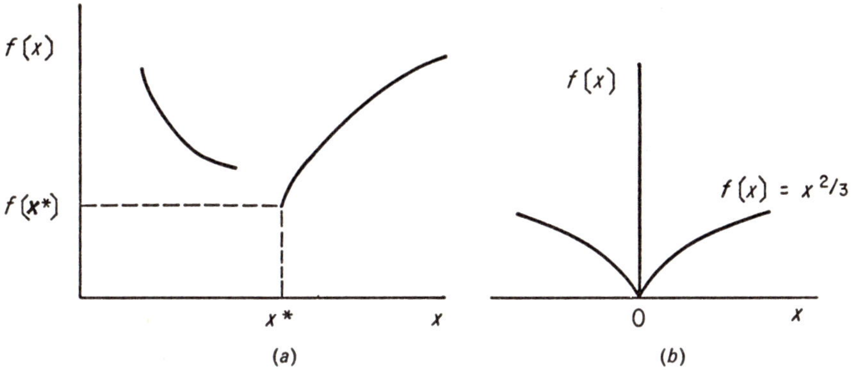

Fig. 2.5-1 (*a*) Minimum of $f(\mathbf{x})$ occurs at a discontinuity in $f(\mathbf{x})$; (*b*) minimum of $f(\mathbf{x})$ occurs where $df(\mathbf{x})/dx$ is undefined.

Problem (2.5-2) is identical with expressions (2.2-1) through (2.2-3), presented in Sec. 2.2. The necessary conditions for $\mathbf{x}^*$ to be a local minimum can be stated in two theorems, the first of which (Theorem 2) may be called the first-order conditions (because the functions involved are assumed to be once-differentiable) and the second of which (Theorem 3) may be termed the second-order conditions (because the functions involved are assumed to be twice-differentiable).

We commence with the following concept: if $\mathbf{x}^*$ is a local minimum, $f(\mathbf{x})$ cannot decrease along any smooth arc directed from $\mathbf{x}^*$ into the feasible region. Let the vector $\mathbf{v}$ be tangent to the arc leading from $\mathbf{x}^*$. Following Fiacco and McCormick,[1] we partition the nonzero vectors $\mathbf{v}$ into three classes, each set V_i comprising the set of $\mathbf{v}$ such that:

Class	*Inequality constraints*		*Equality constraints*	*Objective function*
V_1	$\{\mathbf{v}^T\nabla g_j(\mathbf{x}^*) \geq 0$ for active constraints$\}$	and	$\{\mathbf{v}^T\nabla h_j(\mathbf{x}^*) = 0$ for all $j = 1, \ldots, m\}$	and $\{\mathbf{v}^T\nabla f(\mathbf{x}^*) \geq 0\}$
V_2	$\{\mathbf{v}^T\nabla g_j(\mathbf{x}^*) \geq 0$ for active constraints$\}$	and	$\{\mathbf{v}^T\nabla h_j(\mathbf{x}^*) = 0$ for all $j = 1, \ldots, m\}$	and $\{\mathbf{v}^T\nabla f(\mathbf{x}^*) < 0\}$
V_3	$\{\mathbf{v}^T\nabla g_j(\mathbf{x}^*) < 0$ for at least one active constraint$\}$	or	$\{\mathbf{v}^T\nabla h_j(\mathbf{x}^*) \neq 0$ for at least one constraint$\}$	

[1] A. V. Fiacco and G. P. McCormick, "Nonlinear Programming," John Wiley & Sons, Inc., New York, 1968.

All feasible perturbations of $\mathbf{x}^*$ fall into the union of V_1 and V_2, and if $\mathbf{v}$ is contained in $V_2, f(\mathbf{x})$ decreases, while if $\mathbf{v}$ is contained in $V_1, f(\mathbf{x})$ increases or is constant. In essence the first-order necessary conditions pose the requirement that the set V_2 be empty.

If V_2 is empty, the existence of Lagrange multipliers can be proved resulting in the following theorem.

Theorem 1[1]

If (*a*) $\mathbf{x}^*$ satisfies problem (2.5–2), (*b*) the functions $f(\mathbf{x})$, $g_j(\mathbf{x})$, and $h_j(\mathbf{x})$ are once-differentiable, and (*c*) at $\mathbf{x}^*$ the set V_2 is empty, then there exist vectors (lagrange multipliers) $\mathbf{u}^*$ and $\mathbf{w}^*$ such that $(\mathbf{x}^*,\mathbf{u}^*,\mathbf{w}^*)$ satisfies:

(1) $h_j(\mathbf{x}^*) = 0 \qquad j = 1, \ldots, m$

(2) $g_j(\mathbf{x}^*) \geq 0 \qquad j = m+1, \ldots, p$

(3) $u_j^* g_j(\mathbf{x}^*) = 0 \qquad j = m+1, \ldots, p$

(4) $u_j^* \geq 0 \qquad j = m+1, \ldots, p$

(5) $\nabla L(\mathbf{x}^*,\mathbf{u}^*,\mathbf{w}^*) = \mathbf{0}$

In Eq. (5) the function

$$L(\mathbf{x},\mathbf{u},\mathbf{w}) \equiv f(\mathbf{x}) + \sum_{j=1}^{m} w_j h_j(\mathbf{x}) - \sum_{j=m+1}^{p} u_j g_j(\mathbf{x})$$

can be regarded as a generalized lagrangian function associated with problem (2.5–2); hence Eq. (5) is

$$\nabla L(\mathbf{x}^*,\mathbf{u}^*,\mathbf{w}^*) \equiv \nabla f(\mathbf{x}^*) + \sum_{j=1}^{m} w_j^* \nabla h_j(\mathbf{x}^*) - \sum_{j=m+1}^{p} u_j^* \nabla g_j(\mathbf{x}^*) = \mathbf{0}$$

In order to ascertain under what circumstances the set V_2 is empty one more concept is needed, that of the *first-order constraint qualification.* As outlined in the well-known paper by Kuhn and Tucker,[2] suppose that $\mathbf{x}^{(k)}$ is a feasible point for problem (2.5–2) and that $h_1(\mathbf{x}), \ldots, h_m(\mathbf{x})$, $g_{m+1}(\mathbf{x}), \ldots, g_p(\mathbf{x})$, are once-differentiable at $\mathbf{x}^{(k)}$. The first-order constraint qualification is a condition imposed on the constraint set only, namely, that for each boundary point of the constraint set composed of the equality constraints and active inequality constraints, there must exist a smooth curve

[1] *Ibid.*

[2] W. W. Kuhn and A. W. Tucker, Nonlinear Programming, *Proc. 2d Berkeley Symp. on Mathematical Statistics and Probability,* University of California Press, Berkeley, 1951, pp. 481–492.

terminating on the boundary point and lying wholly within the constraint set. If $\mathbf{x}^*$ is a local minimum, $f(\mathbf{x})$ cannot decrease along any such curve directed from $\mathbf{x}^*$ into the feasible region. *A sufficient condition for the first-order-constraint qualification* to hold is that all the gradients of the active inequality constraints and the gradients of the equality constraints evaluated at a tentative $\mathbf{x}^*$ are linearly independent.

How to ensure that the set V_2 is empty can be specified in different ways, but the best-known is by specifying the *first-order-constraint qualification*, leading to Theorem 2.

Theorem 2[2]

If the functions $f(\mathbf{x}), h_1(\mathbf{x}), \ldots, h_m(\mathbf{x}), g_{m+1}(\mathbf{x}), \ldots, g_p(\mathbf{x})$ are once-differentiable at a point $\mathbf{x}^*$, and if the first-order-constraint qualification holds at $\mathbf{x}^*$, then the necessary conditions that $\mathbf{x}^*$ be a local minimum of problem (2.4–2) are that there exist lagrange multipliers $\mathbf{u}^*$ and $\mathbf{w}^*$ such that $(\mathbf{x}^*,\mathbf{u}^*,\mathbf{w}^*)$ satisfy equations (1) through (5) in Theorem 1.

To take into account the curvature of the functions in problem (2.5–2), McCormick[2] described the necessary second-order conditions for $\mathbf{x}^*$ to be a local minimum. Assume that the functions $f(\mathbf{x}), h_1(\mathbf{x}), \ldots, h_m(\mathbf{x}), g_{m+1}(\mathbf{x}), \ldots, g_p(\mathbf{x})$ are twice-differentiable at $\mathbf{x}^{(k)}$, a point satisfying problem (2.5–2). Let $\mathbf{v}$ be any nonzero vector such that

$$\mathbf{v}^T\nabla g_j(\mathbf{x}^{(k)}) = 0 \qquad \text{for all active inequality constraints}$$

$$\mathbf{v}^T\nabla h_j(\mathbf{x}^{(k)}) = 0 \qquad \text{for all equality constraints}$$

Then if $\mathbf{v}$ is the tangent of a twice-differentiable curve $\psi(\theta)$, $\theta \geq 0$, along which $g_j(\psi(\theta)) = 0$ for all the active inequality constraints and $h_j(\psi(\theta)) = 0$ for all the equality constraints, the *second-order-constraint qualification* holds at $\mathbf{x}^{(k)}$. *A sufficient condition for the second-order-constraint qualification* to hold at $\mathbf{x}^{(k)}$ is that the gradients of the active inequality constraints at $\mathbf{x}^{(k)}$ and the gradients of the equality constraints at $\mathbf{x}^{(k)}$ are linearly independent.

We can now state the *necessary second-order conditions.*

Theorem 3[1]

(*a*) If the functions $f(\mathbf{x}), h_1(\mathbf{x}), \ldots, h_m(\mathbf{x}), g_{m+1}(\mathbf{x}), \ldots, g_p(\mathbf{x})$ are twice-differentiable at the point $\mathbf{x}^*$, and (*b*) if the first- and second-order-constraint qualifications hold at

[1] Fiacco and McCormick, *op. cit.*; G. P. McCormick, *SIAM J. Appl. Math.*, **15**:641 (1967).
[2] McCormick, *op. cit.*
[3] *Ibid.*

$\mathbf{x}^*$, then the necessary conditions that $\mathbf{x}^*$ be a local minimum for problem (2.5–2) are that there exist vectors $\mathbf{w}^* = [w_1^*, \ldots, w_m^*]^T$ and $\mathbf{u}^* = [u_{m+1}^*, \ldots, u_p^*]^T$ such that (*c*)

(1) $h_j(\mathbf{x}^*) = 0 \qquad j = 1, \ldots, m$

(2) $g_j(\mathbf{x}^*) \geq 0 \qquad j = m + 1, \ldots, p$

(3) $u_j^* \geq 0 \qquad j = m + 1, \ldots, p$

(4) $u_j^* g_j(\mathbf{x}) = 0 \qquad j = m + 1, \ldots, p$

(5) $\nabla L(\mathbf{x}^*,\mathbf{u}^*,\mathbf{w}^*) = 0$

and (*d*) for every nonzero vector $\mathbf{v}$, for which $\mathbf{v}^T \nabla g_j(\mathbf{x}^*) = 0$ for all the active inequality constraints and $\mathbf{v}^T \nabla h_j(\mathbf{x}^*) = 0$ for all the equality constraints, the following is true:

$$(6) \qquad \mathbf{v}^T \nabla^2 L(\mathbf{x}^*,\mathbf{u}^*,\mathbf{w}^*)\mathbf{v} \geq 0$$

If only a zero vector $\mathbf{v}$ exists, (6) is satisfied by implication because the active constraints intersect to give a unique solution.

The *sufficient conditions* for $\mathbf{x}^*$ to be a local isolated[1] minimum of problem (2.5–2) are the same as the necessary conditions (*a*), (*c*), and (*d*) of Theorem 3, provided that the following amended condition is substituted for Eq. (6) of part (*d*) of the theorem: (*d'*) For every nonzero vector $\mathbf{v}$ for which $\mathbf{v}^T \nabla g_j(\mathbf{x}^*) = 0$ for the active inequality constraints, $\mathbf{v}^T \nabla g_j(\mathbf{x}^*) \geq 0$ for the nonactive inequality constraints, and $\mathbf{v}^T \nabla h_j(\mathbf{x}^*) = 0$ for all the equality constraints, the following is true.[2]

$$(6') \qquad \mathbf{v}^T \nabla^2 L(\mathbf{x}^*,\mathbf{u}^*,\mathbf{w}^*)\mathbf{v} > 0$$

An alternative sufficiency condition is given by Theorem 4.

Theorem 4[3]

If the functions $f(\mathbf{x})$, $h_1(\mathbf{x}), \ldots, h_m(\mathbf{x})$, $g_{m+1}(\mathbf{x}), \ldots, g_p(\mathbf{x})$ are twice-differentiable with respect to $\mathbf{x}$, if the necessary conditions (1) through (5) of Theorem 3 hold, and if the determinant of the jacobian matrix of the functions $h_j(\mathbf{x})$, $u_j g_j(\mathbf{x})$, and $\nabla L(\mathbf{x},\mathbf{u},\mathbf{w})$ with respect to $(\mathbf{x},\mathbf{u},\mathbf{w})$ does not vanish at $(\mathbf{x}^*,\mathbf{u}^*,\mathbf{w}^*)$, then the sufficiency conditions of Theorem 3 for $\mathbf{x}^*$ to be a local minimum are satisfied at $\mathbf{x}^*$.

Example 2.5–1 Necessary and sufficient conditions with inequality constraints

In this example the problem is:

Minimize: $f(\mathbf{x}) = x_1^2 + x_2$

[1] "Isolated" formally means that, for $0 < \|\mathbf{x}\| < \varepsilon$, and ε sufficiently small, $f(\mathbf{x}) > f(\mathbf{x}^*)$.
[2] L. Pennisi, *Trans. Am. Math. Soc.*, **74**:177 (1953); McCormick, *op. cit.*
[3] McCormick, *op. cit.*

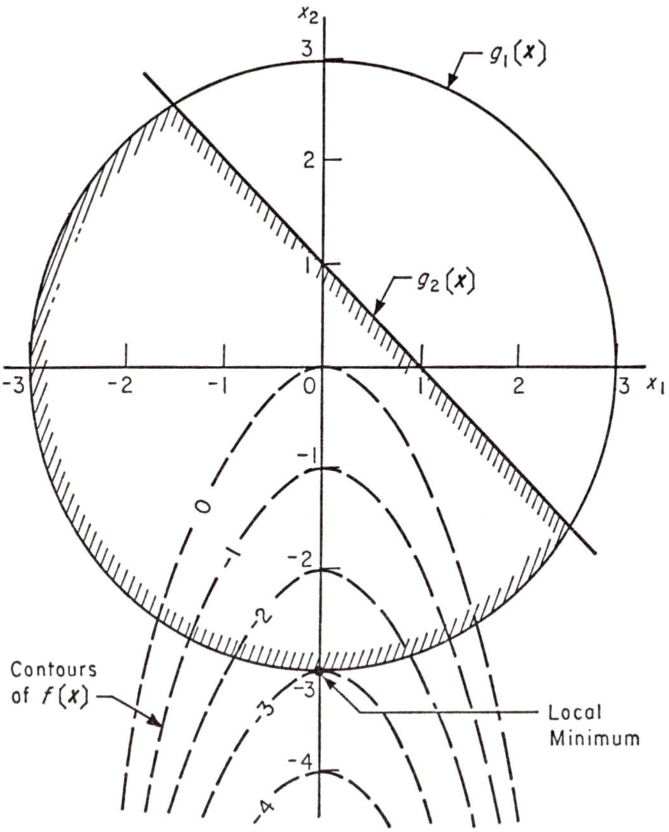

Fig. E2.5-1

Subject to: $g_1(\mathbf{x}) = -(x_1^2 + x_2^2) + 9 \geq 0$

$g_2(\mathbf{x}) = -x_1 - x_2 + 1 \quad \geq 0$

In the problem, $g_1(\mathbf{x})$ will be an active constraint, whereas $g_2(\mathbf{x})$ will be an inactive constraint; refer to Fig. E2.5-1.

We first note by inspection that the functions are twice-differentiable. Because there is only one binding constraint, $g_1(\mathbf{x})$, a test does not have to be carried out to satisfy the first- and second-order constraint qualifications.

By Theorems 1 and 2 we need to show that the vectors $\mathbf{x}^*$ and $\mathbf{u}^*$ exist that satisfy the following listed conditions:

Constraints $g_1(\mathbf{x}^*)$ and $g_2(\mathbf{x}^*)$ are nonnegative, or

$$-x_1^{*2} - x_2^{*2} + 9 \geq 0$$
$$-x_1^* - x_2^* + 1 \geq 0 \qquad (a)$$

Any point within or on the boundaries of the shaded region is a feasible $\mathbf{x}$ vector.

$$1\begin{bmatrix}2x_1^*\\1\end{bmatrix} - u_1^*\begin{bmatrix}-2x_1^*\\-2x_2^*\end{bmatrix} - u_2^*\begin{bmatrix}-1\\-1\end{bmatrix} = \mathbf{0} \tag{b}$$

or

$$2x_1^*u_1^* + u_2^* = 0$$

$$2x_2^*u_1^* + u_2^* = 0$$

$$u_1^*(-x_1^{*2} - x_2^{*2} + 9) = 0$$

$$u_2^*(-x_1^* - x_2^* + 1) = 0 \tag{c}$$

$$u_1^* \geq 0 \qquad \text{and} \qquad u_2^* \geq 0 \tag{d}$$

If we assumed from constraints (c) that both u_1^* and u_2^* were zero, a contradiction would arise from constraints (b) because then $1 = 0$, hence not all the u^*'s may be zero. Suppose we place $u_2^* = 0$. Then, from the first constraint in (b), either $x_1^* = 0$ or $(1 + u_1^*) = 0$, the latter being impossible, because u_i^* cannot be negative. Hence $x_1^* = 0$. From the constraints in (c), because $u_1^* \neq 0$, $x_1^{*2} + x_2^{*2} = 9$ or $x_2^* = \pm 3$ is a possible minimum. However, $x_2^* = +3$ with $x_1^* = 0$ violates the second constraint in (a). Consequently, we have found an $\mathbf{x}^*$ vector, $\mathbf{x}^* = [0 \quad -3]^T$, and a $\mathbf{u}^*$ vector

$$u_1^* = \tfrac{1}{6}$$

$$u_2^* = 0$$

that satisfy the constraints (b), (c), and (d). Thus the first-order necessary conditions are fulfilled.

The second-order necessary condition that must be fulfilled is that for

$$[v_1 \quad v_2]\begin{bmatrix}-2x_1^*\\-2x_2^*\end{bmatrix} = 0$$

or $v_1(0) + v_2(6) = 0$, i.e., v_1 is any value and $v_2 = 0$, the following holds true

$$[v_1 \quad 0]\nabla^2 L(\mathbf{x}^*,\mathbf{u}^*)\begin{bmatrix}v_1\\0\end{bmatrix} \geq 0$$

Because $L = f(\mathbf{x}) - u_1 g_1(\mathbf{x}) - u_2 g_2(\mathbf{x})$

$$\nabla^2 L = \begin{bmatrix}2(1 + u_1) & 0\\0 & 2u_2\end{bmatrix}$$

we find $4v_1^2 u_1^*(1 + u_1^*) \geq 0 > 0$. Consequently the second-order necessary conditions are satisfied and also the sufficient conditions.

To determine if the alternate sufficient conditions are satisfied, we form the jacobian matrix of the functions

$$u_1(-x_1^2 - x_2^2 + 9)$$

$$u_2(-x_1 - x_2 + 1)$$

$$x_1 + 2u_1x_1 + u_2$$

$$2u_1x_2 + u_2$$

with respect to x_1, x_2, u_1, and u_2 respectively.

$$\text{or} \quad \mathbf{J} = \begin{bmatrix} -2x_1u_1 & -2x_2u_1 & (-x_1^2 - x_2^2 + 9) & 0 \\ -u_1 & -u_2 & 0 & (-x_1 - x_2 + 1) \\ (1 + 2u_1) & 0 & 2x_1 & 1 \\ 0 & 2u_1 & 2x_2 & 1 \end{bmatrix}$$

At $x_1^* = 0$, $x_2^* = -3$ and with $u_1^* = \frac{1}{6}$ and $u_2^* = 0$,

$$\det \mathbf{J} = \det \begin{bmatrix} 0 & 1 & 0 & 0 \\ -\frac{1}{6} & 0 & 0 & 4 \\ \frac{14}{6} & 0 & 0 & 1 \\ 0 & \frac{1}{3} & -6 & 1 \end{bmatrix} \neq 0$$

Thus the alternate sufficient conditions are fulfilled for the vector $\mathbf{x}^* = [0 \quad -3]^T$ to be a local minimum.

Example 2.5-2 Necessary and sufficient conditions with both equality and inequality constraints

As an example of a nonlinear programming problem incorporating both equality and inequality constraints, we consider the following problem:

$$\begin{aligned} \text{Minimize:} \quad & f(\mathbf{x}) = x_1^2 + x_2 \qquad \mathbf{x} \in E^n \\ \text{Subject to:} \quad & h_1(\mathbf{x}) = x_1^2 + x_2^2 - 9 = 0 \\ & g_2(\mathbf{x}) = -(x_1 + x_2^2) + 1 \geq 0 \\ & g_3(\mathbf{x}) = -(x_1 + x_2) + 1 \geq 0 \end{aligned}$$

According to Theorem 3, $h_1(\mathbf{x})$, $g_2(\mathbf{x})$, and $g_3(\mathbf{x})$ must be twice-differentiable, as they are, and the gradients of the binding constraints, i.e., the active inequality constraints plus the equality constraints, must be linearly independent to satisfy the first- and second-order-constraint qualifications. Suppose that the point A, where $\mathbf{x}^* = [-2.37 \quad -1.84]^T$ located at the intersection of $h_1(\mathbf{x})$ and $g_2(\mathbf{x})$ in Fig. E2.5-2, is to be considered as a candidate for a local optimum. We can form a linear combination of the gradients of the binding constraints

$$c_1 \nabla h_1(\mathbf{x}^*) + c_2 \nabla g_2(\mathbf{x}^*) = \mathbf{0}$$

or

$$c_1 \begin{bmatrix} 2x_1^* \\ 2x_2^* \end{bmatrix} + c_2 \begin{bmatrix} -1 \\ -2x_2^* \end{bmatrix} = \mathbf{0} \qquad (a)$$

It can be shown in several ways that the only $\mathbf{c}$ vector that satisfies Eq. (a) is $c_1 = c_2 = 0$; hence the gradients of the binding constraints are linearly independent, and thus the first- and second-order-constraint qualifications hold.

Next, we check Theorems 1 and 2 containing the first-order necessary conditions. Each of the following must be true at $\mathbf{x}^*$, as they are by the selection of $\mathbf{x}^* = [-2.37 \quad -1.84]^T$:

1. $h_1(\mathbf{x}^*) = x_1^{*2} + x_2^{*2} - 9 = 0 \qquad (-2.37)^2 + (-1.84)^2 - 9 = 0$

   $g_2(\mathbf{x}^*) = -(x_1^* + x_2^{*2}) + 1 \geq 0 \qquad -(-2.37) - (-1.84)^2 + 1 = 0$

   $g_3(\mathbf{x}^*) = -(x_1^* + x_2^*) + 1 \geq 0 \qquad -(-2.37) - (-1.84) + 1 > 0$

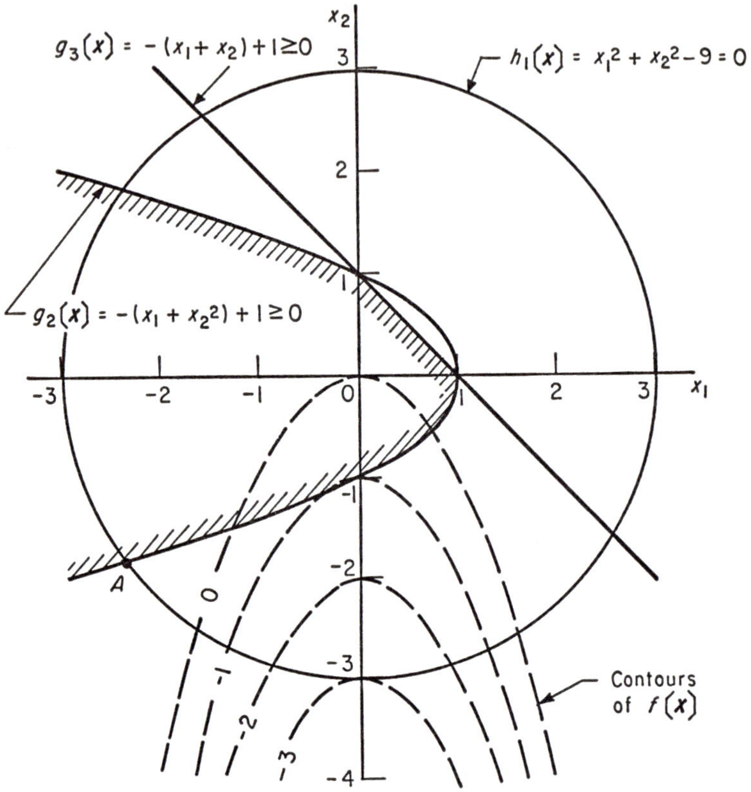

Fig. E2.5-2

2. $u_2^* \geq 0$ and $u_3^* \geq 0$
3. $u_2^*(-x_1^* - x_2^{*2} + 1) = 0$

   $u_3^*(-x_1^* - x_2^* + 1) = 0$
4. $\begin{bmatrix} 2x_1^* \\ 1 \end{bmatrix} + w_1^* \begin{bmatrix} 2x_1^* \\ 2x_2^* \end{bmatrix} - u_2^* \begin{bmatrix} -1 \\ -2x_2^* \end{bmatrix} - u_3^* \begin{bmatrix} -1 \\ -1 \end{bmatrix} = \mathbf{0}$

Because we have picked an $\mathbf{x}^*$ to test for a local minimum in this example, it is easy to substitute $\mathbf{x}^* = [-2.37 \quad -1.84]^T$ into the expressions listed in conditions 2 through 4 and thereafter ascertain if the scalars w_1^*, u_2^*, and u_3^* exist that satisfy the expressions

$$2(-2.37) + w_1^*(2)(-2.37) + u_2^* = 0$$

$$1 + w_1^*(2)(-1.84) + 2u_2^*(-1.84) = 0$$

$$w_1^* = -0.779$$

$$u_2^* = 1.05$$

Consequently, the scalars

$$\begin{aligned} w_1^* &= -0.779 \\ u_2^* &= 1.05 \\ u_3^* &= 0 \end{aligned} \qquad (b)$$

fulfill the requirements of Theorem 2 delineating the first-order necessary conditions.

The additional requirements of Theorem 3 for the second-order necessary conditions beyond those of Theorems 1 and 2 are as follows. The vector **v** is defined by two equations involving the equality constraint and the binding inequality constraint.

$$[v_1 \quad v_2]\begin{bmatrix} -1 \\ -2x_2^* \end{bmatrix} = 0$$

$$[v_1 \quad v_2]\begin{bmatrix} 2x_1^* \\ 2x_2^* \end{bmatrix} = 0$$

or

$$\begin{aligned} -v_1 + 3.68v_2 &= 0 \\ -2.37v_1 - 1.84v_2 &= 0 \end{aligned} \qquad (c)$$

The only vector **v** that exists that satisfies (*c*) is the zero vector, hence there is a unique solution to the problem at the intersection of $g_2(\mathbf{x})$ and $h_1(\mathbf{x})$. Also note in this particular problem that

$$[v_1 \quad v_2]\left\{\begin{bmatrix} 2 & 0 \\ 0 & 0 \end{bmatrix} + w_1^*\begin{bmatrix} 2 & 0 \\ 0 & 2 \end{bmatrix} - u_2^*\begin{bmatrix} 0 & 0 \\ 0 & -2 \end{bmatrix}\right\}\begin{bmatrix} v_1 \\ v_2 \end{bmatrix} \geq 0 > 0$$

or (with $w_1^* = -0.779$ and $u_2^* = 1.05$)

$$0.442v_1^2 + 0.542v_2^2 \geq 0 \qquad (d)$$

is satisfied for all nonzero **v**.

Alternately, the sufficient conditions for $\mathbf{x}^*$ to be a local isolated minimum exist because the determinant of the jacobian matrix described in Theorem 4 is not zero.

$$\mathbf{J} = \begin{bmatrix} 2x_1^* & 2x_2^* & 0 & 0 & 0 \\ -u_2^* & -2u_2^*x_2^* & 0 & (-x_1^* - x_2^{*2} + 1) & 0 \\ -u_3^* & -u_3^* & 0 & 0 & (-x_1^* - x_2^* + 1) \\ 2 + 2w_1^* & 0 & 2x_1^* & 1 & 1 \\ 0 & 2(w_1^* + u_2^*) & 2x_2^* & 2x_2^* & 1 \end{bmatrix}$$

$$\det \mathbf{J} = \det \begin{bmatrix} -4.74 & -3.68 & 0 & 0 & 0 \\ -1.05 & 3.86 & 0 & -0.02 & 0 \\ 0 & 0 & 0 & 0 & +5.21 \\ 0.44 & 0 & -4.74 & 1 & 1 \\ 0 & 0.54 & -3.68 & -3.68 & 1 \end{bmatrix} \neq 0$$

Only simple problems have been used to illustrate the application of the theorems for local optimality. In very largescale problems the theorems still apply, but one may be thwarted from applying them because analytical differentiation of the nonlinear functions $f(\mathbf{x})$, $g(\mathbf{x})$, and $h(\mathbf{x})$ may not be convenient.

2.6 EFFICIENT UNIDIMENSIONAL SEARCHES

Many of the algorithms to be described subsequently require an efficient unidimensional optimization technique to locate the minimum of a function of one variable. Wilde[1] and other general optimization books review one-dimensional search techniques which specify the interval in which the minimum of a function lies. To apply these methods one needs to know an initial uncertainty interval $\Delta^{(0)}$ which contains the minimum of the objective function $f(\mathbf{x})$ and that $f(\mathbf{x})$ is unimodal in the interval. There are various methods, the names of some of which are listed in Table 2.6–1, of reducing the initial interval to a final interval $\Delta^{(n)}$. It is beyond our scope here to do more than make a few remarks concerning these methods and then turn to some others that in practice usually prove more effective.

Wilde defined the efficiency for n functional evaluations as

$$\text{Efficiency} = E = \frac{\Delta^{(n)}}{\Delta^{(0)}}$$

Table 2.6–1 compares E for five different methods.

Table 2.6–1 Efficiency of one-dimensional search techniques (n = number of functional evaluations; F_n = Fibonacci number for n evaluations)

Nonsequential	E	*Sequential*	E
Uniform search	$\frac{2}{n+1}$	Sequential dichotomous search	$\frac{1}{2^{n/2}}$
Uniform dichotomous search	$\frac{1}{(n/2)+1}$	Fibonacci search	$\frac{1}{F_n}$
		Golden section	$(0.618)^{1-n}$

Table 2.6–2 compares the number of functional evaluations of $f(\mathbf{x})$ required to reduce an initial interval of 5×10^{-1} to a smaller interval.

[1] D. J. Wilde, "Optimum Seeking Methods," Prentice-Hall, Inc., Englewood Cliffs, N.J., 1964.

Table 2.6-2 Number of functional evaluations to reduce initial interval of 5×10^{-1}

	Nonsequential		*Sequential*		
Reduction of interval to:	*Uniform*	*Uniform dichotomous*	*Golden section*	*Fibonacci*	*Dichotomous*
5×10^{-3}	199	198	11	11	14
5×10^{-5}	19,999	19,998	21	21	28

Thus the relative efficiency of the two well-known methods of golden section and Fibonacci search are slightly more favorable than the dichotomous search, and distinctly more favorable than the nonsequential methods.

Golden search (search by golden section) is based on the splitting of a line into two segments known in ancient times as the "golden section." The ratio of the whole line to the larger segment is the same as the ratio of the larger segment to the smaller. Two Fibonacci fractions are employed:

$$F_1 = \frac{3 - \sqrt{5}}{2} \approx 0.38$$

$$F_2 = \frac{\sqrt{5} - 1}{2} \approx 0.62$$

Note that $F_1 = (F_2)^2$ and $F_1 + F_2 = 1$. It is necessary to start the search in a direction so as to minimize $f(\mathbf{x})$.

An initial bracket Δ must be obtained on the minimum of $f(\mathbf{x})$ by, say, a sequential series of larger and larger steps in the independent variable. Let the last three x values be designated $x_3^{(0)}$ (the last point), $x_2^{(0)}$, and $x_1^{(0)}$, where $f(x_3^{(0)}) \geq f(x_2^{(0)})$, and let $\Delta^{(k)} = x_3^{(k)} - x_1^{(k)}$. Examine Fig. 2.6-1. Thereafter, for the kth stage, compute the next interval as follows. Determine

$$y_1^{(k)} = x_1^{(k)} + F_1\Delta^{(k)}$$

$$y_2^{(k)} = x_1^{(k)} + F_2\Delta^{(k)} = x_3^{(k)} - F_1\Delta^{(k)}$$

If $f(y_1^{(k)}) < f(y_2^{(k)})$: $\Delta^{(k+1)} = (y_2^{(k)} - x_1^{(k)})$, and $x_1^{(k+1)} = x_1^{(k)}, x_3^{(k+1)} = y_2^{(k)}$

If $f(y_1^{(k)}) > f(y_2^{(k)})$: $\Delta^{(k+1)} = (x_3^{(k)} - y_1^{(k)})$, and $x_1^{(k+1)} = y_1^{(k)}, x_3^{(k+1)} = x_3^{(k)}$

If $f(y_1^{(k)}) = f(y_2^{(k)})$: $\Delta^{(k+1)} = (y_2^{(k)} - x_1^{(k)}) = (x_3^{(k)} - y_1^{(k)})$, and

$$x_1^{(k+1)} = x_1^{(k)}, x_3^{(k+1)} = y_2^{(k)} \text{ or}$$

$$x_1^{(k+1)} = y_1^{(k)}, x_3^{(k+1)} = x_3^{(k)}$$

$$y_1^{(0)} = x_1^{(0)} + 0.38\Delta^{(0)}$$

$$y_2^{(0)} = x_1^{(0)} + 0.62\Delta^{(0)}$$

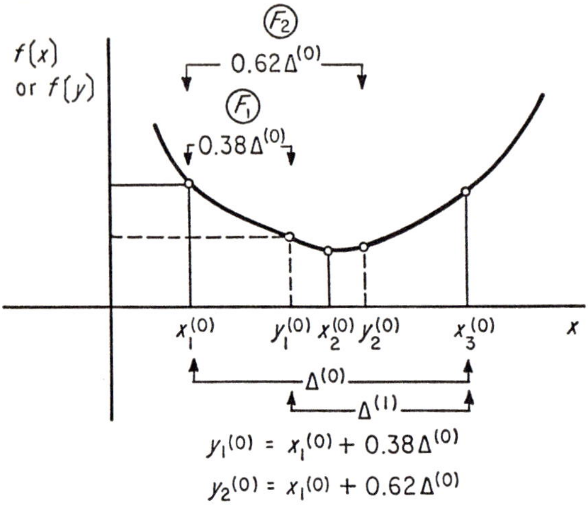

Fig. 2.6-1   Golden search: search by golden section. The initial points occur at $x_1^{(0)}$, $x_2^{(0)}$, and $x_3^{(0)}$. Because $f(y_1^{(0)})$ $> f(y_2^{(0)})$, $\Delta^{(1)} = (x_3^{(0)} - y_1^{(0)})$ and $x_1^{(1)} = y_1^{(0)}$ and $x_3^{(1)} = x_3^{(0)}$ bracket the interval for stage 1.

For precision, two new points are determined each time (rather than one new point) because the values of F_1 and F_2 will not be exact, and with only one new point, numerical roundoff can cause the bracket on the minimum to be lost.

Another class of methods of unidimensional minimization locates a point $\mathbf{x}$ near $\mathbf{x}^*$ (the value of the independent variable corresponding to the minimum of $f(\mathbf{x})$) by extrapolation and interpolation. Both quadratic and cubic estimation have been proposed using function values only and using both function and derivative values. Coggins[1] pointed out that several of the techniques involving the fitting of a polynomial through selected points were better able to locate the minimum of $f(\mathbf{x})$ to within a specified precision than the methods listed in Table 2.6-1. Box, Davies, and Swann[2] recommended that the algorithm of Davies, Swann, and Campey (DSC)[3] be executed to bracket the minimum and that all subsequent calculations follow Powell's algorithm.[4] These two algorithms will now be described.

[1] G. F. Coggins, Univariate Search Methods, *Imperial Chemical Industries Ltd., Central Instr. Lab. Res. Note* 64/11, 1964.

[2] M. J. Box, D. Davies, and W. H. Swann, "Non-linear Optimization Techniques." Chemical Industries Monograph 5, Oliver and Boyd, Edinburgh, 1970.

[3] ICI Note 64/3, 1964.

[4] M. J. D. Powell, *Computer J.*, **7**:155 (1964). See also J. Walsh (ed.), "Numerical Analysis," Academic Press Inc., London, 1966.

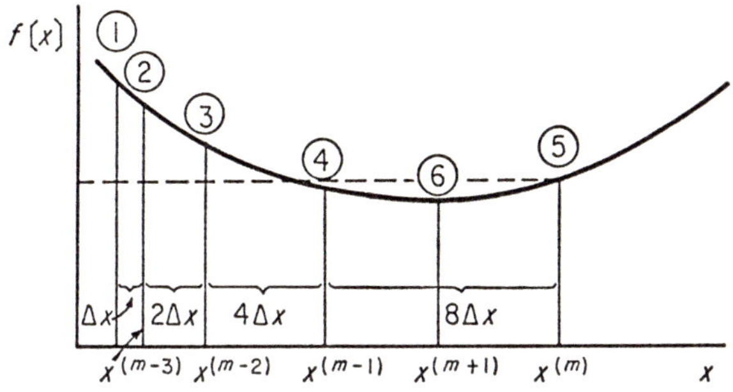

Fig. 2.6–2 DSC unidimensional minimization.

In the DSC unidimensional search, steps of increasing size are taken until the minimum is overshot and then a single quadratic interpolation is performed. Figure 2.6–2 illustrates the procedure ($x^{(m)}$ is the first value of x that overshoots the minimum, and Δx is the step size), of which the steps are:

Step 1: Evaluate $f(x)$ at the initial point $x^{(0)}$. If $f(x^{(0)} + \Delta x) \leq f(x^{(0)})$, go to step 2. If $f(x^{(0)} + \Delta x) > f(x^{(0)})$, let $\Delta x = -\Delta x$ and go to step 2.

Step 2: Compute $x^{(k+1)} = x^{(k)} + \Delta x$.

Step 3: Compute $f(x^{(k+1)})$.

Step 4: If $f(x^{(k+1)}) \leq f(x^{(k)})$, double Δx and return to step 2 with $k = k + 1$. If $f(x^{(k+1)}) > f(x^{(k)})$, denote $x^{(k+1)}$ by $x^{(m)}$, $x^{(k)}$ by $x^{(m-1)}$, etc., reduce Δx by one-half, and return to steps 2 and 3 for one more (only) calculation.

Step 5: Of the four equally spaced values of x in the set $\{x^{(m+1)}, x^{(m)}, x^{(m-1)}, x^{(m-2)}\}$, discard either $x^{(m)}$ or $x^{(m-2)}$, whichever is farthest from the x corresponding to the smallest value of $f(x)$ in the set. Let the remaining three values of x be denoted by $x^{(a)}$, $x^{(b)}$, and $x^{(c)}$, where $x^{(b)}$ is the center point and $x^{(a)} = x^{(b)} - \Delta x$ and $x^{(c)} = x^{(b)} + \Delta x$.

Step 6: Carry out a quadratic interpolation to estimate x^*.

$$x^* \approx \tilde{x}^* = x^{(b)} + \frac{\Delta x[f(x^{(a)}) - f(x^{(c)})]}{2[f(x^{(a)}) - 2f(x^{(b)}) + f(x^{(c)})]}$$

These steps complete the first stage of the DSC method. To continue, a new start is made from $\tilde{x}^*$ or $x^{(c)}$, if $f(x^{(c)}) < f(\tilde{x}^*)$, Δx is reduced, and step 1 begun again.

In Powell's algorithm a quadratic approximation is carried out using the first three points obtained in the direction of search. The x corresponding

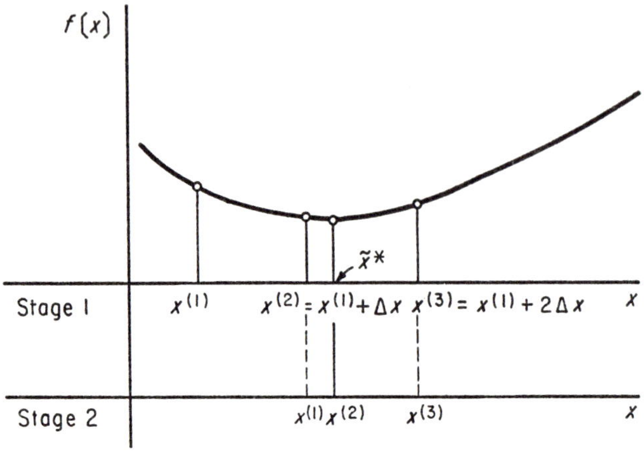

Fig. 2.6-3 Powell's unidimensional minimization.

to the minimum of the quadratic function is determined, and these quadratic approximations are continued until the minimum of $f(x)$ is located to the required precision. Powell's algorithm proceeds as follows; examine Fig. 2.6-3.

Step 1: From the base vector $x^{(1)}$ compute $x^{(2)} = x^{(1)} + \Delta x$.
Step 2: Compute $f(x^{(1)})$ and $f(x^{(2)})$.
Step 3: If $f(x^{(1)}) > f(x^{(2)})$, let $x^{(3)} = x^{(1)} + 2\Delta x$.
If $f(x^{(1)}) \leq f(x^{(2)})$, let $x^{(3)} = x^{(1)} - \Delta x$.
Step 4: Compute $f(x^{(3)})$.
Step 5: Estimate the value of x at the minimum of $f(x)$, $\tilde{x}^*$, by

$$\tilde{x}^* = \frac{1}{2}\frac{[(x^{(2)})^2-(x^{(3)})^2]f(x^{(1)})+[(x^{(3)})^2-(x^{(1)})^2]f(x^{(2)})+[(x^{(1)})^2-(x^{(2)})^2]f(x^{(3)})}{(x^{(2)}-x^{(3)})f(x^{(1)})+(x^{(3)}-x^{(1)})f(x^{(2)})+(x^{(1)}-x^{(2)})f(x^{(3)})}$$

Step 6: If $\tilde{x}^*$ and whichever of $\{x^{(1)},x^{(2)},x^{(3)}\}$ corresponding to the smallest $f(x)$ differ by less than the prescribed accuracy in x, or the accuracy in the corresponding values of $f(x)$, terminate the search. Otherwise, evaluate $f(\tilde{x}^*)$ and discard from the set $\{x^{(1)},x^{(2)},x^{(3)}\}$ the one that corresponds to the greatest value of $f(x)$, unless a bracket on the minimum of $f(x)$ will be lost by so doing, in which case discard the x so as to maintain the bracket. Go to step 5.

The algorithm continues until the desired precision listed in step 6 is obtained.

A combination of the DSC and Powell algorithms has been shown to be better than either of the individual algorithms. The combined DSC-Powell algorithm consists of one stage (steps 1 through 6) of the DSC algorithm to bracket the minimum followed by step 6 of the Powell algorithm, and then successively steps 5 and 6 of the Powell algorithm.

A direct comparison of the DSC-Powell unidimensional search with, say, the golden section search from the viewpoint of the time required or the number of functional evaluations executed is only moderately meaningful. Poor techniques can be discarded from such a comparison, but what really is of importance is how the unidimensional search operates when embedded in a higher-dimensional optimization problem.

To this end Fig. 2.6–4 illustrates the times to execute the solution of two problems, one with two and the other with four independent variables, by the Davidon-Fletcher-Powell method (see Sec. 3.4).

Prob. 1. Rosenbrock's function:

$$f(\mathbf{x}) = 100(x_2 - x_1^2)^2 + (1 - x_1)^2$$

Prob. 2. Fletcher-Powell function:

$$f(\mathbf{x}) = (x_1 + 10x_2)^2 + 5(x_3 - x_4)^2 + (x_2 - 2x_3)^4 + 10(x_1 - x_4)^4$$

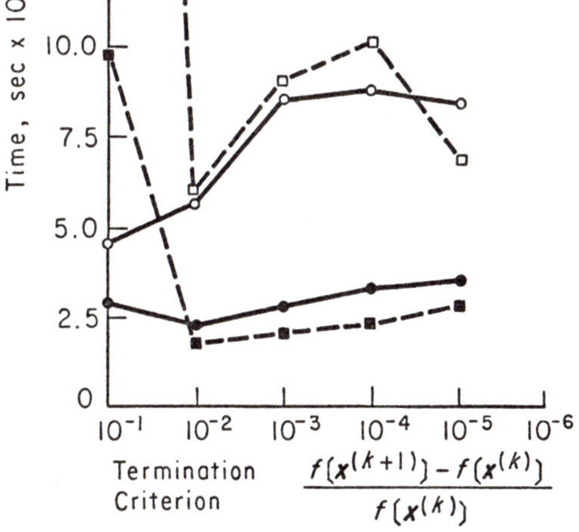

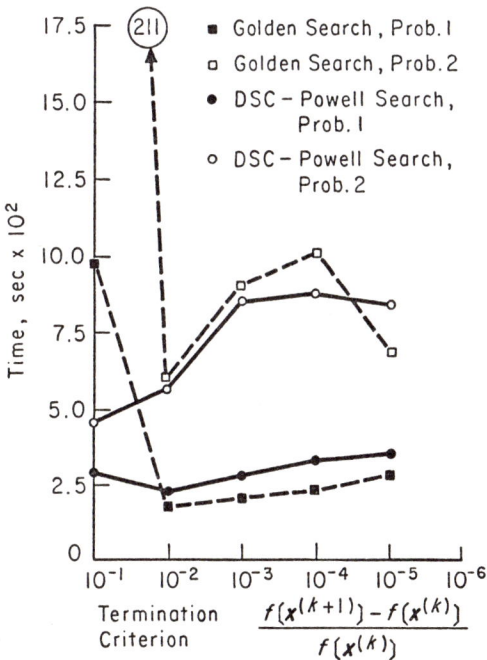

Fig. 2.6–4 Time to solve two different problems using two different unidimensional searches.

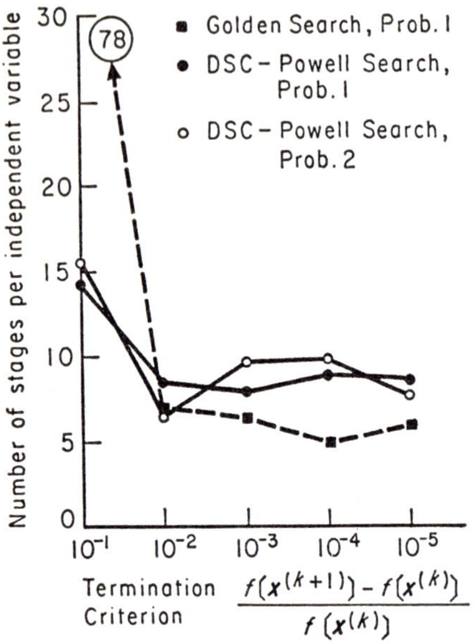

Fig. 2.6-5 Number of stages to termination for two different unidimensional search methods.

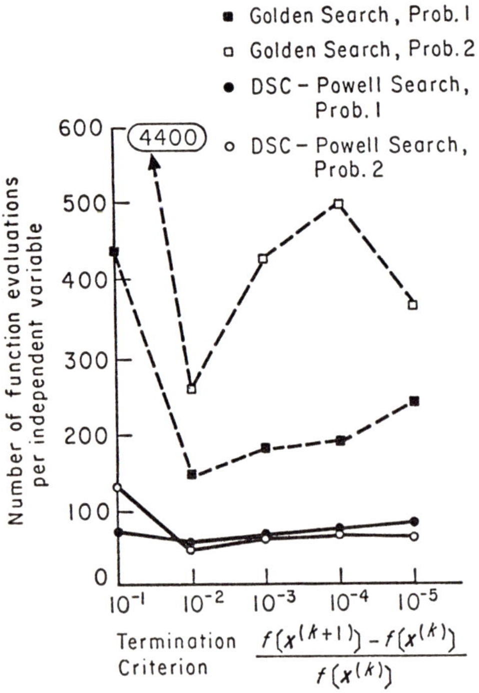

Fig. 2.6-6 Number of functional evaluations per independent variable in the unidimensional search for two different search methods.

For various termination criteria in the fractional change in $f(\mathbf{x})$, the DSC-Powell and golden search were roughly of the same effectiveness as measured by the time of execution, except for the very lowest termination level (10^{-1}).

Figure 2.6–5 shows the number of stages (new search directions) per independent variable. Data for the golden search for Prob. 2 are far enough off the graph so that they have been omitted. Figure 2.6–6 demonstrates how the number of function evaluations in the one-dimensional searches changed with the termination criterion. If the evaluation of the objective function takes any significant amount of time, it would appear as a result of Fig. 2.6–6 that the DSC-Powell search is clearly preferable. The number of partial-derivative (components of the gradient) evaluations are not displayed, but keep in mind that there were two derivative evaluations on each stage of Prob. 1 and 4 on each stage of Prob. 2.

If the function being minimized is not unimodal locally, as has been assumed to be true in the above discussion, extra logic must be added to the unidimensional search code to ensure that the step size is adjusted to fit the local optimum actually sought. For example, Fig. 2.6–7 illustrates how a large initial step can lead to an unbounded solution to a problem when, in fact, a local minimum was sought.

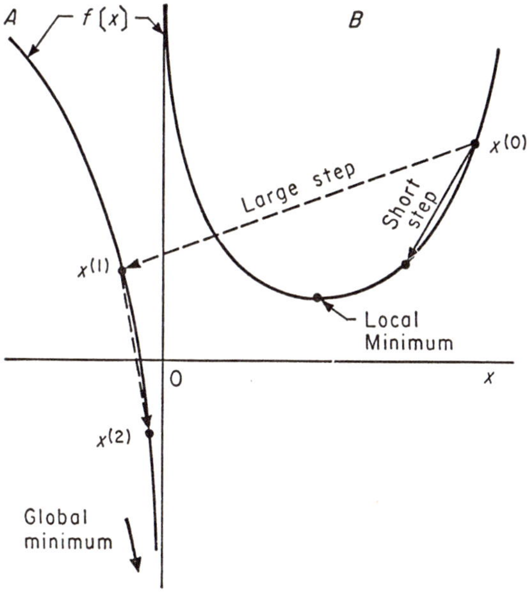

Fig. 2.6–7 A unidimensional search for a local minimum of a multimodal objective function leads to an unbounded solution.

2.7 CLASSIFICATION OF NONLINEAR PROGRAMMING TECHNIQUES

Quite a large number of algorithms have been proposed to solve the general nonlinear programming problem, mainly because no one method appears to be far superior to all the others. The selection of a particular technique at the current state of development rests on the formulation of the problem and the experience of the analyst.

Table 2.7–1 lists a number of methods of classifying nonlinear programming problems. Subsequent chapters in this book are based on the problem-statement-oriented classification scheme that is listed as 1.1 in Table 2.7–1. However, an equally valid scheme is to distinguish between various characteristics of the solution technique as illustrated by classification 2 in the table. Because the hardware and software for computers have been changing so rapidly, this book does not attempt to treat optimization methods specifically from the viewpoint of categories 3 or 4. Gilbert[1] has prepared an annotated bibliography on parameter optimizations suitable for hybrid computers.

Table 2.7–1 Classification of nonlinear programming techniques

1 *Classification by the components of the problem statement*
- 1.1 Constrained vs. unconstrained objective function
  - (*a*) Unconstrained
  - (*b*) Equality constraints
  - (*c*) Inequality constraints
  - (*d*) Both equality and inequality constraints
- 1.2 Discrete (integer) vs. continuous variables
- 1.3 Convex, quadratic, separable, etc., programming

2 *Classification by a characteristic of the solution technique*
- 2.1 Derivative vs. derivative-free (search)
- 2.2 Analytical vs. numerical derivatives
- 2.3 First-order vs. second-order derivatives
- 2.4 Gradient vs. gradient-free
- 2.5 Small-step vs. large-step gradient
- 2.6 Simultaneous iteration on all variables vs. relaxation (one variable at a time) in a search technique
- 2.7 Interior vs. exterior point methods
- 2.8 Deterministic vs. random search
- 2.9 Feasible vs. nonfeasible starting vector

3 *Classification by type of computer to be used in the execution of the algorithm*
- 3.1 Digital vs. hybrid vs. analog

4 *Classification by the programming language used*

[1] E. G. Gilbert, *Simulation*, **10**:350 (1967).

SUPPLEMENTARY REFERENCES

Fiacco, A. V.: Sequential Unconstrained Minimization Methods for Nonlinear Programming, Ph.D. dissertation, Northwestern University, Evanston, Ill., 1967.

———, and G. P. McCormick: "Sequential Unconstrained Minimization Techniques for Nonlinear Programming," Wiley, New York, 1968.

Kunzi, H. P.: Zum heutigen stand der nichtlinearen Optimierungs Theorie, *Unternehmersforsch*, **12**:1 (1968).

———, W. Krelle, and W. Oettli: "Nonlinear Programming," Blaisdell, Waltham, Mass., 1966.

———, H. G. Tzscharch, and C. A. Zehnder: "Numerical Methods of Mathematical Optimization," Academic, New York, 1968.

Mangasarian, O. L.: "Nonlinear Programming," McGraw-Hill, New York, 1969.

———, and Fromovitz: The Fritz-John Necessary Optimality Conditions in the Presence of Equality and Inequality Constraints, *J. Math. Anal. Appl.*, **17**:34 (1967).

Schechter, R. S., and G. S. G. Beveridge: Sufficiency Conditions in Constrained Variations, *Ind. Eng. Chem. Fundamentals*, **5**:571 (1966).

———, and ———: "Optimization: Theory and Practice," McGraw-Hill, New York, 1970.

Wilde, D. J., and C. S. Beightler: "Foundations of Optimization," Prentice-Hall, Englewood Cliffs, N.J., 1967.

Zangwill, W. I.: "Nonlinear Programming: A Unified Approach," Prentice-Hall, Englewood Cliffs, N.J., 1969.

PROBLEMS

2.1 Rewrite the following linear programming problems in matrix notation.

(*a*) Minimize: $f(\mathbf{x}) = 3x_1 + 2x_2 + x_3$

Subject to: $g_1(\mathbf{x}) = 2x_1 + 3x_2 + x_3 \geq 10$

$g_2(\mathbf{x}) = x_1 + 2x_2 + x_3 \geq 15$

(*b*) Maximize: $f(\mathbf{x}) = 5x_1 + 10x_2 + 12x_3$

Subject to: $g_1(\mathbf{x}) = 15x_1 + 10x_2 + 10x_3 \leq 200$

$g_2(\mathbf{x}) = x_1 \geq 0$

$g_3(\mathbf{x}) = x_2 \geq 0$

$g_4(\mathbf{x}) = x_3 \geq 0$

$h_1(\mathbf{x}) = 10x_1 + 25x_2 + 20x_3 = 300$

2.2 Put the following nonlinear objective function into matrix notation by defining suitable matrices; $\mathbf{x} = [x_1 \quad x_2]^T$.

$$f(\mathbf{x}) = 3 + 2x_1 + 3x_2 + 2x_1^2 + 2x_1x_2 + 6x_2^2$$

2.3 Transform Prob. 2.37 to the standard form of the NLP problem given by Eqs. (2.2-1), (2.2-2), and (2.2-3).

2.4 Classify the following problems as (*a*) linear, (*b*) quadratic, (*c*) convex, (*d*) nonlinear programming problems (more than one classification may apply to a problem).

2.1*a*	2.15*a*
2.1*b*	2.15*b*
2.6	2.16
2.11	2.18

2.5 Classify each of the following matrices as (*a*) positive definite, (*b*) negative definite, (*c*) neither.

(*a*) $\begin{bmatrix} 1 & 0 \\ 0 & 1 \end{bmatrix}$ (*c*) $\begin{bmatrix} 0.1 & 0 \\ 3 & 1 \end{bmatrix}$

(*b*) $\begin{bmatrix} 1 & 1 \\ 1 & 1 \end{bmatrix}$ (*d*) $\begin{bmatrix} 1 & -2 \\ -2 & 1 \end{bmatrix}$

2.6 Sketch the objective function and constraints of the following nonlinear programming problems.

(*a*) Minimize: $f(\mathbf{x}) = 2x_1^2 - 2x_1x_2 + 2x_2^2 - 6x_1 + 6$

Subject to: $g_1(\mathbf{x}) = x_1 + x_2 \le 2$

(*b*) Minimize: $f(\mathbf{x}) = x_1^3 - 3x_1x_2 + 4$

Subject to: $g_1(\mathbf{x}) = 5x_1 + 2x_2 \ge 18$

$h_1(\mathbf{x}) = -2x_1 + x_2^2 = 5$

(*c*) Minimize: $f(\mathbf{x}) = -5x_1^2 + x_2^2$

Subject to: $g_1(\mathbf{x}) = \dfrac{x_1^2}{x_2^2} - \dfrac{1}{x_2} \le -1$

$g_2(\mathbf{x}) = x_1 \ge 0$

$g_3(\mathbf{x}) = x_2 \ge 0$

2.7 Examine Problems 2.1*a*, 2.1*b*, 2.38 and Problem 13 (in Appendix A). For each problem state (a) the total number of variables and (2) the number of independent variables. List a suitable set of variables for both categories.

2.8 Formulate the following problems as nonlinear programming problems.

(*a*) Find the length and height and width of a rectangular tank open at the top which provide the maximum volume for a fixed surface area A (A = sides + bottom).

(*b*) Find the "curve of quickest descent" from one point to another, that is, the path a particle should take to minimize the transition time. This classical problem (called the brachistochrone) was first proposed by John Bernoulli in 1696.

(*c*) Condensing steam at temperature T_s in a heat exchanger is used to heat oil from T_1 to T_2. The effective earnings of additional area can be expressed in terms of incremental costs about a reference state

$$R = \underbrace{QC_Q\theta}_{\substack{\text{value of}\\\text{energy}\\\text{recovered}}} - \underbrace{AC_Fr}_{\substack{\text{cost of}\\\text{incremental}\\\text{capacity}}} - rC_C \tag{1}$$

where R = incremental revenue, \$/year
Q = heat transfer rate, Btu/hr
C_Q = value of incremental energy transferred, \$/Btu
θ = hours of operation per year
A = incremental heat transfer area of exchanger, ft^2
C_F = incremental cost of exchanger area, $\$/\text{ft}^2$
r = annual charges, $\dfrac{(\$\text{ charge})}{(\$\text{ cost})(\text{year})}$
C_C = cost of exchanger without adding area, \$/hr

The energy balance which forms the constraint for Eq. (1) is based on a macroscopic steady-state model of the exchanger

$$WC_P(T_2 - T_1) = Q = UA\frac{T_2 - T_1}{\ln[(T_s - T_1)/(T_s - T_2)]}$$

where W = flow rate, a constant, lb/hr
C_P = heat capacity, a constant, Btu/(lb)(°F)
U = overall heat transfer coefficient, a constant, Btu/(hr)(ft^2)(ΔT)

Find the maximum revenue.

(*d*) The investment for piping and pipe fittings constitutes an important part of the total investment for a chemical plant. It is necessary, therefore, to choose pipe sizes which give a minimum total pumping and fixed charges. The optimum economic cost of pipe can be expressed as follows:

$$C = \underbrace{\frac{AqKWH_g}{PD^3E}}_{\substack{\text{pumping}\\\text{cost}}} + \underbrace{XD^n + (1 + F)XD^nK_F}_{\substack{\text{fixed and}\\\text{installation}\\\text{cost}}} \tag{1}$$

where C = total cost, \$/(year)(ft)
A = constant
q = fluid flow rate, ft^3/sec
ρ = fluid density, lb/ft^3
μ_0 = fluid viscosity, cp
K = cost of electric energy, \$/kwhr
W = mechanical work, (ft)(lb)/lb
H_g = hours of operation per year
E = efficiency of motor and pumping, fraction
V = average linear velocity of fluid, ft/sec
D = inside diameter of pipe, in.
L = length of pipe, ft
X = cost of new pipe per foot if pipe diameter = 1 in., \$/ft
n = constant dependent on type of pipe
F = ratio of total cost for fitting and installation to cost of pipe
K_F = annual fixed charges, including maintenance fraction

The mechanical energy balance is the physical relationship that applies to the fluid flow.

$$W = \frac{2fV^2L(1 - J)}{g_c D}$$

For viscous flow ($N_{Re} < 2100$)

$$f = \frac{16}{N_{Re}} \qquad N_{Re} = \frac{LV\rho}{\mu}$$

where f = friction factor
N_{Re} = Reynolds number
g_c = 32.17 (ft)(lb$_m$)/(sec^2)(lb$_f$)
J = fractional loss due to fittings and bends, fraction

Find the minimum cost in terms of the optimum pipe diameter.

2.9 What is a unimodal function, and what is its significance in optimization?

2.10 Distinguish between the local and global extrema of the following objective function.

$$f(\mathbf{x}) = 2x_1^3 + x_2^2 + x_1^2x_2^2 + 4x_1x_2 + 3$$

2.11 How many independent variables are there in the following problem?

Minimize: $(13/2)x_1^2 + (5/2)x_2^2 + (1/2)x_3^2 - 4x_1x_2 + 3x_1x_3 - 2x_2x_3 + y_4^2 + y_4y_5 + y_5^2 + 3y_4 - 2y_5$

Subject to:
$$y_1 \equiv 13x_1 - 4x_2 + 3x_3 + y_4 + 3y_5 \geqq 0$$
$$y_2 \equiv -4x_1 + 5x_2 - 2x_3 + y_5 - 1 \geqq 0$$
$$y_3 \equiv 3x_1 - 2x_2 + x_3 - 2y_4 - 2 \geqq 0$$
$$y_4 \geqq 0$$
$$y_5 \geqq 0$$

2.12 Give an example of a convex objective function; a concave objective function; a convex objective function subject to concave inequality constraints.

2.13 Is the following problem a convex programming problem?

Minimize: $f(\mathbf{x}) = 100x_1 + \dfrac{200}{x_1x_2}$

Subject to: $2x_2 + \dfrac{300}{x_1x_2} \leq 1$

$x_1, x_2 \geq 0$

2.14 Give an example of a positive definite matrix; a semidefinite matrix.

2.15 Obtain an objective function which has more than one local minimum but not an infinite number. Specify the global minimum.

2.16 Are the following vectors (*a*) feasible or nonfeasible vectors with regard to Prob. 2.1*b*; (*b*) interior or exterior vectors?

(1) $\mathbf{x} = [5 \quad 2 \quad 10]^T$

(2) $\mathbf{x} = [10 \quad 2 \quad 7.5]^T$

(3) $\mathbf{x} = [0 \quad 0 \quad 0]^T$

2.17 Shade the feasible region of the nonlinear programming problems of Prob. 2.6. Is $\mathbf{x} = [1 \quad 1]^T$ an interior, boundary, or exterior point in these problems?

2.18 Indicate which portion of the following function is convex and which portion concave.

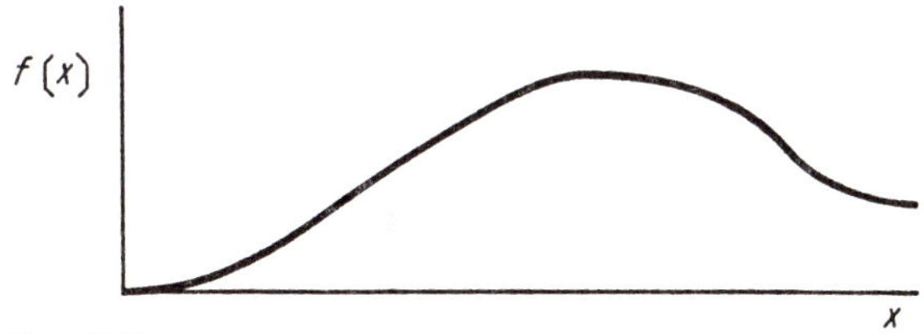

Fig. P2.18

2.19 Is the quadratic function

$$f(\mathbf{x}) = 10 + 10x_1 + x_2 - 6x_1^2 - 3x_2^2$$

convex, concave, neither, or both? Is a general quadratic function always either convex or concave?

2.20 Separable functions are those that can be expressed in the form

$$\psi(\mathbf{x}) = \sum_{i=1}^{n} \psi_i(\mathbf{x})$$

For example, $x_1^2 + x_2^2 + x_3^2$ is a separable function because

$$\psi(\mathbf{x}) = \sum x_i^2$$

Show that if the terms in a separable function are convex, the separable function is convex.

2.21 Find whether or not the following objective functions are convex.

(*a*) $f(\mathbf{x}) = 3x_1^2 - 4x_1x_2 + x_2^2$

(*b*) $f(\mathbf{x}) = e^{x_1} + x_2^2 + 1$

2.22 What is the feasible region for $\mathbf{x}$ given the following constraints? Sketch the feasible region for the two-dimensional problems.

(*a*) $h_1(\mathbf{x}) = x_1 + x_2 - 3 = 0$

$h_2(\mathbf{x}) = 2x_1 - x_2 + 1 = 0$

(*b*) $h_1(\mathbf{x}) = x_1^2 + x_2^2 + x_3^2 = 0$

$h_2(\mathbf{x}) = x_1 + x_2 + x_3 = 0$

(c) $g_1(\mathbf{x}) = x_1 - x_2^2 - 2 \geq 0$

$g_2(\mathbf{x}) = x_1 - x_2 + 4 \geq 0$

(d) $h_1(\mathbf{x}) = x_1^2 + x_2^2 + 3$

$g_1(\mathbf{x}) = x_1 - x_2 + 2 \geq 0$

$g_2(\mathbf{x}) = x_1 \geq 0$

$g_3(\mathbf{x}) = x_2 \geq 0$

2.23 Answer the questions below for the following problem; in each case *justify* your answer.

Minimize: $f(\mathbf{x}) = \frac{1}{4}x_1^4 - \frac{1}{2}x_1^2 - x_2$

Subject to: $x_1^2 + x_2^2 = 4$

$x_1 - x_2 \leq 2$

(a) Is the problem a convex programming problem?
(b) Is the point $\mathbf{x} = [1 \quad 1]^T$ a feasible point?
(c) Is the point $\mathbf{x} = [2 \quad 2]^T$ an interior point?
(d) Is $f(\mathbf{x})$ a unimodal function?

2.24 Under what circumstances is a local minimum guaranteed to be the global minimum? (Be brief.)

2.25 Determine the gradient and the value of the gradient of the following objective functions at the designated points.

(a) $f(\mathbf{x}) = 3x_1^2 - 2x_1x_2 + 6x_2^2$

At $\mathbf{x} = [0 \quad 0]^T$

At $\mathbf{x} = [1 \quad 2]^T$

(b) $f(\mathbf{x}) = 4x_1^2 - 2x_1x_2 + 2x_2^3$

At $\mathbf{x} = [-1 \quad 0]^T$

At $\mathbf{x} = [-1 \quad -1]^T$

2.26 What is the gradient of $f(\mathbf{x}) = x_1e^{x_2} + x_1x_2$ evaluated at $\mathbf{x} = [2 \quad 3]^T$?

2.27 Approximate $f(\mathbf{x})$ given in Prob. 2.26 at the point $\mathbf{x} = [1 \quad 1]^T$ by a second-order (quadratic) approximate.

2.28 Approximate the following objective functions at the designated point by (1) a linear (first-order) expansion in a Taylor series, and (2) a quadratic (second-order) expansion in a Taylor series.

$$f(\mathbf{x}) = e^{x_1^2 + 2x_2^2} - 10x_1x_2 \qquad \text{at } \mathbf{x} = [1 \quad 1]^T$$

2.29 If the second-order-constraint qualification holds, does the first-order-constraint qualification also hold?

2.30 What are the necessary and sufficient conditions to ascertain the maximum of a function of a single variable?

2.31 Two solutions to the nonlinear programming problem

$$\text{Minimize:} \quad f(\mathbf{x}) = 7x_1 - 6x_2 + 4x_3$$
$$\text{Subject to:} \quad h_1(\mathbf{x}) = x_1^2 + 2x_2^2 + 3x_3^2 - 1 = 0$$
$$h_2(\mathbf{x}) = 5x_1 + 5x_2 - 3x_3 - 6 = 0$$

have been reported, apparently a maximum and a minimum.

$$\mathbf{x} = \begin{bmatrix} 0.947 \\ 0.207 \\ -0.0772 \end{bmatrix} \qquad \mathbf{x} = \begin{bmatrix} 0.534 \\ 0.535 \\ -0.219 \end{bmatrix}$$
$$f(\mathbf{x}) = 5.08 \qquad\qquad f(\mathbf{x}) = -0.346$$

Verify that these **x** vectors respectively satisfy the necessary and sufficient conditions for a maximum and a minimum.

2.32 The problem

$$\text{Minimize:} \quad f(\mathbf{x}) = 100(x_2 - x_1^2)^2 + (1 - x_1)^2$$
$$\text{Subject to:} \quad x_1^2 + x_2^2 \leq 2$$

is reported to have a local minimum at the point $\mathbf{x}^* = [1 \quad 1]^T$. Determine if the necessary conditions for a local optimum are satisfied. Is this local optimum also a global optimum?

2.33 The following objective function can be seen by inspection to have a minimum at $x = 0$.

$$f(x) = |x^3|$$

Can the criteria of Sec. 2.5 be applied to this objective function?

2.34 Determine whether or not the saddle point for the function $f(\mathbf{x}) = 1 - x_1^2 - 4x_1x_2 - x_2^2$ constrained by the cylinder $x_1^2 + x_2^2 = 2$ is a local minimum.

2.35 For the problem

$$\text{Minimize:} \quad f(\mathbf{x}) = x_2^2$$
$$\text{Subject to:} \quad g_1(\mathbf{x}) = -x_1^3 + x_2^3 \geq 0$$
$$g_2(\mathbf{x}) = x_1^3 + x_2^3 \geq 0$$
$$g_3(\mathbf{x}) = x_1^2 + x_2^2 + 2x_2 \geq 0$$

test to determine if the proposed solution

$$\mathbf{x} = [0 \quad 0]^T$$

satisfies the Theorems of Sec. 25.

2.36 Determine whether or not the suggested solution $\mathbf{x} = [0.82 \quad 0.43 \quad 0.77]^T$ to the problem

$$\text{Minimize:} \quad f(\mathbf{x}) = \frac{2}{x_1 + 0.5} + \frac{1}{x_2 + 0.2} + \frac{3}{x_3 + 0.5}$$

$$\text{Subject to:}\quad 4x_1 + 7x_2 + 3x_3 \le 10$$
$$3x_1 + 4x_2 + 5x_3 \le 8$$
$$x_1, x_2, x_3 \ge 0$$

is an optimal solution (to two significant figures).

2.37 Determine whether or not the suggested solution $\mathbf{x} = [0.75 \quad 0.57 \quad 0.69]^T$ to the problem

$$\text{Minimize:}\quad f(\mathbf{x}) = \frac{2}{x_1 + 0.5} + \frac{1}{x_2 + 0.2} + \frac{3}{x_3 + 0.5}$$
$$\text{Subject to:}\quad 3x_1 + 4x_2 + 5x_3 = 8$$
$$x_1, x_2, x_3 \ge 0$$

is an optimal solution (to two significant figures).

2.38 The following minimization problem

$$\text{Minimize:}\quad f(\mathbf{x}) = 4x_1 - x_2^2 - 12$$
$$\text{Subject to:}\quad 25 - x_1^2 - x_2^2 = 0$$
$$10x_1 - x_1^2 + 10x_2 - x_2^2 - 34 \ge 0$$
$$(x_1 - 3)^2 + (x_2 - 1)^2 \ge 0$$
$$x_1, x_2 \ge 0$$

has been solved numerically to yield what is thought to be the solution to the problem, namely, the vector $\mathbf{x} = [1.000 \quad 4.900]^T$. Show whether or not the $\mathbf{x}$ vector found satisfies the necessary and sufficient conditions for it to be a solution to the problem. Give all your computational details.

2.39 Minimize $f(\mathbf{x}) = x^2 - x$ starting from the point $x = 3$ by the following unidimensional searches:

(*a*) Golden search
(*b*) DSC-Powell
(*c*) DSC search alone

Let $|\Delta x^{(0)}| = 0.1$. Complete enough function evaluations to reduce $|\Delta x^{(k)}| < 10^{-3}$. Plot the value of $[f(x^{(k+1)}) - f(x^{(k)})]$ vs. sequence number k for each method. You can bracket the minimum for the golden search by the DSC method.

2.40 Find the minimum of $f(\mathbf{x})$ in the direction of steepest descent from the point $\mathbf{x}^{(0)} = [2 \quad 2]^T$ for the objective function $f(\mathbf{x}) = x_1^2 + 25x_2^2$. [*Hint:* Let $\mathbf{x}^{(1)} = \mathbf{x}^{(0)} + \lambda \nabla f(\mathbf{x}^{(0)})$. Minimize $f(\mathbf{x}^{(1)})$ with respect to λ.]

2.41 Suppose it is desired to find the real roots of the equation

$$f_1(\mathbf{x}) = 3000 - 100x^2 - 4x^5 - 6x^6 = 0 \qquad (a)$$

How can this problem be converted into an optimization problem? Suppose further that it is desired to find the real roots of both Eqs. (*a*) and (*b*) simultaneously.

$$f_2(\mathbf{x}) = 6x^4 + 4x^3 + 100x^2 - 3000 = 0 \qquad (b)$$

How can this latter problem be converted into an optimization problem?

2.42 The coefficients in the empirical model $y = \beta_0 + \beta_1 x_1 + \beta_2 x_2$ are to be estimated by least squares, that is, by minimizing the sum of the squares of the deviations between the predicted value of y (using the estimated coefficients) and the experimental values of y. Formulate the problem as an optimization problem.

2.43 Show that the objective function

$$f(\mathbf{x}) = 55.84 + [7.31 \quad 26.65]\mathbf{x} + \mathbf{x}^T \begin{bmatrix} -3.03 & 1.345 \\ 1.345 & -6.96 \end{bmatrix} \mathbf{x}$$

where $\mathbf{x}^T = [x_1 \quad x_2]^T$, is strictly convex. Show that $-g(\mathbf{x})$ is strictly concave, where the constraint is $g(\mathbf{x}) = 85.72 + 21.85x_1 + 8.59x_2 - 9.20x_1^2 - 5.18x_2^2 - 6.26x_1x_2$. Then show that the extremum obtained in minimizing $f(\mathbf{x})$ is a global extremum.

Part Two

Unconstrained nonlinear programming methods

In Table 2.7–1, the first classification of nonlinear programming problems in category 2 is (1) methods that use derivatives in the optimization vs. (2) methods that do not use derivatives—commonly known as search methods. Chapter 3 treats category 1 methods, and Chap. 4 treats category 2—both for unconstrained problems. Chapter 5 compares the effectiveness of the various methods. Of course, this classification is not clear-cut, because some techniques, for example, evaluate the components of the gradient of the objective function by difference schemes or minimize in the direction of a gradient by a search technique. We have the space to consider only a few of the many solution techniques, and these techniques have been selected from the viewpoint of their effectiveness by themselves and in connection with the algorithms discussed in subsequent chapters describing constrained nonlinear programming, because several of the important constrained nonlinear programming algorithms require the use of an effective unconstrained minimization procedure.

3

Unconstrained minimization procedures using derivatives

The general nonlinear programming problem without constraints reduces to just

$$\text{Minimize:} \quad f(\mathbf{x}) \qquad \mathbf{x} \in E^n \tag{3.0-1}$$

where $f(\mathbf{x})$ is the objective function. Guided by the remarks in Sec. 2.5–1, we seek minimization methods that lead to a stationary point of $f(\mathbf{x})$, that is, $\nabla f(\mathbf{x}^*) = \mathbf{0}$. In this chapter we consider how to solve problem (3.0–1) by algorithms that make use of first and second partial derivatives of $f(\mathbf{x})$. We first describe the search directions prescribed by steepest descent, then Newton's method, conjugate directions, and finally, some of the methods of approximating the direction given by Newton's method by using only first derivatives.

3.1 GRADIENT METHODS

In this section we briefly set forth the strategy of gradient (steepest descent) methods of unconstrained optimization; these methods use only first derivatives of the objective function in the calculations. At the kth stage, the transition from a point $\mathbf{x}^{(k)}$ to another point $\mathbf{x}^{(k+1)}$ can be viewed as given by the following expression:

$$\mathbf{x}^{(k+1)} = \mathbf{x}^{(k)} + \Delta\mathbf{x}^{(k)} = \mathbf{x}^{(k)} + \lambda^{(k)}\hat{\mathbf{s}}^{(k)} = \mathbf{x}^{(k)} + \lambda^{*(k)}\mathbf{s}^{(k)} \qquad (3.1\text{–}1)$$

where $\Delta\mathbf{x}^{(k)}$ = vector from $\mathbf{x}^{(k)}$ to $\mathbf{x}^{(k+1)}$
$\hat{\mathbf{s}}^{(k)}$ = a unit vector in direction $\Delta\mathbf{x}^{(k)}$
$\mathbf{s}^{(k)}$ = any vector in direction $\Delta\mathbf{x}^{(k)}$
$\lambda^{(k)}, \lambda^{*(k)}$ = scalars such that $\Delta\mathbf{x}^{(k)} = \lambda^{(k)}\hat{\mathbf{s}}^{(k)} = \lambda^{*(k)}\mathbf{s}^{(k)}$

3.1-1 The Method of Steepest Descent

The method of steepest descent for unconstrained minimization can be traced back to the work of the well-known French mathematician Cauchy. As mentioned in Sec. 2.4–4, the gradient of the objective function $f(\mathbf{x})$ at any point $\mathbf{x}$ is a vector in the direction of the greatest local increase in $f(\mathbf{x})$. Clearly, then, one might proceed in the direction opposite to the gradient of $f(\mathbf{x})$, that is, in the direction of *steepest descent*, for the negative gradient of $f(\mathbf{x})$ at $\mathbf{x}^{(k)}$ points in the direction of the greatest decrease in $f(\mathbf{x})$ with respect to each of the components of $\mathbf{x}$, and is orthogonal to the contour of $f(\mathbf{x})$ at $\mathbf{x}^{(k)}$. Introduction of the negative of the normalized (or unit) gradient of $f(\mathbf{x})$, that is, the direction of steepest descent, defined at $\mathbf{x}^{(k)}$ by

$$\hat{\mathbf{s}}^{(k)} = -\frac{\nabla f(\mathbf{x}^{(k)})}{\|\nabla f(\mathbf{x}^{(k)})\|} \qquad (3.1\text{–}2)$$

into Eq. (3.1–1) gives the transition from $\mathbf{x}^{(k)}$ to $\mathbf{x}^{(k+1)}$ as

$$\begin{aligned}\mathbf{x}^{(k+1)} &= \mathbf{x}^{(k)} - \frac{\lambda^{(k)}\nabla f(\mathbf{x}^{(k)})}{\|\nabla f(\mathbf{x}^{(k)})\|}\\ &= \mathbf{x}^{(k)} - \lambda^{*(k)}\nabla f(\mathbf{x}^{(k)})\end{aligned} \qquad (3.1\text{–}3)$$

The negative of the gradient gives the direction for optimization but not the magnitude of the step to take, so that various steepest descent procedures are possible, depending upon the choice of λ and the meaning of the symbol $\|\nabla f(\mathbf{x}^{(k)})\|$. Because one step in the direction of steepest descent will not, in general, arrive at the minimum of $f(\mathbf{x})$, Eq. (3.1–3) must be applied repetitively until the minimum is reached. At minimum, the value of the elements of the vector gradient will each be equal to zero. As a special case of an objective function, if $f(\mathbf{x}) = \frac{1}{2}\mathbf{x}^T\mathbf{A}\mathbf{x}$, then $\nabla f(\mathbf{x}^{(k)}) = \mathbf{A}\mathbf{x}^{(k)}$ can be substituted into Eq. (3.1–3).

A procedure of strictly steepest descent can terminate at any type of stationary point, i.e., at a point where the elements of gradient of $f(\mathbf{x})$ are zero. It is usually necessary to determine if this point is a local minimum (i.e., a solution) or a saddle point. If it is a saddle point, it is necessary to employ a nongradient method to move away from the point, after which the minimization may continue as before. The stationary point may be tested by examining the hessian matrix of the objective function, if available, evaluated at the stationary point. If the matrix is not positive definite, the stationary point is a saddle point. Various rules are employed to terminate a series of steepest descent steps, based either on the value of $f(\mathbf{x})$, of $\mathbf{x}$ itself, λ, the $\nabla f(\mathbf{x})$, or some combination of these, as well as corresponding values on previous steps. The success of a particular method in converging efficiently to a local minimum depends on the rules, as well as the character of the problem itself.

Two general methods of selecting the step size λ are employed, although many others may be envisioned. In one method the objective function is minimized with respect to λ in order to move from $\mathbf{x}^{(k)}$ to $\mathbf{x}^{(k+1)}$, while in the other method a fixed, or variable, value is selected for λ.

We consider first the adjustment of λ to minimize $f(\mathbf{x})$ in a preselected search direction. All old information is discarded as it is replaced by new information, so that no acceleration of the optimization can be carried out. Convergence of steepest descent in this form can be demonstrated.[1] It can be shown that, with a convex objective function having third-order differentiability (and a few other even less restrictive functions), the method converges in the limit as $k \to \infty$. However, this feature of steepest descent is of little consolation in practice because the rate of convergence can be intolerably slow, as has been shown by numerical experiments and also by theory.[2]

If the point $\mathbf{x}^{(k+1)}$ is to be determined by use of Eq. (3.1–3), then $f(\mathbf{x})$ can be minimized formally by computing λ from the solution of

$$\frac{df(\mathbf{x}^{(k)} + \lambda \hat{\mathbf{s}}^{(k)})}{d\lambda} = 0$$

As a specific example, suppose that $f(\mathbf{x})$ is a quadratic function [insert $\lambda \hat{\mathbf{s}}^{(k)}$ for $(\mathbf{x} - \mathbf{x}^{(k)})$ in Eq. (2.4–5)]. Then

$$\frac{df(\mathbf{x}^{(k)} + \lambda \hat{\mathbf{s}}^{(k)})}{d\lambda} = 0 = \nabla^T f(\mathbf{x}^{(k)}) \hat{\mathbf{s}}^{(k)} + (\hat{\mathbf{s}}^{(k)})^T \mathbf{H} \lambda \hat{\mathbf{s}}^{(k)} \qquad (3.1\text{–}4)$$

yielding a relation for $\lambda^{(k)}$ of

$$\lambda^{(k)} = -\frac{\nabla^T f(\mathbf{x}^{(k)}) \hat{\mathbf{s}}^{(k)}}{(\hat{\mathbf{s}}^{(k)})^T \mathbf{H} \hat{\mathbf{s}}^{(k)}} \qquad (3.1\text{–}5)$$

[1] A. A. Goldstein, *Numerical Math.*, **4**:146 (1962).

[2] H. Akaike, *Ann. Inst. Statist. Math. Tokyo*, **11**:1 (1959).

Alternatively, $f(\mathbf{x})$ can be minimized by a numerical search as described in Sec. 2.6.

An interesting feature of the procedure of minimization for a quadratic function is that $\nabla f(\mathbf{x}^{(k+1)})$ is orthogonal to $\hat{\mathbf{s}}^{(k)}$, demonstrated as follows. Observe that if

$$f(\mathbf{x}) = \mathbf{a} + \mathbf{x}^T\mathbf{b} + \tfrac{1}{2}\mathbf{x}^T\mathbf{H}\mathbf{x}$$

the gradient of $f(\mathbf{x})$ is

$$\nabla f(\mathbf{x}) = \mathbf{b} + \mathbf{H}\mathbf{x} \tag{3.1-6}$$

so that

$$\nabla f(\mathbf{x}^{(0)}) = \mathbf{b} + \mathbf{H}\mathbf{x}^{(0)}$$

$$\cdots\cdots\cdots\cdots\cdots\cdots$$

$$\nabla f(\mathbf{x}^{(k)}) = \mathbf{b} + \mathbf{H}\mathbf{x}^{(k)}$$

Introduction of the expression for $\nabla f(\mathbf{x}^{(k)})$ into Eq. (3.1-4) leads to

$$(\mathbf{b} + \mathbf{H}\mathbf{x}^{(k)})^T\hat{\mathbf{s}}^{(k)} + (\hat{\mathbf{s}}^{(k)})^T\mathbf{H}\lambda^{(k)}\hat{\mathbf{s}}^{(k)} = 0$$

and introduction of $\mathbf{x}^{(k+1)} - \mathbf{x}^{(k)}$ for $\lambda^{(k)}\hat{\mathbf{s}}^{(k)}$ and rearrangement leads to

$$(\hat{\mathbf{s}}^{(k)})^T(\mathbf{b} + \mathbf{H}\mathbf{x}^{(k)}) + (\hat{\mathbf{s}}^{(k)})^T\mathbf{H}(\mathbf{x}^{(k+1)} - \mathbf{x}^{(k)}) = 0$$

or

$$(\hat{\mathbf{s}}^{(k)})^T(\mathbf{b} + \mathbf{H}\mathbf{x}^{(k+1)}) = (\hat{\mathbf{s}}^{(k)})^T\nabla f(\mathbf{x}^{(k+1)}) = 0 \tag{3.1-7}$$

In other words, the gradient at $\mathbf{x}^{(k+1)}$ is orthogonal to the previous search direction $\mathbf{s}^{(k)}$ (see Fig. 3.1-1).

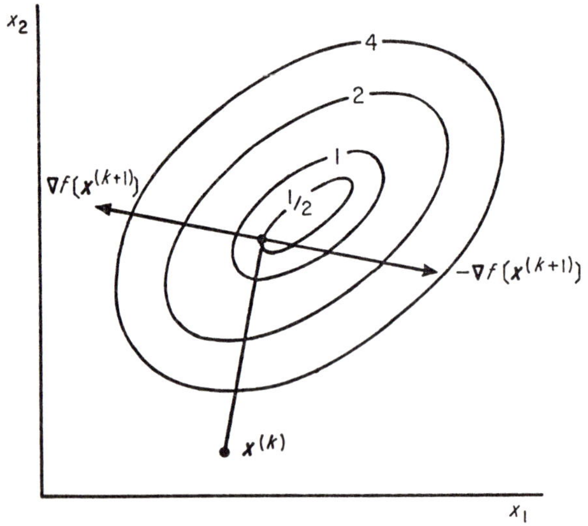

Fig. 3.1-1 Illustrates that $(\mathbf{s}^{(k)})^T\nabla f(\mathbf{x}^{(k+1)}) = 0$ for a quadratic function if $f(\mathbf{x})$ is minimized in the $\mathbf{s}^{(k)}$ direction.

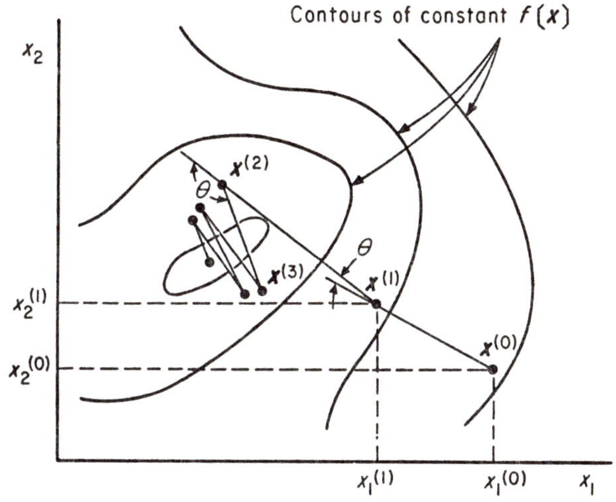

Fig. 3.1-2 Oscillation in the method of steepest descent.

If a fixed or adjustable value of the scalar λ is selected for the method of steepest descent, the value of λ must be controlled carefully in order to avoid either an unexpected increase in $f(\mathbf{x})$ or an excessive number of steps in reaching the solution. The first event will occur if λ is too large, and the second if λ is very small, or if λ is so large as to result in oscillation about the minimum as illustrated in Fig. 3.1-2. Thus the value of λ must be reduced as the minimum is approached. One possible method of controlling λ involves establishing a criterion for λ based on the angle θ between successive vector steps in the minimization. For example, if the angle is smaller than a given value, then λ should be multiplied by some predetermined constant α; if the angle is larger, then λ should be divided by α.

Example 3.1-1 Method of steepest descent

A few cycles of the method of steepest descent will be described to illustrate the technique for the problem.

Minimize: $f(\mathbf{x}) = x_1^2 + 25x_2^2$

Consider first using a fixed step length λ having an initial value of unity. On each stage values of the following functions are required:

$$\frac{\partial f(\mathbf{x}^{(k)})}{\partial x_1} = 2x_1^{(k)} \qquad \frac{\partial f(\mathbf{x}^{(k)})}{\partial x_2} = 50x_2^{(k)}$$

$$\|\nabla f(\mathbf{x}^{(k)})\| = \sqrt{\left(\frac{\partial f(\mathbf{x}^{(k)})}{\partial x_1}\right)^2 + \left(\frac{\partial f(\mathbf{x}^{(k)})}{\partial x_2}\right)^2}$$

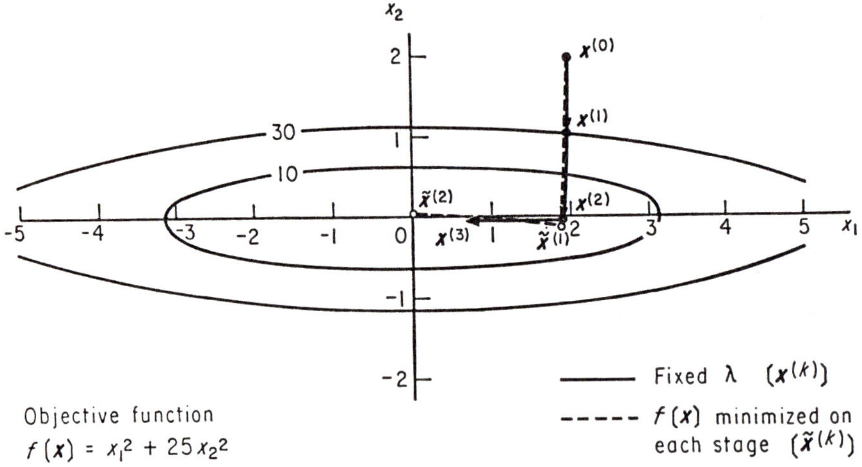

Fig. E3.1–1a

After starting at $\mathbf{x}^{(0)} = [2 \quad 2]^T$, the following steps are taken:

Stage	x_1	x_2	$\frac{\partial f(\mathbf{x}^{(k)})}{\partial x_1}$	$\frac{\partial f(\mathbf{x}^{(k)})}{\partial x_2}$	$\lVert \nabla f(\mathbf{x}^{(k)}) \rVert$	*Step to next stage* Δx_1	Δx_2
0	2	2	4	100	~100	−0.04	−1.00
1	1.96	1.00	3.92	50	50.1	−0.078	−1.00
2	1.88	0	3.76	0	3.76	−1.00	0
3	0.88	0					

Refer to Fig. E3.1–1a for the trajectory of the path of the search.

For the method to converge, λ usually must be successively reduced by some fraction or the search will oscillate back and forth. Note that at the minimum, $\mathbf{x} = [0 \quad 0]^T$, $\nabla f(\mathbf{x}) = \mathbf{0}$.

The results of the three corresponding stages of calculation in which, rather than using a fixed λ, the minimum of $f(\mathbf{x})$ is sought in the direction of steepest descent are:

Stage k	$\lambda^{(k)}$	x_1	x_2	$\frac{\partial f(\mathbf{x}^{(k)})}{\partial x_1}$	$\frac{\partial f(\mathbf{x}^{(k)})}{\partial x_2}$	$f(\mathbf{x}^{(k)})$
0		2	2	4	100	104
1	2.003	1.92	−0.003	3.84	−0.15	3.19
2	1.850	0.070	0.070	0.14	3.50	0.13
3	0.070	0.070	−0.000			

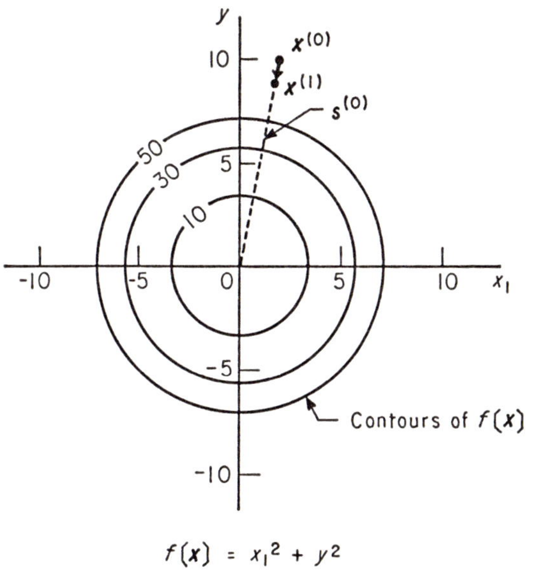

Fig. E3.1-1*b*

Observe in Fig. 3.1-1*a* that the gradient of $f(\mathbf{x})$ does not point in the direction of the minimum at the start of the search because the scale of x_1 and x_2 is quite different. By a change of variable

$$y = 5x_2$$

the function to be minimized becomes

$$f(\mathbf{x}) = x_1^2 + y^2$$

and the vector at $x_1 = 1$, $y = 5x_2 = 10$, does indeed point to the minimum, because the scales of x_1 and y are now the same; examine Fig. E3.1-1*b*.

If the nonlinear objective function is too complex to differentiate analytically, the partial derivative components of the gradient can be approximated by difference relations. For example, with two variables the forward difference relations are

$$\frac{\partial f(\mathbf{x}^{(k)})}{\partial x_1} \approx \frac{f((x_1^{(k)} + \delta_1), x_2^{(k)}) - f(x_1^{(k)}, x_2^{(k)})}{\delta_1} \qquad (a)$$

$$\frac{\partial f(\mathbf{x}^{(k)})}{\partial x_2} \approx \frac{f(x_1^{(k)}, (x_2^{(k)} + \delta_2)) - f(x_1^{(k)}, x_2^{(k)})}{\delta_2} \qquad (b)$$

where the δ_i are some small perturbations. Only three evaluations of the objective function are needed, namely, at the points $(x_1^{(k)}, x_2^{(k)})$, $[(x_1^{(k)} + \delta_1), x_2^{(k)}]$, and $[x_1^{(k)}, (x_2^{(k)} + \delta_2)]$, on each cycle k. The values of δ_i in general are selected so that the numerical error in the approximation to the derivative is reduced to a reasonable level, but inasmuch as (1) the gradient does not necessarily point in the direction of the minimum at $\mathbf{x}^{(k)}$ and (2) the gradient is reevaluated at each stage, the numerical error is important primarily in the vicinity of the minimum where $\nabla f(\mathbf{x}) \to \mathbf{0}$.

For illustrative purposes only we evaluate the gradient components by the difference formulas (*a*) and (*b*) in this example. Let $\delta_1 = \delta_2 = 0.05$. Then:

Point				$\frac{\partial f(\mathbf{x}^{(k)})}{\partial x_1}$		$\frac{\partial f(\mathbf{x}^{(k)})}{\partial x_2}$	
x_1	x_2	$x_1 + \delta_1$	$x_2 + \delta_2$	*Approximate*	*Exact*	*Approximate*	*Exact*
2	2	2.05	2.05	4.05	4.00	101.25	100.0
0.01	0.01	0.06	0.06	0.070	0.02	1.80	0.50

At some distance from the minimum the difference approximations for the derivatives are quite good, but near the minimum they are not as satisfactory. Of course, it would be possible to reduce the value of δ_i as the search progressed or use better approximation relations for the derivatives, but these matters need not be discussed here, inasmuch as alternative methods of unconstrained optimization are available that are superior to the method of steepest descent.

The main handicap in using the method of steepest descent, as pointed out in the example, is its dependence on the relative scaling of the decision variables. If the hyperspace is very elongated so as to form a "ridge," or "valley" (the ratio of the maximum to minimum eigenvalue of $\mathbf{H}(\mathbf{x})$ at any point is large), steepest descent techniques converge too slowly to be effective, and may fail to converge at all in a reasonable time. Figure 3.1–3 demonstrates the difficulty; the direction of steepest descent proves to be nearly orthogonal to the best direction to go to get to the minimum of $f(\mathbf{x})$. One way out of this difficulty is to make use of second-order information (information provided by the second partial derivatives of the objective function with respect to the independent variables, or their approximates), a subject to be discussed in Secs. 3.2 and 3.4. Another approach, which we will describe first, is to adjust the scaling of the independent variables in the objective function.

3.1–2 Scaling of the Independent Variables

Example 3.1–1 has indicated that as the scale for a coordinate changes, the direction of steepest descent changes. Thus an arbitrary change in the units of the independent variables will change the direction of steepest descent and influence the effectiveness of the gradient minimization. One way to circumvent the difficulty might be to substitute dimensionless variables

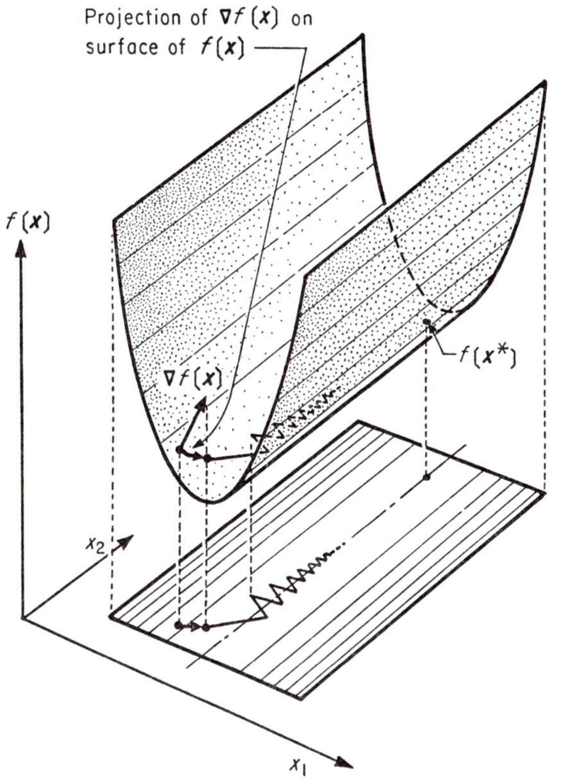

Fig. 3.1-3 Characteristic oscillation of the method of steepest descent in a narrow valley.

obtained by dividing each variable by its range, such as

$$\hat{T} = \frac{T - T_1}{T_2 - T_1} \qquad \hat{p} = \frac{p - p_1}{p_2 - p_1}$$

where T stands for temperature and p for pressure, for the original variables, but even this adjustment artificially fixes the distance between $p_2 - p_1$ to be the same as between $T_2 - T_1$.

If the general definition of distance in E^n is taken to be

$$ds^r = \frac{|dx_1|^r + |dx_2|^r + \cdots + |dx_n|^r}{n}$$

in an n-dimensional problem, where r is the matrix index, it can be shown[1]

[1] H. Elder, Ph.D. dissertation, Purdue University, Lafayette, Ind., 1966.

that the ratio of the change in any two unscaled coordinates is given by

$$\frac{dx_i}{dx_j} = \pm \left| \frac{\partial f(\mathbf{x})/\partial x_i}{\partial f(\mathbf{x})/\partial x_j} \right|^{1/(r-1)} \tag{3.1-8}$$

The plus sign is used when the partial derivatives have the same sign, and the minus sign is used when they have the opposite sign. For the usual metric ($r = 2$), one obtains

$$\frac{dx_i}{dx_j} = \pm \frac{\partial f(\mathbf{x})/\partial x_i}{\partial f(\mathbf{x})/\partial x_j}$$

which corresponds to the direction obtained from the gradient.

Suppose, though, that a change in scale (units) is made for the decision variables so that

$$x_i = \psi(\tilde{x}_i)$$

where $\tilde{x}_i$ is the scaled variable. Normally, such a change is linear, as for example, a temperature conversion

$$T\,(\text{in }^\circ\text{F}) = 1.8T\,(\text{in }^\circ\text{C}) + 32$$

so that $\mu_i = \partial\psi(\tilde{x}_i)/\partial\tilde{x}_i$ is a constant. Then the ratio of the change in any two unscaled variables can be shown to be

$$\frac{dx_i}{dx_j} = \pm \left| \frac{\partial f(\mathbf{x})/\partial x_i}{\partial f(\mathbf{x})/\partial x_j} \right|^{1/(r-1)} \left| \frac{\mu_i}{\mu_j} \right|^{r/(r-1)} \tag{3.1-9}$$

The effect of the scale choice is given by $|\mu_i/\mu_j|^{r/(r-1)}$. For the case of $r = 2$,

$$\frac{dx_i}{dx_j} = \frac{\partial f(\mathbf{x})/\partial x_i}{\partial f(\mathbf{x})/\partial x_j} \left(\frac{\mu_i}{\mu_j} \right)^2$$

from which it can be concluded that the relative change in the variables x_i and x_j can be anything, depending on what the scale factors are. Consequently, there is no unique direction of steepest descent.

Certain interesting conclusions can be drawn by selecting other metric indexes, such as $r = 0$, $r = 1$, and $r = \infty$. For $r = 0$, corresponding to $ds = (|dx_1|\ |dx_2| \cdots |dx_n|)^{-n}$, the ratio dx_i/dx_j is the same for both the unscaled and scaled variables. Box and Wilson[1] effected the same scaling by making the rate of change of the objective function with respect to one dimensionless variable be equal to that obtained with respect to another dimensionless variable.

[1] G. E. P. Box and K. B. Wilson, *J. Roy. Statist. Soc.*, **B13**:1 (1951).

For the case of $r = 1$, Eq. (3.1–8) yields

$$\frac{dx_i}{dx_j} = \pm\infty$$

indicating that a step is taken in one coordinate direction only, the one with the largest associated partial derivative. Such a step corresponds to a univariate search, the step being selected by the magnitude of the $\partial f/\partial x_i$.

As a final case, when $r = \pm\infty$, corresponding to $ds = \pm dx_k$, where $|dx_k| = \max_j(|dx_j|)$ for $r = +\infty$ and $|dx_k| = \min_j(|dx_j|)$ for $r = -\infty$, from Eq. (3.1–8),

$$\frac{dx_i}{dx_j} = \pm 1$$

implying that each coordinate is varied to the same extent on each successive stage of the optimization. Clearly, by selecting a suitable metric index and by scaling, a wide choice of directions can be used for the direction of steepest descent. Adjustment of the metric index itself during optimization has not been studied but might be the foundation for improved algorithms.

3.2 SECOND-DERIVATIVE (NEWTON'S) AND RELATED METHODS

From one viewpoint the search direction of steepest descent can be interpreted as contriving a linear approximation of the objective function; examine Fig. 3.2–1*a*. On the other hand, second-derivative methods, among which the best-known is Newton's method,[1] originate from the quadratic approximation of $f(\mathbf{x})$ given by Eq. (2.4–5). They make use of second-order information, that is, information obtained from the second partial derivatives of $f(\mathbf{x})$ with respect to the independent variables.

3.2–1 Newton's Method

The direction of search $\mathbf{s}$ for Newton's method is chosen as follows. If $(\mathbf{x} - \mathbf{x}^{(k)})$ of Eq. (2.4–5) is replaced by $\Delta\mathbf{x}^{(k)} = \mathbf{x}^{(k+1)} - \mathbf{x}^{(k)}$ as defined by Eq. (3.1–1), the quadratic approximation of $f(\mathbf{x})$ in terms of $\Delta\mathbf{x}^{(k)}$ is

$$f(\mathbf{x}^{(k+1)}) = f(\mathbf{x}^{(k)}) + \nabla^T f(\mathbf{x}^{(k)})\Delta\mathbf{x}^{(k)} + \tfrac{1}{2}(\Delta\mathbf{x}^{(k)})^T\nabla^2 f(\mathbf{x}^{(k)})\Delta\mathbf{x}^{(k)} \qquad (3.2\text{–}1)$$

[1] So called because the solution of the set of equations $\nabla f(\mathbf{x}) = \mathbf{0}$ by Newton's method yields Eq. (3.2–2); alternatively termed *quasilinearization methods*.

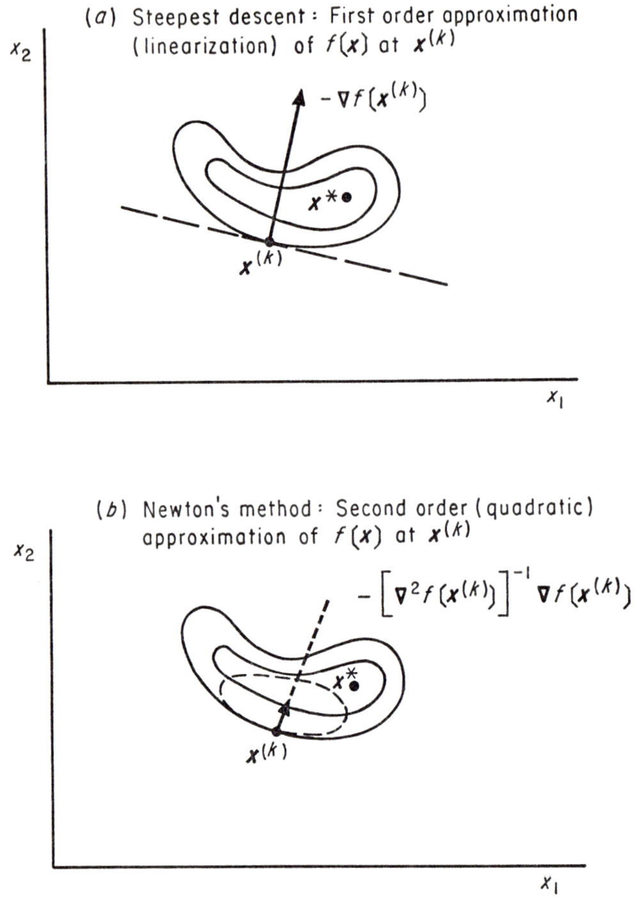

Fig. 3.2-1 Comparison of steepest descent with Newton's method from the viewpoint of objective function approximation. (*a*) Steepest descent: first-order approximation (linearization) of $f(\mathbf{x})$ at $\mathbf{x}^{(k)}$; (*b*) Newton's method: second-order (quadratic) approximation of $f(\mathbf{x})$ at $\mathbf{x}^{(k)}$.

The minimum of $f(\mathbf{x})$ in the direction of $\Delta\mathbf{x}^{(k)}$ is obtained by differentiating $f(\mathbf{x})$ with respect to each of the components of $\Delta\mathbf{x}$ and equating the resulting expressions to zero to give

$$\Delta\mathbf{x}^{(k)} = -[\nabla^2 f(\mathbf{x}^{(k)})]^{-1}\nabla f(\mathbf{x}^{(k)}) \tag{3.2-2}$$

where $[\nabla^2 f(\mathbf{x}^{(k)})]^{-1}$ is the inverse of hessian matrix $H(\mathbf{x}^{(k)})$ defined in Sec. 2.4 [the matrix of second partial derivatives of $f(\mathbf{x})$ with respect to $\mathbf{x}$ evaluated at $\mathbf{x}^{(k)}$].

Introduction of Eq. (3.2–2) into Eq. (3.1–1) yields the transition from $\mathbf{x}^{(k)}$ to $\mathbf{x}^{(k+1)}$ for Newton's method.

$$\mathbf{x}^{(k+1)} = \mathbf{x}^{(k)} - [\nabla^2 f(\mathbf{x}^{(k)})]^{-1}\nabla f(\mathbf{x}^{(k)}) \tag{3.2–3}$$

Note that both the direction *and* step length are specified. If $f(\mathbf{x})$ is actually quadratic, only one step is required to reach the minimum of $f(\mathbf{x})$. But for a general nonlinear objective function the minimum of $f(\mathbf{x})$ will not be reached in one step, so that Eq. (3.2–3) is usually modified to conform to Eq. (3.1–3) by introducing the parameter for the step length λ into Eq. (3.2–3).

$$\mathbf{x}^{(k+1)} = \mathbf{x}^{(k)} - \lambda^{(k)} \frac{[\nabla^2 f(\mathbf{x}^{(k)})]^{-1}[\nabla f(\mathbf{x}^{(k)})]}{\|[\nabla^2 f(x^{(k)})]^{-1}[\nabla f(\mathbf{x}^{(k)})]\|} \tag{3.2–4}$$

The ratio $\lambda^{(k)}/\|[\nabla^2 f(\mathbf{x}^{(k)})]^{-1}[\nabla f(\mathbf{x}^{(k)})]\|$ is just some scalar $\lambda^{*(k)}$; hence Eq. (3.2–4) is more frequently written as follows:

$$\mathbf{x}^{(k+1)} = \mathbf{x}^{(k)} - \lambda^{*(k)}\mathbf{H}^{-1}(\mathbf{x}^{(k)})\nabla f(\mathbf{x}^{(k)}) \tag{3.2–4a}$$

Observe that the search direction $\mathbf{s}$ is now given by $\mathbf{s}^{(k)} = -\mathbf{H}^{-1}(\mathbf{x}^{(k)})\nabla f(\mathbf{x}^{(k)})$. Equation (3.2–4*a*) is applied iteratively, as is Eq. (3.1–3), until some termination criterion is satisfied.

Note that in Eq. (3.2–4*a*) a matrix inversion is required, and one must be very cautious to use a technique that guarantees a positive definite inverse, as will be explained subsequently. Many standard digital computer programs for matrix inversion are unsatisfactory in this respect.[1] Also note that analytical second partial derivatives must be evaluated or approximated, which may not be practical in some instances. The criterion to guarantee convergence in Newton's method, assuming the function $f(\mathbf{x})$ is twice-differentiable, is that the inverse of the hessian matrix of the objective function should be positive definite (refer to Appendix C).

$$[\nabla^2 f(\mathbf{x}^{(k)})]^{-1} \equiv \mathbf{H}^{-1}(\mathbf{x}^{(k)}) > \mathbf{0} \tag{3.2–5}$$

Example 3.2–1 Comparison of first- and second-order derivative methods

To demonstrate the use of Eqs. (3.1–3) and (3.2–3), consider the poorly scaled objective function devised by Rosenbrock,[2] two contours of which ($f(\mathbf{x}) = 8$ and $f(\mathbf{x}) = 4$) are illustrated in Fig. E3.2–1.

$$f(\mathbf{x}) = 100(x_2 - x_1^2)^2 + (1 - x_1)^2 \tag{a}$$

[1] J. W. Langley, *J. Am. Statist. Assoc.*, **62**:819 (1967).
[2] H. H. Rosenbrock, *Computer J.*, **3**:174 (1960).

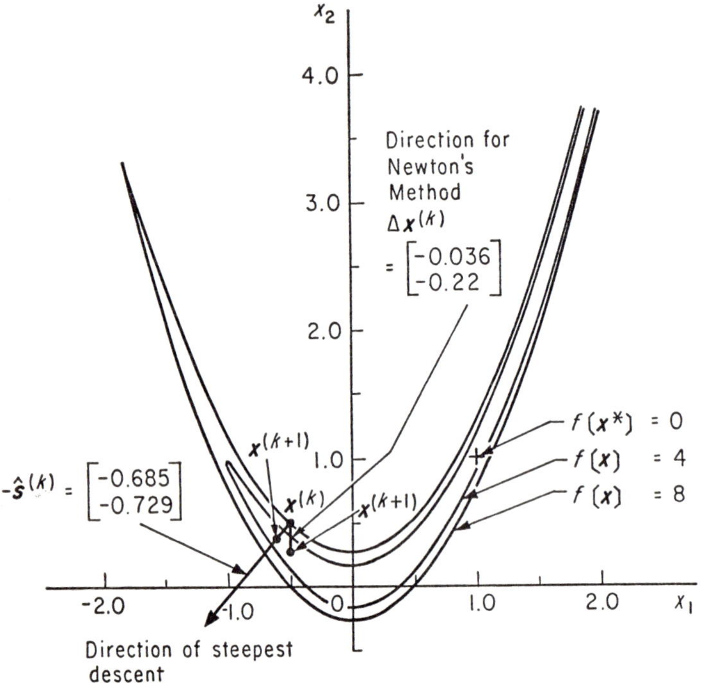

Fig. E3.2-1 The gradient and second-derivative methods for Rosenbrock's function.

Geometrically, $f(\mathbf{x})$ is interpreted as a slowly falling curved valley with its lowest point at $\mathbf{x}^* = [1 \quad 1]^T$, where $f(\mathbf{x}^*) = 0$.

METHOD OF STEEPEST DESCENT

Consider the point $\mathbf{x}^{(k)} = [-0.5 \quad 0.5]^T$, at which $f(\mathbf{x}^{(k)}) = 8.5$. The normalized gradient of $f(\mathbf{x})$ at $\mathbf{x}^{(k)} = [-0.5 \quad 0.5]^T$ is

$$\frac{1}{[(\partial f/\partial x_1)^2 + (\partial f/\partial x_2)^2]^{\frac{1}{2}}_{\mathbf{x}^{(k)}}} \begin{bmatrix} \partial f/\partial x_1 \\ \partial f/\partial x_2 \end{bmatrix}_{\mathbf{x}^{(k)}} = \frac{1}{68.6} \begin{bmatrix} 47 \\ 50 \end{bmatrix} = [0.685 \quad 0.729]^T \qquad (b)$$

The negative of the normalized gradient at $\mathbf{x}^{(k)}$, $\hat{\mathbf{s}}^{(k)} = [-0.685, -0.729]^T$, as shown in Fig. E3.2-1, points in the direction of steepest descent and is orthogonal to the contour of $f(\mathbf{x})$ that passes through $\mathbf{x}^{(k)}$.

To find the new vector $\mathbf{x}^{(k+1)}$, it is necessary to select a value for λ. For example, one can choose a specific value for λ or find that value of λ at which $f(\mathbf{x})$ achieves its minimum in the direction given by the unit vector $\hat{\mathbf{s}}^{(k)}$. At $\mathbf{x}^{(k)} = [-0.5 \quad 0.5]^T$,

Eq. (3.1–1) is

$$\mathbf{x}^{(k+1)} = \begin{bmatrix} -0.5 \\ 0.5 \end{bmatrix} - \lambda^{(k)} \begin{bmatrix} 0.685 \\ 0.729 \end{bmatrix} \qquad (c)$$

Consequently,

$$f(\mathbf{x}^{(k+1)}) = f(\lambda) = 100[0.5 - 0.729\lambda - (0.5 + 0.685\lambda)^2]^2 + (1.5 + 0.685\lambda)^2 \qquad (d)$$

The minimum of $f(\lambda)$ with respect to λ occurs at $\lambda = 0.164$. Introduction of $\lambda^{(k)} = 0.164$ into Eq. (c) gives the new point $\mathbf{x}^{(k+1)} = [-0.612 \quad 0.381]^T$, at which $f(\mathbf{x}) = 2.6$; examine Fig. E3.3–1. The new $\hat{\mathbf{s}}^{(k+1)}$ is determined at $\mathbf{x}^{(k+1)}$ by Eq. (3.1–2), and then $\mathbf{x}^{(k+2)}$ is found in the direction of $\hat{\mathbf{s}}^{(k+1)}$ in the same manner as $\mathbf{x}^{(k+1)}$ was found. This iterative procedure is continued until it is no longer possible to reduce the value of $f(\mathbf{x})$ or until some specified convergence criterion has been satisfied. As a matter of interest we should mention that the method of steepest descent will not be successful in rounding the curve in the valley of Rosenbrock's function.

NEWTON'S METHOD

Consider next Newton's method, starting from the same point, $\mathbf{x}^{(k)} = [-0.5 \quad 0.5]^T$; $\mathbf{x}^{(k+1)}$ is found using Eq. (3.2–3) or (3.2–4*a*) as follows:

$$\nabla^2 f(\mathbf{x}^{(k)}) = \begin{bmatrix} (-400x_2 + 1200x_1^2 + 2) & (-400x_1) \\ (-400x_1) & (200) \end{bmatrix}_{\mathbf{x}^{(k)}} = \begin{bmatrix} 102 & 200 \\ 200 & 200 \end{bmatrix}$$

$$\Delta\mathbf{x}^k = -[\nabla^2 f(\mathbf{x}^{(k)})]^{-1}\nabla f(\mathbf{x}^{(k)}) = \frac{1}{98}\begin{bmatrix} 1 & 1 \\ -1 & 0.51 \end{bmatrix}\begin{bmatrix} 47 \\ 50 \end{bmatrix} = \begin{bmatrix} -0.03 \\ -0.22 \end{bmatrix}$$

$$\mathbf{x}^{(k+1)} = \begin{bmatrix} -0.5 \\ 0.5 \end{bmatrix} + \begin{bmatrix} -0.03 \\ -0.22 \end{bmatrix} = \begin{bmatrix} -0.53 \\ 0.28 \end{bmatrix}$$

At $\mathbf{x}^{(k+1)} = [-0.53 \quad 0.28]^T$, the value of $f(\mathbf{x})$ is $f(\mathbf{x}) = 2.33$. The vector $\Delta\mathbf{x}^{(k)} = [-0.03 \quad -0.22]^T$ is shown in Fig. E3.2–1. The new $\Delta\mathbf{x}^{(k+1)}$ is evaluated at $\mathbf{x}^{(k+1)}$ by Eq. (3.2–2), and $\mathbf{x}^{(k+2)}$ is found by Eq. (3.2–3).

An alternative procedure would be to compute $\mathbf{s}^{(k)} = -\mathbf{H}^{-1}(\mathbf{x}^{(k)})\nabla f(\mathbf{x}^{(k)})$ as above but search in the direction of $\mathbf{s}^{(k)}$ for a λ that minimizes $f(\mathbf{x})$ as indicated by Eq. (3.2–4*a*). In either instance, the iterative procedure is repeated until a specified convergence criterion is satisfied or until it is no longer possible to reduce the value of $f(\mathbf{x})$. In practice, to reduce the computation time, the elements of $\mathbf{H}(\mathbf{x})$ may be computed less frequently than at every stage.

If Eq. (3.2–3) is used, Newton's method automatically provides a sequence of step lengths corresponding to the distance to minimize the respective quadratic approximates of $f(\mathbf{x})$ at successive values of $\mathbf{x}^{(k)}$. For instance, the quadratic approximation to Rosenbrock's function at $\mathbf{x}^{(k)} = [-0.5 \quad 0.5]^T$ is $q(\mathbf{x}^{(k)}) = -5.25 - 2x_1 + 50x_2 + 200x_1x_2 + 51x_1^2 + 100x_2^2$, and the minimum of $q(\mathbf{x}^{(k)})$ is at $\tilde{\mathbf{x}} = [-0.53 \quad 0.28]^T$. On the other hand, the first-derivative methods linearize $f(\mathbf{x})$ at $\mathbf{x}^{(k)}$, but a linear function has no minimum (or maximum) except at its extremities; hence a specific step length must be chosen in a direction orthogonal to the linearized $f(\mathbf{x})$.

3.2-2 Geometric Interpretation

We next provide a geometric interpretation of the local quadratic approximation to the objective function and illustrate the significance of the requirement that $\mathbf{H}^{-1}(\mathbf{x})$ be positive definite. A second-order (quadratic) function, as illustrated in Fig. 3.2-2, can be transformed to a new coordinate system by translation of the center of the old coordinates to the extremum of the function, and subsequent rotation of the axes to achieve symmetry. Let the old coordinates be designated by x_1 and x_2, and the new coordinates, termed *principal axes*, by $\tilde{x}_1$ and $\tilde{x}_2$. The two transformations yield a new relationship for the objective function, termed the *canonical function*, expressed in terms of the principal axes, a function that is much simpler than the original function, inasmuch as all the first-order and cross-product terms have been eliminated.

For example, for two independent variables the general quadratic objective function or approximate thereto from Eq. (2.4-5) is

$$f(\mathbf{x}) = b_0 + b_1x_1 + b_2x_2 + b_{11}x_1^2 + b_{22}x_2^2 + b_{12}x_1x_2 + b_{21}x_2x_1 \quad (3.2\text{-}6)$$

Equation (3.2-6) transforms to the canonical equation

$$f(\mathbf{x}) - f(\mathbf{x}^*) = \tilde{b}_{11}\tilde{x}_1^2 + \tilde{b}_{22}\tilde{x}_2^2 \quad (3.2\text{-}7)$$

where $f(\mathbf{x}^*)$ is the value of $f(\mathbf{x})$ at the center of the quadratic surface, $\tilde{b}_{11}$ and $\tilde{b}_{22}$ are the transformed coefficients, and the overlay tilde designates "in canonical form." The translation indicated in Fig. 3.2-2 corresponds to the

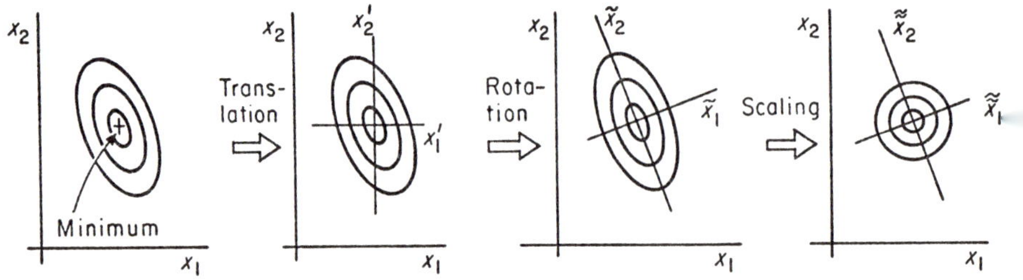

Fig. 3.2-2 Transformation of coordinates into the principal axes. The original coordinates are x_1, x_2; the canonical coordinates are $\tilde{x}_1$, $\tilde{x}_2$.

elimination of the linear terms, and the rotation corresponds to the elimination of the cross-product terms in Eq. (3.2–6). In Fig. 3.2–2, the right-hand panel depicts the result of scaling the transformed variables, so that the contours of the objective function become circles. Figure 3.2–3 illustrates typical examples of two-dimensional functions in terms of their original and principal axes. The elements of the hessian matrix of the objective function $\mathbf{H}(\mathbf{x})$ are easily related to the coefficients in Eq. (3.2–6).

$$\frac{\partial^2 f(\mathbf{x})}{\partial x_1^2} = 2b_{11} \qquad \frac{\partial^2 f(\mathbf{x})}{\partial x_1\,\partial x_2} = 2b_{12} = \frac{\partial^2 f(\mathbf{x})}{\partial x_2\,\partial x_1} = 2b_{21}$$

$$\frac{\partial^2 f(\mathbf{x})}{\partial x_2^2} = 2b_{22}$$

Furthermore, the coefficients $\tilde{b}_{11}$ and $\tilde{b}_{22}$ in Eq. (3.2–7), as shown in most books on matrices or linear algebra, are the eigenvalues of the matrix $\frac{1}{2}\mathbf{H}(\mathbf{x}^{(k)})$. The inverse of the hessian matrix of the objective function evaluated at $\mathbf{x}^{(k)}$ provides a measure of the curvative of $f(\mathbf{x})$ in the vicinity of $\mathbf{x}^{(k)}$.

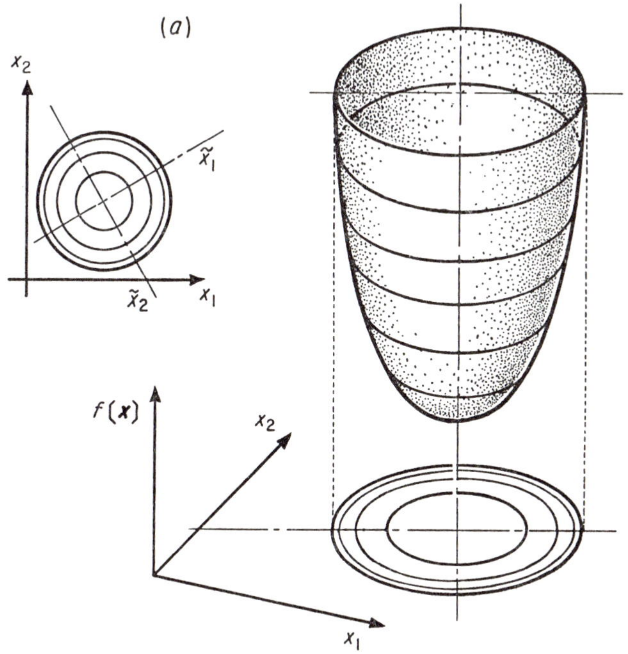

Fig. 3.2–3(*a*) Geometry of second-order objective functions of two independent variables.

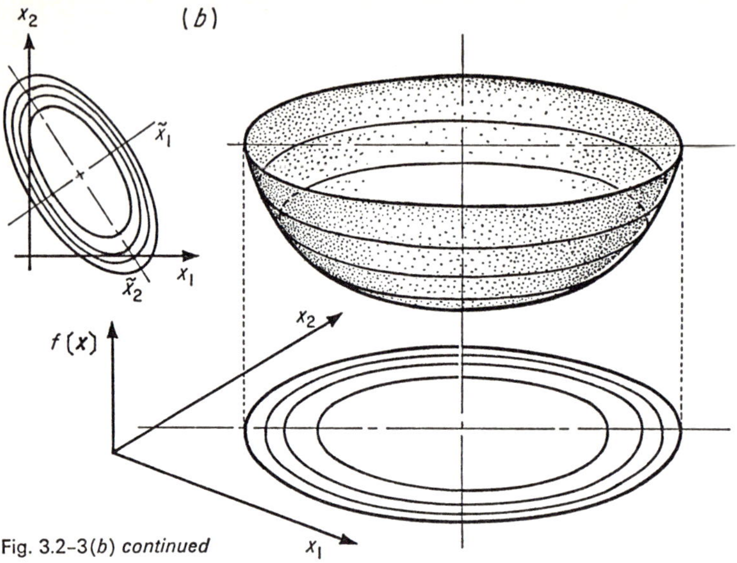

Fig. 3.2–3(*b*) *continued*

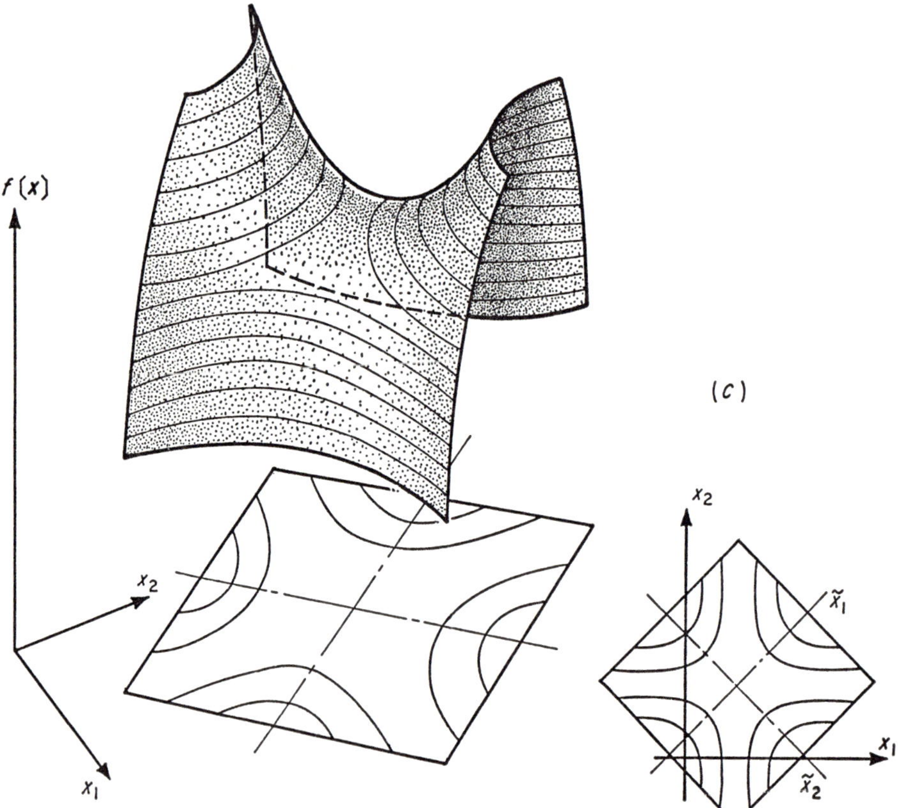

Fig. 3.2–3(*c*) *continued*

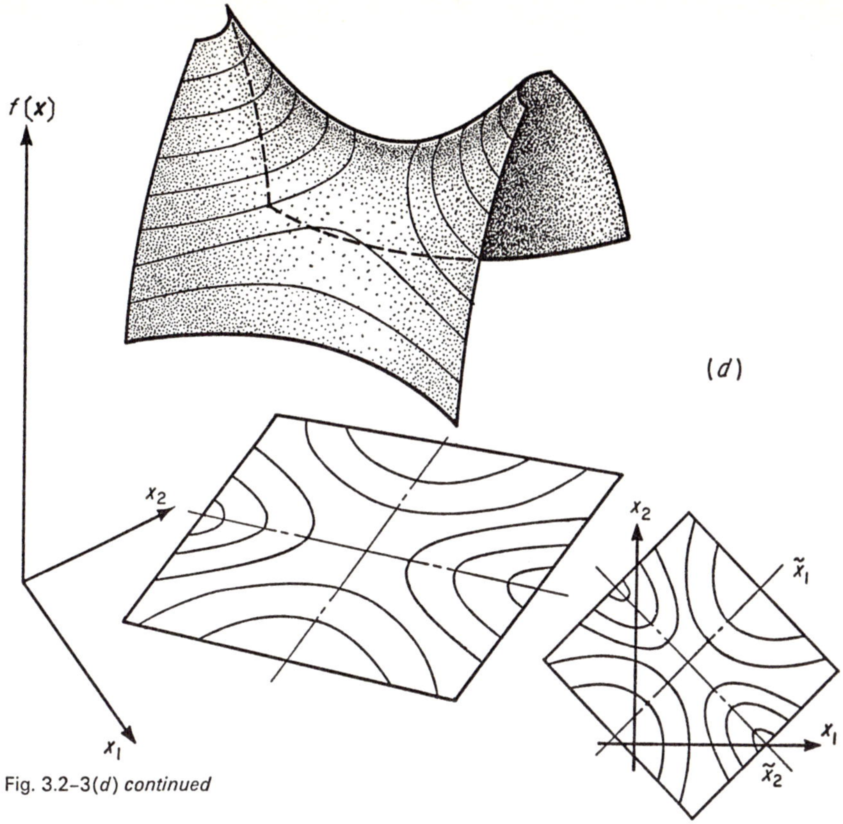

Fig. 3.2–3(*d*) *continued*

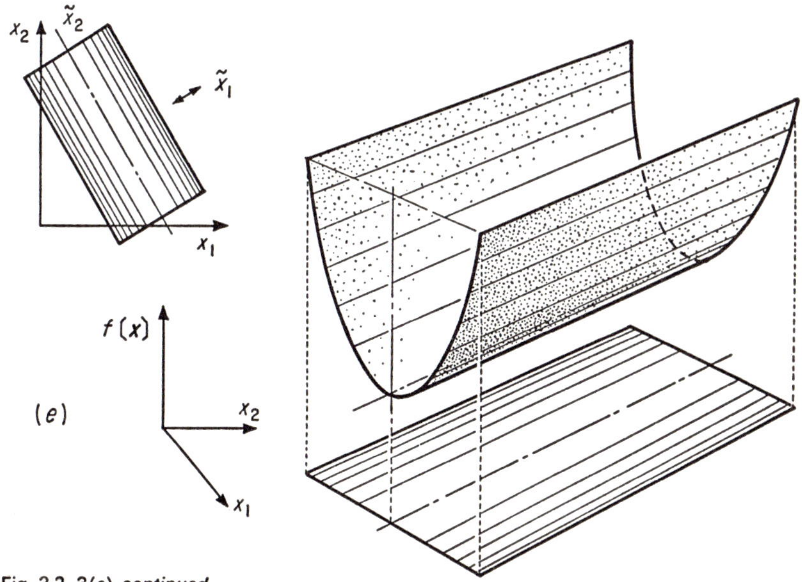

Fig. 3.2–3(*e*) *continued*

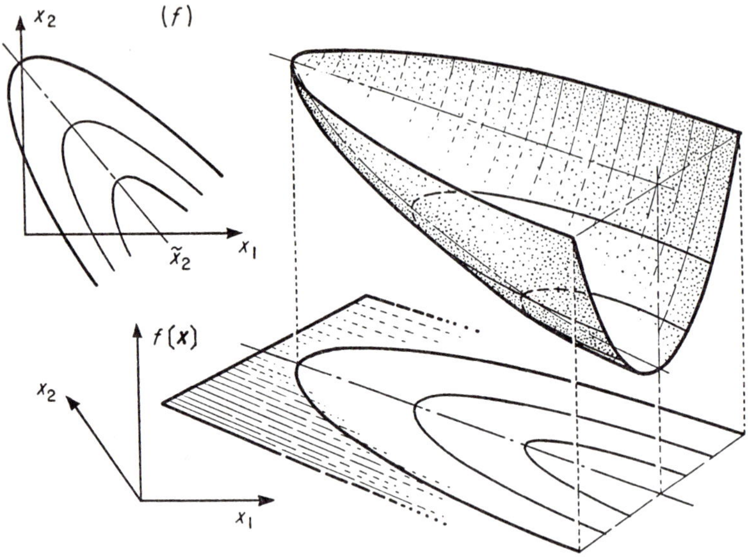

Fig. 3.2-3(*f*) *continued*

Table 3.2-1 Interpretation of the canonical function $f(\mathbf{x}) - f(\mathbf{x}^*) = \tilde{b}_{11}\tilde{x}_1^2 + \tilde{b}_{22}\tilde{x}_2^2$

Coefficient		*Signs*					
Case	*Relations*	$\tilde{b}_{11}$	$\tilde{b}_{22}$	*Types of contours*	*Geometric interpretation*	*Center*	*Figure*
1	$\tilde{b}_{11} = \tilde{b}_{22}$	−	−	Circles	Circular hill	Maximum	(*a*)
2	$\tilde{b}_{11} = \tilde{b}_{22}$	+	+	Circles	Circular hollow	Minimum	(*a*)
3	$\tilde{b}_{11} > \tilde{b}_{22}$	−	−	Ellipses	Elliptical hill	Maximum	(*b*)
4	$\tilde{b}_{11} > \tilde{b}_{22}$	+	+	Ellipses	Elliptical hollow	Minimum	(*b*)
5	$\tilde{b}_{11} = \tilde{b}_{22}$	+	−	Hyperbolas	Symmetrical saddle	Saddle point	(*c*)
6	$\tilde{b}_{11} = \tilde{b}_{22}$	−	+	Hyperbolas	Symmetrical saddle	Saddle point	(*c*)
7	$\tilde{b}_{11} > \tilde{b}_{22}$	+	−	Hyperbolas	Elongated saddle	Saddle point	(*d*)
8	$\tilde{b}_{22} = 0$	−		Straight lines	Stationary* ridge	None	(*e*)
9	$\tilde{b}_{22} = 0$	+		Straight lines	Stationary* valley	None	(*e*)
10	$\tilde{b}_{22} = 0$	−		Parabolas	Rising ridge,*†	At ∞	(*f*)
11	$\tilde{b}_{22} = 0$	+		Parabolas	Falling valley,*†	At ∞	(*f*)

*These are "degenerate" surfaces.

†To the relation given at the top of the table add two linear terms.

Table 3.2–1 interprets the information provided by the canonical function (3.2–7) in terms of the shape of the original function (3.2–6). If $|\tilde{b}_{11}| > |\tilde{b}_{22}|$, the contours are elongated along the $\tilde{x}_2$ (smaller-coefficient) axis, and vice versa. If the center on the $\tilde{x}_2$ axis is at infinity and $\tilde{b}_{11}$ is negative, the contours are parabolas, as illustrated in Fig. 3.2–3*f*. Either of the degenerate surfaces shown in Fig. 3.2–3*e* is known as a valley, or ridge, and appears when one of the coefficients is extremely small in magnitude compared with the other. As a simple example, let $f(\mathbf{x}) = x_1^2 + x_2^2 + 2x_1x_2$, which by inspection (let $x = x_1 + x_2$) can be seen to transform to $f(\mathbf{x}) = f(\mathbf{x}) = x^2$. Then $\tilde{b}_{11} = 1$ and $\tilde{b}_{22} = 0$, corresponding to case 9 in Table 3.2–1. These concepts can easily be extended to functions of more than two independent variables. For instance, when all the $\tilde{b}_{ii}$ are equal, the equal-level surfaces of the objective function are hyperspheres; when one or more of the $\tilde{b}_{ii}$ are relatively small, a hypervalley (ridge) exists; and so forth.

One of the major requirements of any successful optimization technique is the ability to be able to move rapidly in a local region along a narrow valley (in minimization) toward the minimum of the objective function. In other words, a good algorithm will give a search direction having a large component along the valley. Valleys (ridges in maximization) occur remarkably frequently, at least locally. It is not necessary that the approximate objective function be degenerate, because in the typical case of Fig. 3.2–3*b*, in the upper and lower regions the contours resemble a valley. A valley lies in the direction of the eigenvector associated with a small eigenvalue of the hessian matrix of the objective function. For example, referring to the function $f(\mathbf{x}) = x_1^2 + 25x_2^2$ in Example 3.1–1 (illustrated by Fig. E3.1–1*a*), the hessian matrix is a constant and equal to

$$\mathbf{H} = \begin{bmatrix} 2 & 0 \\ 0 & 50 \end{bmatrix}$$

The eigenvalues obtained from the characteristic equation $(2 - \beta)(50 - \beta) = 0$ are $\beta_{11} = 2$ and $\beta_{22} = 50$. (In a diagonal matrix the eigenvalues are the elements on the main diagonal.) The eigenvector associated with β_{11} can have any value for the element in the x_1 direction as long as the x_2 direction element is zero. Note how the valley in Fig. E3.1–1*a* is aligned in the x_1 direction. The direction $-\mathbf{H}^{-1}\nabla f(\mathbf{x})$ evaluated at different points in the x space always points toward the minimum of $f(\mathbf{x})$.

Function	$\mathbf{x} = [2 \quad 2]^T$	$\mathbf{x} = [2 \quad 0]^T$
$\nabla f(\mathbf{x})$	$\begin{bmatrix} 4 \\ 100 \end{bmatrix}$	$\begin{bmatrix} 4 \\ 0 \end{bmatrix}$
$-\mathbf{H}^{-1}\nabla f(\mathbf{x})$	$(-1)\begin{bmatrix} \frac{1}{2} & 0 \\ 0 & \frac{1}{50} \end{bmatrix}\begin{bmatrix} 4 \\ 100 \end{bmatrix} = \begin{bmatrix} -2 \\ -2 \end{bmatrix}$	$(-1)\begin{bmatrix} \frac{1}{2} & 0 \\ 0 & \frac{1}{50} \end{bmatrix}\begin{bmatrix} 4 \\ 0 \end{bmatrix} = \begin{bmatrix} -2 \\ 0 \end{bmatrix}$

In the example the vector $-\mathbf{H}^{-1}(\mathbf{x})\nabla f(\mathbf{x})$ points in exactly the correct direction because $f(\mathbf{x})$ is quadratic, but even if the objective function is not quadratic, in general, $-\mathbf{H}^{-1}\nabla f(\mathbf{x})$ has a large component parallel to the eigenvector corresponding to a small eigenvalue of $\mathbf{H}(\mathbf{x})$, and the search directions as desired line up roughly with the principal axes as approximated at $\mathbf{x}^k$.

A major drawback to Newton's method (other than the difficulty of obtaining analytical derivatives) is that the value of the objective function is guaranteed to be improved on each cycle only if the hessian matrix of the objective function, $\mathbf{H}(\mathbf{x}) = \nabla^2 f(\mathbf{x}^k)$, is positive definite. $\mathbf{H}(\mathbf{x})$ is positive definite for strictly convex functions, but for general functions Newton's method may lead to search directions diverging from the minimum of $f(\mathbf{x})$. To see why criterion (3.2–5) is necessary to guarantee convergence, recall that a real symmetric matrix is positive definite if and only if its eigenvalues are positive. Consequently, in minimization, we observe from Fig. 3.2–3 that when the eigenvalues of $H(\mathbf{x}^k)$ are all positive, the quadratic approximation corresponds locally to a circular or elliptical hollow having a minimum. On the other hand, if a pair of eigenvalues have opposite signs, we observe from Fig. 3.2–3 that a saddle exists that does not have a local minimum. In this latter case the direction given by Eq. (3.2–3) [or (3.2–4*a*)] will indicate that the best search direction is toward the saddle point instead of away from it in the "downhill" direction.

3.2–3 Forcing the Hessian Matrix to Be Positive Definite

Certain authors have proposed that the hessian matrix be forced to be positive definite at each stage of the minimization. Greenstadt[1] devised a scheme of eigenvalue analysis that guaranteed that an *estimate* of the inverse of the hessian matrix would be positive definite. Let $\tilde{\mathbf{H}}(\mathbf{x})$ be the

[1] J. Greenstadt, *Math. Computation*, **21**:360 (1967).

approximate to $\mathbf{H}(\mathbf{x})$. Scale the matrix $\tilde{\mathbf{H}}(\mathbf{x})$ as follows:

$$\mathbf{\Pi}(\mathbf{x}) = \mathbf{C}^{-1}(\mathbf{x})\tilde{\mathbf{H}}(\mathbf{x})\mathbf{C}^{-1}(\mathbf{x}) \tag{3.2-8}$$

where $\mathbf{C}(\mathbf{x})$ is a diagonal matrix whose elements are $c_{ii} = (|\tilde{h}_{ii}|)^{\frac{1}{2}}$, that is, the positive square roots of the absolute values of the elements on the main diagonal of $\tilde{\mathbf{H}}(\mathbf{x})$. $\mathbf{\Pi}$ will have all positive or negative ones on its main diagonal. For example, let

$$\tilde{\mathbf{H}} = \begin{bmatrix} 1 & 1 \\ 1 & 4 \end{bmatrix}$$

Then

$$\mathbf{C} = \begin{bmatrix} 1 & 0 \\ 0 & 2 \end{bmatrix} \qquad \mathbf{C}^{-1} = \begin{bmatrix} 1 & 0 \\ 0 & \frac{1}{2} \end{bmatrix}$$

and

$$\mathbf{\Pi} = \begin{bmatrix} 1 & 0 \\ 0 & \frac{1}{2} \end{bmatrix}\begin{bmatrix} 1 & 1 \\ 1 & 4 \end{bmatrix}\begin{bmatrix} 1 & 0 \\ 0 & \frac{1}{2} \end{bmatrix} = \begin{bmatrix} 1 & \frac{1}{2} \\ \frac{1}{2} & 1 \end{bmatrix}$$

Because $\mathbf{C}^{-1}(\mathbf{x})$ and $\tilde{\mathbf{H}}(\mathbf{x})$ are nonsingular and of order n, the inverse of their product is the product of the inverses in reverse order, or

$$\mathbf{\Pi}^{-1}(\mathbf{x}) = \mathbf{C}(\mathbf{x})\tilde{\mathbf{H}}(\mathbf{x})^{1}\mathbf{C}(\mathbf{x})$$

Then $\tilde{\mathbf{H}}^{-1}(\mathbf{x})$ can be calculated from the scaled matrix.

$$\tilde{\mathbf{H}}^{-1}(\mathbf{x}) = \mathbf{C}^{-1}(\mathbf{x})\mathbf{\Pi}^{-1}(\mathbf{x})\mathbf{C}^{-1}(\mathbf{x}) \tag{3.2-9}$$

Greenstadt pointed out that $\mathbf{\Pi}^{-1}(\mathbf{x})$ can be expressed in terms of the eigenvalues α_i and eigenvectors of $\mathbf{\Pi}(\mathbf{x})$. The eigenvectors of the inverse of a matrix are the same as those of the matrix itself, and the eigenvalues of the inverse matrix are simply the inverse of the eigenvalues of the original matrix (α_i^{-1}). Consequently,

$$\mathbf{\Pi}^{-1}(\mathbf{x}) = \sum_{i=1}^{n} \alpha_i^{-1}\mathbf{e}_i\mathbf{e}_i^T$$

where $\mathbf{e}_i$ is the normalized eigenvector corresponding to the eigenvalue α_i. Instead of using $\mathbf{\Pi}^{-1}(\mathbf{x})$, however, $\tilde{\mathbf{\Pi}}^{-1}(\mathbf{x})$ is used.

$$\tilde{\mathbf{\Pi}}^{-1}(\mathbf{x}) = \sum_{i=1}^{n} |\alpha_i|^{-1}\mathbf{e}_i\mathbf{e}_i^T$$

(in which any $\alpha_i = 0$ is replaced by a small positive number), so that $\tilde{\mathbf{H}}^{-1}(\mathbf{x})$ can now be guaranteed positive definite if computed from

$$\tilde{\mathbf{H}}^{-1}(\mathbf{x}) = \mathbf{C}^{-1}(\mathbf{x})\tilde{\mathbf{\Pi}}^{-1}(\mathbf{x})\mathbf{C}^{-1}(\mathbf{x}) \tag{3.2-10}$$

As a simple example, suppose that the matrix $\tilde{\mathbf{H}} = \begin{bmatrix} 1 & 2 \\ 2 & 1 \end{bmatrix}$; $\tilde{\mathbf{H}}^{-1}$ is not positive definite. Compute

$$\mathbf{\Pi} = \begin{bmatrix} 1 & 0 \\ 0 & 1 \end{bmatrix} \begin{bmatrix} 1 & 2 \\ 2 & 1 \end{bmatrix} \begin{bmatrix} 1 & 0 \\ 0 & 1 \end{bmatrix} = \begin{bmatrix} 1 & 2 \\ 2 & 1 \end{bmatrix}$$

The eigenvalues of $\mathbf{\Pi}$ are $\alpha_1 = -1$ and $\alpha_2 = 3$, and the associated normalized eigenvectors are

$$\mathbf{e}_1 = \begin{bmatrix} \dfrac{1}{\sqrt{2}} \\ \dfrac{1}{\sqrt{2}} \end{bmatrix} \qquad \mathbf{e}_2 = \begin{bmatrix} \dfrac{1}{\sqrt{2}} \\ -\dfrac{1}{\sqrt{2}} \end{bmatrix}$$

Hence

$$\mathbf{\Pi}^{-1} = \frac{1}{-1} \begin{bmatrix} \dfrac{1}{\sqrt{2}} & 0 \\ \dfrac{1}{\sqrt{2}} & 0 \end{bmatrix} \begin{bmatrix} \dfrac{1}{\sqrt{2}} & \dfrac{1}{\sqrt{2}} \\ 0 & 0 \end{bmatrix} + \frac{1}{3} \begin{bmatrix} \dfrac{1}{\sqrt{2}} & 0 \\ -\dfrac{1}{\sqrt{2}} & 0 \end{bmatrix} \begin{bmatrix} \dfrac{1}{\sqrt{2}} & -\dfrac{1}{\sqrt{2}} \\ 0 & 0 \end{bmatrix}$$

$$= \begin{bmatrix} -\frac{1}{3} & \frac{2}{3} \\ \frac{2}{3} & -\frac{1}{3} \end{bmatrix}$$

However, instead of $\mathbf{\Pi}^{-1}$, one uses

$$\tilde{\mathbf{\Pi}}^{-1} = \left|\frac{1}{-1}\right| \begin{bmatrix} \dfrac{1}{\sqrt{2}} & 0 \\ \dfrac{1}{\sqrt{2}} & 0 \end{bmatrix} \begin{bmatrix} \dfrac{1}{\sqrt{2}} & \dfrac{1}{\sqrt{2}} \\ 0 & 0 \end{bmatrix} + \left|\frac{1}{3}\right| \begin{bmatrix} \dfrac{1}{\sqrt{2}} & 0 \\ -\dfrac{1}{\sqrt{2}} & 0 \end{bmatrix} \begin{bmatrix} \dfrac{1}{\sqrt{2}} & -\dfrac{1}{\sqrt{2}} \\ 0 & 0 \end{bmatrix}$$

$$= \begin{bmatrix} \frac{2}{3} & \frac{1}{3} \\ \frac{1}{3} & \frac{2}{3} \end{bmatrix}$$

and inserting $\tilde{\mathbf{\Pi}}^{-1}$ into Eq. (3.2–10), the $\tilde{\mathbf{H}}^{-1}$ used becomes positive definite.

$$\tilde{\mathbf{H}}^{-1} = \begin{bmatrix} \frac{2}{3} & \frac{1}{3} \\ \frac{1}{3} & \frac{2}{3} \end{bmatrix}$$

Any eigenvalue whose absolute value is less than 10^{-4} is replaced by 10^{-4}.

Marquardt,[1] Levenberg,[2] and Goldfeld, Quandt, and Trotter[3] suggested an alternative computation scheme to ensure that the estimate of $\mathbf{H}^{-1}(\mathbf{x})$ was positive definite.

$$\tilde{\mathbf{H}}^{*-1}(\mathbf{x}) = \mathbf{C}^{-1}(\mathbf{x})(\mathbf{\Pi}(\mathbf{x}) + \beta\mathbf{I})^{-1}\mathbf{C}^{-1}(\mathbf{x}) = (\tilde{\mathbf{H}}(\mathbf{x}) + \beta\mathbf{C}^2(\mathbf{x}))^{-1} \tag{3.2-11}$$

where β is a positive constant such that $\beta > -\min\{\alpha_i\}$. Because the eigenvalues of $(\mathbf{\Pi}(\mathbf{x}) + \beta\mathbf{I})$ are $(\alpha_i + \beta)$, Eq. (3.2–11) guarantees that $\tilde{\mathbf{H}}^{*-1}(\mathbf{x})$ is positive definite, since use of an appropriate β in Eq. (3.2–11) in effect destroys negative and small eigenvalues of the approximate to the hessian matrix. Note that, with β sufficiently large, $\beta\mathbf{I}$ can overwhelm $\mathbf{\Pi}(\mathbf{x})$ and the minimization approaches a steepest descent search.

Zwart[4] suggested a third way of maintaining the estimate of $\mathbf{H}(\mathbf{x})$ positive definite. The essential step is to find a real unitary matrix $\mathbf{U}$ such that, upon application of the transformation $\mathbf{x} = \mathbf{U}\tilde{\mathbf{x}}$, one obtains a diagonalized hessian matrix of the objective function.

$$\tilde{\mathbf{H}}(\mathbf{x}^{(k)}) = \mathbf{U}^T\mathbf{H}(\mathbf{x}^{(k)})\mathbf{U} = \begin{bmatrix} \tilde{h}_{11} & & & 0 \\ & \tilde{h}_{22} & & \\ & & \ddots & \\ 0 & & & \tilde{h}_{nn} \end{bmatrix} \tag{3.2-12}$$

This step corresponds to the rotation of axes in Fig. 3.2–2. To set up the unitary matrix $\mathbf{U}$, one needs to determine the eigenvalues and eigenfunctions of $\mathbf{H}(\mathbf{x}^{(k)})$. Then, if any of the elements of the diagonal matrix $\tilde{\mathbf{H}}(\mathbf{x}^{(k)})$ are negative or small, they are replaced by some positive small number to yield a modified matrix $\tilde{\mathbf{H}}^*(\mathbf{x}^{(k)})$. Thus the direction corresponding to any eigenvalue that has the wrong sign is not considered, and any extremely small eigenvalue is not allowed to dominate the selection of the search direction. Finally, the search direction is established from the relation

$$\mathbf{s}^{(k)} = -\tilde{\mathbf{H}}^*(\mathbf{x}^{(k)})\nabla f(\mathbf{x}^{(k)}) \tag{3.2-13}$$

Newton's method does have the distinct advantage of quadratic convergence in the vicinity of the minimum of the objective function [if

[1] D. W. Marquardt, *J. SIAM*, **11**:431 (1963).

[2] K. Levenberg, *Quart. Appl. Math.*, **2**:164 (1944).

[3] S. M. Goldfeld, R. E. Quandt, and H. F. Trotter, *Econometrica*, **34**:541 (1966).

[4] P. B. Zwart, "Nonlinear Programming: A Quadratic Analysis of Ridge Paralysis," Washington Univ., Rep. COO-1493-21, St. Louis, Mo., January, 1969.

$\mathbf{H}(\mathbf{x}) > \mathbf{O}$ and if the objective function can be approximated reasonably well by a quadratic function], which is just the region in which steepest descent methods perform the poorest. Far away from the minimum, steepest descent methods may be superior. One can conclude that a suitable combination of steepest descent and Newton's method should exhibit superior performance to either method alone, and such procedures are described in Sec. 3.4.

3.3 CONJUGACY AND CONJUGATE DIRECTIONS

As explained subsequently in this section, a quadratic objective function of n independent variables that has a minimum can be minimized in n steps (or less) if the steps are taken in what are termed *conjugate directions.* Although the use of optimization schemes that prove effective for quadratic functions may be occasionally misleading (and will not in general yield conjugate search directions) for more complex objective functions, nevertheless this concept provides the motivation for this section. Before describing any specific algorithms we need first to define and illustrate the property of conjugacy. In this section we assume, unless stated specifically otherwise, that the objective function is quadratic of the form

$$f(\mathbf{x}) = a + \mathbf{b}^T\mathbf{x} + \tfrac{1}{2}\mathbf{x}^T\mathbf{H}\mathbf{x}$$

in which $\mathbf{H}$ is positive definite.

3.3-1 Conjugacy

Suppose the minimization of $f(\mathbf{x})$ starts at $\mathbf{x}^{(0)}$ in an initial direction $\hat{\mathbf{s}}^{(0)}$ picked arbitrarily or by some particular algorithm. For convenience we choose to make $(\hat{\mathbf{s}}^{(0)})^T\hat{\mathbf{s}}^{(0)} = 1$ so that $\hat{\mathbf{s}}^{(0)}$ is a unit vector. The vector $\mathbf{x}^{(1)}$ will be determined from

$$\mathbf{x}^{(1)} = \mathbf{x}^{(0)} + \lambda^{(0)}\hat{\mathbf{s}}^{(0)} \tag{3.3-1}$$

and the step length $\lambda^{(0)}$ will be determined by minimizing $f(\mathbf{x}^{(0)} + \lambda\mathbf{s}^{(0)})$ with respect to λ, as indicated by Eq. (3.1-4)

$$\frac{df(\mathbf{x}^{(0)} + \lambda\hat{\mathbf{s}}^{(0)})}{d\lambda} = 0 = \nabla^T f(\mathbf{x}^{(0)})\hat{\mathbf{s}}^{(0)} + (\hat{\mathbf{s}}^{(0)})^T\nabla^2 f(\mathbf{x}^{(0)})\lambda\hat{\mathbf{s}}^{(0)}$$

which leads to

$$\lambda^{(0)} = -\frac{\nabla^T f(\mathbf{x}^{(0)})\hat{\mathbf{s}}^{(0)}}{(\hat{\mathbf{s}}^{(0)})^T\nabla^2 f(\mathbf{x}^{(0)})\hat{\mathbf{s}}^{(0)}} \tag{3.3-2}$$

After $\mathbf{x}^{(1)}$ is computed from Eqs. (3.1–1) and (3.3–2), a new direction must be selected for the minimization of $f(\mathbf{x})$. The new direction $\hat{\mathbf{s}}^{(1)}$ is said to be *conjugate* (or conjugated) with the old direction $\hat{\mathbf{s}}^{(0)}$ if $(\hat{\mathbf{s}}^{(1)})^T[\nabla^2 f(\mathbf{x}^{(0)})]\hat{\mathbf{s}}^{(0)} = 0$. In general, a set of n linearly independent directions of search $\mathbf{s}^{(0)}, \mathbf{s}^{(1)}, \ldots, \mathbf{s}^{(n-1)}$ are said to be conjugate with respect to a positive definite (square) matrix $\mathbf{Q}$[1] if

$$(\mathbf{s}^{(i)})^T\mathbf{Q}\mathbf{s}^{(j)} = 0 \qquad 0 \le i \ne j \le n-1 \tag{3.3–3}$$

(We assume $\mathbf{Q}$ is of full rank.) A specific example of $\mathbf{Q}$ is the hessian matrix of the objective function $\mathbf{H}$.

Conjugacy is quite analogous to orthogonality; in fact, when $\mathbf{H} = \mathbf{I}$, $(\mathbf{s}^{(i)})^T\mathbf{s}^{(j)} = 0$ in Eq. (3.3–3). From the viewpoint of the topological characteristics of the quadratic function discussed in the previous section, if the objective function is transformed to a type of canonical form, say, $f(\mathbf{x}) = \tilde{b}_{11}\tilde{x}_1^2 + \tilde{b}_{22}\tilde{x}_2^2 = \tilde{\mathbf{x}}^T\tilde{\mathbf{H}}\tilde{\mathbf{x}}$, the eigenvalues of $\frac{1}{2}\mathbf{H}$ are on the diagonal of $\tilde{\mathbf{H}}$.

$$\tilde{\mathbf{H}} = \begin{bmatrix} \tilde{b}_{11} & 0 \\ 0 & \tilde{b}_{22} \end{bmatrix}$$

Thus conjugacy can be interpreted as orthogonality in a space of the transformed coordinates if the search directions are scaled by appropriate functions of the eigenvalues. Specifically, in the new coordinates,

$$(\tilde{\mathbf{s}}^{(i)})^T\tilde{\mathbf{H}}\tilde{\mathbf{s}}^{(j)} = \tilde{b}_{11}\tilde{s}_1^{(i)}\tilde{s}_1^{(j)} + \tilde{b}_{22}\tilde{s}_2^{(i)}\tilde{s}_2^{(j)} = \frac{\tilde{s}_1^{(i)}\tilde{s}_1^{(j)}}{\tilde{b}_{22}} + \frac{\tilde{s}_2^{(i)}\tilde{s}_2^{(j)}}{\tilde{b}_{11}} = 0$$

$$= (\tilde{\tilde{\mathbf{s}}}^{(i)})^T\tilde{\tilde{\mathbf{s}}}^{(j)} = 0$$

where $\quad \tilde{\tilde{s}}_1^{(i)} = \dfrac{\tilde{s}_1^{(i)}}{\sqrt{\tilde{b}_{22}}} \quad$ and $\quad \tilde{\tilde{s}}_2^{(i)} = \dfrac{\tilde{s}_2^{(i)}}{\sqrt{\tilde{b}_{11}}}$

Because conjugate directions are linearly independent, any vector $\mathbf{v}$ in E^n can be represented in terms of $\mathbf{s}^{(0)}, \mathbf{s}^{(1)}, \ldots,$ as follows:

$$\mathbf{v} = \sum_{j=0}^{n-1} v^{(j)}\mathbf{s}^{(j)} \tag{3.3–4}$$

where $\quad v^{(j)} = \dfrac{(\mathbf{s}^{(j)})^T\mathbf{H}(\mathbf{x})\mathbf{v}}{(\mathbf{s}^{(j)})^T\mathbf{H}(\mathbf{x})\mathbf{s}^{(j)}}$

[1] M. R. Hestenes, The Conjugate Gradient Method for Solving Linear Systems, in *Proceedings of the Symposium on Applied Mathematics*, vol. VI, McGraw-Hill Book Company, New York, 1956, pp. 83–102.

There always exists at least one set of n mutually conjugate directions (with respect to $\mathbf{H}$) because the eigenvectors of $\mathbf{H}$ form such a set.

Also, we will subsequently need the following relation for a quadratic function if conjugate directions are used:

$$\mathbf{H}^{-1} = \sum_{j=0}^{n-1} \frac{\mathbf{s}^{(j)}(\mathbf{s}^{(j)})^T}{(\mathbf{s}^{(j)})^T\mathbf{H}\mathbf{s}^{(j)}} \tag{3.3–4a}$$

Consider the matrix $\sum_{j=0}^{n-1} \alpha_j \mathbf{s}^{(j)}(\mathbf{s}^{(j)})^T$. Postmultiplication by $\mathbf{H}\mathbf{s}^{(k)}$ gives

$$\left[\sum_{j=0}^{n-1} \alpha_j \mathbf{s}^{(j)}(\mathbf{s}^{(j)})^T\right]\mathbf{H}\mathbf{s}^{(k)} = \alpha_k \mathbf{s}^{(k)}(\mathbf{s}^{(k)})^T\mathbf{H}\mathbf{s}^{(k)}$$

$$= \mathbf{s}^{(k)}$$

if we make $\alpha_k = [(\mathbf{s}^{(k)})^T\mathbf{H}\mathbf{s}^{(k)}]^{-1}$. Thus Eq. (3.3–4$a$) is true.

A numerical example will clarify the concept of conjugacy.

Example 3.3–1 Conjugate directions

As an example of the selection and generation of conjugate directions, we will consider the problem

Minimize: $f(\mathbf{x}) = x_1^2 + x_2^2 - 4$

starting at $\mathbf{x}^{(0)} = [4 \quad 4]^T$. Since $f(\mathbf{x})$ is a quadratic expression to start with, it will not have to be approximated. The vectors and matrices we will need are

$$(\mathbf{x} - \mathbf{x}^{(k)}) = \begin{bmatrix} x_1 - x_1^{(k)} \\ x_2 - x_2^{(k)} \end{bmatrix}$$

$$\nabla f(\mathbf{x}) = \begin{bmatrix} 2x_1 \\ 2x_2 \end{bmatrix}$$

$$\mathbf{H}(\mathbf{x}) \equiv \nabla^2 f(\mathbf{x}) = \begin{bmatrix} 2 & 0 \\ 0 & 2 \end{bmatrix}$$

The vector $\mathbf{x}^{(1)}$ is computed from $\mathbf{x}^{(1)} = \mathbf{x}^{(0)} + \lambda^{(0)}\hat{\mathbf{s}}^{(0)}$.

$$\begin{bmatrix} x_1^{(1)} \\ x_2^{(1)} \end{bmatrix} = \begin{bmatrix} x_1^{(0)} \\ x_2^{(0)} \end{bmatrix} + \lambda^{(0)} \begin{bmatrix} \hat{s}_1^{(0)} \\ \hat{s}_2^{(0)} \end{bmatrix} = \begin{bmatrix} 4 \\ 4 \end{bmatrix} + \lambda^{(0)} \begin{bmatrix} \hat{s}_1^{(0)} \\ \hat{s}_2^{(0)} \end{bmatrix}$$

Any direction can be picked for $\hat{\mathbf{s}}^{(0)}$, such as the direction of the gradient, but we will pick an arbitrary direction for illustrative purposes

$$\hat{\mathbf{s}}^{(0)} = \begin{bmatrix} \dfrac{1}{2} \\ \dfrac{\sqrt{3}}{2} \end{bmatrix}$$

Note that

$$(\hat{\mathbf{s}}^{(0)})^T\hat{\mathbf{s}}^{(0)} = 1: \quad \begin{bmatrix} \frac{1}{2} & \frac{\sqrt{3}}{2} \end{bmatrix} \begin{bmatrix} \frac{1}{2} \\ \frac{\sqrt{3}}{2} \end{bmatrix} = 1$$

The step length $\lambda^{(0)}$ is computed from Eq. (3.3–2).

$$\lambda^{(0)} = -\frac{[8 \quad 8]\begin{bmatrix} \frac{1}{2} \\ \frac{\sqrt{3}}{2} \end{bmatrix}}{\begin{bmatrix} \frac{1}{2} & \frac{\sqrt{3}}{2} \end{bmatrix}\begin{bmatrix} 2 & 0 \\ 0 & 2 \end{bmatrix}\begin{bmatrix} \frac{1}{2} \\ \frac{\sqrt{3}}{2} \end{bmatrix}} = -5.46$$

Then

$$\lambda^{(0)}\hat{\mathbf{s}}^{(0)} = \begin{bmatrix} -2.73 \\ -4.74 \end{bmatrix}$$

and

$$\mathbf{x}^{(1)} = \begin{bmatrix} 1.27 \\ -0.74 \end{bmatrix}$$

The next direction for minimization, $\hat{\mathbf{s}}^{(1)}$, is picked to be conjugate to $\hat{\mathbf{s}}^{(0)}$ by using Eq. (3.3–3) with $\mathbf{Q} = \mathbf{H}$.

$$[\hat{s}_1^{(1)} \quad \hat{s}_2^{(1)}]\begin{bmatrix} 2 & 0 \\ 0 & 2 \end{bmatrix}\begin{bmatrix} \frac{1}{2} \\ \frac{\sqrt{3}}{2} \end{bmatrix} = 0$$

The additional equation needed is

$$[\hat{s}_1^{(1)} \quad \hat{s}_2^{(1)}]\begin{bmatrix} \hat{s}_1^{(1)} \\ \hat{s}_2^{(1)} \end{bmatrix} = 1$$

leading to

$$\left.\begin{aligned} \hat{s}_1^{(1)} + \sqrt{3}\,\hat{s}_2^{(1)} &= 0 \\ (\hat{s}_1^{(1)})^2 + (\hat{s}_2^{(1)})^2 &= 1 \end{aligned}\right\} \quad \text{so that} \quad \hat{\mathbf{s}}^{(1)} = \begin{bmatrix} -\frac{\sqrt{3}}{2} \\ \frac{1}{2} \end{bmatrix}$$

The step length $\lambda^{(1)}$ is computed next from the equivalent of Eq. (3.3–2).

$$\lambda^{(1)} = -\frac{[2.54 \quad -1.48]\begin{bmatrix} -\dfrac{\sqrt{3}}{2} \\ \dfrac{1}{2} \end{bmatrix}}{\begin{bmatrix} -\dfrac{\sqrt{3}}{2} & \dfrac{1}{2} \end{bmatrix}\begin{bmatrix} 2 & 0 \\ 0 & 2 \end{bmatrix}\begin{bmatrix} -\dfrac{\sqrt{3}}{2} \\ \dfrac{1}{2} \end{bmatrix}} = 1.47$$

$$\begin{bmatrix} x_1^{(2)} \\ x_2^{(2)} \end{bmatrix} = \begin{bmatrix} 1.27 \\ -0.74 \end{bmatrix} + 1.47 \begin{bmatrix} -\dfrac{\sqrt{3}}{2} \\ \dfrac{1}{2} \end{bmatrix} = \begin{bmatrix} 0 \\ 0 \end{bmatrix}$$

Figure E3.3-1 illustrates the path of the search. For this special case the objective function is spherical; hence the search directions are not only conjugate but also orthogonal.

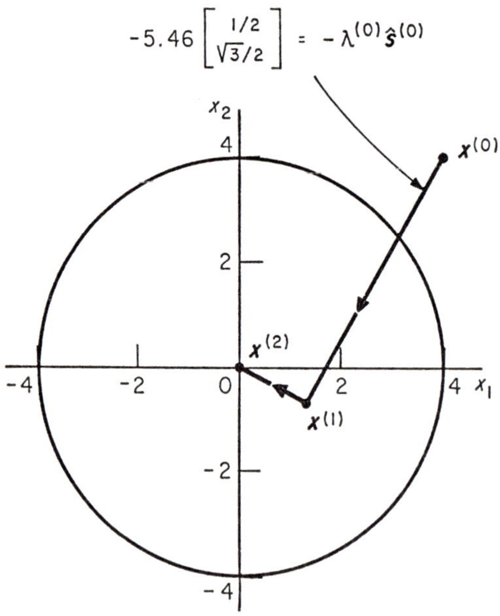

Fig. E3.3-1

The vectors $\hat{\mathbf{s}}^{(k)}$ generated as conjugate directions can be shown to be linearly independent in the sense described in Sec. 2.1. The only additional vector that can exist that is mutually conjugate to all the n directions $\hat{\mathbf{s}}^{(0)}, \ldots, \hat{\mathbf{s}}^{(n-1)}$ is the zero vector. Thus we observe in the foregoing example an illustration of the general rule that *if conjugate directions are employed, any quadratic function of n variables that has a minimum can be minimized in n steps*, one in each conjugate direction. Furthermore, the order in which the directions are used is immaterial.

We can prove this rule for conjugate directions as follows. The objective function can be written $f(\mathbf{x}) = a + \mathbf{x}^T\mathbf{b} + \frac{1}{2}\mathbf{x}^T\mathbf{H}\mathbf{x}$, so that the $\nabla f(\mathbf{x}) = \mathbf{b} + \mathbf{H}\mathbf{x}$, and at the minimum of $f(\mathbf{x})$, where $\nabla f(\mathbf{x}^*) = \mathbf{0}$, $\mathbf{x}^* = -\mathbf{H}^{-1}\mathbf{b}$. We will also need to note, as can be demonstrated by multiplication of the elements, that $\nabla^T f(\mathbf{x}^{(k)})\hat{\mathbf{s}}^{(k)} = (\hat{\mathbf{s}}^{(k)})^T \nabla f(\mathbf{x}^{(k)})$. For the nth stage, after using Eqs. (3.1–1) and (3.3–2),

$$\mathbf{x}^{(n)} = \mathbf{x}^{(0)} + \sum_{k=0}^{n-1} \lambda^{(k)}\hat{\mathbf{s}}^{(k)}$$

On each stage we minimize $f(\mathbf{x}^{(k)} + \lambda\hat{\mathbf{s}}^{(k)})$ in the direction $\hat{\mathbf{s}}^{(k)}$ in order to obtain $\lambda^{(k)}$, with the result that

$$\mathbf{x}^{(n)} = \mathbf{x}^{(0)} - \sum_{k=0}^{n-1} \left(\frac{(\hat{\mathbf{s}}^{(k)})^T \nabla f(\mathbf{x}^{(k)})}{(\hat{\mathbf{s}}^{(k)})^T \mathbf{H}\hat{\mathbf{s}}^{(k)}} \right) \hat{\mathbf{s}}^{(k)} \qquad (3.3\text{–}5a)$$

Furthermore,

$$\begin{aligned}
(\hat{\mathbf{s}}^{(k)})^T \nabla f(\mathbf{x}^{(k)}) &= (\hat{\mathbf{s}}^{(k)})^T (\mathbf{H}\mathbf{x}^{(k)} + \mathbf{b}) \\
&= (\hat{\mathbf{s}}^{(k)})^T \left\{ \mathbf{H} \left[\mathbf{x}^{(0)} + \sum_{i=1}^{k-1} \lambda^{(i)}\hat{\mathbf{s}}^{(i)} \right] + \mathbf{b} \right\} \\
&= (\hat{\mathbf{s}}^{(k)})^T \{ \mathbf{H}\mathbf{x}^{(0)} + \mathbf{b} \}
\end{aligned}$$

because the products $(\hat{\mathbf{s}}^{(k)})^T \mathbf{H}\hat{\mathbf{s}}^{(i)}$ all vanish, inasmuch as the s's are conjugate. Finally,

$$\mathbf{x}^{(n)} = \mathbf{x}^{(0)} - \sum_{k=0}^{n-1} \frac{(\hat{\mathbf{s}}^{(k)})^T (\mathbf{H}\mathbf{x}^{(0)} + \mathbf{b})\hat{\mathbf{s}}^{(k)}}{(\hat{\mathbf{s}}^{(k)})^T \mathbf{H}\hat{\mathbf{s}}^{(k)}} \qquad (3.3\text{–}5b)$$

Identification of

$$\mathbf{x}^{(0)} = \sum_{k=0}^{n-1} \frac{(\hat{\mathbf{s}}^{(k)})^T \mathbf{H}\mathbf{x}^{(0)}\hat{\mathbf{s}}^{(k)}}{(\hat{\mathbf{s}}^{(k)})^T \mathbf{H}\hat{\mathbf{s}}^{(k)}}$$

and
$$\mathbf{H}^{-1}\mathbf{b} = \sum_{k=0}^{n-1} \frac{(\hat{\mathbf{s}}^{(k)})^T \mathbf{H}(\mathbf{H}^{-1}\mathbf{b})\hat{\mathbf{s}}^{(k)}}{(\hat{\mathbf{s}}^{(k)})^T \mathbf{H}\hat{\mathbf{s}}^{(k)}}$$

from Eq. (3.3–4) and introduction of these terms into Eq. (3.3–5*b*) yield

$$\mathbf{x}^{(n)} = -\mathbf{H}^{-1}\mathbf{b} \tag{3.3-6}$$

showing that $\mathbf{x}^{(n)}$ is at the minimum of $f(\mathbf{x})$.

A method that is guaranteed to reach the minimum of a quadratic objective function in a specified number of steps is said to have the property of quadratic termination. Conjugate gradient methods take n steps, while Newton's method takes only one step, for example.

For conjugate directions (or simply linearly independent directions for that matter), if in each case $f(\mathbf{x})$ is minimized in the conjugate direction $\mathbf{s}$ as indicated by Eq. (3.1–4), it can be shown as follows that $[(\mathbf{s}^{(j)})^T\nabla f(\mathbf{x}^{(l)})] = 0$, $0 \leq j \leq \ell - 1$, as long as no more than n directions are used. We have seen earlier, in Sec. 3.1, that for a quadratic function,

$$\nabla f(\mathbf{x}^{(l)}) = \mathbf{b} + \mathbf{H}\mathbf{x}^{(l)}$$

Hence

$$\nabla f(\mathbf{x}^{(l)}) = \mathbf{b} + \mathbf{H}(\mathbf{x}^{(k)} + \sum_{j=k}^{l-1} \lambda^{(j)}\mathbf{s}^{(j)}) = \mathbf{b} + \mathbf{H}\mathbf{x}^{(k)} + \mathbf{H}\sum_{j=k}^{l-1} \lambda^{(j)}\mathbf{s}^{(j)}$$

where $\mathbf{x}^{(k)}$ is the arbitrary point from which the conjugate searches start. Since

$$\nabla f(\mathbf{x}^{(k)}) = \mathbf{b} + \mathbf{H}\mathbf{x}^{(k)}$$

then
$$\nabla f(\mathbf{x}^{(l)}) = \nabla f(\mathbf{x}^{(k)}) + \sum_{j=k}^{l-1} \lambda^{(j)}\mathbf{H}\mathbf{s}^{(j)}$$

Premultiplication of this equation by $(\mathbf{s}^{(k-1)})^T$ yields

$$(\mathbf{s}^{(k-1)})^T\nabla f(\mathbf{x}^{(l)}) = (\mathbf{s}^{(k-1)})^T\nabla f(\mathbf{x}^{(k)}) + \sum_{j=k}^{l-1} \lambda^j(\mathbf{s}^{(k-1)})^T\mathbf{H}\mathbf{s}^{(j)}$$

The first term on the right-hand side is zero because, as shown in Sec. 3.1–1, the gradient at a point is orthogonal to the previous search direction if the function is minimized in that search direction to reach the point. All the terms in the sum vanish because of conjugacy. Hence $(\mathbf{s}^{(k-1)})^T\nabla f(\mathbf{x}^{(l)}) = 0$, and because the analysis above is still valid for k having any index number between 1 and ℓ

$$(\mathbf{s}^{(j)})^T\nabla f(\mathbf{x}^{(l)}) = 0 \qquad 0 \leq j \leq \ell - 1 \tag{3.3-7}$$

Let us define an $n \times i$ matrix $\mathbf{X}^{(i)}$ in which each element is $\mathbf{x}^{(i+1)} - \mathbf{x}^{(i)} \equiv \Delta\mathbf{x}^{(i)} = \lambda^{(i)}\hat{\mathbf{s}}^{(i)}$.

$$\mathbf{X}^{(i)} = [(\mathbf{x}^{(1)} - \mathbf{x}^{(0)}) \quad (\mathbf{x}^{(2)} - \mathbf{x}^{(1)}) \quad \ldots \quad (\mathbf{x}^{(i)} - \mathbf{x}^{(i-1)})]$$
$$= [\Delta\mathbf{x}^{(0)} \quad \Delta\mathbf{x}^{(1)} \quad \Delta\mathbf{x}^{(i-1)}]$$

or

$$(\mathbf{X}^{(i)})^T = \begin{bmatrix} (\Delta\mathbf{x}^{(0)})^T \\ (\Delta\mathbf{x}^{(1)})^T \\ \cdot \\ \cdot \\ \cdot \\ (\Delta\mathbf{x}^{(i-1)})^T \end{bmatrix} = \begin{bmatrix} \lambda^{(0)}(\hat{\mathbf{s}}^{(0)})^T \\ \lambda^{(1)}(\hat{\mathbf{s}}^{(1)})^T \\ \cdot \\ \cdot \\ \cdot \\ \lambda^{(i-1)}(\hat{\mathbf{s}}^{(i-1)})^T \end{bmatrix}$$

$$\begin{bmatrix} \lambda^{(0)}\hat{s}_1^{(0)} & \lambda^{(0)}\hat{s}_2^{(0)} & \ldots & \lambda^{(0)}\hat{s}_n^{(0)} \\ \lambda^{(1)}\hat{s}_1^{(1)} & \lambda^{(1)}\hat{s}_2^{(1)} & \ldots & \lambda^{(1)}\hat{s}_n^{(1)} \\ \cdots & \cdots & \cdots & \cdots \\ \lambda^{(i-1)}\hat{s}_1^{(i-1)} & \lambda^{(i-1)}\hat{s}_2^{(i-1)} & \ldots & \lambda^{(i-1)}\hat{s}_n^{(i-1)} \end{bmatrix}$$

Using Eq. (3.3–7), we find

$$(\mathbf{X}^{(i)})^T \nabla f(\mathbf{x}^{(i)}) = 0 \qquad i \le n - 1 \tag{3.3–8}$$

Another useful matrix is the $n \times i$ matrix

$$\mathbf{G}^{(i)} = [(\nabla f(\mathbf{x}^{(1)}) - \nabla f(\mathbf{x}^{(0)})) \quad (\nabla f(\mathbf{x}^{(2)}) - \nabla f(\mathbf{x}^{(1)}))$$
$$\ldots \quad (\nabla f(\mathbf{x}^{(i)}) - \nabla f(\mathbf{x}^{(i-1)}))]$$
$$= [\Delta\mathbf{g}^{(0)} \quad \Delta\mathbf{g}^{(1)} \quad \ldots \quad \Delta\mathbf{g}^{(i-1)}]$$

where $\Delta\mathbf{g}^{(i)} \equiv \nabla f(\mathbf{x}^{(i+1)}) - \nabla f(\mathbf{x}^{(i)})$. From the gradient of $f(\mathbf{x})$,

$$\nabla f(\mathbf{x}) = \nabla f(\mathbf{x}^{(k)}) + \nabla^2 f(\mathbf{x}^{(k)})(\mathbf{x} - \mathbf{x}^{(k)}) \tag{3.3–9}$$

and if we let $\mathbf{x} = \mathbf{x}^{(k+1)}$,

$$\nabla f(\mathbf{x}^{(k+1)}) - \nabla f(\mathbf{x}^{(k)}) = \nabla^2 f(\mathbf{x}^{(k)})(\mathbf{x}^{(k+1)} - \mathbf{x}^{(k)}) \equiv \mathbf{H}(\lambda^{(k)}\hat{\mathbf{s}}^{(k)}) \tag{3.3–10}$$

Consequently,

$$\left.\begin{aligned} (\mathbf{X}^{(i)})^T[\nabla f(\mathbf{x}^{(j+1)}) - \nabla f(\mathbf{x}^{(j)})] &= 0 \\ (\mathbf{G}^{(i)})^T[\mathbf{x}^{(j+1)} - \mathbf{x}^{(j)}] &= 0 \end{aligned}\right\} \quad 0 \le i < j \le n - 1 \qquad \begin{aligned} &(3.3–11) \\ &(3.3–12) \end{aligned}$$

when the steps $\lambda^{(0)}\hat{\mathbf{s}}^{(0)}, \lambda^{(1)}\hat{\mathbf{s}}^{(1)}, \ldots$ are in conjugate directions.

With the important properties of conjugacy now described, we can turn to consideration of algorithms for minimization of $f(\mathbf{x})$ that use conjugate directions.

3.3-2 The Conjugate Gradient Method

The Fletcher-Reeves conjugate gradient method[1] generates a sequence of search directions $\mathbf{s}$ that are linear combinations of $-\nabla f(\mathbf{x}^{(k)})$, that is, the current steepest descent direction, and $\mathbf{s}^{(0)}, \ldots, \mathbf{s}^{(k-1)}$, that is, the previous search directions, the weighting factors chosen to make the search directions conjugate. The weights turn out to be such that at $\mathbf{x}^{(k)}$ only the current gradient and the most recent gradient are used to compute the new search direction. This idea evolved from the method of solution of sets of linear equations by Hestenes and Stiefel[2] and Beckman.[3]

To illustrate the idea, let the initial direction of search be $\mathbf{s}^{(0)} = -\nabla f(\mathbf{x}^{(0)})$. Then let $\mathbf{x}^{(1)} - \mathbf{x}^{(0)} = \lambda^{*(0)}\mathbf{s}^{(0)}$ and make

$$\mathbf{s}^{(1)} = -\nabla f(\mathbf{x}^{(1)}) + \omega_1 \mathbf{s}^{(0)}$$

where ω_1 is a scalar weight that will be chosen so as to make $\mathbf{s}^{(1)}$ and $\mathbf{s}^{(0)}$ conjugate with respect to $\mathbf{H}$.

$$(\mathbf{s}^{(0)})^T \mathbf{H} \mathbf{s}^{(1)} = 0 \tag{3.3-13}$$

Equation (3.3-10) is used to eliminate $(\mathbf{s}^{(0)})^T$ from Eq. (3.3-13); note $\mathbf{H} = \mathbf{H}^T$ for a quadratic function.

$$(\mathbf{s}^{(0)})^T = \frac{(\mathbf{x}^{(1)} - \mathbf{x}^{(0)})^T}{\lambda^{*(0)}} = \frac{[\nabla f(\mathbf{x}^{(1)}) - \nabla f(\mathbf{x}^{(0)})]^T \mathbf{H}^{-1}}{\lambda^{*(0)}}$$

Hence $\quad [\nabla f(\mathbf{x}^{(1)}) - \nabla f(\mathbf{x}^{(0)})]^T[-\nabla f(\mathbf{x}^{(1)}) + \omega_1 \mathbf{s}^{(0)}] = 0$

All the cross-product terms vanish because of the properties discussed in Sec. 3.3-1, so that

$$\omega_1 = \frac{\nabla^T f(\mathbf{x}^{(1)}) \nabla f(\mathbf{x}^{(1)})}{\nabla^T f(\mathbf{x}^{(0)}) \nabla f(\mathbf{x}^{(0)})}$$

Search direction $\mathbf{s}^{(2)}$ is made a linear combination of $-\nabla f(\mathbf{x}^{(2)})$, $\mathbf{s}^{(1)}$, and $\mathbf{s}^{(0)}$, and forced to be conjugate to $\mathbf{s}^{(1)}$. Extension of these developments

[1] R. Fletcher and C. M. Reeves, *Computer J.*, **7**:149 (1964).

[2] M. R. Hestenes and E. L. Stiefel, *J. Res. Natl. Bur. Std.*, **B49**:409 (1952).

[3] F. S. Beckman, The Solution of Linear Equations by the Conjugate Gradient Method, in A. Ralston and H. S. Wilf (eds.), "Mathematical Methods for Digital Computers," vol. 1, John Wiley & Sons, Inc., New York, 1960.

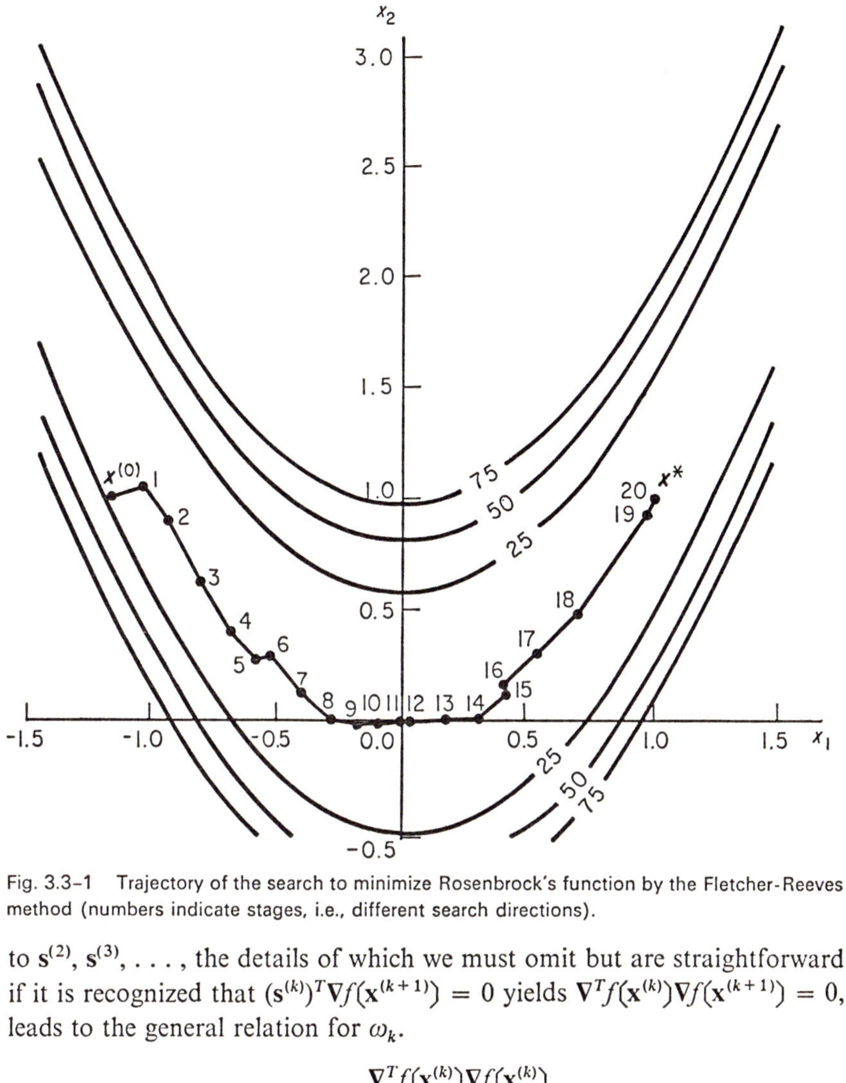

Fig. 3.3–1 Trajectory of the search to minimize Rosenbrock's function by the Fletcher-Reeves method (numbers indicate stages, i.e., different search directions).

to $\mathbf{s}^{(2)}, \mathbf{s}^{(3)}, \ldots$, the details of which we must omit but are straightforward if it is recognized that $(\mathbf{s}^{(k)})^T \nabla f(\mathbf{x}^{(k+1)}) = 0$ yields $\nabla^T f(\mathbf{x}^{(k)}) \nabla f(\mathbf{x}^{(k+1)}) = 0$, leads to the general relation for ω_k.

$$\omega_k = \frac{\nabla^T f(\mathbf{x}^{(k)}) \nabla f(\mathbf{x}^{(k)})}{\nabla^T f(\mathbf{x}^{(k-1)}) \nabla f(\mathbf{x}^{(k-1)})} \tag{3.3-14}$$

All the weighting factors prior to ω_k, namely, $\omega_{k-1}, \omega_{k-2}, \ldots$, prove to be zero—a very neat arrangement.

The major steps in the algorithm are:

1. At $\mathbf{x}^{(0)}$ compute

$$\mathbf{s}^{(0)} = -\nabla f(\mathbf{x}^{(0)})$$

2. On the kth stage determine the minimum of $f(\mathbf{x})$ by a unidimensional search in the $\mathbf{s}^{(k)}$ direction. This locates $\mathbf{x}^{(k+1)}$.
3. Evaluate $f(\mathbf{x}^{(k+1)})$ and $\nabla f(\mathbf{x}^{(k+1)})$.
4. The direction $\mathbf{s}^{(k+1)}$ is determined from

$$\mathbf{s}^{(k+1)} = -\nabla f(\mathbf{x}^{(k+1)}) + \mathbf{s}^{(k)} \frac{\nabla^T f(\mathbf{x}^{(k+1)}) \nabla f(\mathbf{x}^{(k+1)})}{\nabla^T f(\mathbf{x}^{(k)}) \nabla f(\mathbf{x}^{(k)})}$$

   After $(n + 1)$ iterations $(k = n)$, the procedure cycles again, $\mathbf{x}^{(n+1)}$ becoming $\mathbf{x}^{(0)}$.
5. Terminate the algorithm when $\|\mathbf{s}^{(k)}\| < \varepsilon$, where ε is an arbitrary constant.

Note that matrix inversion is not required. Another advantage of the algorithm is that it requires only a limited amount of storage in a computer compared with the $n \times n$ matrices described in Sec. 3.4. Figure 3.3–1 illustrates the trajectory of the minimization for Rosenbrock's function. The Fletcher-Reeves algorithm is evaluated in Chap. 5 for a number of test problems.

3.3–3 Partan Methods

Shah, Buehler, and Kempthorne[1] described several algorithms that made use of conjugate directions (general Partan) and conjugate gradients (steepest descent Partan, continued Partan). A commercial program is available

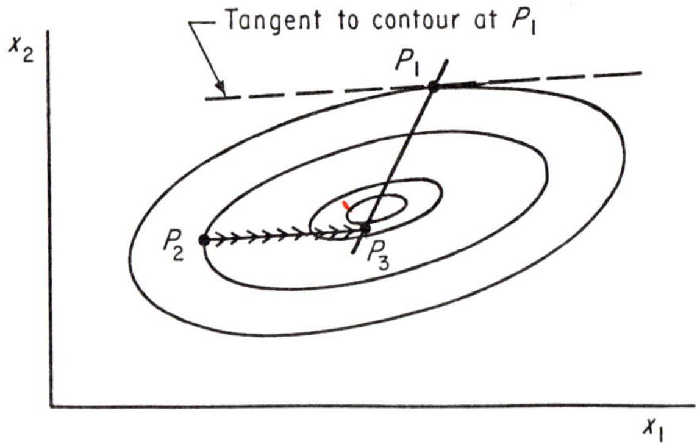

Fig. 3.3–2 Parallel tangents (Partan) method in two dimensions.

[1] B. V. Shah, R. J. Buehler and O. Kempthorne, *J. SIAM*, **12**:74 (1964).

from Electronic Associates Inc., Princeton, N.J. Partan is short for "parallel tangents." Figure 3.3–2 illustrates the essence of the procedure for a quadratic objective function of two independent variables. P_1 and P_2 are any two points in the $(x_1 - x_2)$ plane. One proceeds from P_2 parallel to the tangent to the contour at P_1 until the minimum of $f(\mathbf{x})$ is reached at P_3. The tangents at P_1 and P_3 are parallel, and the minimum of $f(\mathbf{x})$ is found on the line through P_1 and P_3.

The method makes use of the fact that parallelism of lines is retained under a general affine (i.e., essentially canonical) transformation of the space of independent variables, so that some aspects of the search for a minimum will be unaffected by the scale of the variables involved. Part of the procedure is based on an acceleration technique devised by Forsythe and Motzkin[1] for use with steepest ascent.

The *general Partan* algorithm is essentially as follows; examine Fig. 3.3–3. Let $\mathbf{x}^{(0)}, \mathbf{x}^{(2)}, \mathbf{x}^{(3)}, \ldots$ denote the successive $\mathbf{x}$ vectors in E^n and denote by π_k the plane tangent to the contour of $f(\mathbf{x})$ at $\mathbf{x}^{(k)}$. Each step is to the minimum of $f(\mathbf{x})$. From $\mathbf{x}^{(0)}$ (so numbered for symmetry) proceed along a polygonal line $\mathbf{x}^{(0)}\mathbf{x}^{(2)}\mathbf{x}^{(3)}\mathbf{x}^{(4)} \ldots$, on which $\mathbf{x}^{(m)}$ is at the minimum of $f(\mathbf{x})$ on the extended line $\mathbf{x}^{(m-1)}\mathbf{x}^{(m)}$. The initial direction $\mathbf{x}^{(0)}\mathbf{x}^{(2)}$ is arbitrary; $\mathbf{x}^{(2)}\mathbf{x}^{(3)}$ is arbitrary but parallel to π_0; $\mathbf{x}^{(4)}$ is then colinear with $\mathbf{x}^{(0)}$ and $\mathbf{x}^{(3)}$. Thereafter, for $k = 2, 3, \ldots, \mathbf{x}^{(2k)}\mathbf{x}^{(2k+1)}$ is parallel to $\pi_0, \pi_2, \pi_4, \ldots, \pi_{2k-2}$, and $\mathbf{x}^{(2k+2)}$ is colinear with $\mathbf{x}^{(2k-2)}$ and $\mathbf{x}^{(2k+1)}$. Shah, Buehler, and Kempthorne demonstrated that if $f(\mathbf{x})$ is a quadratic function in n dimensions having a unique minimum, that is, is a positive definite quadratic form, or a monotone function thereof, the general Partan algorithm reaches the minimum at $\mathbf{x}^{(2n)}$, if not sooner. Thus the method has the property of quadratic termination.

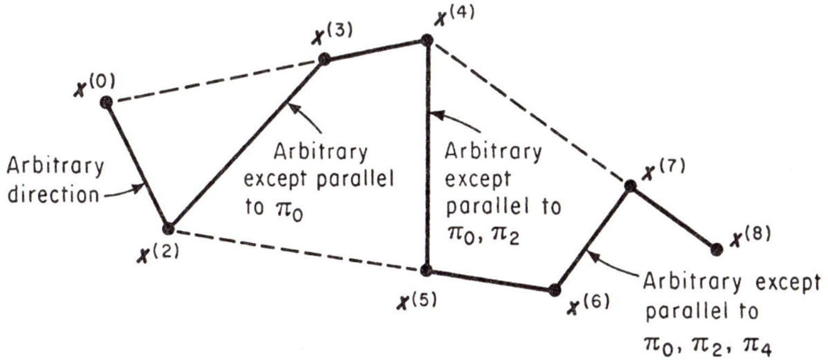

Fig. 3.3–3 General Partan algorithm.

[1] G. E. Forsythe and T. S. Motzkin, *Bull. Am. Math. Soc.*, **57**:183 (1951).

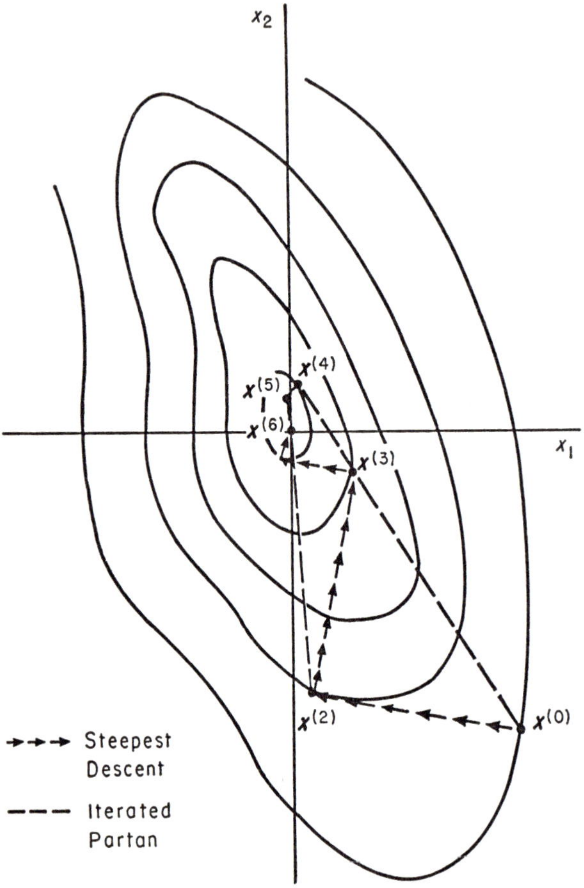

Fig. 3.3-4 Comparison of steepest descent, iterated, and continued Partan trajectories.

Directions obtained by the general Partan algorithm are conjugate, as demonstrated for the quadratic objective function $f(\mathbf{x}) = \frac{1}{2}\mathbf{x}^T\mathbf{H}\mathbf{x}$ of n independent variables. The gradient of $f(\mathbf{x})$ is $\nabla f(\mathbf{x}) = \mathbf{H}\mathbf{x}$. Because the optimization path from $\mathbf{x}^{(0)}$ proceeds along the vector $(\mathbf{x}^{(0)} - \mathbf{x}^{(2)})$ (examine Fig. 3.3-4) until the minimum of $f(\mathbf{x})$ is reached, whereupon the point so located is designated $\mathbf{x}^{(2)}$, the vector $(\mathbf{x}^{(0)} - \mathbf{x}^{(2)})$ is parallel to π_2, the tangent plane at $\mathbf{x}^{(2)}$. Also, $(\mathbf{x}^{(0)} - \mathbf{x}^{(2)})$ is normal to the gradient of $f(\mathbf{x})$ at $\mathbf{x}^{(2)}$, $\nabla f(\mathbf{x}^{(2)}) = \mathbf{H}\mathbf{x}^{(2)}$. Consequently,

$$(\mathbf{x}^{(0)} - \mathbf{x}^{(2)})^T\nabla f(\mathbf{x}^{(2)}) = (\mathbf{x}^{(0)} - \mathbf{x}^{(2)})^T\mathbf{H}\mathbf{x}^{(2)} = 0$$

$$\nabla^T f(\mathbf{x}^{(2)})(\mathbf{x}^{(0)} - \mathbf{x}^{(2)}) = (\mathbf{x}^{(2)})^T\mathbf{H}(\mathbf{x}^{(0)} - \mathbf{x}^{(2)}) = 0$$

so that $(\mathbf{x}^{(0)})^T\mathbf{H}\mathbf{x}^{(2)} = (\mathbf{x}^{(2)})^T\mathbf{H}\mathbf{x}^{(2)}$. Extending the construction,

$$\begin{aligned}(\mathbf{x}^{(0)})^T\mathbf{H}\mathbf{x}^{(2)} &= (\mathbf{x}^{(2)})^T\mathbf{H}\mathbf{x}^{(2)} = (\mathbf{x}^{(4)})^T\mathbf{H}\mathbf{x}^{(2)} = \cdots = (\mathbf{x}^{(2k)})^T\mathbf{H}\mathbf{x}^{(2)} \\ &= (\mathbf{x}^{(2)})^T\mathbf{H}\mathbf{x}^{(0)} = (\mathbf{x}^{(2)})^T\mathbf{H}\mathbf{x}^{(2)} = (\mathbf{x}^{(2)})^T\mathbf{H}\mathbf{x}^{(4)} = \cdots = (\mathbf{x}^{(2)})^T\mathbf{H}\mathbf{x}^{(2k)}\end{aligned}$$

and in general, these quantities are all equal to $(\mathbf{x}^{(2j)})^T\mathbf{H}\mathbf{x}^{(2k)}$. Also, the construction requires that the vector $(\mathbf{x}^{(2)} - \mathbf{x}^{(3)})$ (examine Fig. 3.3–4) be parallel to π_0, or $(\mathbf{x}^{(2)} - \mathbf{x}^{(3)})^T\nabla f(\mathbf{x}^{(0)}) = 0$, and a similar analysis leads to

$$\mathbf{x}^{(2j)}\mathbf{H}\mathbf{x}^{(2k)} = \mathbf{x}^{(2j)}\mathbf{H}\mathbf{x}^{(2k+1)} \qquad j = 0, 1, \ldots, k-1, k = 1, 2, \ldots, n-1$$

Specifically, we are interested in the differences

$$\begin{aligned}(\mathbf{x}^{(k+2)})^T\mathbf{H}\mathbf{x}^{(2n)} - (\mathbf{x}^{(k+2)})^T\mathbf{H}\mathbf{x}^{(2n-2)} &= 0 \\ (\mathbf{x}^{(k)})^T\mathbf{H}\mathbf{x}^{(2n)} - (\mathbf{x}^{(k)})^T\mathbf{H}^{(2n-2)} &= 0\end{aligned}$$

which yield, after subtracting the second equation from the first,

$$(\mathbf{x}^{(k+2)} - \mathbf{x}^{(k)})^T\mathbf{H}(\mathbf{x}^{(2n)} - \mathbf{x}^{(2n-2)}) = 0 \qquad (3.3\text{–}15)$$

Equation (3.3–15) states that the directions $(\mathbf{x}^{(2)} - \mathbf{x}^{(0)})$, $(\mathbf{x}^{(4)} - \mathbf{x}^{(2)})$, . . . up to $(\mathbf{x}^{(2n)} - \mathbf{x}^{(2n-2)})$ are mutually conjugate.

There are various Partan methods. In *steepest descent Partan* the arbitrary directions in the general Partan algorithm are chosen as follows. At the points $\mathbf{x}^{(0)}, \mathbf{x}^{(2)}, \mathbf{x}^{(4)}, \ldots \mathbf{x}^{(2k)}$ proceed in the direction of the negative gradient. This approach is consistent with the case in which $f(\mathbf{x})$ is quadratic and there are no errors in determining first derivatives, so that steepest descent Partan has finite convergence. Hence the arbitrariness in the choice of certain directions is removed, and the procedure is now invariant under rotations, that is, transformations $\mathbf{y} = \mathbf{U}\mathbf{x}$, where $\mathbf{U}$ is an orthogonal matrix. The choice of scale in steepest descent Partan does affect the performance of intermediate steps, though.

Iterated Partan operates as follows:

1. Determine the direction of the negative gradient (steepest descent) at $\mathbf{x}^{(0)}$.
2. Locate $\mathbf{x}^{(2)}$ at the minimum of $f(\mathbf{x})$ along the negative gradient from $\mathbf{x}^{(0)}$.
3. Determine the direction of the negative gradient at $\mathbf{x}^{(2)}$.
4. Locate $\mathbf{x}^{(3)}$ at the minimum of $f(\mathbf{x})$ along the negative gradient from $\mathbf{x}^{(2)}$.
5. Connect $\mathbf{x}^{(0)}$ and $\mathbf{x}^{(3)}$ with a straight line and locate the minimum of $f(\mathbf{x})$ along this line; denote the point by $\mathbf{x}^{(4)}$.
6. Let $\mathbf{x}^{(4)}$ be a new starting point and repeat the procedure.

If the problem contains n variables, one takes n gradient steps and then connects $\mathbf{x}^{(0)}$ with $\mathbf{x}^{(n+1)}$. In Fig. 3.3–4 the steps from $\mathbf{x}^{(0)}$ to $\mathbf{x}^{(2)}$, $\mathbf{x}^{(2)}$ to $\mathbf{x}^{(3)}$, $\mathbf{x}^{(4)}$ to $\mathbf{x}^{(5)}$, and $\mathbf{x}^{(5)}$ to $\mathbf{x}^{(6)}$ (not shown) are steepest descent steps.

Iterated Partan has proved to be much less effective than *continued Partan*, which is initiated with the first five steps of iterated Partan, and then continues as follows (for two variables):

6′. Determine the direction of the negative gradient at $\mathbf{x}^{(4)}$.
7. Locate $\mathbf{x}^{(5)}$ at the minimum of $f(\mathbf{x})$ along the negative gradient.
8. Connect $\mathbf{x}^{(2)}$ and $\mathbf{x}^{(5)}$ with a straight line and locate the minimum along the line; denote the point by $\mathbf{x}^{(6)}$.
9. Repeat step 6′ with the point determined in step 8, replacing $\mathbf{x}^{(4)}$. On each cycle the steepest descent direction is used at $\mathbf{x}^{(2k)}$, $k = 2, 3, \ldots,$ and $\mathbf{x}^{(2k-2)}$ is connected to $\mathbf{x}^{(2k+1)}$ for the acceleration step.

The Partan algorithm is evaluated in Chap. 5.

3.3–4 Zoutendijk's Method (Projection Method)

An algorithm using conjugate directions computed with the aid of a projection matrix has been proposed by Zoutendijk.[1] Projection matrices are described in Sec. 6.3, but we can summarize the steps of the algorithm here:

1. Start at $\mathbf{x}^{(0)}$ and let the projection matrix $\mathbf{P}^{(0)} = \mathbf{I}$.
2. For the kth step compute the projection matrix

$$\begin{aligned}\mathbf{P}^{(k)} &= \mathbf{I} - \mathbf{G}^{(k)}[(\mathbf{G}^{(k)})^T\mathbf{G}^{(k)}]^{-1}(\mathbf{G}^{(k)})^T \\ &= \mathbf{P}^{(k-1)} - \mathbf{P}^{(k-1)}\Delta\mathbf{g}^{(k)}[(\Delta\mathbf{g}^{(k)})^T\mathbf{P}^{(k-1)}\Delta\mathbf{g}^{(k)}]^{-1}(\Delta\mathbf{g}^{(k)})^T\mathbf{P}^{(k-1)}\end{aligned} \tag{3.3–16}$$

3. If $\mathbf{P}^{(k)}\nabla f(\mathbf{x}^{(k)}) \neq \mathbf{0}$, let $\mathbf{s}^{(k)} = -\mathbf{P}^{(k)}\nabla f(\mathbf{x}^{(k)})$, and minimize $f(\mathbf{x})$ in the $\mathbf{s}^{(k)}$ direction to reach $\mathbf{x}^{(k+1)}$. Repeat step 2. After n search directions are selected, start at step 1 again, with $\mathbf{x}^{(0)} = \mathbf{x}^{(n)}$.
4. If $\mathbf{P}^{(k)}\nabla f(\mathbf{x}^{(k)}) = \mathbf{0}$ and $\nabla f(\mathbf{x}^{(k)}) = \mathbf{0}$, terminate the search.
5. If $\mathbf{P}^{(k)}\nabla f(\mathbf{x}^{(k)}) = \mathbf{0}$ and $\nabla f(\mathbf{x}^{(k)}) \neq \mathbf{0}$, start at step 1 again, with $\mathbf{x}^{(0)} = \mathbf{x}^{(k)}$.

[1] G. Zoutendijk, "Methods of Feasible Directions," American Elsevier Publishing Company, New York, 1960.

After n iterations are carried out, $\mathbf{P}^{(n)} = 0$; hence a new cycle of iterations must be started. Because the first search direction on restart is that of steepest descent, it can be shown[1] that the algorithm minimizes a quadratic function having a positive definite hessian matrix in n or fewer stages. Compare Eq. (3.3–16) with Eq. (3.4–11) in the next section.

3.3–5 Multiparameter Adjustment

Miele and Cantrell[2] proposed a method of search that involved the selection of two parameters to minimize $f(\mathbf{x})$ in each search direction. In their algorithm

$$\mathbf{x}^{(k+1)} = \mathbf{x}^{(k)} - \lambda_0^{(k)}\nabla f(\mathbf{x}^{(k)}) + \lambda_1^{(k)}\Delta\mathbf{x}^{(k-1)} \tag{3.3–17}$$

The objective function $f(\mathbf{x}^{(k)} - \lambda_0\nabla f(\mathbf{x}^{(k)}) + \lambda_1\Delta\mathbf{x}^{(k-1)})$ is minimized with respect to both λ_0 and λ_1, and thereafter $\mathbf{x}^{(k+1)}$ computed by Eq. (3.3–17). Under these circumstances it can be shown that $\nabla^T f(\mathbf{x}^{(k)})\nabla f(\mathbf{x}^{(k+1)}) = 0$, that $\nabla^T f(\mathbf{x}^{(k+1)})\Delta\mathbf{x}^{(k+1)} = 0$, and that $\nabla^T f(\mathbf{x}^{(k+1)})\Delta\mathbf{x}^{(k)} = 0$.

On the first iteration, $\Delta\mathbf{x}^{(k-1)} = \mathbf{0}$ and $\mathbf{x}^{(0)}$ must be given. Thereafter, for the kth stage:

1. Compute $\mathbf{x}^{(k)}$, $\nabla f(\mathbf{x}^{(k)})$, and $\Delta\mathbf{x}^{(k-1)} = \mathbf{x}^{(k)} - \mathbf{x}^{(k-1)}$.
2. Evaluate $\lambda_0^{(k)}$ and $\lambda_1^{(k)}$ to the desired precision by an efficient two-dimensional search such as the ones described in this or the next chapter.
3. Use Eq. (3.3–17) to initiate step 1 again.
4. Restart every $(n + 1)$ iterations with $\Delta\mathbf{x}^{(k-1)} = \mathbf{0}$.
5. Terminate when $|\Delta f(\mathbf{x})| < \varepsilon$.

For a quadratic function, the above algorithm is the same as the Fletcher-Reeves algorithm but takes longer to execute because of the two-dimensional search on each stage. For nonquadratic functions, the Fletcher-Reeves algorithm in effect selects the best value of λ_0 on each stage while keeping the ratio of λ_1/λ_0 constant, whereas the algorithm of Miele and Cantrell optimizes both λ_0 and λ_1. Figure 3.3–5 illustrates Miele and Cantrell's results for a test of their algorithm using function VI in Table 5.2–1 and a version of Newton's method for the two-dimensional

[1]G. P. McCormick and J. D. Pearson, Chap. 21 in R. Fletcher (ed.), "Optimization," Academic Press Inc., London, 1969.

[2]A. Miele and J. W. Cantrell, *Rice Univ. Aero-Astronautics Rept.* 56, Houston, Tex., 1969.

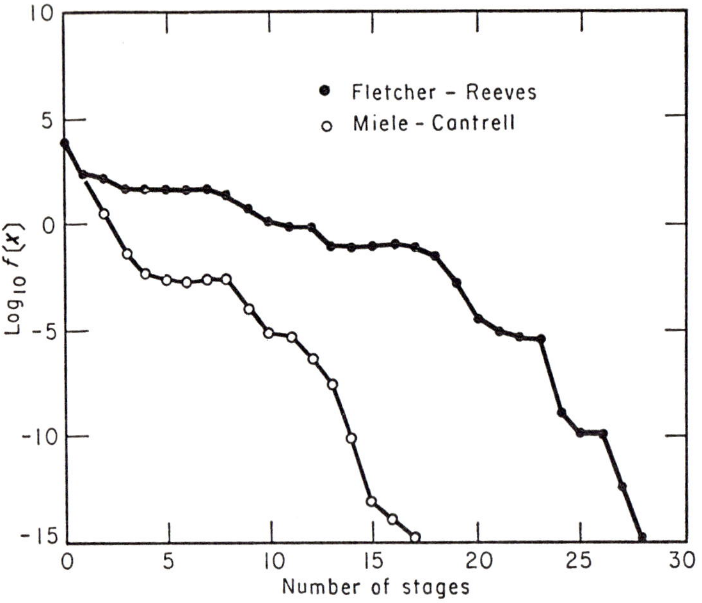

Fig. 3.3-5 Two-parameter adjustment algorithm of Miele and Cantrell for function VI in Table 5.2-1.

search. The times on a Burroughs B 5500 computer were 8.8 and 11.9 sec for the Miele-Cantrell and Fletcher-Reeves algorithms, respectively.

Cragg and Levy[1] extended the two-parameter adjustment method to a greater number of parameters at the expense of a higher-dimensional search on each stage to obtain the values of the parameters that minimize $f(\mathbf{x})$. The next $\mathbf{x}$ vector is computed from

$$\mathbf{x}^{(k+1)} = \mathbf{x}^{(k)} - \lambda_0^{(k)}\nabla f(\mathbf{x}^{(k)}) + \sum_{i=1}^{m} \lambda_i^{(k)}\Delta\mathbf{x}^{(i-1)} \tag{3.3-18}$$

with $m \leq n - 1$. For the initial stages of the algorithm the unknown $\Delta\mathbf{x}^i$ can be set equal to zero. Table 3.3-1 compares several of the algorithms with the Cragg-Levy algorithm in which a modified form of Newton's method was used to carry out the $(m + 1)$-dimensional search for the λ's. The fact that Newton's search was used undoubtedly contributed to the better performance of these algorithms. Function evaluations were not reported.

[1] E. E. Cragg and A. V. Levy, *Rice. Univ. Aero-Astronautics Rept.* 58, Houston, Tex., 1969.

Table 3.3-1 Comparison of multiparameter optimization algorithms to reduce $f(\mathbf{x}) < 10^{-13}$

		*Function I**		*Function VI**		*Function X**	
Method	*Sec. ref.*	*Stages*	*Time*†	*Stages*	*Time*†	*Stages*	*Time*†
Gradient	3.1	‡	‡	‡	‡	‡	‡
Fletcher-Reeves	3.3-2	29	1.2	29	2.4	68	14.0
Davidon-Fletcher-Powell	3.4-2	21	1.1	39	4.5	30	6.7
Miele-Cantrell (two-parameter)§	3.3-5	2	0.6	18	2.0	32	12.8
Cragg-Levy (four-parameter)¶	3.3-5	2	0.6	4	1.4	7	5.0
Newton, uncorrected	3.2	6	0.1	‖	‖	25	1.6
Newton, corrected	3.2	21	0.3	39	1.5	25	1.6

*See Table 5.2-1.

†Time is in seconds on a Burroughs B 5500 computer.

‡Not successful in solving problem.

§Uses Newton's method, corrected to make the hessian matrix positive definite, in the parameter optimization.

¶Two parameters only for Rosenbrock's function (function I).

‖Converges to nonoptimal stationary point.

Source: E. E. Cragg and A. V. Levy, *Rice Univ.*, Houston, Tex., *Aero-Astronautics Rep.* 58, 1969.

3.4 VARIABLE METRIC METHODS

A class of methods termed *variable metric*,[1] *quasi-Newton*, or *large-step gradient* exists that approximate the hessian matrix or its inverse but use information from only first-order derivatives to do so. Most of these methods employ conjugate directions, while others do not. Variable metric methods compute a new $\mathbf{x}$ vector from the one on the preceding stage by an equation analogous to Eqs. (3.1-3) and (3.2-4*a*).

$$\mathbf{x}^{(k+1)} = \mathbf{x}^{(k)} + \lambda^{(k)}\hat{\mathbf{s}}^{(k)} = \mathbf{x}^{(k)} - \lambda^{*(k)}\boldsymbol{\eta}(\mathbf{x}^{(k)})\nabla f(\mathbf{x}^{(k)}) \qquad (3.4\text{-}1)$$

where $\boldsymbol{\eta}(\mathbf{x}^{(k)})$ is sometimes called the direction matrix and represents an approximation of $\mathbf{H}^{-1}(\mathbf{x})$. From this viewpoint, in Sec. 3.1, $\boldsymbol{\eta}(\mathbf{x}^{(k)})$ is the identity matrix, and in Sec. 3.2, $\boldsymbol{\eta}(\mathbf{x}^{(k)})$ is the inverse of the hessian matrix of the objective function $\mathbf{H}^{-1}(\mathbf{x})$. However, to use $\mathbf{H}^{-1}(\mathbf{x})$ it was necessary

[1] In a more restrictive sense variable metric refers to only those methods in which a transformation is made on the independent variables to scale them more equally, but we will not use the term in this way.

to compute the second partial derivatives of $f(\mathbf{x})$ explicitly and to invert the matrix $\mathbf{H}(\mathbf{x})$, whereas in the variable metric methods various relations are used to compute $\boldsymbol{\eta}(\mathbf{x}^{(k)})$ without having to do either.

Another useful relation between $\mathbf{x}^{(k+1)}$ and $\mathbf{x}^{(k)}$ was given, by Eq. (3.3–10), for a quadratic objective function (or a quadratic approximate to the objective function).

$$\nabla f(\mathbf{x}^{(k+1)}) - \nabla f(\mathbf{x}^{(k)}) = \mathbf{H}(\mathbf{x}^{(k)})(\mathbf{x}^{(k+1)} - \mathbf{x}^{(k)}) \qquad (3.4\text{–}2a)$$

By premultiplying both sides of Eq. (3.4–2*a*) by $\mathbf{H}^{-1}(\mathbf{x}^{(k)})$, we get

$$\mathbf{x}^{(k+1)} - \mathbf{x}^{(k)} = \mathbf{H}^{-1}(\mathbf{x}^{(k)})[\nabla f(\mathbf{x}^{(k+1)}) - \nabla f(\mathbf{x}^{(k)})] \qquad (3.4\text{–}2b)$$

If $f(\mathbf{x})$ is quadratic, then $\mathbf{H}(\mathbf{x}^{(k)}) = \mathbf{H}$, a constant matrix. We can look upon Eq. (3.4–2*b*) as a set of n linear equations containing a set of unknown parameters that must be estimated in order to approximate $\mathbf{H}^{-1}(\mathbf{x})$, or $\mathbf{H}(\mathbf{x})$ itself, given a previous history of the values of $f(\mathbf{x})$, $\nabla f(\mathbf{x})$, and $\Delta\mathbf{x}$ on the earlier stages of the search. Various techniques can be used to solve the linear equations, and each technique leads to a different variable metric method.

In a large group of methods, $\mathbf{H}^{-1}(\mathbf{x}^{(k+1)})$ is to be approximated from information collected in the kth stage, or

$$\mathbf{H}^{-1}(\mathbf{x}^{(k+1)}) \approx \omega\boldsymbol{\eta}^{(k+1)} = \omega(\boldsymbol{\eta}^{(k)} + \Delta\boldsymbol{\eta}^{(k)}) \qquad (3.4\text{–}3)$$

where $\boldsymbol{\eta}$ is the approximating matrix for $\mathbf{H}^{-1}(\mathbf{x})$ (the argument $\mathbf{x}$ of $\boldsymbol{\eta}$ will be suppressed to save space; hence the superscript on $\boldsymbol{\eta}$ will designate the stage), $\Delta\boldsymbol{\eta}^{(k)}$ is a matrix to be specified and ω is a scaling factor, a constant, generally equal to unity. The selcction of $\Delta\boldsymbol{\eta}^{(k)}$ essentially determines the type of variable metric method. To guarantee convergence, $\omega\boldsymbol{\eta}^{(k+1)}$ must be positive definite and should satisfy Eq. (3.4–2*b*) when it replaces $\mathbf{H}^{-1}$.

At the stage $\mathbf{x}^{(k+1)}$ we know $\mathbf{x}^{(k)}$, $\nabla f(\mathbf{x}^{(k)})$, $\nabla f(\mathbf{x}^{(k+1)})$, and $\boldsymbol{\eta}^{(k)}$, and wish to compute $\boldsymbol{\eta}^{(k+1)}$ so that the relation

$$\boldsymbol{\eta}^{(k+1)}\Delta\mathbf{g}^{(k)} = \frac{1}{\omega}\Delta\mathbf{x}^{(k)} \qquad (3.4\text{–}2c)$$

is satisfied. Let $\Delta\boldsymbol{\eta}^{(k)} = \boldsymbol{\eta}^{(k+1)} - \boldsymbol{\eta}^{(k)}$. Then the equation

$$\Delta\boldsymbol{\eta}^{(k)}\Delta\mathbf{g}^{(k)} = \frac{1}{\omega}\Delta\mathbf{x}^{(k)} - \boldsymbol{\eta}^{(k)}\Delta\mathbf{g}^{(k)} \qquad (3.4\text{–}2d)$$

is to be solved for $\Delta\boldsymbol{\eta}^{(k)}$. It can be shown by direct substitution of the result that Eq. (3.4–2*d*) has the solution

$$\Delta\boldsymbol{\eta}^{(k)} = \frac{1}{\omega}\frac{\Delta\mathbf{x}^{(k)}\mathbf{y}^T}{\mathbf{y}^T\Delta\mathbf{g}^{(k)}} - \frac{\boldsymbol{\eta}^{(k)}\Delta\mathbf{g}^{(k)}\mathbf{z}^T}{\mathbf{z}^T\Delta\mathbf{g}^{(k)}} \qquad (3.4\text{–}4)$$

where $\mathbf{y}$ and $\mathbf{z}$ are arbitrary $n \times 1$ vectors. If for $\omega = 1$ we choose a special linear combination of the two directions $\Delta\mathbf{x}^{(k)}$ and $\boldsymbol{\eta}^{(k)}\Delta\mathbf{g}^{(k)}$

$$\mathbf{y} = \mathbf{z} = \Delta\mathbf{x}^{(k)} - \boldsymbol{\eta}^{(k)}\Delta\mathbf{g}^{(k)}$$

then Broyden's algorithm (described in Sec. 3.4–1) results, whereas if we choose

$$\mathbf{y} = \Delta\mathbf{x}^{(k)} \qquad \mathbf{z} = \boldsymbol{\eta}^{(k)}\Delta\mathbf{g}^{(k)}$$

then the matrix $\boldsymbol{\eta}^{(k+1)}$ is updated by the Davidon-Fletcher-Powell algorithm (described in Sec. 3.4–2). Because $\mathbf{y}$ and $\mathbf{z}$ are arbitrary vectors, other choices are feasible, and these will be discussed in subsequent sections. If the steps $\Delta\mathbf{x}^{(k)}$ are consecutively determined by minimizing $f(\mathbf{x})$ in the $\mathbf{s}^{(k)}$ direction, all the methods that compute a symmetric $\boldsymbol{\eta}^{(k+1)}$ satisfying Eq. (3.4–2c) generate directions that are mutually conjugate (for a quadratic objective function).

3.4-1 $\Delta\eta^k$ Has Rank 1

Broyden,[1] in describing techniques of solving sets of linear equations, showed that if $\Delta\boldsymbol{\eta}^{(k)}$ is to be a symmetric matrix with a rank of 1 and the relation $\boldsymbol{\eta}^{(k+1)}\Delta\mathbf{g}^{(k)} = \Delta\mathbf{x}^{(k)}$ is to be satisfied, then the only possible choice of $\Delta\boldsymbol{\eta}^{(k)}$ is

$$\Delta\boldsymbol{\eta}^{(k)} = \frac{[(\Delta\mathbf{x}^{(k)}) - \boldsymbol{\eta}^{(k)}(\Delta\mathbf{g}^{(k)})][(\Delta\mathbf{x}^{(k)}) - \boldsymbol{\eta}^{(k)}(\Delta\mathbf{g}^{(k)})]^T}{[(\Delta\mathbf{x}^{(k)}) - \boldsymbol{\eta}^{(k)}(\Delta\mathbf{g}^{(k)})]^T(\Delta\mathbf{g}^{(k)})} \tag{3.4–5}$$

where, to save space, we let

$$(\Delta\mathbf{x}^{(k)}) = \mathbf{x}^{(k+1)} - \mathbf{x}^{(k)}$$
$$(\Delta\mathbf{g}^{(k)}) = \nabla f(\mathbf{x}^{(k+1)}) - \nabla f(\mathbf{x}^{(k)})$$

In the simplest algorithm the minimization starts by choosing $\mathbf{x}^{(0)}$ and $\boldsymbol{\eta}^{(0)} > \mathbf{0}$, and then applying Eqs. (3.4–1), (3.4–3), and (3.4–5) in sequence until, say, $\|\nabla f(\mathbf{x}^k)\| < \varepsilon$. If in each search direction $\lambda^{(k)}$ is the scalar that minimizes $f(\mathbf{x})$ in that direction, then the method generates conjugate directions of search. Thus, under certain restricted conditions, the algorithm just described is guaranteed to converge. Specifically, if the objective function of n independent variables is quadratic, so that the nonsingular hessian matrix $\mathbf{H}$ is constant, then if $\boldsymbol{\eta}^{(0)} > \mathbf{0}$, if $\boldsymbol{\eta}^{(k+1)}$ is computed by

[1] C. G. Broyden, *Math. Computation*, **21**:368 (1967).

Eqs. (3.4–3) and (3.4–5), if $\mathbf{x}^{(k+1)}$ is computed by Eq. (3.4–1), and if the $(\Delta\mathbf{x}^{(k)})$ are linearly independent directions, it can be proved that after n steps, $\boldsymbol{\eta}^{(n)} = \mathbf{H}^{-1}$. One interesting feature of the rank 1 methods is that λ (or λ^*) in Eq. (3.4–1) does not necessarily have to be the parameter that minimizes $f(\mathbf{x})$. Broyden shows that λ can be an arbitrary parameter as long as it does not cause $\boldsymbol{\eta}$ to become singular nor the denominator of the right-hand side of Eq. (3.4–5) to become zero. This feature permits abandoning the unidimensional search if an adequate alternative method of establishing λ can be determined (see Sec. 3.4–5). The theorems detailing the sufficient conditions for the convergence of the rank 1 algorithms are given by Goldfarb.[1] Note that no matrix inversion is required for the methods in this subsection.

If the objective function is not quadratic, some of the less satisfactory aspects of the use of Eq. (3.4–5) are:

1. $\boldsymbol{\eta}$ may cease to become positive definite, in which case it is necessary to make sure that $\boldsymbol{\eta}^{(k+1)}$ is made positive definite by one of the methods mentioned in Sec. 3.2.
2. The correction $\Delta\boldsymbol{\eta}^{(k)}$ may become unbounded (sometimes even for quadratic functions, because of roundoff).
3. If $\Delta\mathbf{x}^{(k)} = -\lambda^{*(k)}\boldsymbol{\eta}(\mathbf{x}^{(k)})\nabla f(\mathbf{x}^{(k)})$ by chance is in the direction of the preceding stage, $\boldsymbol{\eta}(\mathbf{x}^{(k+1)})$ becomes singular or undetermined.

Consequently, in Broyden's algorithm, if either

$$\boldsymbol{\eta}^{(k)}\Delta\mathbf{g}^{(k)} = \Delta\mathbf{x}^{(k)}$$

or

$$(\boldsymbol{\eta}^{(k)}\Delta\mathbf{g}^{(k)} - \Delta\mathbf{x}^{(k)})^T\Delta\mathbf{g}^{(k)} = 0$$

set $\boldsymbol{\eta}^{(k+1)} = \boldsymbol{\eta}^{(k)}$, that is, $\Delta\boldsymbol{\eta}^{(k)} = 0$, in determining the search direction in Eq. (3.4–1). Figure 3.4–1 illustrates the trajectory of the search for the minimum of Rosenbrock's function by Broyden's algorithm with the DSC-Powell unidimensional search. Note how a large initial step (one negative gradient step) in the unidimensional search bypasses the left-hand portion of the curved valley, whereas a small initial step causes the minimization to be confined to the valley entirely. A computer code for Broyden's algorithm will be found in Appendix B.

Davidon[2] proposed essentially the same computation for $\Delta\boldsymbol{\eta}^{(k)}$ as Eq. (3.4–5), except that $\Delta\boldsymbol{\eta}^{(k)}$ was multiplied by a function of two parameters

[1] D. Goldfarb, Chap. 18 in R. Fletcher (ed.), "Optimization," Academic Press Inc., New York, 1969.

[2] W. C. Davidon, *Computer J.*, **10**:406 (1968); Chap. 2 in R. Fletcher (ed.), "Optimization," Academic Press Inc., New York, 1969.

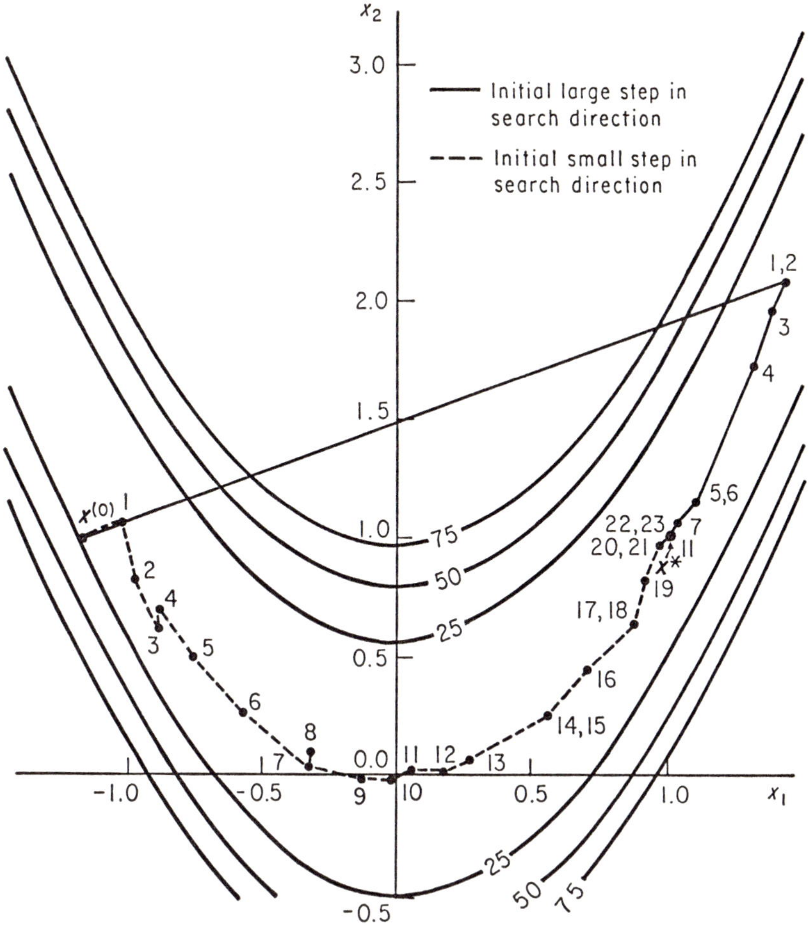

Fig. 3.4–1 Trajectory of the search to minimize Rosenbrock's function by Broyden's algorithm (numbers designate stages, i.e., different search directions).

that restricted the change in $\boldsymbol{\eta}^{(k)}$ on each stage to be not "too great" and that kept $\boldsymbol{\eta}^{(k+1)}$ positive definite. The algorithm used a step length of $\lambda^* = 1$. If $f(\mathbf{x}^{(k+1)}) > f(\mathbf{x}^{(k)})$, after $\boldsymbol{\eta}^{(k+1)}$ is calculated, $\mathbf{x}^{(k+1)}$ is replaced by $\mathbf{x}^{(k)}$ on the next iteration. Although unidimensional searches are avoided, good choices of λ^* and the two parameters have considerable effect on the usefulness of the algorithm. Powell[1] lists a number of additional investigators who have proposed the use of Eq. (3.4–5) or its equivalent.

[1] M. J. D. Powell, Rank One Methods for Unconstrained Optimization, *AERE Rept.* TP 372, 1969.

Murtagh and Sargent[1] showed that among the conditions required for convergence to a stationary point, the norm of $\boldsymbol{\eta}^{(k)}$ must be bounded above and below. For the lower bound, direct computation of the matrix norm can be avoided by using the stronger condition from the available vectors

$$\frac{\|\boldsymbol{\eta}^{(k)}\nabla f(\mathbf{x}^{(k)})\|}{\|\nabla f(\mathbf{x}^{(k)})\|} \geq \rho_1$$

where the ρ_i are constants. Another condition required for convergence restricts the angle between the search direction and direction of steepest descent so that $f(\mathbf{x})$ decreases for $\lambda^* > 0$ (with $\boldsymbol{\eta}^{(k)} > \mathbf{0}$, of course).

$$|\nabla^T f(\mathbf{x}^{(k)})\boldsymbol{\eta}^{(k)}\nabla f(\mathbf{x}^{(k)})| \geq \rho_2 \|\nabla f(\mathbf{x}^{(k)})\| \, \|\boldsymbol{\eta}^{(k)}\nabla f(\mathbf{x}^{(k)})\|$$

With these conditions satisfied, plus a few other minor ones, it is possible to choose a λ^* such that

$$f(\mathbf{x}^{(k)}) - f(\mathbf{x}^{(k+1)}) \geq \rho_3 \lambda^{*(k)} \nabla^T f(\mathbf{x}^{(k)})\boldsymbol{\eta}^{(k)}\nabla f(\mathbf{x}^{(k)})$$

Based on these concepts, they proposed the following algorithm. For the kth stage:

1. Set $\lambda^{*(k)} = 1$.
2. Take a step using Eq. (3.4–1).
3. If $\|\nabla f(\mathbf{x}^{(k)})\| \leq \nu_1$, continue the unidimensional search for the minimum.
4. Test to determine if

$$f(\mathbf{x}^{(k)}) - f(\mathbf{x}^{(k+1)}) \geq \rho_3 \lambda^{*(k)} \nabla^T f(\mathbf{x}^{(k)})\boldsymbol{\eta}^{(k)}\nabla f(\mathbf{x}^{(k)}) > 0$$

If the inequality is not satisfied, execute one step of the unidimensional search, and return to step 2. If the unidimensional search has converged but the test is not satisfied, reduce λ^* by one-half, and return to step 2.

In the unidimensional search, convergence was assumed when either $|\nabla^T f(\mathbf{x}^{(k+1)})\Delta\mathbf{x}^{(k)}| < \nu_1$ or $\Delta\lambda^* \|\boldsymbol{\eta}^{(k)}\nabla f(\mathbf{x}^{(k)})\| < \nu_1$, where $\Delta\lambda^*$ is the change in λ^*.

5. Test to determine if $\lambda^* > \nu_2$ and

$$\frac{\|\boldsymbol{\eta}^{(k)}\nabla f(\mathbf{x}^{(k)})\|}{\|\nabla f(\mathbf{x}^{(k)})\|} > \rho_1$$

Scale $\lambda^{*(k)}$ up and $\boldsymbol{\eta}^{(k)}$ down, if necessary, to satisfy tests 4 and 5.

[1] B. A. Murtagh and R. W. H. Sargent, in R. Fletcher (ed.), "Optimization," Academic Press Inc., London, 1969.

6. Test to determine if the direction matrix is still positive definite. If not, reset $\boldsymbol{\eta}^{(k)}$; otherwise, update $\boldsymbol{\eta}^{(k)}$ by Eq. (3.4–5). One reset method is to let $\boldsymbol{\eta}^{(k+1)} = \mathbf{I}$. Another is to use $\boldsymbol{\eta}^{(k+1)} = \boldsymbol{\eta}^{(k)}$.

3.4–2 Davidon-Fletcher-Powell Method

In the well-known Davidon method,[1] as modified by Fletcher and Powell,[2] the matrix $\Delta\boldsymbol{\eta}$ was in effect[3] chosen to have a rank of 2. No matrix inversion is required. The direction matrix $\boldsymbol{\eta}$ is updated in such a way that, for a quadratic objective function in the limit of n stages, $\boldsymbol{\eta}$ is equal to $\mathbf{H}^{-1}$. The initial $\boldsymbol{\eta}$ is usually chosen as the identity matrix, $\boldsymbol{\eta}^{(0)} = \mathbf{I}$ (but can be any symmetric positive definite matrix), so that the initial direction in the minimization is one of steepest descent. A good estimate of the elements of $\mathbf{H}^{-1}$ at $\mathbf{x}^*$ (the extremum) is a better initial selection for $\boldsymbol{\eta}^{(0)}$ than the identity matrix, but the choice of $\boldsymbol{\eta}^{(0)} = \mathbf{I}$ is definitely preferable to letting the elements of $\boldsymbol{\eta}^{(0)}$ be equal to the values of the analytical partial derivatives or their finite-difference approximates at the initial point $\mathbf{x}^{(0)}$. A gradual changeover is made from the gradient direction to Newton's direction as the optimization takes place, thus taking advantage of the best characteristics of each of the two methods at the appropriate stage. Proof of convergence of the algorithm can be demonstrated only for a quadratic objective function with a positive definite hessian matrix [see Eq. (3.4–6) below].

We can obtain the relation for $\Delta\boldsymbol{\eta}^{(k)}$ in the Davidon-Fletcher-Powell algorithm, as mentioned earlier, by substituting $\mathbf{y}^{(k)} = \Delta\mathbf{x}^{(k)}$ and $\mathbf{z}^{(k)} = \boldsymbol{\eta}^{(k)}\Delta\mathbf{g}^{(k)}$ into Eq. (3.4–4) to obtain

$$\begin{aligned}\boldsymbol{\eta}^{(k+1)} &= \boldsymbol{\eta}^{(k)} + \mathbf{A}^{(k)} - \mathbf{B}^{(k)} \\ &= \boldsymbol{\eta}^{(k)} + \frac{(\Delta\mathbf{x}^{(k)})(\Delta\mathbf{x}^{(k)})^T}{(\Delta\mathbf{x}^{(k)})^T(\Delta\mathbf{g}^{(k)})} - \frac{\boldsymbol{\eta}^{(k)}(\Delta\mathbf{g}^{(k)})(\Delta\mathbf{g}^{(k)})^T(\boldsymbol{\eta}^{(k)})^T}{(\Delta\mathbf{g}^{(k)})^T\boldsymbol{\eta}^{(k)}(\Delta\mathbf{g}^{(k)})} \end{aligned} \qquad (3.4\text{–}5a)$$

where the notation is the same as used in connection with Eq. (3.4–5). Note that the second and third matrices on the right side of Eq. (3.4–5*a*) are symmetric matrices, so that if $\boldsymbol{\eta}^{(k)}$ is symmetric, $\boldsymbol{\eta}^{(k+1)}$ is also symmetric.

[1] W. C. Davidon, *USAEC Doc.* ANL–5990 (rev.), November, 1959.

[2] R. Fletcher and M. J. D. Powell, *Computer J.*, **6**:163 (1963).

[3] Broyden, *op. cit.*

The recursion relation (3.4–5*a*) is satisfactory in practice provided that:

1. The error in evaluating $\nabla f(\mathbf{x}^{(k)})$ is not large.
2. $\boldsymbol{\eta}^{(k)}$ does not become ill-conditioned.

The role of the matrix $\mathbf{A}^{(k)}$ in Eq. (3.4–5*a*) ensures that $\boldsymbol{\eta} \to \mathbf{H}^{-1}$, while the matrix $\mathbf{B}^{(k)}$ ensures that $\boldsymbol{\eta}^{(k+1)}$ remains positive definite at all stages and in the limit cancels out $\boldsymbol{\eta}^{(0)}$. Let us apply Eq. (3.4–5*a*) for a few stages starting from $\boldsymbol{\eta}^{(0)}$.

$$\boldsymbol{\eta}^{(1)} = \mathbf{I} + \mathbf{A}^{(0)} - \mathbf{B}^{(0)}$$

$$\boldsymbol{\eta}^{(2)} = \boldsymbol{\eta}^{(1)} + \mathbf{A}^{(1)} - \mathbf{B}^{(1)} = \mathbf{I} + (\mathbf{A}^{(0)} + \mathbf{A}^{(1)}) - (\mathbf{B}^{(0)} + \mathbf{B}^{(1)})$$

$$\cdots\cdots\cdots\cdots\cdots\cdots\cdots\cdots\cdots\cdots\cdots\cdots$$

$$\boldsymbol{\eta}^{(k+1)} = \mathbf{I} + \sum_{i=0}^{k} \mathbf{A}^{(i)} - \sum_{i=0}^{k} \mathbf{B}^{(i)}$$

For a quadratic function the sum of matrices $\mathbf{A}^{(i)}$ must equal $\mathbf{H}^{-1}$ when $k = n - 1$, and the sum of the matrices $\mathbf{B}^{(i)}$ is designed to cancel out the initial choice for $\boldsymbol{\eta}^{(0)}$ (here the identity matrix). Thus the Davidon-Fletcher-Powell method reflects all prior information to some extent in the current $\boldsymbol{\eta}$.

We should point out that the Davidon-Fletcher-Powell algorithm uses conjugate directions if the objective function is quadratic. For the last direction, $\mathbf{s}^{n-1}$, to be conjugate to all the earlier directions,

$$(\mathbf{X}^{(n-1)})^T\mathbf{H}\mathbf{s}^{(n-1)} = 0$$

or substituting $\mathbf{s}^{(n-1)} = -\boldsymbol{\eta}^{(n-1)}\nabla f(\mathbf{x}^{(n-1)})$,

$$(\mathbf{X}^{(n-1)})^T\mathbf{H}\boldsymbol{\eta}^{(n-1)}\nabla f(\mathbf{x}^{(n-1)}) = 0 \qquad (3.4\text{–}6)$$

[where $\mathbf{X}$ is defined in connection with Eq. (3.3–8)]. Equation (3.4–6) will hold if $\mathbf{H}\boldsymbol{\eta}^{(n-1)} = \mathbf{I}$ or $\boldsymbol{\eta}^{(n-1)} = \mathbf{H}^{-1}$, because then Eq. (3.4–6) reduces to Eq. (3.3–8). Thus the Davidon-Fletcher-Powell method can be placed in the category of methods that use conjugate directions. For a general objective function it is the property of using conjugate search directions that makes the Davidon-Fletcher-Powell method efficient rather than the close approximation of $\mathbf{H}^{-1}$ by $\boldsymbol{\eta}$.

Knowing now that the search directions are conjugate for a quadratic function, we can easily show that $\sum_{i=0}^{n-1} \mathbf{A}^{(i)} = \mathbf{H}^{-1}$. Note that $\Delta\mathbf{g}^{(k)} = \mathbf{H}\Delta\mathbf{x}^{(k)}$ from Eq. (3.4–2*b*). The numerator and denominator of $\mathbf{A}^{(k)}$ are, respectively,

$$(\Delta\mathbf{x}^{(k)})(\Delta\mathbf{x}^{(k)})^T = (\lambda^{*(k)}\mathbf{s}^{(k)})(\lambda^{*(k)}\mathbf{s}^{(k)})^T$$

and

$$(\Delta\mathbf{x}^{(k)})^T\Delta\mathbf{g}^{(k)} = (\lambda^{*(k)}\mathbf{s}^{(k)})^T(\mathbf{H}\lambda^{*(k)}\mathbf{s}^{(k)})$$

so that

$$\sum_{i=0}^{n-1} \mathbf{A}^{(i)} = \sum_{i=0}^{n-1} \frac{\mathbf{s}^{(i)}(\mathbf{s}^{(i)})^T}{(\mathbf{s}^{(i)})^T\mathbf{H}\mathbf{s}^{(i)}} = \mathbf{H}^{-1} \tag{3.4–7}$$

The right-hand equality comes from Eq. (3.3–4*a*).

Although Davidon in his original report used only one step in the search direction of length $\lambda^{*(k)}$, determined by a cubic interpolation between $\lambda^* = 0$ and

$$\lambda^* = \min\left\{1, \frac{2[f(\mathbf{x}^{(k)}) - f_0]}{\nabla^T f(\mathbf{x}^{(k)})\boldsymbol{\eta}^{(k)}\nabla f(\mathbf{x}^{(k)})}\right\} \tag{3.4–8}$$

where f_0 is the expected lowest value of $f(\mathbf{x})$, most variations of the Davidon algorithm minimize the function in the selected search direction. To determine the minimum of $f(\mathbf{x})$ with respect to λ in a given direction, almost any efficient unidimensional search technique can be employed (see Sec. 2.6). It is quite important that the technique be efficient, because a relatively large proportion of the total computation time is spent in this unidimensional search mode.

Fletcher and Powell recommend picking the first of the sequence of λ^*'s by Eq. (3.4–8), or $\lambda^{*(0)}$ can be placed equal to 1. Two different well-known unidimensional searches are utilized in the evaluation in Chap. 5, and Appendix B contains computer routines to execute the searches.

The sensitivity of the Davidon-Fletcher-Powell method to the termination criterion for the unidimensional search proves to be less significant in both the time required and number of functional evaluations carried out than might be anticipated. For example, Table 3.4–1 lists the number of stages, functional evaluations, and the value of Rosenbrock's function starting from $\mathbf{x}^{(0)} = [-1.2 \quad 1]^T$. It is clear from the table that even though many more stages are required if the unidimensional search is not carried out precisely, nevertheless the total number of functional evaluations and the time required to minimize Rosenbrock's function are roughly the same, though perhaps slightly more favorable for $\varepsilon = 10^{-3}$ than for $\varepsilon = 10^{-1}$ or $\varepsilon = 10^{-5}$, where ε is the termination criterion in terms of $\lambda^{*(k)}$ [in Eq. (3.4–1)] for the unidimensional search.

$$\left|\frac{\lambda^{*(k+1)} - \lambda^{*(k)}}{\lambda^{*(k+1)} + \lambda^{*(k)}}\right| < \varepsilon$$

Table 3.4-1 Number of functional evaluations, *n*, to reduce Rosenbrock's function to a value of 10^{-10} as a function of the unidimensional search termination criterion ε

$\varepsilon = 10^{-1}$			$\varepsilon = 10^{-3}$			$\varepsilon = 10^{-5}$		
Stage *k*	*n*†	*f*(**x**)‡	*Stage* *k*	*n*†	*f*(**x**)‡	*Stage* *k*	*n*†	*f*(**x**)‡
0	16	1.4×10^{-1}	0	27	1.9×10^{-1}	0	36	1.9×10^{-1}
1	22	2.3×10^{-1}	1	32	1.9×10^{-1}	1	31	1.9×10^{-1}
2	11	1.6×10^{-1}	2	24	1.2×10^{-1}	2	34	1.2×10^{-1}
3	16	1.5×10^{-1}	3	25	8.2×10^{-2}	3	34	7.6×10^{-2}
4	15	1.5×10^{-1}	4	25	4.3×10^{-2}	4	35	4.2×10^{-2}
5	16	1.4×10^{-1}	5	27	2.2×10^{-2}	5	36	2.1×10^{-2}
2	14	1.4×10^{-1}	6	27	1.1×10^{-2}	6	36	9.5×10^{-3}
6	18	1.0×10^{-1}	7	23	3.9×10^{-3}	7	33	3.2×10^{-3}
8	15	1.0×10^{-1}	8	25	8.6×10^{-4}	8	34	6.1×10^{-4}
9	18	6.6×10^{-2}	9	25	1.7×10^{-5}	9	35	2.6×10^{-5}
10	15	6.3×10^{-2}	10	19	2.0×10^{-7}	10	28	4.5×10^{-7}
11	18	2.5×10^{-2}	11	11	8.8×10^{-11}	11	9	4.6×10^{-11}
12	17	2.0×10^{-2}						
13	18	1.6×10^{-2}						
14	16	7.2×10^{-3}						
15	13	5.2×10^{-3}						
16	17	4.1×10^{-4}						
17	13	1.6×10^{-4}						
18	16	6.6×10^{-6}						
19	6	1.5×10^{-6}						
20	9	7.6×10^{-10}						
21	1	1.2×10^{-10}						

† = function evaluations per stage.
‡ At the end of the stage.

	$\varepsilon = 10^{-1}$	$\varepsilon = 10^{-3}$	$\varepsilon = 10^{-5}$
Total number of function evaluations	320	290	380
Relative time	1.14	1.00	1.12

Experience has demonstrated that for some problems variable metric methods will fail to reach the minimum of the objective function if the degree of precision of the unidimensional search is not fine enough; hence

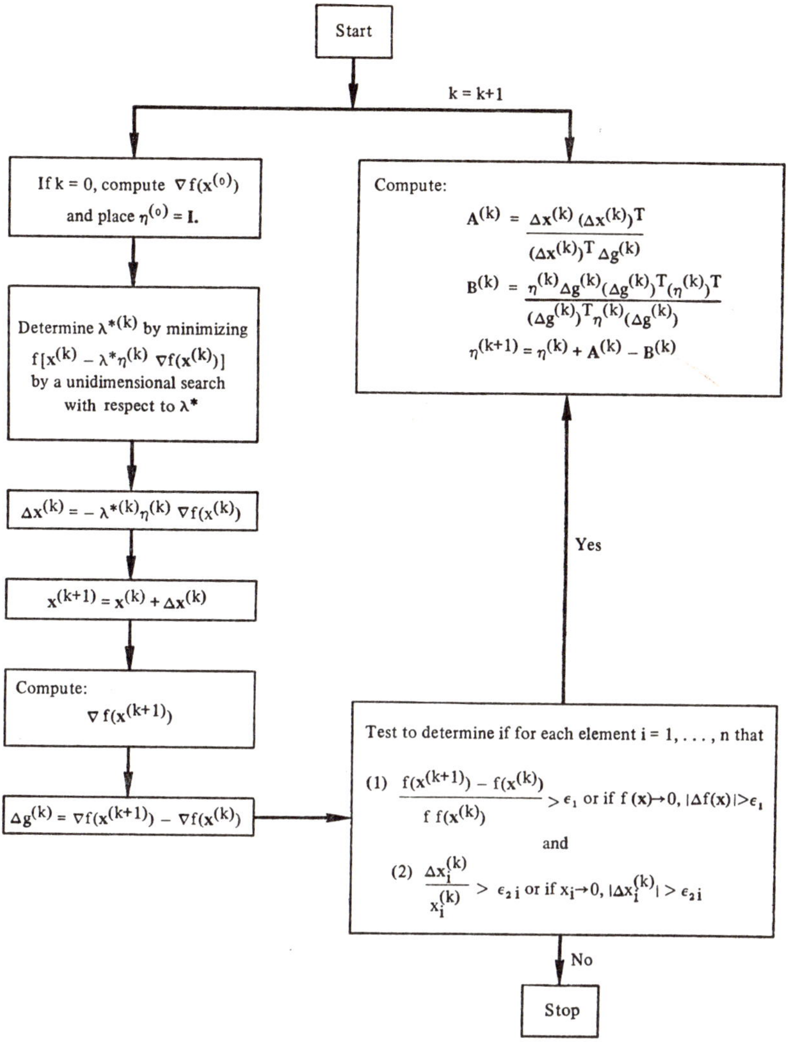

Fig. 3.4-2 Information flow chart for the Davidon-Fletcher-Powell method.

it is recommended that the precision in the unidimensional search be at least equivalent to that required for termination of the main algorithm. The cost in terms of time and/or function evaluations of doing this is relatively small, while the reliability of any of the variable metric methods is improved.

Fletcher and Powell recommended that the minimization be terminated if, on evaluating both the vectors $-\boldsymbol{\eta}^{(k)}\nabla f(\mathbf{x}^{(k)})$ and $-\lambda^{*(k)}\boldsymbol{\eta}^{(k)}\nabla f(\mathbf{x}^{(k)})$, either of the following occur:

1. Every component of the two vectors is less than a prescribed value.
2. The predicted lengths (‖ ‖) of each of the vectors from the minimum is less than a prescribed value.

The two alternative termination criteria shown in Fig. 3.4–2, the information flow chart of the Davidon-Fletcher-Powell method, have been employed instead with success in the results reported in Chap. 5. Figure 3.4–3 illustrates the trajectory of the Davidon-Fletcher-Powell algorithm for two different initial step sizes in the unidimensional search, $\lambda^* = 1$ and $\lambda^* = 10^{-3}$, for Rosenbrock's function; the trajectories are quite similar to those in Fig. 3.4–1.

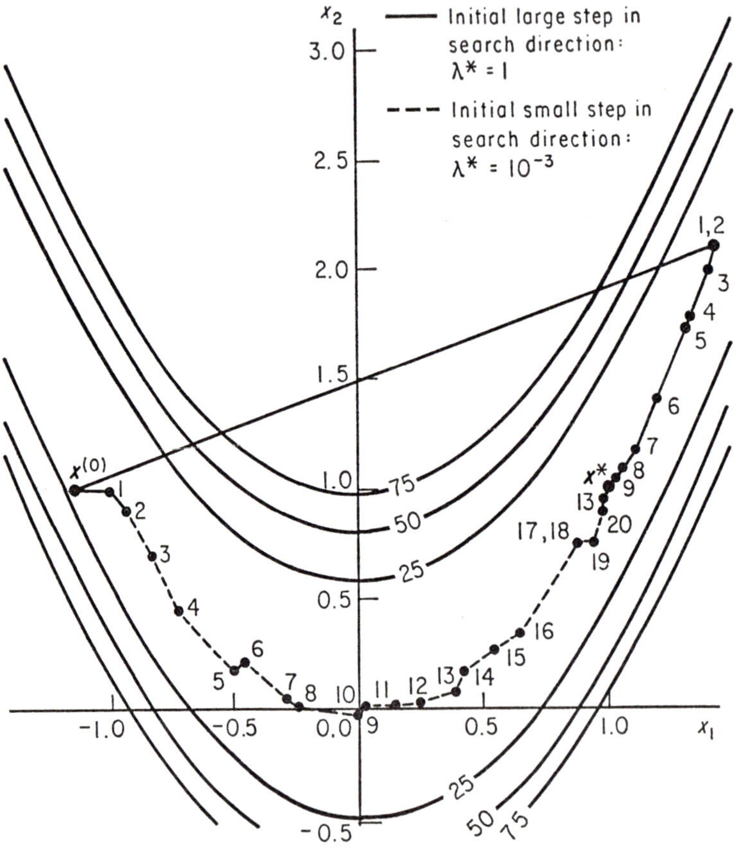

Fig. 3.4–3 Trajectory of the search to minimize Rosenbrock's function by the Davidon-Fletcher-Powell method (numbers indicate stages, i.e., different search directions).

Example 3.4-1 Davidon-Fletcher-Powell Method

The Davidon-Fletcher-Powell method is now illustrated for the problem

Minimize: $4(x_1 - 5)^2 + (x_2 - 6)^2$

The recursion relation to be used is

$$\mathbf{x}^{(k+1)} = \mathbf{x}^{(k)} - \lambda^{*(k)}\boldsymbol{\eta}^{(k)}\nabla f(\mathbf{x}^{(k)}) \tag{a}$$

where

$$\nabla f(\mathbf{x}^{(k)}) = \begin{bmatrix} 8(x_1 - 5) \\ 2(x_2 - 6) \end{bmatrix}$$

and $\boldsymbol{\eta}^{(k)}$ is given by Eq. (3.4–5a).

Let $\boldsymbol{\eta}^{(0)} = \mathbf{I}$ and let the initial $\mathbf{x}$ vector be $\mathbf{x}^{(0)} = [8 \quad 9]^T$. Then the new $\mathbf{x}$ vector $\mathbf{x}^{(1)}$ is computed from Eq. (a).

$$\begin{bmatrix} x_1^{(1)} \\ x_2^{(1)} \end{bmatrix} = \begin{bmatrix} 8 \\ 9 \end{bmatrix} - \lambda^{*(0)} \begin{bmatrix} 1 & 0 \\ 0 & 1 \end{bmatrix} \begin{bmatrix} 24 \\ 6 \end{bmatrix}$$

Because the objective function is quite simple, for the purposes of illustration we can determine $\lambda^{*(0)}$ by minimizing $f(\mathbf{x}^{(1)})$ with respect to λ^*, using analytical methods rather than a search.

$$f(\mathbf{x}^{(1)}) = 4[(8 - 24\lambda^*) - 5]^2 + [(9 - 6\lambda^*) - 6]^2$$

$$\frac{df(\mathbf{x}^{(1)})}{d\lambda^*} = 0 = 51 - 390\lambda^*$$

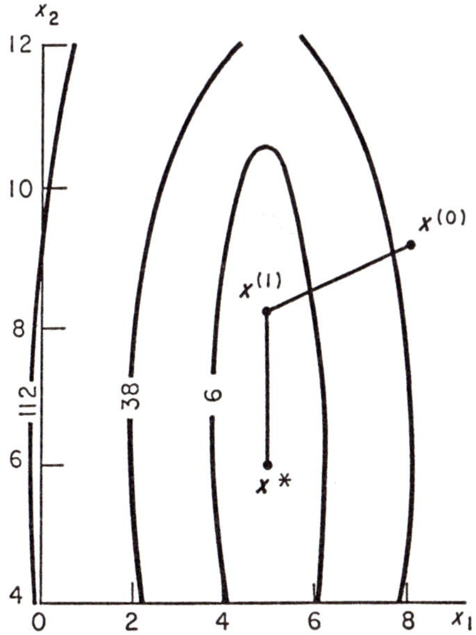

Fig. E3.4–1 Trajectory of search for the Davidon-Fletcher-Powell algorithm.

or $\lambda^{*(0)} = 0.1307$, at which stage $\mathbf{x}^{(1)} = [4.862 \quad 8.215]^T$ and $f(\mathbf{x}) = 4.985$, as shown in Fig. E3.4–1. At $\mathbf{x}^{(1)}$

$$\nabla f(\mathbf{x}^{(1)}) = [-1.108 \quad 4.431]^T$$

so that
$$(\Delta \mathbf{g})^{(0)} = [-25.108 \quad -1.569]^T$$

Next, $\boldsymbol{\eta}^{(1)}$ is computed.

$$\boldsymbol{\eta}^{(1)} = \begin{bmatrix} 1 & 0 \\ 0 & 1 \end{bmatrix} + \frac{\begin{bmatrix} -3.13 & 0 \\ -0.785 & 0 \end{bmatrix}\begin{bmatrix} -3.13 & -0.785 \\ 0 & 0 \end{bmatrix}}{[-3.13 \quad -0.785]\begin{bmatrix} -25.108 \\ -1.569 \end{bmatrix}}$$

$$- \frac{\begin{bmatrix} 1 & 0 \\ 0 & 1 \end{bmatrix}\begin{bmatrix} -25.108 & 0 \\ 1.569 & 0 \end{bmatrix}\begin{bmatrix} -25.108 & -1.569 \\ 0 & 0 \end{bmatrix}\begin{bmatrix} 1 & 0 \\ 0 & 1 \end{bmatrix}}{[-25.108 \quad -1.569]\begin{bmatrix} 1 & 0 \\ 0 & 1 \end{bmatrix}\begin{bmatrix} -25.108 \\ -1.569 \end{bmatrix}}$$

$$= \begin{bmatrix} 1.270 \times 10^{-1} & -3.149 \times 10^{-2} \\ -3.149 \times 10^{-2} & 1.0038 \end{bmatrix}$$

Now $\mathbf{x}^{(2)}$ can be computed using Eq. (*a*).

$$\begin{bmatrix} x_1^{(2)} \\ x_2^{(2)} \end{bmatrix} = \begin{bmatrix} 4.862 \\ 8.215 \end{bmatrix} - \lambda^{*(1)} \begin{bmatrix} 1.270 \times 10^{-1} & -3.149 \times 10^{-2} \\ -3.149 \times 10^{-2} & 1.0038 \end{bmatrix}\begin{bmatrix} -1.108 \\ 4.431 \end{bmatrix}$$

As before, $\lambda^{*(1)}$ is formed by minimizing $f(\mathbf{x}^{(2)})$ with respect to λ^*. Additional stages of the optimization yield the information in Table E3.4–1*a*. Table E3.4–1*b* lists the matrix $\boldsymbol{\eta}$ at each stage of the search, which can be compared with the inverse of the hessian matrix, $\mathbf{H}^{-1}$, at $\mathbf{x}^* = [5 \quad 6]^T$:

$$\mathbf{H} = \begin{bmatrix} 8 & 0 \\ 0 & 2 \end{bmatrix} \quad \text{and} \quad \mathbf{H}^{-1} = \begin{bmatrix} \frac{1}{8} & 0 \\ 0 & \frac{1}{2} \end{bmatrix}$$

Table E3.4–1*a*

Stage k	$x_1^{(k)}$	$x_2^{(k)}$	$\dfrac{\partial f(\mathbf{x}^{(k)})}{\partial x_1}$	$\dfrac{\partial f(\mathbf{x}^{(k)})}{\partial x_2}$	$f(\mathbf{x}^{(k)})$	$\lambda^{*(k)}$
0	8.000	9.000	24.000	6.000	45.000	0.1307
1	4.862	8.215	−1.108	4.431	4.985	0.4942
2	5.000	6.000	3.81×10^{-7}	2.55×10^{-9}	9.06×10^{-15}	1.000
3	5.000	6.000	0	0	0	

Table E3.4-1*b*

	Stage 0	*Stage* 1
$\boldsymbol{\eta}$	$\begin{bmatrix} 1 & 0 \\ 0 & 1 \end{bmatrix}$	$\begin{bmatrix} 1.270 \times 10^{-1} & -3.149 \times 10^{-2} \\ -3.149 \times 10^{-2} & 1.0038 \end{bmatrix}$

Stage 2	*Stage* 3
$\begin{bmatrix} 1.250 \times 10^{-1} & -8.882 \times 10^{-16} \\ -8.882 \times 10^{-16} & 5.000 \times 10^{-1} \end{bmatrix}$	$\begin{bmatrix} 1.250 \times 10^{-1} & 1.387 \times 10^{-17} \\ -1.387 \times 10^{-17} & 5.000 \times 10^{-1} \end{bmatrix}$

It has been found that the Davidon-Fletcher-Powell and other variable metric methods can take negative steps occasionally or terminate at a nonstationary point. Bard[1] pointed out how this behavior invariably has been the result of the matrix $\boldsymbol{\eta}$ becoming singular. If $\boldsymbol{\eta}$ becomes almost singular, then the search directions may be chosen as if the problem were badly scaled, when it is not. Near-singularity can be avoided by increasing the number of significant figures carried or by scaling the elements of the $\mathbf{x}$ vector to make the diagonal elements of $\mathbf{A}^{(0)}$ more nearly the order of 1. If these steps are not feasible, then, when the cosine of the angle between $\nabla f(\mathbf{x}^{(k)})$ and $\boldsymbol{\eta}^{(k)}\nabla f(\mathbf{x}^{(k)})$ is less than 10^{-5}, $\boldsymbol{\eta}$ can be reinitialized to a diagonal matrix in which the element η_{ii} is the ratio of the ith element of $(\Delta\mathbf{x}^{(k)})$ to the ith element of $\nabla f(\mathbf{x}^{(k)})$. Other methods of starting the search over with a revised direction matrix have been proposed, and a few examples are included in the evaluation in Chap. 5.

One final matter remains to be examined. Can the Davidon-Fletcher-Powell method be carried out successfully with the derivatives estimated by difference schemes? If so, then the disadvantage of having to provide analytical formulas to evaluate the derivatives disappears, and the Davidon procedure becomes more closely aligned to derivative-free (search) procedures. Of primary concern are the difficulties that may arise from rounding and approximation errors in the computations that bias the estimates of the derivatives.

Stewart[2] showed one way in which the components of the gradient can be estimated by difference quotients, thus extending the Davidon method

[1] Y. Bard, On a Numerical Instability of Davidon-like Methods, *IBM N.Y. Sci. Center Rept.* 320-2913, August, 1967.
[2] G. W. Stewart, *J. Assoc. Computer Machinery*, **14**:72 (1967).

Table 3.4-2 Comparison of variable metric methods employing numerical estimates of the derivatives with Powell's algorithm for five test problems*

(Figures shown are function evaluations. See Chap. 5 for corresponding data for analytical derivatives.)

Method	*Prob.* 2 (*App. A*)	*Prob.* 29 (*App. A*)	*Prob.* 32 (*App. A*)	*Prob.* 34 (*App. A*)	*Prob. VI, Table* 5 (*App. A*)
Powell†	262	136	700	86	291
Davidon-Fletcher-Powell:					
(*a*)	132	1625	305	218	702
(*b*)	121	1123	205	231	*f*
Broyden:					
(*a*)	139	4336	167	230	1251
(*b*)	112	*f*	*f*	176	*f*

*With DSC-Powell unidimensional search.

†See Chap. 4.

(*a*) is for $\eta = 10^{-8}$, $m = 10^{-8}$, $\delta = 10^{-7}$; (*b*) is for $\eta = 10^{-14}$, $m = 10^{-14}$, $\delta = 10^{-13}$; f = failed.

to unconstrained nonlinear programming problems in which derivatives cannot, or cannot easily, be formed analytically. Information gathered in the course of the minimization is used to determine optimal step sizes for the difference relations. Although Stewart's method (as corrected) of computing approximate derivatives works exceptionally well for certain problems, it occasionally fails to work, or else takes excessive function evaluations to reach the same degree of precision as the variable metric method using analytical derivatives.

Table 3.4–2 compares the number of function evaluations for Powell's algorithm, one of the best derivative-free algorithms, with the Davidon-Fletcher-Powell and Broyden algorithms in which Stewart's method of estimating derivatives has been substituted for the analytical derivatives. Stewart's method requires that three arbitrary parameters be supplied by the user:

η = roughly the significant figures permitted by the computer

m = an upper bound on the negative logarithm of the error in the current estimated derivative compared with the previous estimated derivative

δ = step size to be used in calculating the components of the first two gradients

Both η and m depend on the computer being used, while δ is related to the function being minimized. Two selections of the parameters are shown in the table. Corresponding data for the Davidon-Fletcher-Powell and Broyden algorithms employing analytical derivatives are not included in the table—although the data can be found in Chap. 5—because it is difficult to decide how to weight the derivative calls relative to the function evaluation calls.

Results for the helical valley (Problem 34 in Appendix A) and Rosenbrock's function (Problem 2 in Appendix A) are different from those published by Stewart, but this is not surprising in view of the fact that different δ's were employed and different termination criteria involved. In the problems other than Problem 2, the initial choice of $\delta = 10^{-7}$ yielded estimates of the derivatives that had little error initially, but subsequent error became substantial. In one problem the error fortuitously reduced the number of function evaluations below that of the analytical technique. On the other hand, letting $\delta = 10^{-13}$ gave large initial errors. Because the components of the initial two gradients had to be computed with user-supplied parameters, it is difficult to recommend Stewart's methods in preference to analytical derivatives, and as Table 3.4–2 indicates, Stewart's method would not, overall, be as efficient as Powell's algorithm.

3.4-3 Pearson's Algorithms

Pearson[1] proposed several methods of computing $\boldsymbol{\eta}$ using search directions that were conjugate. Pearson's algorithms can be obtained by substitution of different vectors for $\mathbf{y}$ and $\mathbf{z}$ in Eq. (3.4-4).

1. Pearson No. 2. Let $\mathbf{y} = \mathbf{z} = \Delta\mathbf{x}^{(k)}$ and $\omega = 1$ in Eq. (3.4-4). Then

$$\boldsymbol{\eta}^{(k+1)} = \boldsymbol{\eta}^{(k)} + \frac{(\Delta\mathbf{x}^{(k)} - \boldsymbol{\eta}^{(k)}\Delta\mathbf{g}^{(k)})(\Delta\mathbf{x}^{(k)})^T}{(\Delta\mathbf{x}^{(k)})^T(\Delta\mathbf{g}^{(k)})} \tag{3.4-9}$$

$$\boldsymbol{\eta}^0 = \mathbf{R}^0$$

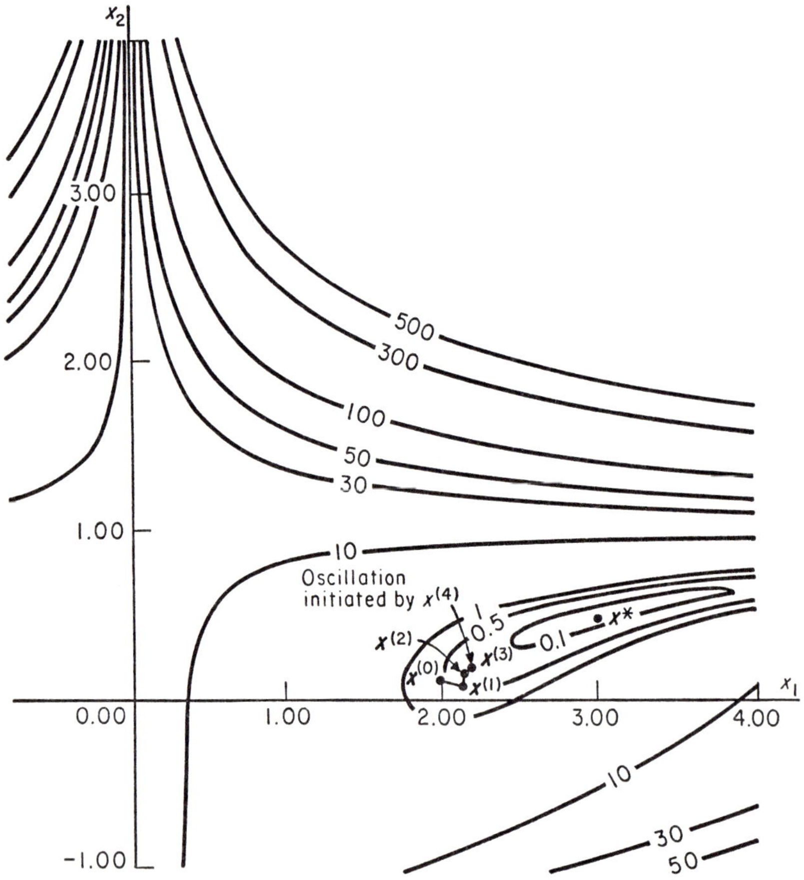

Fig. 3.4-4 Problem 35 of Appendix A.

[1] J. D. Pearson, *Computer J.*, **13**:171 (1969).

where $\mathbf{R}^0$ is any symmetric positive definite matrix. Pearson's No. 2 algorithm usually leads to ill-conditioned direction matrices. Figure 3.4–4 illustrates Problem 35 of Appendix A, for which (starting from $\mathbf{x}^{(0)} = [2 \quad 0.2]^T$ with $\boldsymbol{\eta}^{(0)} = \mathbf{I}$) the following sequence of direction matrices was obtained:

Stage	*Direction matrix* $\boldsymbol{\eta}^{(k)}$	*Determinant of* $\boldsymbol{\eta}^{(k)}$
0	$\begin{bmatrix} 1 & 0 \\ 0 & 1 \end{bmatrix}$	1.00000
1	$\begin{bmatrix} 0.36754 & 0.15788 \\ 0.99148 & 0.75250 \end{bmatrix}$	0.12004
2	$\begin{bmatrix} 0.36636 & 0.15383 \\ 0.88737 & 0.39527 \end{bmatrix}$	0.00831
3	$\begin{bmatrix} 0.35793 & 0.11330 \\ 0.85656 & 0.32020 \end{bmatrix}$	0.00043
4	$\begin{bmatrix} 0.35576 & 0.12809 \\ 0.85077 & 0.30633 \end{bmatrix}$	−0.00001

Hence in four stages the direction matrix no longer is positive definite and on subsequent stages continues to be badly conditioned, oscillating between positive definite and not positive definite. A restart of the algorithm after n stages helps avoid such difficulties, that is, resetting $\boldsymbol{\eta}^{(k+1)}$ to $\mathbf{R}^{(0)}$ after every n steps.

2. Pearson No. 3. Let $\mathbf{y} = \mathbf{z} = \boldsymbol{\eta}^{(k)}\Delta\mathbf{g}^{(k)}$ in Eq. (3.4–4), with $\omega = 1$. Then

$$\boldsymbol{\eta}^{(k+1)} = \boldsymbol{\eta}^{(k)} + [(\Delta\mathbf{x}^{(k)}) - \boldsymbol{\eta}^{(k)}(\Delta\mathbf{g}^{(k)})]\frac{[\boldsymbol{\eta}^{(k)}(\Delta\mathbf{g}^{(k)})]^T}{(\Delta\mathbf{g}^{(k)})^T\boldsymbol{\eta}^{(k)}(\Delta\mathbf{g}^{(k)})} \qquad (3.4\text{–}10)$$

$$\boldsymbol{\eta}^{(0)} = \mathbf{R}^{(0)}$$

The trajectory of search for Pearson No. 3 in minimizing Rosenbrock's function is essentially the same as that depicted in Fig. 3.4–3, except that smaller steps are taken on each stage. Pearson also tested the reset form of the algorithm.

3. Projected Newton-Raphson. Pearson also proposed the projected Newton-Raphson (PNR) calculation that can be obtained from Eq. (3.4–4) with $\omega \to \infty$ and $\mathbf{z} = \boldsymbol{\eta}^{(k)}\Delta\mathbf{g}^{(k)}$:

$$\boldsymbol{\eta}^{(k+1)} = \boldsymbol{\eta}^{(k)} - \frac{(\boldsymbol{\eta}^{(k)}\Delta\mathbf{g}^{(k)})(\boldsymbol{\eta}^{(k)}\Delta\mathbf{g}^{(k)})^T}{(\Delta\mathbf{g}^{(k)})^T\boldsymbol{\eta}^{(k)}(\Delta\mathbf{g}^{(k)})} \tag{3.4–11}$$

$$\boldsymbol{\eta}^{(0)} = \mathbf{R}^{(0)}$$

Equation (3.4–11) is analogous to Zoutendijk's method (described in Sec. 3.3–4) if the projection matrix in Eq. (3.3–12) is replaced by the direction matrix $\boldsymbol{\eta}^{(k)}$. The quantity $(\boldsymbol{\eta}^{(k)}\Delta\mathbf{g}^{(k)})$ is the projection of $\Delta\mathbf{g}^{(k)}$ orthogonal to $\mathbf{G}^{(k)}$, and every n steps $\mathbf{R}^{(k)}$ is an approximation to $\mathbf{H}^{-1}(\mathbf{x}^{(k)})$, so that a Newton search is (approximately) carried out. When k is a multiple of n, the number of independent variables, $\boldsymbol{\eta}^{(k)}$, is reset to $\mathbf{R}^{(k)}$ and

$$\mathbf{R}^{(k+1)} = \mathbf{R}^{(k)} + \frac{(\Delta\mathbf{x}^{(k)} - \mathbf{R}^{(k)}\Delta\mathbf{g}^{(k)})(\boldsymbol{\eta}^{(k)}\Delta\mathbf{g}^{(k)})^T}{(\Delta\mathbf{g}^{(k)})^T\boldsymbol{\eta}^{(k)}(\Delta\mathbf{g}^{(k)})} \tag{3.4–12}$$

Some results for Pearson's algorithms are included in the evaluation in Chap. 5.

3.4–4 Other Methods of Updating the Direction Matrix

Greenstadt[1] derived a general relation for $\Delta\boldsymbol{\eta}$ by minimizing the norm, defined as follows with respect to $\Delta\boldsymbol{\eta}$:

$$N(\Delta\boldsymbol{\eta}) = \text{trace}\,[\mathbf{W}\Delta\boldsymbol{\eta}^{(k)}\mathbf{W}(\Delta\boldsymbol{\eta}^{(k)})^T]$$

(where $\mathbf{W}$ is a positive definite symmetric matrix) subject to the conditions:

1. $\Delta\boldsymbol{\eta}^{(k)}$ is always symmetric: $\Delta\boldsymbol{\eta}^{(k)} = (\Delta\boldsymbol{\eta}^{(k)})^T$.

2. $\boldsymbol{\eta}^{(k+1)}\Delta\mathbf{g}^{(k)} = \Delta\mathbf{x}^{(k)}$, or its equivalent, Eq. (3.4–2c), with the aid of Lagrange multipliers.

The relation obtained was

$$\begin{aligned}\Delta\boldsymbol{\eta}^{(k)} = \frac{1}{(\Delta\mathbf{g}^{(k)})^T\mathbf{W}^{-1}\Delta\mathbf{g}^{(k)}}\Big\{&\Delta\mathbf{x}^{(k)}(\Delta\mathbf{g}^{(k)})^T\mathbf{W}^{-1} + \mathbf{W}^{-1}\Delta\mathbf{g}^{(k)}(\Delta\mathbf{x}^{(k)})^T\\ &-\boldsymbol{\eta}^{(k)}\Delta\mathbf{g}^{(k)}(\Delta\mathbf{g}^{(k)})^T\mathbf{W}^{-1} - \mathbf{W}^{-1}\Delta\mathbf{g}^{(k)}(\Delta\mathbf{g}^{(k)})^T\boldsymbol{\eta}^{(k)}\\ &-\frac{1}{(\Delta\mathbf{g}^{(k)})^T\mathbf{W}^{-1}\Delta\mathbf{g}^{(k)}}\left[(\Delta\mathbf{g}^{(k)})^T\Delta\mathbf{x}^{(k)} - (\Delta\mathbf{g}^{(k)})^T\boldsymbol{\eta}^{(k)}\Delta\mathbf{g}^{(k)}\right]\\ &\times\mathbf{W}^{-1}\Delta\mathbf{g}^{(k)}(\Delta\mathbf{g}^{(k)})^T\mathbf{W}^{-1}\Big\}\end{aligned} \tag{3.4–13}$$

[1] J. Greenstadt, *Math. Computation*, **24**:1 (1970).

Greenstadt let $\mathbf{W}^{-1} = \boldsymbol{\eta}^{(k)}$ and $\mathbf{W}^{-1} = \mathbf{I}$, but application of Eq. (3.4–13) with $\mathbf{W}^{-1} = \mathbf{I}$ to test problems gave poor results, while letting $\mathbf{W}^{-1} = \boldsymbol{\eta}^{(k)}$ gave results comparable with the Davidon-Fletcher-Powell algorithm.

Goldfarb[1] noted that if $\mathbf{W}^{-1} = \boldsymbol{\eta}^{(k)}$, the following equation results:

$$\Delta\boldsymbol{\eta}_{\mathrm{I}}^{(k)} = \frac{1}{(\Delta\mathbf{g}^{(k)})^T\boldsymbol{\eta}^{(k)}\Delta\mathbf{g}^{(k)}}\Bigg\{\Delta\mathbf{x}^{(k)}(\Delta\mathbf{g}^{(k)})^T\boldsymbol{\eta}^{(k)} + \boldsymbol{\eta}^{(k)}\Delta\mathbf{g}^{(k)}(\Delta\mathbf{x}^{(k)})^T - \left[1 + \frac{(\Delta\mathbf{g}^{(k)})^T\Delta\mathbf{x}^{(k)}}{(\Delta\mathbf{g}^{(k)})^T\boldsymbol{\eta}^{(k)}\Delta\mathbf{g}^{(k)}}\right]\boldsymbol{\eta}^{(k)}\Delta\mathbf{g}^{(k)}(\Delta\mathbf{g}^{(k)})^T\boldsymbol{\eta}^{(k)}\Bigg\} \tag{3.4–14}$$

whereas if $\mathbf{W}^{-1} = \boldsymbol{\eta}^{(k+1)}$, the following equation results:

$$\Delta\boldsymbol{\eta}_{\mathrm{II}}^{(k)} = \frac{1}{(\Delta\mathbf{g}^{(k)})^T\Delta\mathbf{x}^{(k)}}\Bigg\{-\Delta\mathbf{x}^{(k)}(\Delta\mathbf{g}^{(k)})^T\boldsymbol{\eta}^{(k)} - \boldsymbol{\eta}^{(k)}\Delta\mathbf{g}^{(k)}(\Delta\mathbf{x}^{(k)})^T + \left[1 + \frac{(\Delta\mathbf{g}^{(k)})^T\boldsymbol{\eta}^{(k)}\Delta\mathbf{g}^{(k)}}{(\Delta\mathbf{g}^{(k)})^T\Delta\mathbf{x}^{(k)}}\right]\Delta\mathbf{x}^{(k)}(\Delta\mathbf{x}^{(k)})^T\Bigg\} \tag{3.4–15}$$

If $\mathbf{W}^{-1} = \boldsymbol{\eta}^{(k+1)} - \boldsymbol{\eta}^{(k)} = \Delta\boldsymbol{\eta}^{(k)}$, Eq. (3.4–5) results [even though $\mathbf{W}^{-1}$ has no inverse, since $\Delta\boldsymbol{\eta}^{(k)}$ in Eq. (3.4–5) is of rank 1]. Similarly, substitution of

$$\mathbf{W}^{-1} = \boldsymbol{\eta}^{(k)} - \frac{\boldsymbol{\eta}^{(k)}\Delta\mathbf{g}^{(k)}(\Delta\mathbf{g}^{(k)})^T\boldsymbol{\eta}^{(k)}}{(\Delta\mathbf{g}^{(k)})^T\boldsymbol{\eta}^{(k)}\Delta\mathbf{g}^{(k)}}$$

or

$$\mathbf{W}^{-1} = \boldsymbol{\eta}^{k} - \frac{\Delta\mathbf{x}^{(k)}(\Delta\mathbf{x}^{(k)})^T}{(\Delta\mathbf{x}^{(k)})^T\Delta\mathbf{g}^{(k)}}$$

gives Eq. (3.4–5). Equation (3.4–5*a*) can be obtained by letting

$$\begin{aligned}\mathbf{W}^{-1} &= [(\Delta\mathbf{g}^{(k)})^T\boldsymbol{\eta}^{(k)}\Delta\mathbf{g}^{(k)}]^{\frac{1}{2}}\boldsymbol{\eta}^{(k+1)} - [(\Delta\mathbf{g}^{(k)})^T\Delta\mathbf{x}^{(k)}]^{\frac{1}{2}}\boldsymbol{\eta}^{(k)} \\ &= [(\Delta\mathbf{g}^{(k)})^T\boldsymbol{\eta}^{(k+1)}\Delta\mathbf{g}^{(k)}]^{-\frac{1}{2}}\boldsymbol{\eta}^{(k+1)} - [(\Delta\mathbf{g}^{(k)})^T\boldsymbol{\eta}^{(k)}\Delta\mathbf{g}^{(k)}]^{-\frac{1}{2}}\boldsymbol{\eta}^{(k)} \\ &= \boldsymbol{\eta}^{(k+1)} - \left[\frac{(\Delta\mathbf{g}^{(k)})^T\Delta\mathbf{x}^{(k)}}{(\Delta\mathbf{g}^{(k)})^T\boldsymbol{\eta}^{(k)}\Delta\mathbf{g}^{(k)}}\right]^{\frac{1}{2}}\frac{\boldsymbol{\eta}^{(k)}\Delta\mathbf{g}^{(k)}(\Delta\mathbf{g}^{(k)})^T\boldsymbol{\eta}^{(k)}}{(\Delta\mathbf{g}^{(k)})^T\boldsymbol{\eta}^{k}\Delta\mathbf{g}^{(k)}} \\ &= \boldsymbol{\eta}^{(k)} - \left[\frac{(\Delta\mathbf{g}^{(k)})^T\boldsymbol{\eta}^{(k)}\Delta\mathbf{g}^{(k)}}{(\Delta\mathbf{g}^{(k)})^T\Delta\mathbf{x}^{(k)}}\right]^{\frac{1}{2}}\frac{\Delta\mathbf{x}^{(k)}(\Delta\mathbf{x}^{(k)})^T}{(\Delta\mathbf{g}^{(k)})^T\Delta\mathbf{x}^{(k)}}\end{aligned}$$

Both Eqs. (3.4–14) and (3.4–15) yield corrections to $\boldsymbol{\eta}^{(k)}$ that provide quadratic termination for a strictly convex quadratic objective function, just as do Eqs. (3.4–5) and (3.4–5*a*). However, only Eqs. (3.4–5*a*) and (3.4–15) preserve the positive definiteness of $\boldsymbol{\eta}$. Goldfarb shows how each of the

[1] D. Goldfarb, *Math. Computation*, **24**:23 (1970).

equations (3.4–5), (3.4–5*a*), (3.4–14), and (3.4–15) can be written as linear combinations of the others, and in particular,

$$\Delta\boldsymbol{\eta}_{\mathrm{I}} = \gamma\Delta\boldsymbol{\eta}_{(3.4\text{-}5a)} + (1-\gamma)\Delta\boldsymbol{\eta}_{(3.4\text{-}5)}$$

$$\Delta\boldsymbol{\eta}_{\mathrm{II}} = \gamma^{-1}\Delta\boldsymbol{\eta}_{(3.4\text{-}5a)} + (1-\gamma^{-1})\Delta\boldsymbol{\eta}_{(3.4\text{-}5)}$$

where
$$\gamma = \frac{(\Delta\mathbf{g}^{(k)})^T\,\Delta\mathbf{x}^{(k)}}{(\Delta\mathbf{g}^{(k)})^T\boldsymbol{\eta}^{(k)}\,\Delta\mathbf{g}^{(k)}}$$

Consequently, we can write, in general,

$$\Delta\boldsymbol{\eta}^{(k)} = \alpha\,\Delta\boldsymbol{\eta}_{\mathrm{I}}^{(k)} + (1-\alpha)\,\Delta\boldsymbol{\eta}_{\mathrm{II}}^{(k)} \qquad (3.4\text{–}16)$$

By various choices of α any of the equations for $\Delta\boldsymbol{\eta}^{(k)}$ given so far can be obtained.

3.4–5 Fletcher's Method

In all the minimization techniques described so far, after the search direction is computed, the objective function is minimized in the search direction. Because much of the computation takes place in these unidimensional searches, the question naturally arises as to whether or not one or a few steps of minimization would be adequate. Fletcher[1] proposed an algorithm that abandoned the characteristic of quadratic termination, i.e., termination in n steps for a quadratic function, while at the same time retaining the property that the direction matrix $\boldsymbol{\eta} \to \mathbf{H}^{-1}(\mathbf{x})$ in the sense that for quadratic functions the eigenvalues of $\boldsymbol{\eta}$ tend to those of $\mathbf{H}^{-1}$. The relationship for $\Delta\boldsymbol{\eta}^{(k)}$ in Eq. (3.4–3) is based on this property plus the satisfaction of

$$\boldsymbol{\eta}^{(k+1)}\Delta\mathbf{g}^{(k)} = \Delta\mathbf{x}^{(k)} \qquad \text{that is} \qquad \Delta\mathbf{g}^{(k)} = (\boldsymbol{\eta}^{(k+1)})^{-1}\,\Delta\mathbf{x}^{(k)}$$

Fletcher's updating relation was based on the recursion relation for inverting matrices:

$$(\boldsymbol{\eta}^{(k+1)})^{-1} = \left[\mathbf{I} - \frac{\Delta\mathbf{g}^{(k)}(\Delta\mathbf{x}^{(k)})^T}{(\Delta\mathbf{x}^{(k)})^T\,\Delta\mathbf{g}^{(k)}}\right](\boldsymbol{\eta}^{(k)})^{-1}\left[\mathbf{I} - \frac{\Delta\mathbf{x}^{(k)}(\Delta\mathbf{g}^{(k)})^T}{(\Delta\mathbf{x}^{(k)})^T\,\Delta\mathbf{g}^{(k)}}\right] + \frac{\Delta\mathbf{g}^{(k)}(\Delta\mathbf{g}^{(k)})^T}{(\Delta\mathbf{x}^{(k)})^T\,\Delta\mathbf{g}^{(k)}} \qquad (3.4\text{–}17)$$

a relation that forced $(\boldsymbol{\eta}^{(k+1)})^{-1}\,\Delta\mathbf{x}^{(k)} = \Delta\mathbf{g}^{(k)}$. Interchanging $\Delta\mathbf{x}^{(k)}$ and $\Delta\mathbf{g}^{(k)}$ and $\boldsymbol{\eta}^{(k+1)}$ and $(\boldsymbol{\eta}^{(k+1)})^{-1}$ in Eq. (3.4–17) leads to the recursion relation

[1] R. Fletcher, *Computer J.*, **13**:317 (1970).

$$\boldsymbol{\eta}^{(k+1)} = \left[\mathbf{I} - \frac{\Delta\mathbf{x}^{(k)}(\Delta\mathbf{g}^{(k)})^T}{(\Delta\mathbf{x}^{(k)})^T\,\Delta\mathbf{g}^{(k)}}\right]\boldsymbol{\eta}^{(k)}\left[\mathbf{I} - \frac{\Delta\mathbf{g}^{(k)}(\Delta\mathbf{x}^{(k)})^T}{(\Delta\mathbf{x}^{(k)})^T\,\Delta\mathbf{g}^{(k)}}\right] + \frac{\mathbf{x}^{(k)}(\Delta\mathbf{x}^{(k)})^T}{(\Delta\mathbf{x}^{(k)})^T\,\Delta\mathbf{g}^{(k)}} \quad (3.4\text{–}18)$$

The algorithm uses relation (3.4–5*a*) when $(\Delta\mathbf{g}^{(k)})^T\mathbf{H}^{-1}(\mathbf{x}^{(k)})\,\Delta\mathbf{g}^{(k)} < (\Delta\mathbf{g}^{(k)})^T\boldsymbol{\eta}^{(k)}\,\Delta\mathbf{g}^{(k)}$, and Eq. (3.4–18) when $(\Delta\mathbf{g}^{(k)})^T\mathbf{H}^{-1}(\mathbf{x}^{(k)})\,\Delta\mathbf{g}^{(k)} \geq (\Delta\mathbf{g}^{(k)})^T\boldsymbol{\eta}^{(k)}\,\Delta\mathbf{g}^{(k)}$. Linear combinations of Eqs. (3.4–18) and (3.4–5*a*) can also be used. Experience with the test problems described in Chap. 5 indicates that, usually, most of the early directions are based on Eq. (3.4–5*a*), and it is only in the later stages of the optimization that Eq. (3.4–18) is called. Because $\boldsymbol{\eta}$ computed by Eq. (3.4–5*a*) tends to zero whereas $\boldsymbol{\eta}$ computed by Eq. (3.4–18) tends to infinity as the number of stages increases, use of both equations seems to have some merit.

However, it is the cubic interpolation for a minimum in a given search direction and the limited step length, rather than the computation of $\boldsymbol{\eta}$, that makes Fletcher's technique quite efficient.[1] The scalar λ is chosen from an equation similar to Eq. (3.4–8):

$$\lambda' = \frac{2[(f(\mathbf{x}^{(k)}) - f_{\text{low}}]}{\nabla^T f(\mathbf{x}^{(k)})\mathbf{s}^{(k)}}$$

where f_{low} is the lowest estimated value of $f(\mathbf{x})$. [If $f(\mathbf{x})$ turns out to be lower than f_{low}, termination takes place.] A cubic interpolation is used between $\mathbf{x}^{(k)}$ and $\mathbf{x}^{(k)} + \lambda'\mathbf{s}^{(k)}$ to get the minimum in a search direction. Because no bracket is required for a cubic interpolation and the result of interpolation may be unsatisfactory if $\mathbf{x}^{(k)}$ is on a concave portion of the approximating polynomial. Fletcher limited the value of λ to be the smaller of (1) the λ' found by the cubic interpolation or (2)

$$\lambda^{(s+1)} = 0.1\lambda^{(s)}$$

where the superscript s denotes the number in the sequence of steps in the unidimensional search.

After each step the test

$$-\frac{f(\mathbf{x}^{(k)}) - f(\mathbf{x}^{(k)} + \lambda^{(s)}\mathbf{s}^{(k)})}{\lambda^{(s)}\nabla^T f(\mathbf{x}^{(k)})\mathbf{s}^{(k)}} \geq 10^{-4}$$

is carried out, and if satisfied, the stage is completed. Otherwise, the cubic interpolation is continued. Final termination takes place when

[1] The DSC-Powell search with scaling (see Appendix B) performs equally well.

$\Delta x_i \le \varepsilon = 10^{-5}$. To avoid the effects of roundoff error or incorrectly programmed derivatives, the code also terminated when (1) $f(\mathbf{x}^{(k+1)}) > f(\mathbf{x}^{(k)})$ and $(\Delta\mathbf{x}^{(k)})^T \Delta\mathbf{g}^{(k+1)} < 0$, and/or (2) $(\Delta\mathbf{x}^{(k)})^T \Delta\mathbf{g}^{(k)} \ge 0$.

Fletcher compared the above algorithm with the Davidon-Fletcher-Powell algorithm using a number of test problems and showed that it was about as effective as the latter. The number of iterations in a search direction was reduced, but to compensate, the number of search directions selected increased. Some results of applying Fletcher's algorithm to other test problems are described in Chap. 5.

3.4-6 Approximation of the Hessian Matrix

Instead of approximating $\mathbf{H}^{-1}(\mathbf{x}^{(k+1)})$ as in Eq. (3.4-3), we can approximate $\mathbf{H}(\mathbf{x}^{(k+1)})$ itself and then invert to get the approximation of $\mathbf{H}^{-1}$.

$$\mathbf{H}(\mathbf{x}^{(k+1)}) \approx \boldsymbol{\Upsilon}^{(k+1)} = \boldsymbol{\Upsilon}^{(k)} + \Delta\boldsymbol{\Upsilon}^{(k)}$$

where $\boldsymbol{\Upsilon}^{(k)}$ is the estimate of $\mathbf{H}(\mathbf{x}^{(k)})$, and the matrix $\Delta\boldsymbol{\Upsilon}^{(k)}$ is the only symmetric matrix of rank 1 that enables $\boldsymbol{\Upsilon}^{(k+1)}$ to satisfy the equation $\boldsymbol{\Upsilon}^{(k+1)}\Delta\mathbf{x}^{(k)} = \Delta\mathbf{g}^{(k)}$.

$$\Delta\boldsymbol{\Upsilon}^{(k)} = \frac{[(\Delta\mathbf{g}^{(k)}) - \boldsymbol{\Upsilon}^{(k)}(\Delta\mathbf{x}^{(k)})][(\Delta\mathbf{g}^{(k)}) - \boldsymbol{\Upsilon}^{(k)}(\Delta\mathbf{x}^{(k)})]^T}{[(\Delta\mathbf{g}^{(k)}) - \boldsymbol{\Upsilon}^{(k)}(\Delta\mathbf{x}^{(k)})]^T(\Delta\mathbf{x}^{(k)})} \qquad (3.4\text{–}20)$$

The conditions for convergence are the same as those described in Sec. 3.4-1. Because $(\boldsymbol{\Upsilon}^{(k+1)})^{-1}$ may not be positive definite, the suggestions in Sec. 3.2 also must be applied to guarantee positive definiteness. The initial $\boldsymbol{\Upsilon}^{(0)}$ can be chosen to be $(\boldsymbol{\eta}^{(0)})^{-1}$.

Equation (3.4-20) is analogous to Eq. (3.4-5) if we keep in mind that for a quadratic approximate $\Delta\mathbf{g}^{(k)} = \mathbf{H}\,\Delta\mathbf{x}^{(k)}$ (here) and $\Delta\mathbf{x}^{(k)} = \mathbf{H}^{-1}\Delta\mathbf{g}^{(k)}$ (in Sec. 3.4-1). In principle, it should be possible to write expressions for $\Delta\boldsymbol{\Upsilon}^{(k)}$ equivalent to each of those given in Secs. 3.4-2 through 3.4-4, but it is questionable as to whether the corresponding computation times to solve a problem would be reduced inasmuch as a matrix inversion must take place on each stage.

An algorithm by Goldstein and Price[1] that has been demonstrated to be efficient will now be summarized. Even though it does not strictly fall into the variable metric category, on each stage it does attempt to approximate $\mathbf{H}(\mathbf{x})$ by a difference scheme, based on a half factorial design, and then executes a matrix inversion. Only information about $f(\mathbf{x}^{(k)})$ and $\nabla f(\mathbf{x}^{(k)})$ is required to estimate $\mathbf{H}(\mathbf{x}^{(k)})$. Goldstein and Price prove that the algorithm

[1] A. A. Goldstein and J. F. Price, *Numerical Math.*, **10**:184 (1967).

minimizes $f(\mathbf{x})$ for a convex objective function subject to some minor conditions. The algorithm on the kth stage is as follows; the values of $0 < \delta < \frac{1}{2}$ and $r > 0$ are specified in advance.

Step 1: Compute as the approximation to $\mathbf{H}(\mathbf{x}^{(k)})$ the $n \times n$ matrix $\tilde{\mathbf{H}}(\mathbf{x}^{(k)})$, a matrix whose jth column is given by

$$\frac{\nabla f(\mathbf{x}^{(k)} + \theta^{(k)}\mathbf{I}_j) - \nabla f(\mathbf{x}^{(k)})}{\theta^{(k)}}$$

where

$$\theta^{(k)} = r\|\varphi(\mathbf{x}^{(k-1)})\| \qquad \text{for } k > 0$$

$$\theta^{(0)} = r$$

$$\mathbf{I}_j = j\text{th column of } n \times n \text{ identity matrix } \mathbf{I}$$

$$\varphi(\mathbf{x}^{(k)}) = \text{a column vector given by}$$

$$\varphi(\mathbf{x}^{(k)}) = \begin{cases} -\nabla f(\mathbf{x}^{(k)}) & \text{if } k = 0 \text{ or } \tilde{\mathbf{H}}(\mathbf{x}^{(k)}) \text{ is singular, or } [\nabla^T f(\mathbf{x}^{(k)})\tilde{\mathbf{H}}^{-1}(\mathbf{x}^{(k)})\nabla f(\mathbf{x}^{(k)})] \leq 0, \\ & \text{so that } \tilde{\mathbf{H}}^{-1} \text{ is not positive definite;} \\ -\tilde{\mathbf{H}}^{-1}(\mathbf{x}^{(k)})\nabla f(\mathbf{x}^{(k)}) & \text{otherwise} \end{cases}$$

Note that (1) $\tilde{\mathbf{H}}(\mathbf{x}^{(k)})$ is not necessarily a symmetric matrix, and (2) if $\nabla^T f(\mathbf{x}^{(k)})[\mathbf{H}^{-1}(\mathbf{x}^{(k)})\nabla f(\mathbf{x}^{(k)})] \leq 0$, then the proposed search direction $\varphi(\mathbf{x}^{(k)})$ and $\nabla f(\mathbf{x}^{(k)})$ are more than 90° apart. Since the search is conducted in the minus direction, the negative of the quadratic form implies a component in the positive gradient direction.

Step 2: Compute

$$F(\mathbf{x}^{(k)}, \lambda) = \frac{f(\mathbf{x}^{(k)}) - f(\mathbf{x}^{(k)} + \lambda\varphi(\mathbf{x}^{(k)}))}{\lambda[\nabla^T f(\mathbf{x}^{(k)})\varphi(\mathbf{x}^{(k)})]}$$

Select $\lambda^{(k)}$ such that $\delta \leq F(\mathbf{x}^{(k)}, 1)$ or $\delta \leq F(\mathbf{x}^{(k)}, \lambda^{(k)}) \leq 1 - \delta$, $\lambda^{(k)} \neq 1$. These criteria help keep the search from taking steps that far exceed the linear region of behavior of the objective function near $\mathbf{x}^{(k)}$ assumed in the approximation of $\mathbf{H}(\mathbf{x})$.

Step 3: Set $\mathbf{x}^{(k+1)} = \mathbf{x}^{(k)} + \lambda^{(k)}\varphi(\mathbf{x}^{(k)})$.

Step 4: Terminate when $\|\varphi(\mathbf{x}^{(k)})\| < \varepsilon$.

Thus, if $\tilde{\mathbf{H}}(\mathbf{x}^{(k)})$ is singular or does not give a "downhill direction," the method reduces to that of steepest descent. Preferably, r should be chosen so that $\tilde{\mathbf{H}}(\mathbf{x}^{(k)})$ approximates $\mathbf{H}(\mathbf{x}^{(k)})$ as closely as possible. The value of δ is selected so that the values of $f(\mathbf{x}^{(k)})$, $k = 1, 2, \ldots,$ are a monotonic decreasing sequence; the closer to 1/2 the value of δ is, the more $f(\mathbf{x}^{(k)} + \lambda\varphi(\mathbf{x}^{(k)}))$ is forced to approach its minimum with respect to λ. Goldstein and Price reported that the algorithm was equivalent in effectiveness, insofar as the functional and gradient evaluation count was concerned, to the Davidon-Fletcher-Powell algorithm for Rosenbrock's function. For poorly scaled problems it can be less satisfactory because it relapses into steepest descent steps. The most interesting feature of the algorithm is the small number of unidimensional searches per new search direction (stage), something on the order of one to two per stage. Some results of using the algorithm to solve test problems are given in Chap. 5.

3.5 SUMMARY OF UNCONSTRAINED ALGORITHMS

In this chapter we have examined a number of unconstrained optimization methods. By way of summary of the principal algorithms, Table 3.5-1 lists the recursive relations used to calculate $\boldsymbol{\eta}(\mathbf{x}^{(k)}) \equiv \boldsymbol{\eta}^{(k)}$ or to calculate $\mathbf{s}^{(k)}$ in $\Delta\mathbf{x}^{(k)} = \mathbf{x}^{(k+1)} - \mathbf{x}^{(k)} = \lambda^{*(k)}\mathbf{s}^{(k)} = -\lambda^{*(k)}\boldsymbol{\eta}(\mathbf{x}^{(k)})\nabla f(\mathbf{x}^{(k)})$. We will defer until Chap. 5 the comparison of the relative effectiveness of the algorithms so that the search methods of Chap. 4 can be included in the comparison.

Table 3.5-1 Summary of unconstrained NLP methods employing derivatives

Method	*Section no.*	*Recursion relation*
Steepest descent	3.1-1	$\boldsymbol{\eta}^{(k)} = \mathbf{I}$
Newton	3.2	$\boldsymbol{\eta}^{(k)} = -[\nabla^2 f(\mathbf{x}^{(k)})]^{-1} \equiv \mathbf{H}^{-1}(\mathbf{x}^{(k)})$
Greenstadt	3.2	$\boldsymbol{\eta}^{(k)} = \mathbf{C}^{-1}(\mathbf{x}^{(k)})\boldsymbol{\Pi}^{-1}\mathbf{C}^{-1}(\mathbf{x}^{(k)})$
Marquardt	3.2	$\boldsymbol{\eta}^{(k)} = \mathbf{C}^{-1}(\mathbf{x}^{(k)})(\boldsymbol{\Pi} + \beta\mathbf{I})^{-1}\mathbf{C}^{-1}(\mathbf{x}^{(k)})$
Broyden, rank 1	3.4-1	$\boldsymbol{\eta}^{(k+1)} = \boldsymbol{\eta}^{(k)} + \left\{\dfrac{[\Delta\mathbf{x}^{(k)} - \boldsymbol{\eta}^{(k)}\Delta\mathbf{g}^{(k)}][\Delta\mathbf{x}^{(k)} - \boldsymbol{\eta}^{(k)}\Delta\mathbf{g}^{(k)}]^T}{[\Delta\mathbf{x}^{(k)} - \boldsymbol{\eta}^{(k)}\Delta\mathbf{g}^{(k)}]^T\Delta\mathbf{g}^{(k)}}\right\}$
Davidon-Fletcher-Powell	3.4-2	$\boldsymbol{\eta}^{(k+1)} = \boldsymbol{\eta}^{(k)} + \left\{\dfrac{\Delta\mathbf{x}^{(k)}(\Delta\mathbf{x}^{(k)})^T}{(\Delta\mathbf{x}^{(k)})^T\Delta\mathbf{g}^{(k)}} - \dfrac{\boldsymbol{\eta}^{(k)}\Delta\mathbf{g}^{(k)}[\boldsymbol{\eta}^{(k)}\Delta\mathbf{g}^{(k)}]^T}{(\Delta\mathbf{g}^{(k)})^T\boldsymbol{\eta}^{(k)}\Delta\mathbf{g}^{(k)}}\right\}$
Pearson No. 2	3.4-3	$\boldsymbol{\eta}^{(k+1)} = \boldsymbol{\eta}^{(k)} + \left\{\dfrac{[\Delta\mathbf{x}^{(k)} - \boldsymbol{\eta}^{(k)}\Delta\mathbf{g}^{(k)}](\Delta\mathbf{x}^{(k)})^T}{(\Delta\mathbf{x}^{(k)})^T\Delta\mathbf{g}^{(k)}}\right\}$
Pearson No. 3	3.4-3	$\boldsymbol{\eta}^{(k+1)} = \boldsymbol{\eta}^{(k)} + \left\{\dfrac{[\Delta\mathbf{x}^{(k)} - \boldsymbol{\eta}^{(k)}\Delta\mathbf{g}^{(k)}][\boldsymbol{\eta}^{(k)}\Delta\mathbf{g}^{(k)}]^T}{(\Delta\mathbf{g}^{(k)})^T\boldsymbol{\eta}^{(k)}\Delta\mathbf{g}^{(k)}}\right\}$
Projected Newton Zoutendijk projection (if $\mathbf{P} = \boldsymbol{\eta}$)	3.4-3 3.3-4	$\boldsymbol{\eta}^{(k+1)} = \boldsymbol{\eta}^{(k)} - \left\{\dfrac{[\boldsymbol{\eta}^{(k)}\Delta\mathbf{g}^{(k)}][\boldsymbol{\eta}^{(k)}\Delta\mathbf{g}^{(k)}]^T}{(\Delta\mathbf{g}^{(k)})^T\boldsymbol{\eta}^{(k)}\Delta\mathbf{g}^{(k)}}\right\}$
Greenstadt and Goldfarb	3.4-4	$\boldsymbol{\eta}^{(k+1)} = \boldsymbol{\eta}^{(k)} + \text{Eq. (3.4-13)}$

Table 3.5-1 *continued*

Method	*Section no.*	*Recursion relation*
Fletcher	3.4–5	$\boldsymbol{\eta}^{(k+1)} = \text{Eq. (3.4–18)}$
Fletcher-Reeves	3.3–2	$\mathbf{s}^{(k+1)} = -\nabla f(\mathbf{x}^{(k)}) + \left\{\dfrac{\mathbf{s}^{(k)}\nabla^T f(\mathbf{x}^{(k+1)})\nabla f(\mathbf{x}^{(k+1)})}{\nabla^T f(\mathbf{x}^{(k)})\nabla f(\mathbf{x}^{(k)})}\right\}$
Approximation of $\mathbf{H}(\mathbf{x})$	3.4–6	$\tilde{\mathbf{H}}^{(k+1)} = \tilde{\mathbf{H}}^{(k)} + \left\{\dfrac{[\Delta\mathbf{g}^{(k)} - \tilde{\mathbf{H}}^{(k)}\Delta\mathbf{x}^{(k)}][\Delta\mathbf{g}^{(k)} - \tilde{\mathbf{H}}^{(k)}\Delta\mathbf{x}^{(k)}]^T}{[\Delta\mathbf{g}^{(k)} - \tilde{\mathbf{H}}^{(k)}\Delta\mathbf{x}^{(k)}]^T\Delta\mathbf{x}^{(k)}}\right\}$
Goldstein and Price	3.4–6	Uses difference scheme to approximate elements of $\mathbf{H}(\mathbf{x}^{(k)})$ or uses $\mathbf{s}^{(k)} = -\nabla f(\mathbf{x}^{(k)})$.

SUPPLEMENTARY REFERENCES

General References

Box, M. J.: A Comparison of Several Current Optimization Methods, and the Use of Transformations in Constrained Problems, *Computer J.*, **9**:67 (1966).

Dorn, W. S.: Nonlinear Programming: A Survey, *Management Sci.*, **9**:171 (1963).

Hestenes, M. R.: *J. Opt. Theory and Appl.*, **4**:303 (1969).

Hurt, J. J.: A Review of Algorithms for Optimization, *Univ. of Iowa Rep.* 22, June, 1970.

Kowalik, J., and M. R. Osborne: "Methods for Unconstrained Optimization Problems," American Elsevier, New York, 1968.

Meyers, G. E.: Properties of the Conjugate Gradient and Davidon Methods, *J. Opt. Theory Appl.*, **2**:1968.

Powell, M. J. D.: A Survey of Numerical Methods for Unconstrained Optimization, *SIAM Rev.*, **12**:79(1970).

Ribière, G.: Sur la methode de Davidon-Fletcher-Powell pour la minimisation des fonctions, *Management Sci.*, **16**:572 (1970).

Schechter, R. S., and G. S. C. Beveridge: "Optimization: Theory and Practice," McGraw-Hill, New York, 1970.

Spang, H. A., III: A Review of Minimization Techniques for Nonlinear Functions, *SIAM Rev.*, **4**:343 (1962).

Topkis, D. M., and A. F. Veinott: On the Convergence of Some Feasible Direction Algorithms for Nonlinear Programming, *J. SIAM Control*, **5**:268 (1967).

Wilde, D. J.: "Optimum Seeking Methods," Prentice-Hall, Englewood Cliffs, N.J., 1964.

———, and C. S. Beightler: "Foundations of Optimization," Prentice-Hall, Englewood Cliffs, N.J., 1967.

Wolfe, P.: Recent Developments in Nonlinear Programming, *Advan. Computers*, **3**:155–187 (1962).

Additional Methods of Unconstrained Nonlinear Programming Using Derivatives

Booth, A. D.: An Application of the Method of Steepest Descents to the Solution of Systems of Nonlinear Simultaneous Equations, *Quart. J. Mech. Appl. Math.*, **11**:460, 191 (1949).

Broyden, C. G.: The Convergence of a Class of Double-Rank Minimization Algorithms; 1. General Considerations, *J. Inst. Math. Appl.*, **6**:76 (1970).

———, G. C.: The Convergence of a Class of Double-Rank Minimization Algorithms; 2. The New Algorithm, *J. Inst. Math. Appl.*, **6**:222 (1970).

Crockett, J. G., and H. Chernoff: Gradient Methods of Maximization, *Pacific J. Math.*, **5**:33 (1955).

Curry, H. D.: The Method of Steepest Descent for Non-linear Minimization Problems, *Quart. Appl. Math.*, **2**:258 (1944).

Dixon, L. C. W., and M. C. Biggs: Meander—A Newton Based Procedure for *N*-Dimensional Function Minimization, *Technical Rep.* No. 9, The Hatfield Polytechnic, Hatfield, England, April, 1970.

Goldfield, S. M., R. E. Quandt, and H. F. Trotter: Maximization by Quadratic Hill Climbing, *Econometrica*, **34**:541 (1966).

Huang, H. Y., and A. B. Levy: *J. Opt. Theory and Appl.*, **6**:269 (1970).

Jacobson, D. H., and W. Oksman: An Algorithm That Minimizes Homogeneous Functions of *N* Variables in $N + 2$ Iterations and Rapidly Minimizes General Functions, *Technical Rept.* No. 618, Division of Engineering and Applied Physics, Harvard University, Cambridge, Mass., October, 1970.

Marquardt, D. W.: An Algorithm for Least Squares Estimation of Nonlinear Parameters, *SIAM J.*, **11**:431 (1963).

Murtagh, B. A., and R. W. H. Sargent: A Constrained Minimization Method with Quadratic Convergence, Chap. 14 in R. Fletcher (ed.), "Optimization," Academic Press Inc., London, 1969.

———, B. A., and R. W. H. Sargent: *Computer J.*, **13**:185 (1970).

Papaioannou, T., and O. Kempthorne: Parallel Tangents and Steepest Descent Optimization Algorithm, *Wright-Patterson Air Force Base Rept.* ARL 70–0117, July, 1970.

Powell, M. J. D.: An Iterative Method for Finding Stationary Values of a Function of Several Variables, *Computer J.*, vol. 5, 1962.

Shah, B. V., R. J. Buehler, and O. Kempthorne: *Iowa State Univ. Statist. Lab. Tech. Rept.* 3, 1961; 2 (rev.), 1962; *J. Soc. Ind. Appl. Math.*, vol. 12, 1964.

Shanno, D. F.: *SIAM J. Numer. Anal.*, **7**:366 (1970).

———, D. F.: *Math. Computation*, **24**:647 (1970).

———, D. F., and P. C. Kettler: *Math. Computation*, **24**:657 (1970).

Siddall, J. N.: Optisep Designers' Optimization Subroutines, *McMaster Univ. Rept.* ME/70/DSN/REP/1, Faculty of Engineering, Hamilton, Ontario, Canada, 1970.

PROBLEMS[1]

3.1 Answer the following questions about the method of steepest descent:

(*a*) Given that the unconstrained objective function is poorly scaled, will the initial progress of the search be fast or slow? Will the progress near the extremum be fast or slow?

(*b*) Once a gradient search direction is selected at a point $\mathbf{x}^{(k)}$, how should the step size be selected to reach the next point, $\mathbf{x}^{(k+1)}$?

[1] Additional problems suitable for this chapter can be found in the problem set at the end of Chap. 4.

3.2 Demonstrate by proof whether or not the method of steepest descent is a method that uses conjugate directions (in minimizing a quadratic function with a positive definite hessian matrix).

3.3 What is the direction of steepest descent at the point $\mathbf{x} = [1 \quad 1]^T$ for the objective function $f(\mathbf{x}) = x_1^2 + 2x_2^2$? Is this function badly scaled?

3.4 Determine the vector that represents the direction of steepest ascent at the point $\mathbf{x} = [1 \quad 1]^T$ for the objective function in problem

(*a*) 2.1*a* (*b*) 2.6*a* (*c*) 2.13 (*d*) 2.32

3.5 Carry out two stages in the method of steepest descent starting from $\mathbf{x} = [1 \quad 1]^T$ for the objective function $f(\mathbf{x}) = x_1^2 + 2x_2^2$. First use a fixed step size. Then minimize $f(\mathbf{x})$ in each stage either numerically or analytically.

3.6 Consider the following objective functions:

(*a*) $f(\mathbf{x}) = 1 + x_1 + x_2 + \dfrac{4}{x_1} + \dfrac{9}{x_2}$

(*b*) $f(\mathbf{x}) = (x_1 + 5)^2 + (x_2 + 8)^2 + (x_3 + 7)^2 + 2x_1^2x_2^2 + 4x_1^2x_3^2$

Will Newton's method converge for these functions?

3.7 Consider the minimization of the objective function

$$f(\mathbf{x}) = x_1^3 + x_1x_2 - x_2^2x_1^2$$

by Newton's method starting from the point $\mathbf{x}^{(0)} = [1 \quad 1]^T$. A computer code carefully programmed to execute Newton's method has not been successful. Explain the probable reason(s) for the failure.

3.8 What is the initial direction of search determined by Newton's method for Prob. 3.3? What is the step length? How many steps (search directions) are needed to solve Prob. 3.17? to solve Prob. 3.37?

3.9 Explain the topology of the following objective functions with the aid of Fig. 3.2-2 and Table 3.2-1.

(*a*) $3x_1 + 2x_2^2$

(*b*) $3 + 2x_1 + 3x_2 + 2x_1^2 + 2x_1x_2 + 6x_2^2$

(*c*) $3 + 2x_1 - 3x_2 + 2x_1^2 + 2x_1x_2 + 6x_2^2$

(*d*) $3x_1^2 - 4x_1x_2 + x_2^2$

3.10 Approximate the objective function in Prob. 3.34*f* by a quadratic. Interpret the topology of the objective function in terms of its approximate.

3.11 Is the hessian matrix of $f(\mathbf{x}) = 5x_1^2 + 3x_2^2 + x_3^2 - 2x_1x_2$ always positive definite? Repeat for $2x_1^2 - x_2^2 - x_1x_2$.

3.12 How can the hessian matrix for the function $f(\mathbf{x}) = 2x_1^2 - 2x_2^2 - x_1x_2$ be approximated by a positive definite matrix by (*a*) the method of Greenstadt, (*b*) the method of Marquardt?

3.13 What can be said about the convergence of Newton's method from an examination of the hessian matrix of the objective function in problem

(*a*) 3.34*b* (*b*) 3.34*e* (*c*) 3.36

3.14 What kinds of surfaces are represented by the following expressions (in terms of Fig. 3.2–3 and Table 3.2–1):

(*a*) $x_1^2 - x_1x_2 + x_2^2$

(*b*) $x_1^2 + 2x_1x_2 + x_2^2$

(*c*) $2x_1^2 + 2x_2^2 + 8x_3^2 - 4x_1x_2 + 12x_1x_3 + 8x_2x_3$

3.15 Given the function $f(\mathbf{x}) = x_1^2 + x_2^2 + 2x_3^2 - x_1x_2$, generate a set of conjugate directions. Carry out two stages of the minimization in the conjugate directions minimizing $f(\mathbf{x})$ in each direction. Illustrate the search path and a few selected contours of the objective function.

3.16 For what values of $\mathbf{x}$ are the following directions conjugate for the function $f(\mathbf{x}) = x_1^2 + x_1x_2 + 16x_2^2 + x_3^2 - x_1x_2x_3$?

$$\mathbf{s}^{(1)} = \begin{bmatrix} -\dfrac{1}{\sqrt{3}} \\ \dfrac{1}{\sqrt{3}} \\ -\dfrac{1}{\sqrt{3}} \end{bmatrix} \qquad \mathbf{s}^{(2)} = \begin{bmatrix} -\dfrac{1}{\sqrt{3}} \\ \dfrac{2}{\sqrt{3}} \\ 0 \end{bmatrix}$$

3.17 Are the directions $\begin{bmatrix} 0 \\ 1 \end{bmatrix}$ and $\begin{bmatrix} 1 \\ 0 \end{bmatrix}$ linearly independent? orthogonal? conjugate?

3.18 Are orthogonal directions ever conjugate directions? Explain.

3.19 Show that the search directions $\mathbf{s}^{(1)} = [0.453 \quad -0.892]^T$ and $\mathbf{s}^{(2)} = [0.608 \quad -0.794]^T$ used in minimizing Rosenbrock's function $f(\mathbf{x}) = 100(x_2 - x_1^2)^2 + (1 - x_1)^2$ at the point $\mathbf{x} = [-0.702 \quad 0.462]^T$ are conjugate.

3.20 Show that Eq. (3.3–14) is the correct weighting factor for the conjugate gradient method.

3.21 Do methods that use conjugate directions, if started from the same initial $\mathbf{x}^{(0)}$ with the same $\mathbf{s}^{(0)}$, choose the same sequence of search directions $\mathbf{s}^{(1)}$, $\mathbf{s}^{(2)}$, etc.? Answer yes or no and provide a simple example to explain your answer.

3.22 Compare the variable metric methods in three ways:

(*a*) The values of the elements of the direction matrix

(*b*) The search directions

(*c*) The $\mathbf{x}$ vectors

for problems———for several stages starting from the same $\mathbf{x}$ vector.

3.23 For each of the variable metric methods in Sec. 3.4 give the values of the elements of the direction matrix for the first three stages of search for the following problems:

(*a*) 3.34*d* (*b*) 3.37 (*c*) 3.40*a*

3.24 Evaluate the direction matrix by the———variable metric method for one of the objective functions listed in Prob. 3.39.

3.25 Given the initial direction matrix $\boldsymbol{\eta}^{(0)} = \mathbf{I}$, what is $\boldsymbol{\eta}^{(1)}$ by the Davidon-Fletcher-Powell algorithm if $f(\mathbf{x}) = x_1^2 + 2x_2^2$ and $\mathbf{x}^{(0)} = [1 \quad 1]^T$?

3.26 After an initial search to minimize Rosenbrock's function, the direction matrix at $\mathbf{x}^{(1)} = [1.441 \quad 2.078]^T$ is

$$\boldsymbol{\eta}^{(1)} = \begin{bmatrix} 1.544 \times 10^{-1} & -3.467 \times 10^{-1} \\ -3.467 \times 10^{-1} & 8.578 \times 10^{-1} \end{bmatrix}$$

What is the next search direction for the———method?

3.27 After 13 stages of minimization for the Rosenbrock function, the computer code terminates at $x = [1 \quad 1]^T$. The gradient is essentially a zero vector. What is the direction matrix for the———method and problem number———?

3.28 Does the Goldstein-Price algorithm make use of conjugate directions?

3.29 Develop the recursive equation to calculate the direction matrix by (*a*) the Davidon-Fletcher-Powell algorithm, (*b*) the Pearson algorithms, (*c*) Broyden's algorithm, if the objective function is to be maximized rather than minimized.

3.30 All the algorithms in Chap. 3 have been expressed as minimization problems. What is the simplest way to use the algorithms to maximize instead of minimize?

3.31 On the seventh stage of the Davidon-Fletcher-Powell method the following information is available for the Rosenbrock function: $f(\mathbf{x}) = 0.19469$; $x_1 = 1.4409$; $x_2 = 2.0779$; $\partial f(\mathbf{x})/\partial x_1 = -0.1455$; $\partial f(\mathbf{x})/\partial x_2 = 0.3565$; and the direction matrix is

$$\begin{bmatrix} 0.1544 & -0.3467 \\ -0.3467 & 0.8577 \end{bmatrix}$$

What are the next two directions of search?

3.32 The following objective function is bimodal and has a saddle point at $\mathbf{x} = [2 \quad 2]^T$, where $f(\mathbf{x}) = 2$.

$$f(\mathbf{x}) = (1 + 8x_1 - 7x_2^2 + \tfrac{7}{3}x_1^3 - \tfrac{1}{4}x_1^4)(x_2^2 e^{-x_2})$$

Ascertain which of the local optima is the global optimum. Make one search starting at the saddle point. A contour plotting or outline can be used to portray $f(x)$ in the $(x_1 - x_2)$ plane, if desired.

3.33 Solve each of the following sets of equations by minimizing the sum of the square of the differences, $\sum(d_i - 0)^2$.

(*a*) $x_1 + 3\log_{10}x_1 - x_2^2 = 0$
$2x_1^2 - x_1x_2 - 5x_1 + 1 = 0$

(*b*) $x_1^2 + (x_2 - 1)^2 - 5 = 0$
$(x_1 - 1)^2 + x_2^2 - 1 = 0$

(*c*) Solve the set of 24 nonlinear equations with 24 variables listed by Pack and Swan.[1]

[1] D. C. Pack and G. W. Swan, *J. Fluid Mech.*, **25**:165 (1966).

3.34 Minimize the following functions of two independent variables.

(*a*) $\frac{1}{2}\{1 - \cos 360[(2x - 1)^2 + (2y - 1)^2]^{1/2}\}\left[1 - \frac{(y - 3x)^2}{8}\right]$

(*b*) $y + \sin x$

(*c*) $-1(y - x)^4 + (1 - x)^2$

(*d*) $-x^2 + x - y^2 + y + 4$

(*e*) $\exp\left[-(x - 1)^2\right] - \frac{(y^2 - 0.5)^2}{0.132}$

3.35 A manufacturer can produce a certain consumer item A for 20 cents/lb and consumer item B for 10 cents/lb. The manufacturer's sales research staff believes that the company can sell $1{,}000{,}000/x^2y$ lb/day of A and $2{,}000{,}000/xy^2$ lb/day of B, where x is the selling price of A in cents per pound, and y is the selling price of B in cents per pound. If A and B are sold at the same price, determine the maximum profit. What are x and y? If A and B are sold at different prices, determine the maximum profit. What are x and y?

3.36 The annual operating expenses of a gas compressor on a transcontinental pipeline are given by

$$C = \frac{KQZ}{10^6 L}\left(\ln \frac{P_1}{P_2} + b\right) + K_1 D^2 \left[\frac{P_1}{2(s - P_1)} + \frac{P_1^2}{4(s + P_1)^2}\right]$$

where C = operating cost, \$/year
Q = amount of gas pumped, ft³/day
L = distance between compressor stations, miles
P_1 = discharge pressure, psia
P_2 = suction pressure, psia
D = diameter of line, in.
K, K_1, Z, s, b = constants

Also
$$Q = K_2 \frac{D^{2.6}(P_1^2 - P_2^2)^{0.54}}{L^{0.54} Z^{0.54}}$$

If $Z = 1$, $K = 1370$, $L = 20$, $b = 1.476$, $K_1 = 0.081$, $s = 100$, and $K_2 = 1.13$, determine P_1 and P_2 to minimize C.

3.37 Maximize the following objective function:

$$f(\mathbf{x}) = x_1^3 \exp[x_2 - x_1^2 - 10(x_1 - x_2)^2]$$

Compare the trajectories of the optimization in the **x** space by the following methods:

(*a*) Steepest descent
(*b*) Continued Partan
(*c*) Newton's method
(*d*) A variable metric method
(*e*) Fletcher-Reeves
(*f*) Goldstein-Price

3.38 Maximize the following objective function:

$$f(\mathbf{x}) = (0.35 + 0.40x_1 + 0.35x_2)^4(0.85 - 0.60x_1 + 0.85x_2)^4 \exp[2.00 - (0.35 + 0.40x_1 + 0.35x_2)^4 - (0.85 - 0.60x_1 + 0.85x_2)^4]$$

Compare the trajectories of the optimization in the **x** space by the following methods:

(*a*) Steepest descent
(*b*) Continued Partan
(*c*) Newton's method
(*d*) A variable metric method
(*e*) Fletcher-Reeves
(*f*) Goldstein-Price

3.39 From the point $\mathbf{x}^{(k)} = [1 \quad -2 \quad 3]^T$, determine the (next) point $\mathbf{x}^{(k+1)}$ by (1) the method of steepest descent, (2) continued Partan, (3) Newton's method, (4) Davidon-Fletcher-Powell method, (5) the conjugate gradient method for the following objective functions:

(*a*) $f(\mathbf{x}) = x_1^2 + x_2^2 + x_3^2$
(*b*) $f(\mathbf{x}) = 2x_1^2 + 2x_1x_2 + 3x_2^2 + x_3$
(*c*) $f(\mathbf{x}) = \exp(x_1^2 + x_2^2 - x_3 - x_1 + 4)$

3.40 Minimize the following functions starting with an initial vector $\mathbf{x}^{(0)} = [2 \quad -2.5 \quad 2 \quad -2.5]^T$.

(*a*) $f(\mathbf{x}) = x_1^2 + x_2^2 + x_3^2 + x_4^2$
(*b*) $f(\mathbf{x}) = (x_1 - x_2)^2 + (x_3 - x_4)^2$
(*c*) $f(\mathbf{x}) = x_1^3 + x_2 + x_3^3 + x_4 + 16x_1^2x_2 + 8x_2^2x_3 + x_3^2x_4 + 2$

3.41 A function described by Wheeling[1] provides a test of the ability of an algorithm to overcome discontinuities. The function

$$f(\mathbf{x}) = -3|x_1| - |x_2|$$

has a pyramid shape in three dimensions, and its contours in the $(x_1 - x_2)$ plane are diamond-shaped, with discontinuities along the principal axes. Find the maximum of $f(\mathbf{x})$, and also find $\mathbf{x}^*$ by (*a*) steepest descent, (*b*) continued Partan, (*c*) Newton's method, (*d*) a variable metric method, (*e*) the conjugate gradient method. (The maximum is at the origin.) Wheeling started the optimization at $\mathbf{x}^{(0)} = [10 \quad 10]^T$, where $f(\mathbf{x}) = -40$; try other starting vectors.

3.42 If the objective function is of the general form

$$f(\mathbf{x}) = \prod_{i=1}^{n} (x_i^i e^{-x_i}) \qquad (a)$$

the maximum of $f(\mathbf{x})$ can be shown to occur at the maximum of each factor, i.e., at $x_i = i$. Use function (*a*) as a test function and compute the maximum

[1] R. F. Wheeling, *Comm. Assoc. Computer Mach.*, **3**:632 (1960).

value of the following function by the———method:

$$f(\mathbf{x}) = x_1 x_2^2 x_3^3 x_4^4 e^{-(x_1+x_2+x_3+x_4)}$$

Compare with the known maximum. Let $\mathbf{x}^{(0)} = [3 \quad 4 \quad \frac{1}{2} \quad 1]^T$ and also $\mathbf{x}^{(0)} = [1 \quad 1 \quad 1 \quad 1]^T$.

3.43 The following function due to Brooks[1] has a long narrow ridge and a maximum value at $\mathbf{x}^* = [1 \quad 1]^T$.

$$f(\mathbf{x}) = x_1^2 \exp[1 - x_1^2 - 20.25(x_1 - x_2)^2]$$

Ascertain the maximum of $f(\mathbf{x})$ from the initial vectors $\mathbf{x}^{(0)} = [0.1 \quad 0.1]^T$ and also $\mathbf{x}^{(0)} = [1.9 \quad 0.1]^T$, using the method of ———. Plot the function and the trajectory of the optimization in $(x_1 - x_2)$ space.

3.44 In statistical analysis the fitting of exponential functions is difficult because of parameter interaction that leads to hyperbolic ridges in parameter space. For example, minimize the sum of the squares of the deviations

$$\phi = \sum_{i=1}^{n} (y_{\text{observed}} - y_{\text{predicted}})_i^2$$

where $$y_{\text{predicted}} = \frac{k_1}{k_1 - k_2}(e^{-k_2 t} - e^{-k_1 t})$$

for the following data:

t	y_{observed}
0.5	0.263
1.0	0.455
1.5	0.548

Plot the sum-of-squares surface with the estimated coefficients.

3.45 Repeat Prob. 3.44 for the following model and data:

$$y = \frac{k_1 x_1}{1 + k_2 x_1 + k_3 x_2}$$

y_{observed}	x_1	x_2
0.126	1	1
0.219	2	1
0.076	1	2
0.126	2	2
0.186	0.1	0

[1] S. H. Brooks, *Operations Res.*, **7**:430 (1959).

3.46 Approximate the minimum value of the integral

$$\int_0^1 \left[\left(\frac{dy}{dx}\right)^2 - 2yx^2 \right] dx$$

subject to the boundary conditions $dy/dx = 0$ at $x = 0$ and $y = 0$ at $x = 1$. *Hint:* Assume a trial function $y(\mathbf{x}) = a(1 - x_2)$ that satisfies the boundary conditions and find the value of a that minimizes the integral. Will a more complicated trial function that satisfies the boundary conditions improve the estimate of the minimum of the integral?

3.47 In a decision problem it is desired to minimize the expected risk defined as follows:

$$\mathscr{E}\,\{\text{risk}\} = (1 - P)c_1[1 - F(b)] + Pc_2\theta\left(\frac{b}{2} + \frac{2\pi}{4}\right)\mathrm{F}\left(\frac{b}{2} - \frac{\sqrt{2\pi}}{4}\right)$$

where $f(b) = \int_{-\infty}^{b} e^{-u^2/2\theta^2}\,du$

$c_1 = 1.25 \times 10^5$

$c_2 = 15$

$\theta = 2000$

$P = 0.25$

Find the minimum expected risk and b.

3.48 A bakery producing 1-lb loaves of bread normally produces 10,000 lb bread per day. Due to a period of severe competition, the market price of the product has dropped so low that the plant is operating at a loss. Under normal operation (10,000 lb product per day, 300 days per year) the costs are as follows:

1. Labor, supervision, steam, sales, social security, etc.: $600/day
2. Raw material cost: $0.075/lb of product
3. Yearly depreciation, taxes, insurance, etc., amounting to 25 per cent of investment: $300,000

Assume that items 1 and 2 will vary linearly with production while item 3 remains constant with change of production. The bread has a stable demand, and no new process for its manufacture is considered feasible by experts in the field.

The production department working together with the sales and accounting departments finds from the best available data that the cost in dollars per unit of production is given (within the production limits of 0 to 20,000 lb/day) by the equation

$$C = \frac{(\$300{,}000)\,(0.25/\text{year})}{(300\ \text{day/year})\,(P\ \text{lb/year})} + \frac{\$400/\text{day}}{P_N\ \text{lb/day}} + 0.075/\text{lb} + 10^{-7}P^{1.3}$$

where P is the actual production in pounds per day, and P_N is the normal production, 10,000 lb/day. The sales department has estimated that the selling price (including returns) will average 18.1 cents/lb for the next month. Based on the data above, what production would you recommend as the optimum for the next month?

3.49 A question has been asked as to whether insulation is economically justified for a large storage tank, and if so, what the optimum insulation thickness is. The costs can be divided into two categories: (*a*) installed costs and (*b*) operating costs. The installed cost (in \$/year) of the insulation is c_1c_2Ax.

A heating coil must also be installed to maintain the oil in the tank at the proper viscosity, and its installed cost (in \$/year) is

$$c_3c_4\frac{Q}{U(t_st_o)}$$

where

$$Q = \frac{A(t_o - t_a)}{(x/k + 1/h_a + 1/h_o)}$$

The operations costs of the tank (in \$/year) are c_5c_6Q. Find the minimum cost and the insulation required for the following case: $A = 8000$; $t_o = 120$; $t_a = 40$; $t_s = 250$; $k = 0.024$; $c_1 = 4$; $c_2 = 0.20$; $c_3 = 0.8$; $c_4 = 0.262$; $c_5 = 1.5 \times 10^{-6}$; $c_6 = 4000$; $h_o = 15 + 60x + 10x^2$; $h_a = 4.0 - 10x$; $U = 17$. What does a negative value of x mean?

Notation

c_1 = cost of insulating material, \$/(ft² surface) (ft thickness)
c_2 = amortization of cost, fraction
c_3 = cost of heating surface, \$/ft²
c_4 = amortization of cost, fraction
c_5 = cost of steam, \$/Btu
c_6 = hours of operation per year, hr
A = insulation area, ft²
h_a = heat transfer coefficient, tank wall to air, Btu/hr (ft²)(°F)
h_o = heat transfer coefficient, oil to tank wall, Btu/hr (ft²)(°F)
k = thermal conductivity of insulation, Btu/hr (ft)(°F)
Q = heat lost, Btu/hr
U = heat transfer coefficient between coil and product, Btu/hr (ft²)(°F)
t_a = ambient air temperature, °F
t_o = product temperature, °F
t_s = heating coil temperature, °F
x = insulation thickness, ft

4

Unconstrained minimization procedures without using derivatives (search methods)

In contrast to Chap. 3, which described methods of solving Problem (3.0–1) by derivative-type methods (and their approximates), this chapter is concerned with the derivative-free types of methods, more commonly called *search* methods of optimization. In the purest of the search methods the direction(s) for minimization are determined solely from successive evaluations of the objection function $f(\mathbf{x})$.

As a general rule, in solving unconstrained nonlinear programming problems, gradient and second-derivative methods converge faster than direct search methods. However, in practice, the derivative-type methods have two main barriers to their implementation. First, in problems with a modestly large number of variables, it is laborious or impossible to provide analytical functions for the derivatives needed in a gradient or second-derivative algorithm. Although evaluation of the derivatives by difference schemes can be substituted for evaluation of the analytical derivatives, as described in Sec. 3.4, the numerical error introduced, particularly in the vicinity of the extremum can impair the use of such substitutions. In principle, symbolic manipulation to evolve analytical derivatives is possible, but this technique still requires considerable development before it becomes a feasible tool in practice. In any case, search methods do not require regularity and continuity of the objective function and the existence of derivatives. Second, and a related point, optimization techniques based on the evaluation of first and possibly second derivatives require a relatively large amount of problem preparation by the user before he introduces the problem into the algorithm, as compared with search techniques.

Because of the difficulties described above, direct search optimization algorithms have been devised that, although slower to execute for simple problems, in practice may prove more satisfactory from the user's viewpoint than gradient or second-derivative methods, and may cost less to use if the cost of problem preparation time is high relative to the computation time. We have the space to consider only a few of the many existing search algorithms in this chapter, and the methods described have been selected from the viewpoint of their effectiveness in solving test problems.

4.1 DIRECT SEARCH

Conceptually, the simplest type of search method is to change one variable at a time while keeping all the others constant until the minimum is reached. For example, one method would set one of the variables, say x_1, constant and vary x_2 until a minimum was obtained. Then, keeping the new value of x_2 constant, change x_1 until an optimum for the value of x_2 is achieved, and so on. This process, however, performs poorly if there are interactions between x_1 and x_2, that is, if in effect terms involving products of x_1 and x_2 occur in the objective function. Hence this method cannot be recommended unless the user has an objective function such that the interactions are insignificant.

Hooke and Jeeves[1] proposed a logically simple strategy of search that made use of prior knowledge and at the same time rejected obsolete information concerning the nature of the topology of the objective function in E^n. As implemented by Wood,[2] the algorithm consists of two major phases, an "exploratory search" around the base point and a "pattern search" in a direction selected for minimization. Figure 4.1-1 is a simplified information flow diagram of the direct search algorithm.

[1] R. Hooke and T. A. Jeeves, *J. Assoc. Computer Mach.*, **8**:212 (1962).

[2] C. F. Wood, Application of "Direct Search" to the Solution of Engineering Problems, *Westinghouse Res. Lab. Sci. Paper* 6-41210-1-P1, 1960.

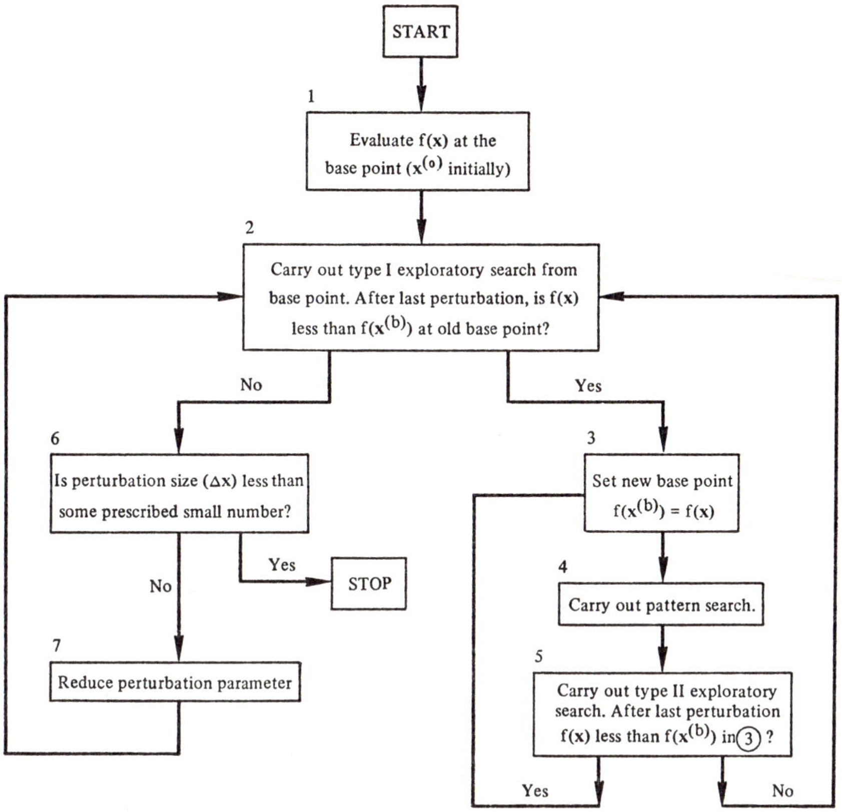

Fig. 4.1-1 Information flow diagram for direct search minimization.

The direct search algorithm operates in the following manner. Initial values for all the elements of **x** must be provided, as well as an initial incremental change $\Delta\mathbf{x}$. To initiate an exploratory search, $f(\mathbf{x})$ is evaluated at a base point (the base point is the vector of initial guesses of the independent variables for the first cycle). Then each variable is changed in rotation, one at a time, by incremental amounts, until all the parameters have been so changed. To be specific, $x_1^{(0)}$ is changed by an amount $+\Delta x_1^{(0)}$, so that $x_1^{(1)} = x_1^{(0)} + \Delta x_1^{(0)}$. If $f(\mathbf{x})$ is reduced, $x_1^{(0)} + \Delta x_1^{(0)}$ is adopted as the new element in **x**. If the increment fails to improve the objective function, $x_1^{(0)}$ is changed by $-\Delta x_1^{(0)}$, and the value of $f(\mathbf{x})$ again checked as before. If the value of $f(\mathbf{x})$ is not improved by either $x_1^{(0)} \pm \Delta x_1^{(0)}$, $x_1^{(0)}$ is left unchanged. Then $x_2^{(0)}$ is changed by an amount $\Delta x_2^{(0)}$, and so on, until all the independent variables have been changed to complete one exploratory search. For each step or move in the independent variable, the value of the objective function is compared with the value at the previous point. If the objective function is improved for the given step, then the new value of the objective function replaces the old one in the testing. However, if a perturbation is a failure, then the old value of $f(\mathbf{x})$ is retained.

After making one (or more) exploratory searches in this fashion, a "pattern search" is made. The successfully changed variables (i.e., those variable changes that decreased $f(\mathbf{x})$) define a vector in E^n that represents a successful direction for minimization. A series of accelerating steps, or pattern searches, is made along this vector as long as $f(\mathbf{x})$ is decreased by each pattern search. The magnitude of the step for the pattern search in each coordinate direction is roughly proportional to the number of successful steps previously en-

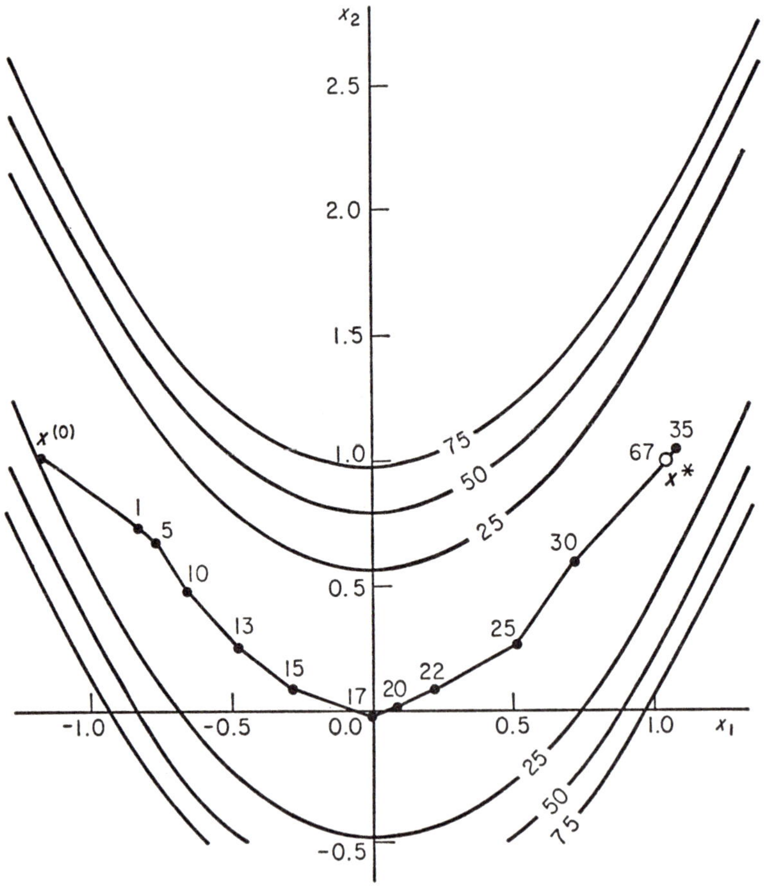

Fig. 4.1-2 Direct search for the minimum of Rosenbrock's function starting from $\mathbf{x}^{(0)} = [-1.2 \quad 1.0]^T$. Points indicate number of successful pattern moves.

countered in each coordinate direction during the exploratory searches for several previous cycles. The change in step size, $\Delta\mathbf{x}$, in the pattern search is taken as some multiple of the $\Delta\mathbf{x}$ used in the exploratory searches in order to accelerate the search. An exploratory search conducted after a pattern search is termed a type II exploratory search, and the success or failure of a pattern move is not established until after the type II exploratory search has been completed.

If $f(\mathbf{x})$ is not decreased after the type II exploratory search, the pattern search is said to fail, and a new type I exploratory search is made in order to define a new successful direction. If the type I exploratory search fails to give a new successful direction, $\Delta\mathbf{x}$ is reduced gradually, until either a new successful direction can be defined or each Δx_i becomes smaller than some preset tolerance. Failure to decrease $f(\mathbf{x})$ for a very small $\Delta\mathbf{x}$ indicates that a local optimum has been reached. Three basic tests must be satisfied for the sequence of searches to terminate. The first test occurs after each exploratory search and pattern search—the change in the objective function is compared with a prespecified small number. If the value of the objective function did not vary by an amount more than the specified number from the previous base value of the objective function, the exploratory search or pattern search is considered a failure. In the absence of such a failure, a test is made to determine if the objective function was increased (a failure) or decreased (a successful search). This second test ensures that the value of the objective function is always being improved. The third test is conducted after an exploratory-search failure on the fractional change in $\Delta\mathbf{x}$. The search can terminate if the change in each variable, $\Delta x_i^{(k)}$, is less than some prespecified number.

Figure 4.1-2 illustrates the path of direct search in minimizing Rosenbrock's function from the starting vector $\mathbf{x}^{(0)} = [-1.2 \quad 1.0]^T$.

Example 4.1-1 Unconstrained maximization by Hooke and Jeeves' direct search

The objective function

$$f(\mathbf{x}) = \frac{1}{(x_1 + 1)^2 + x_2^2}$$

is to be maximized starting at $\mathbf{x}^{(0)} = [2.00 \quad 2.80]^T$, with an initial $\Delta\mathbf{x}$ of $[0.60 \quad 0.84]^T$. The initial value of $f(2.00, 2.80)$ at the base point $\mathbf{x}^{(0)}$ is 0.059. A type I exploratory search is made to define a successful direction. (Such a move is called a type I exploratory search in contrast to the type II exploratory search that follows a pattern search. After a type II exploratory move, a decision is made as to whether the previous pattern moves were a success or failure.)

$$
\begin{array}{lll}
x_1^{(1)} = 2.00 + 0.60 = 2.60 & f(2.60,2.80) = 0.048 & \text{failure} \\
x_1^{(1)} = 2.00 - 0.60 = 1.40 & f(1.40,2.80) = 0.073 & \text{success} \\
x_2^{(1)} = 2.80 + 0.84 = 3.64 & f(1.40,3.64) = 0.052 & \text{failure} \\
x_2^{(1)} = 2.80 - 0.84 = 1.96 & f(1.40,1.96) = 0.104 & \text{success}
\end{array}
$$

The exploratory search is a success. Note that the last successful $\mathbf{x}$ vector is picked up on each search. The new base vector will be (1.40, 1.96).

Now a pattern search is made from the point (1.40,1.96) according to the acceleration rule

$$x_i^{(k+1)} = 2x_i^{(k)} - x_i^{(b)}$$

where $x_i^{(b)}$ is the old base $\mathbf{x}$ vector, here at the start $\mathbf{x}^{(0)}$.

$$
\begin{aligned}
x_1^{(2)} &= 2(1.40) - 2.00 = 0.80 \\
x_2^{(2)} &= 2(1.96) - 2.80 = 1.12 \\
f(0.8,1.12) &= 0.22
\end{aligned}
$$

Finally, a type II exploratory search is made; failure or success is based on a comparison with $f(0.8,1.12) = 0.22$.

$$
\begin{array}{lll}
x_1^{(3)} = 0.80 + 0.60 = 1.40 & f(1.40,1.12) = 0.14 & \text{failure} \\
x_1^{(3)} = 0.80 - 0.60 = 0.20 & f(0.20,1.12) = 0.38 & \text{success} \\
x_2^{(3)} = 1.12 + 0.84 = 1.96 & f(0.20,1.96) = 0.19 & \text{failure} \\
x_2^{(3)} = 1.12 - 0.84 = 0.28 & f(0.20,0.28) = 0.67 & \text{success}
\end{array}
$$

To determine if the pattern search is a success, $f(0.20,0.28) = 0.67$ is compared with $f(1.40,1.96) = 0.104$. Because the pattern search is a success, the new base point is $\mathbf{x}^{(3)} = [0.20 \quad 0.28]^T$ and the old base point becomes $\mathbf{x}^{(1)} = [1.40 \quad 1.96]^T$.

Another pattern search is made.

$$
\begin{aligned}
x_1^{(4)} &= 2(0.20) - 1.40 = -1.00 \\
x_2^{(4)} &= 2(0.28) - 1.96 = -1.40 \\
f(-1.00,-1.40) &= 0.51
\end{aligned}
$$

Now a type II exploratory search is carried out.

$$
\begin{array}{lll}
x_1^{(5)} = -1.00 + 0.60 = -0.40 & f(-0.40,-1.40) = 0.43 & \text{failure} \\
x_1^{(5)} = -1.00 - 0.60 = -1.60 & f(-1.60,-1.40) = 0.43 & \text{failure} \\
x_2^{(5)} = -1.40 + 0.84 = -0.56 & f(-1.00,-0.53) = 3.18 & \text{success}
\end{array}
$$

Since $f(-1.00,-0.56) = 3.18 > f(0.20,0.28) = 0.67$, the pattern move is a success, and $\mathbf{x}^{(5)} = [-1.00 \quad -0.56]^T$ becomes the new base point and $\mathbf{x}^{(3)}$ the old base point.

This sequence of steps continues until the conditions are reached in which, at the end of a type II exploratory search, the value of $f(\mathbf{x})$ is less than the value of $f(\mathbf{x}^{(b)})$ at the new base point. Then even if the type II exploratory search is a success on one or more of the perturbations, the pattern search is said to fail, and a type I exploratory move is initiated from the old base point to define a new successful direction. To illustrate, we continue the search from $\mathbf{x}^{(5)} = [-1.00 \quad -0.56]^T$.

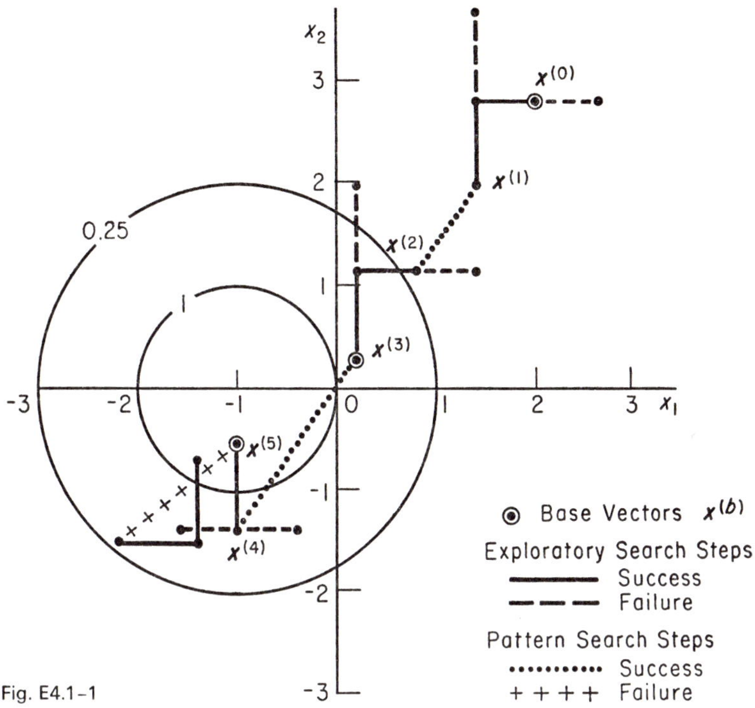

Fig. E4.1-1

Pattern search:

$$\left.\begin{aligned} x_1^{(6)} &= 2(-1.00) - 0.20 = -2.20 \\ x_2^{(6)} &= 2(-0.56) - 0.28 = -1.40 \end{aligned}\right\} f(-2.20, -1.40) = 0.29$$

Type II exploratory search:

$$x_1^{(7)} = -2.20 + 0.60 = -1.60 \qquad f(-1.60, -1.40) = 0.43 \quad \text{success}$$

$$x_2^{(7)} = -1.40 + 0.84 = -0.56 \qquad f(-1.60, -0.56) = 1.49 \quad \text{success}$$

However, because $f(-1.60, -0.56) = 1.49 < f(-1.00, -0.56) = 3.18$, even though the type II exploratory search was a success, the pattern move is deemed a failure, and a type I exploratory search is initiated from $\mathbf{x}^{(5)} = [-1.00 \quad -0.56]^T$.

When the stage is reached in which neither the type I exploratory search nor the pattern search (together with the type II exploratory search) has a success in any coordinate direction, both are said to fail and the perturbation $\Delta\mathbf{x}$ is reduced as follows:

$$\Delta x_{i,\,\text{new}} = \Delta x_{i,\,\text{previous}} \frac{\Delta x_i^{(0)}}{e^{\xi}}$$

where ξ is the number of consecutive exploratory search failures at the given step size since the last successful exploratory search.
(In this example the maximum of $f(\mathbf{x}) \to \infty$ as $x_1 \to -1$ and $x_2 \to 0$.)

4.2 FLEXIBLE POLYHEDRON SEARCH

Nelder and Mead[1] proposed a method of search somewhat more complex than direct search, but one that has proved to be an effective strategy, easily implemented on a digital computer. To provide the background necessary to appreciate the strategy of Nelder and Mead, we will very briefly describe a predecessor technique, the simplex search of Spendley, Hext and Himsworth,[2] devised in connection with the statistical design of experiments. Recall that regular polyhedrons in E^n are simplexes. For example, as indicated in Fig 4.2–1, for two variables a regular simplex is an equilateral triangle (three points); for three variables, the regular simplex is a regular tetrahedron (four points), and so forth.

In the search for a minimum of the objective function $f(\mathbf{x})$, trial $\mathbf{x}$ vectors can be selected at points in E^n located at the vertices of the simplex, as originally suggested by Spendley, Hext and Himsworth. From texts on analytical geometry it can be shown that the coordinates of the vertices of the regular simplex are designated by the following matrix $\mathbf{D}$, in which the columns represent the components of the vertices, numbered from 1 to $(n + 1)$, and the rows represent the coordinates, $i = 1$ to n.

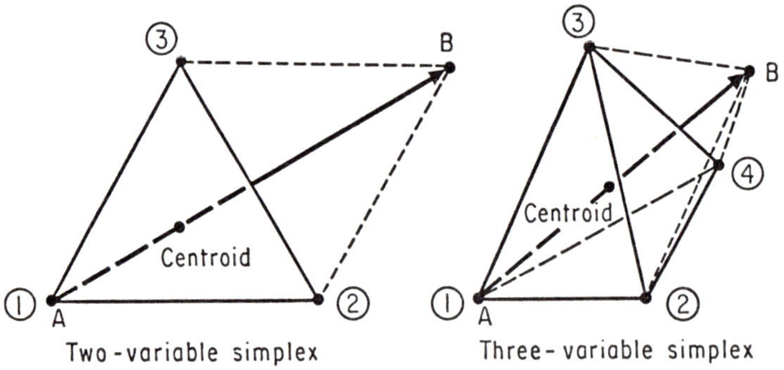

Fig. 4.2–1 Regular simplexes for two and three independent variables. ① indicates the highest value of $f(\mathbf{x})$. The arrow points in the direction of greatest improvement.

[1] J. A. Nelder and R. Mead, *Computer J.*, **7**:308 (1964).
[2] W. Spendley, G. R. Hext and F. R. Himsworth, *Technometrics*, **4**:441 (1962).

$$\mathbf{D} = \begin{bmatrix} 0 & d_1 & d_2 & \dots & d_2 \\ 0 & d_2 & d_1 & \dots & d_2 \\ 0 & d_2 & d_2 & \dots & d_2 \\ \dots & \dots & \dots & \dots & \dots \\ 0 & d_2 & d_2 & \dots & d_1 \end{bmatrix} \qquad \text{an } n \times (n+1) \text{ matrix}$$

where

$$d_1 = \frac{t}{n\sqrt{2}}(\sqrt{n+1} + n - 1)$$

$$d_2 = \frac{t}{n\sqrt{2}}(\sqrt{n+1} - 1)$$

$$t = \text{distance between two vertices}$$

For example, for $n = 2$ and $t = 1$, the triangle given in Fig. 4.2–1 has the following coordinates:

Vertex	$x_{1,i}$	$x_{2,i}$
1	0	0
2	0.965	0.259
3	0.259	0.965

The objective function can be evaluated at each of the vertices of the simplex, and a projection made from the point yielding the highest value of the objective function, point A in Fig. 4.2–1, through the centroid of the simplex. Point A is deleted, and a new simplex, termed a *reflection*, is formed, composed of the remaining old points and the one new point, B, located along the projected line at the proper distance from the centroid. Continuation of this procedure, always deleting the vertex that yields the highest value of the objective function, plus rules for reducing the size of the simplex and for preventing cycling in the vicinity of the extremum, permit a derivative-free search in which the step size on any stage k is fixed but the direction of search is permitted to change. Figure 4.2–2 illustrates the successive simplexes formed in a two-dimensional space with a well-behaved objective function.

Certain practical difficulties in the regular simplex procedure, namely, that it did not provide for acceleration of the search and encountered difficulty in carrying on the search in curving valleys or on curving ridges, led to several improvements.[1] We describe in this section the Nelder and Mead technique, in which the simplex is permitted to alter in shape and thus no

[1] M. J. Box, *Computer J.*, **8**:42 (1965); I. G. Campey and D. G. Nickols, "Simplex Minimization," Imperial Chemical Industries, Ltd., 1961.

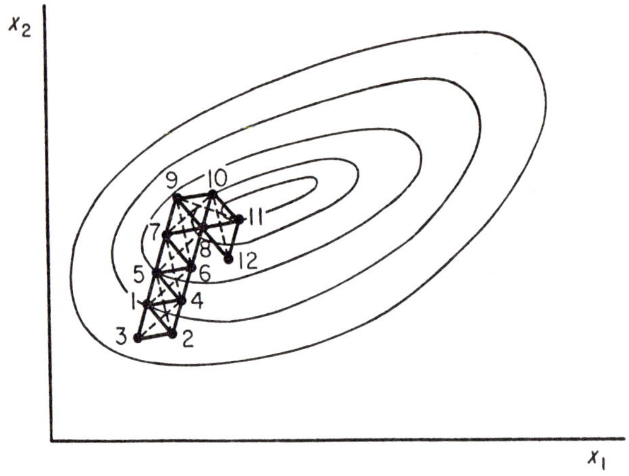

Fig. 4.2-2 Sequence of regular simplexes obtained in minimizing $f(\mathbf{x})$. - - - indicates projection.

longer stays a simplex; hence the use of the more descriptive name "flexible polyhedron."

The method of Nelder and Mead minimizes a function of n independent variables using $(n + 1)$ vertices of a flexible polyhedron in E^n. Each vertex can be defined by a vector $\mathbf{x}$. The vertex (point) in E^n which yields the highest value of $f(\mathbf{x})$ is projected through the center of gravity (centroid) of the *remaining* vertices. Improved (lower) values of the objective function are found by successively replacing the point with the highest value of $f(\mathbf{x})$ by better points until the minimum of $f(\mathbf{x})$ is found.

The details of the algorithm are as follows.

Let $\mathbf{x}_i^{(k)} = [x_{i1}^{(k)}, \ldots, x_{ij}^{(k)}, \ldots, x_{in}^{(k)}]^T$, $i = 1, \ldots, n + 1$, be the ith vertex (point) in E^n on the kth stage of the search, $k = 0, 1, \ldots$, and let the value of the objective function at $\mathbf{x}_i^{(k)}$ be $f(\mathbf{x}_i^{(k)})$. In addition, we need to label $\mathbf{x}$ vectors in the polyhedron that give the maximum and minimum values of $f(\mathbf{x})$. Define

$$f(\mathbf{x}_h^{(k)}) = \max\{f(\mathbf{x}_1^{(k)}), \ldots, f(\mathbf{x}_{n+1}^{(k)})\}$$

with the corresponding $\mathbf{x}_i^{(k)} = \mathbf{x}_h^{(k)}$, and

$$f(\mathbf{x}_l^{(k)}) = \min\{f(\mathbf{x}_1^{(k)}), \ldots, f(\mathbf{x}_{n+1}^{(k)})\}$$

with the corresponding $\mathbf{x}_i^{(k)} = \mathbf{x}_l^{(k)}$. Since the polyhedron in E^n is made up of $(n + 1)$ vertices, $\mathbf{x}_1, \ldots, \mathbf{x}_{n+1}$, let $\mathbf{x}_{n+2}$ be the centroid of all the vertices excluding $\mathbf{x}_h$. The coordinates of the centroid are given by

$$x_{n+2,j}^{(k)} = \frac{1}{n}\left[\left(\sum_{i=1}^{n+1} x_{ij}^{(k)}\right) - x_{hj}^{(k)}\right] \qquad j = 1, \ldots, n \tag{4.2-1}$$

where the index j designates each coordinate direction.

The initial polyhedron usually is selected to be a regular simplex (it does not have to be), with point 1 as the origin, or perhaps the centroid as the origin, as in the computer code in Appendix B. The procedure of finding a vertex in E^n at which $f(\mathbf{x})$ has a better value involves four operations:

1. *Reflection.* Reflect $\mathbf{x}_h^{(k)}$ through the centroid by computing

$$\mathbf{x}_{n+3}^{(k)} = \mathbf{x}_{n+2}^{(k)} + \alpha(\mathbf{x}_{n+2}^{(k)} - \mathbf{x}_h^{(k)}) \tag{4.2-2}$$

where $\alpha > 0$ is the reflection coefficient,

$$\mathbf{x}_{n+2}^{(k)} = \text{centroid computed by Eq. (4.2-1)}$$

$$\mathbf{x}_h^{(k)} = \text{vertex at which } f(\mathbf{x}) \text{ is the largest of } (n + 1) \text{ values of } f(\mathbf{x}) \text{ on } k\text{th stage}$$

2. *Expansion.* If $f(\mathbf{x}_{n+3}^{(k)}) \leq f(\mathbf{x}_l^{(k)})$, expand the vector $(\mathbf{x}_{n+3}^{(k)} - \mathbf{x}_{n+2}^{(k)})$ by computing

$$\mathbf{x}_{n+4}^{(k)} = \mathbf{x}_{n+2}^{(k)} + \gamma(\mathbf{x}_{n+3}^{(k)} - \mathbf{x}_{n+2}^{(k)}) \tag{4.2-3}$$

where $\gamma > 1$ is the expansion coefficient. If $f(\mathbf{x}_{n+4}^{(k)}) < f(\mathbf{x}_l^{(k)})$, replace $\mathbf{x}_h^{(k)}$ by $\mathbf{x}_{n+4}^{(k)}$ and continue from step 1 with $k = k + 1$. Otherwise, replace $\mathbf{x}_h^{(k)}$ by $\mathbf{x}_{n+3}^{(k)}$ and continue from step 1 with $k = k + 1$.

3. *Contractions.* If $f(\mathbf{x}_{n+3}^{(k)}) > f(\mathbf{x}_i^{(k)})$ for all $i \neq h$, contract the vector $(\mathbf{x}_h^{(k)} - \mathbf{x}_{n+2}^{(k)})$ by computing

$$\mathbf{x}_{n+5}^{(k)} = \mathbf{x}_{n+2}^{(k)} + \beta(\mathbf{x}_h^{(k)} - \mathbf{x}_{n+2}^{(k)}) \tag{4.2-4}$$

where $0 < \beta < 1$ is the contraction coefficient. Replace $\mathbf{x}_h^{(k)}$ by $\mathbf{x}_{n+5}^{(k)}$ and return to step 1 to continue the search on the $(k + 1)$st stage.

4. *Reduction.* If $f(\mathbf{x}_{n+3}^{(k)}) > f(\mathbf{x}_h^{(k)})$, reduce all the vectors $(\mathbf{x}_i^{(k)} - \mathbf{x}_l^{(k)})$, $i = 1, \ldots, n + 1$, by one-half from $\mathbf{x}_l^{(k)}$ by computing

$$\mathbf{x}_i^{(k)} = \mathbf{x}_l^{(k)} + 0.5(\mathbf{x}_i^{(k)} - \mathbf{x}_l^{(k)}) \qquad i = 1, \ldots, n + 1 \tag{4.2-5}$$

and return to step 1 to continue the search on the $(k + 1)$st stage.

The criterion used by Nelder and Mead to terminate the search was to test to determine if

$$\left\{\frac{1}{n+1}\sum_{i=1}^{n+1}[f(\mathbf{x}_i^{(k)}) - f(\mathbf{x}_{n+2}^{(k)})]^2\right\}^{\frac{1}{2}} \leq \varepsilon \tag{4.2-6}$$

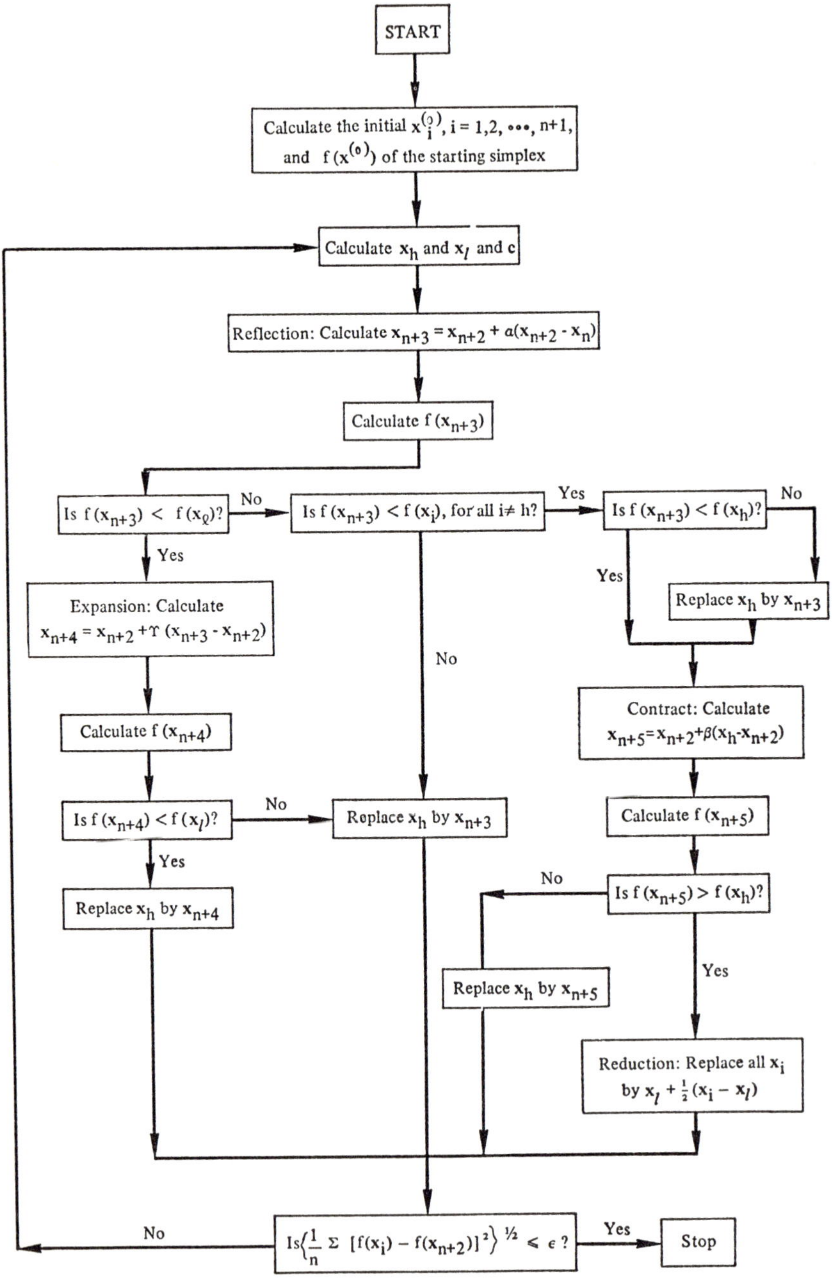

Fig. 4.2-3 Information flow chart for flexible polygon search.

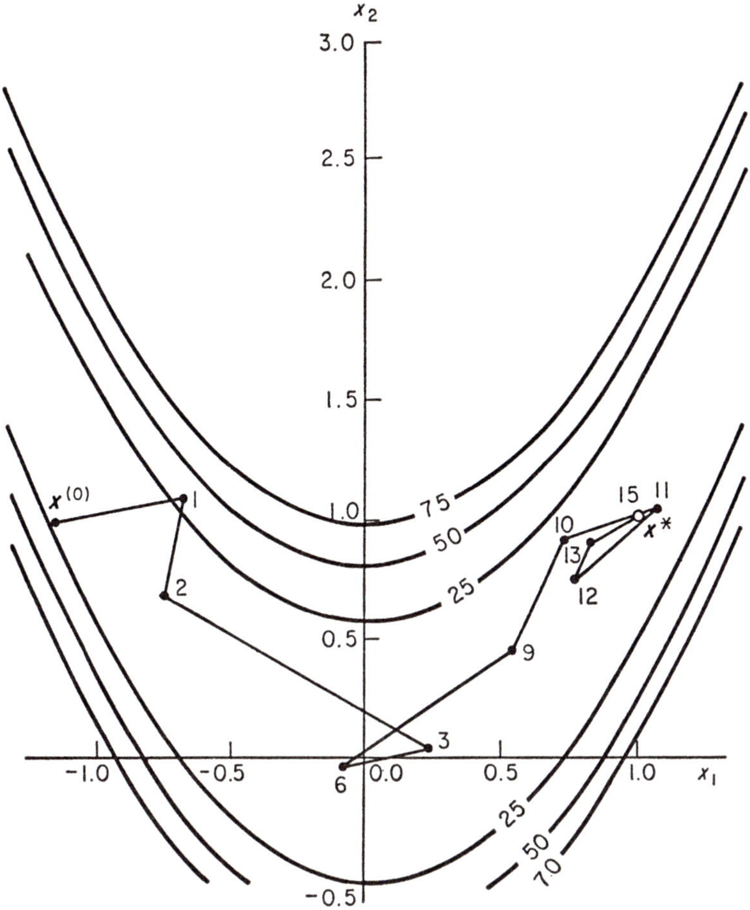

Fig. 4.2-4 Flexible polygon search for the minimum of Rosenbrock's function from $\mathbf{x}^{(0)} = [-1.2 \quad 1.0]^T$ (the numbers represent the number of the stage).

where ε is an arbitrarily small number, and $f(\mathbf{x}_{n+2}^{(k)})$ is the value of the objective function at the centroid $\mathbf{x}_{n+2}^{(k)}$.

Figure 4.2-3 is an information flow diagram of the flexible polygon method, and Fig. 4.2-4 illustrates the progress of the search starting at $\mathbf{x}^{(0)} = [-1.2 \quad 1.0]^T$ for Rosenbrock's function. The flexible polyhedron, as opposed to the rigid simplex, is designed to adapt itself to the topography of the objective function, elongating down long inclined planes, changing directions in curving valleys, and contracting in the neighborhood of a minimum.

The reflection coefficient α is used to project the vertex with the largest value of $f(\mathbf{x})$ through the centroid of the flexible polyhedron. The expansion coefficient γ is used to elongate the search vector if the reflection has produced a vertex with a value of $f(\mathbf{x})$ smaller than the smallest $f(\mathbf{x})$ obtained prior to the reflection. The contraction coefficient β is used to reduce the search vector if the reflection has not produced a vertex with a value of $f(\mathbf{x})$ smaller than the second largest value of $f(\mathbf{x})$ obtained prior to the reflection. Therefore, by means of either expansions or contractions, the size and shape of the flexible polyhedron are scaled to fit into the particular topology of the problem being solved.

A question naturally arises as to what values should be selected for the parameters α, β, and γ. Once the flexible polyhedron has been scaled appropriately, its size should be maintained unchanged until a change in the topology of the problem calls for a different-shape polyhedron. This is possible only if $\alpha = 1$. In addition, Nelder and Mead demonstrated that less functional evaluations were required to solve a problem with $\alpha = 1$ than with $\alpha < 1$. On the other hand, α should not be much greater than unity because (1) the flexible polyhedron is more easily adapted to the topology of the problem if a small value of α is used, particularly when it is necessary to change the direction of search because a curved valley has been encountered, and (2) the size of the polyhedron must be reduced at a local minimum, and a large α will slow the convergence. Therefore the value of $\alpha = 1$ should be chosen as a compromise.

To determine what effect the choice of β and γ have on the progress of the search, Nelder and Mead, and also Paviani,[1] solved several test problems using a large number of different combinations of values for β and γ. Nelder and Mead recommended the values of $\alpha = 1$, $\beta = 0.5$, and $\gamma = 2$ as being generally satisfactory for unconstrained minimization. The size and orientation of the initial polyhedron had some effect on the amount of computer time required, but appropriate values for α, β, and γ were considerably more influential. Paviani observed that there was no clear-cut decision as to the choices of β and γ, and that the effect of the choice of β on the efficiency of the search was slightly more pronounced than that of γ. Table 4.2-1 lists typical results for Test Problem 3 (in Appendix A), in which the Nelder and Mead algorithm was used as the optimizing subroutine. Paviani recommended as conservative choices the following:

$$0.4 \leq \beta \leq 0.6$$

$$2.8 \leq \gamma \leq 3.0$$

[1] D. Paviani, Ph.D. dissertation, The University of Texas, Austin, Tex., 1969.

Table 4.2-1 The effect of the values of β and γ on the solution of test problem 3 (Appendix A)†

β	γ	$f(\mathbf{x}^*)$	*No. of stages, k*	*Execution time,* sec	*Accuracy* $\mathbf{x}^*$ *and* $f(\mathbf{x}^*)$
0.2	3	58.903	90	0.381	2.7×10^{-7}
0.4	3	58.903	55	0.287	7.1×10^{-8}
0.6	3	58.903	81	0.388	2.8×10^{-7}
0.8	3	58.903	95	0.414	9.3×10^{-7}
0.5	2.2	58.903	47	0.238	9.1×10^{-7}
0.5	2.4	58.903	45	0.247	6.5×10^{-7}
0.5	2.6	58.903	49	0.287	8.5×10^{-7}
0.5	2.8	58.903	57	0.304	8.1×10^{-7}
0.5	3.0	58.903	70	0.343	8.6×10^{-7}
0.5	3.2	58.903	46	0.266	8.5×10^{-7}

†Values of the other parameters used to solve Test Problem 3 were

$$\alpha = 1 \qquad t = 0.5 \qquad \varepsilon = 10^{-5}$$

The initial vector was $\mathbf{x}^{(0)} = [90 \quad 10]^T$.

With $0 < \beta < 0.4$, there is the possibility that premature termination can take place because of flattening of the polyhedron. With $\beta > 0.6$, the search may require an excessive number of stages and computer time to reach the final solution of the problem.

Example 4.2-1 Flexible polygon search

To illustrate the method of Nelder and Mead, consider the minimization of the function $f(\mathbf{x}) = 4(x_1 - 5)^2 + (x_2 - 6)^2$ that has a minimum at $\mathbf{x}^* = [5 \quad 6]^T$. Because two variables are involved in $f(\mathbf{x})$, a polygon with three vertices is used to initiate the search. In this example a triangle with vertices at $\mathbf{x}_1^{(0)} = [8 \quad 9]^T$, $\mathbf{x}_2^{(0)} = [10 \quad 11]^T$, and $x_3^{(0)} = [8 \quad 11]^T$ is set up, although any configuration of three points could be used as the initial polyhedron.

For the zeroth stage of the search, $k = 0$; we compute $f(8,9) = 45, f(10,11) = 125$, and $f(8,11) = 65$. Then we reflect $\mathbf{x}_2^{(0)} = [10 \quad 11]^T$ through the centroid of $\mathbf{x}_1^{(0)}$ and $\mathbf{x}_3^{(0)}$ [computed from Eq. (4.2-1)], namely, $\mathbf{x}_4^{(0)}$.

$$x_{4,1}^{(0)} = \tfrac{1}{2}[(8 + 10 + 8) - 10] = 8$$
$$x_{4,2}^{(0)} = \tfrac{1}{2}[(9 + 11 + 11) - 11] = 10$$

to obtain $x_5^{(0)}$.

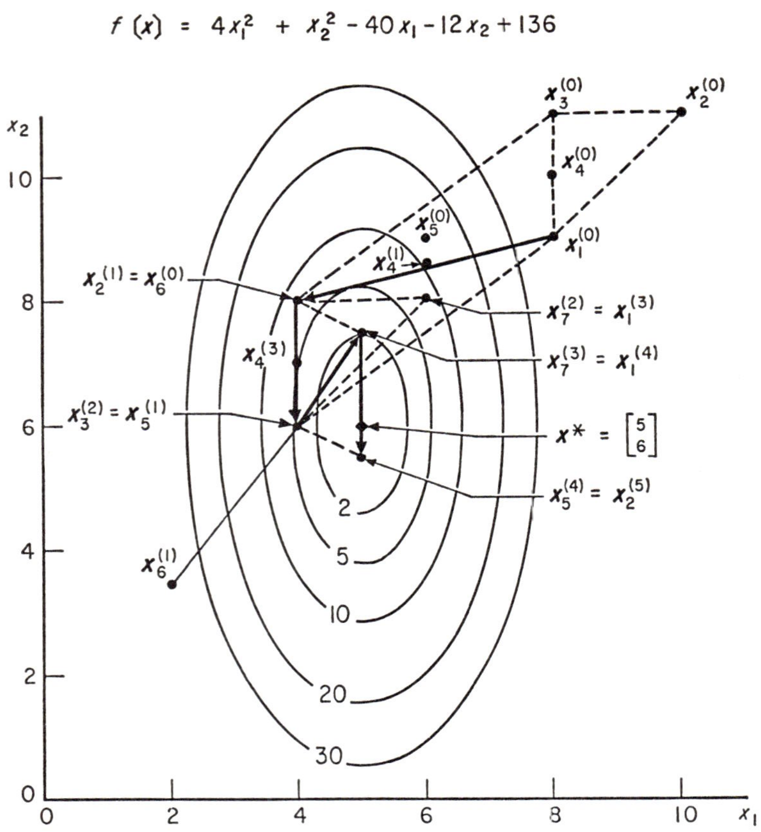

Fig. E4.2–1*a* The unconstrained method of Nelder and Mead.

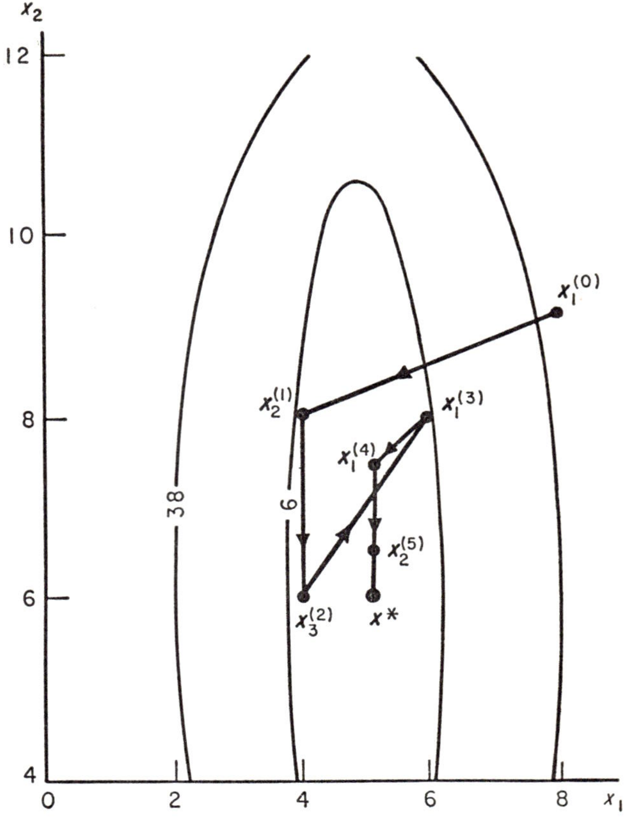

Fig. E4.2–1*b* Trajectory of the search by the Nelder and Mead algorithm.

Table E4.2-1 Five stages of calculation by the method of Nelder and Mead to minimize $f(\mathbf{x}) = 4(x_1 - 5)^2 + (x_2 - 6)^2$

Stage	Vertices of the polyhedron			Values of $f(\mathbf{x})$	Remarks
		x_1	x_2		
0	$x_1^{(0)}$	8	9	45	$\mathbf{x}_l = \mathbf{x}_1^{(0)}$
0	$x_2^{(0)}$	10	11	125	$x_h = \mathbf{x}_2^{(0)}$
0	$x_3^{(0)}$	8	11	65	
0	$x_5^{(0)}$	6	9	13	Obtained by reflection by Eq. (4.2-2)
0	$x_2^{(1)} = x_6^{(0)}$	4	8	8	Obtained by expansion by Eq. (4.2-3); replace $x_2^{(0)}$ by $x_6^{(0)} = x_2^{(1)}$
1	$x_3^{(2)} = x_5^{(1)}$	4	6	4	Replace $x_3^{(0)}$ by $x_5^{(1)} = x_3^{(2)}$
2	$x_1^{(3)} = x_7^{(2)}$	6	8	8	Replace $x_1^{(0)}$ by $x_7^{(3)} = x_1^{(4)}$
3	$x_1^{(4)} = x_7^{(3)}$	5	7.5	2.25	Replace $x_1^{(3)}$ by $x_7^{(4)}$
4	$x_2^{(5)} = x_5^{(4)}$	5	5.5	0.25	Replace $x_2^{(1)}$ by $x_5^{(5)}$

$$x_{5,1}^{(0)} = 8 + 1(8 - 10) = 6$$

$$x_{5,2}^{(0)} = 10 + 1(10 - 11) = 9$$

and

$$f(6,9) = 13$$

Because $f(6,9) = 13 < f(8,9) = 45$, an expansion takes place next.

$$x_{6,1}^{(0)} = 8 + 2(6 - 8) = 4$$

$$x_{6,2}^{(0)} = 10 + 2(9 - 10) = 8$$

$$f(4,8) = 8$$

Because $f(4,8) = 8 < f(8,9) = 45$, we replace $\mathbf{x}_2^{(0)}$ by $\mathbf{x}_6^{(0)}$, and will designate $\mathbf{x}_6^{(0)}$ as $\mathbf{x}_2^{(1)}$ on the next stage of the search.

Finally, because

$$\tfrac{1}{3}[7^2 + 13^2 + 44^2]^{\frac{1}{2}} = 26.8 > 10^{-6}$$

stage $k = 1$ of the search is begun. Figure E4.2–1*a* illustrates the path of the search in its initial stages and Table E4.2–1 tabulates the coordinates of the vertices and the values of $f(\mathbf{x})$ for four additional stages of search. Figure E4.2–1*b* shows the entire search trajectory to termination. It took 32 stages to reduce $f(\mathbf{x})$ to 1×10^{-6}.

4.3 METHODS OF ROSENBROCK AND DAVIES, SWANN, AND CAMPEY

Rosenbrock's method[1] is an iterative procedure that bears some correspondence to the exploratory search of Hooke and Jeeves (described in Sec. 4.1) in that small steps are taken during the search in orthogonal coordinates. However, instead of continually searching the coordinates corresponding to the directions of the independent variables, an improvement can be made after one cycle of coordinate search by lining the search directions up into an orthogonal system, with the overall step on the previous stage as the first building block for the new search coordinates. Rosenbrock's method locates $x^{(k+1)}$ by successive unidimensional searches from an initial point $x^{(k)}$ along a set of *orthonormal directions* $\mathbf{s}_1^{(k)}, \ldots, \mathbf{s}_n^{(k)}$ generated by the Gram-Schmidt procedure, so that the search directions tend to line up with the principal axes of the quadratic approximate to the objective function. Since these axes are the eigenvectors of $\mathbf{H}(\mathbf{x})$ and form a special case of conjugate directions, the method behaves somewhat like a conjugate direction method in its convergence behavior if applied to a quadratic approximate of the objective function.

The method is executed as follows. Let $\hat{\mathbf{s}}_1^{(k)}, \ldots, \hat{\mathbf{s}}_n^{(k)}$ be unit vectors in E^n, where $k = 0, 1, \ldots$ identifies the stages of the search. The orthonormal vectors $\hat{\mathbf{s}}_1^{(k)}, \ldots, \hat{\mathbf{s}}_n^{(k)}$ are generated from information obtained on the $(k-1)$st stage as given by Eq. (4.3–1) and (4.3–2) below. For the initial stage, $k = 0$, the directions $\hat{\mathbf{s}}_1^{(0)}, \ldots, \hat{\mathbf{s}}_n^{(0)}$ are usually taken to be parallel to the axes of $x_1, \ldots, x_n$. In general, the orthogonal search directions can be expressed as combinations of all the coordinates of the independent variables as follows:

$$\begin{aligned}
\hat{\mathbf{s}}_1^{(k)} &= a_{11}^{(k)}\boldsymbol{\delta}_1 + a_{12}^{(k)}\boldsymbol{\delta}_2 + \cdots + a_{1n}^{(k)}\boldsymbol{\delta}_n \\
\hat{\mathbf{s}}_2^{(k)} &= a_{21}^{(k)}\boldsymbol{\delta}_1 + a_{22}^{(k)}\boldsymbol{\delta}_2 + \cdots + a_{2n}^{(k)}\boldsymbol{\delta}_n \\
&\cdots\cdots\cdots\cdots\cdots\cdots\cdots\cdots \\
\hat{\mathbf{s}}_n^{(k)} &= a_{n1}^{(k)}\boldsymbol{\delta}_1 + a_{n2}^{(k)}\boldsymbol{\delta}_2 + \cdots + a_{nn}^{(k)}\boldsymbol{\delta}_n
\end{aligned}$$

where $\boldsymbol{\delta}_i$ is a unit vector in the x_i direction, and the a_{ij} are termed the direction cosines of $\hat{\mathbf{s}}_i$. In matrix notation

$$\hat{\mathbf{s}}^{(k)} = \mathbf{a}^{(k)}\boldsymbol{\delta}$$

On the kth stage, let $\mathbf{x}_0^{(k)} = \mathbf{x}_n^{(k-1)}$ be the point in E^n at which the search is initiated. Let $\lambda_1, \ldots, \lambda_n$ be the respective step lengths associated with the directions $\hat{\mathbf{s}}_1, \ldots, \hat{\mathbf{s}}_n$.

From $\mathbf{x}_0^{(k)}$ the search begins by making a perturbation $\lambda_1^{(k)}\hat{\mathbf{s}}_1^{(k)}$ in the first

[1] H. H. Rosenbrock, *Computer J.*, **3**:175 (1960).

coordinate direction in the sequence. If the value of $f(\mathbf{x}_0^{(k)} + \lambda_1^{(k)}\hat{\mathbf{s}}_1^{(k)})$ is equal to or less than $f(\mathbf{x}_0^{(k)})$, the step is deemed a success and the trial point replaces $\mathbf{x}_0^{(k)}$, $\lambda_1^{(k)}$ is multiplied by a factor $\alpha > 0$, and the search direction $\hat{\mathbf{s}}_2^{(k)}$ is perturbed next. If the value of $f(\mathbf{x}_0^{(k)} + \lambda_1^{(k)}\hat{\mathbf{s}}_1^{(k)})$ is greater than $f(\mathbf{x}_0^{(k)})$, the step is deemed a failure, $\mathbf{x}_0^{(k)}$ is not replaced, $\lambda_1^{(k)}$ is multiplied by a factor $\beta < 0$, and the search direction $\hat{\mathbf{s}}_2^{(k)}$ is perturbed next. Rosenbrock recommended that $\alpha = 3$ and $\beta = -0.5$ for general programming.

After each of the n search directions $\hat{\mathbf{s}}_1^{(k)}, \ldots, \hat{\mathbf{s}}_n^{(k)}$ has been perturbed, the first direction $\hat{\mathbf{s}}_1^{(k)}$ is perturbed again, with a magnitude of the step length equal to $\alpha\lambda^{(k)}$, or $\beta\lambda^{(k)}$, depending upon the outcome of the most recent perturbation in the $\hat{\mathbf{s}}_1^{(k)}$ direction. Perturbations are continued sequentially in the search directions until a success is followed by a failure in every direction, at which time the kth stage is terminated. Since an equal value of a function counts as a success, a success is eventually reached in each direction as the multipliers of $\lambda_i^{(k)}$ reduce the magnitude of the step length. The final point obtained becomes the initial point for the succeeding stage, $\mathbf{x}_0^{(k+1)} = \mathbf{x}_n^{(k)}$. The normalized direction $\hat{\mathbf{s}}_1^{(k+1)}$ is chosen parallel to $(\mathbf{x}_0^{(k+1)} - \mathbf{x}_0^{(k)})$, and the remaining directions are chosen orthonormal to each other and to $\hat{\mathbf{s}}_1^{(k+1)}$ by one of the methods to be described shortly.

Davies, Swann, and Campey (DSC), as described by Swann,[1] modified the Rosenbrock search in the $\mathbf{s}_1^{(k)}, \ldots, \mathbf{s}_n^{(k)}$ directions by locating the minimum of $f(\mathbf{x})$ in each of the directions $\mathbf{s}_i^{(k)}$, much in the manner of the Davidon-Fletcher-Powell search. For clarity, let $\mathbf{x}_i^{(k)}$ indicate the point at which $f(\mathbf{x}_i^{(k)})$ is a minimum in the direction $\mathbf{s}_i^{(k)}$. For each stage (k) there are n vectors $\mathbf{x}_i^{(k)}$ and n optimal values of the objective function $f(\mathbf{x}_i^{(k)})$. From $\mathbf{x}_0^{(k)}$, determine $\lambda_1^{*(k)}$ in the direction of $\mathbf{s}_1^{(k)}$ so that $f(\mathbf{x}_0^{(k)} + \lambda_1^{*(k)}\mathbf{s}_1^{(k)})$ is a minimum. Let $\mathbf{x}_1^{(k)} = \mathbf{x}_0^{(k)} + \lambda_1^{*(k)}\mathbf{s}_1^{(k)}$. From $\mathbf{x}_1^{(k)}$, determine $\lambda_2^{*(k)}$ so that $f(\mathbf{x}_1^{(k)} + \lambda_2^{*(k)}\mathbf{s}_2^{(k)})$ is a minimum. Let $\mathbf{x}_2^{(k)} = \mathbf{x}_1^{(k)} + \lambda_2^{*(k)}\mathbf{s}_2^{(k)}$.

The search pattern is generalized as follows. From $\mathbf{x}_{i-1}^{(k)}$, determine $\lambda_i^{*(k)}$ in the direction of $\mathbf{s}_i^{(k)}$ so that $f(\mathbf{x}_{i-1}^{(k)} + \lambda_i^{*(k)}\mathbf{s}_i^{(k)})$ is a minimum and let $\mathbf{x}_i^{(k)} = \mathbf{x}_{i-1}^{(k)} + \lambda_i^{*(k)}\mathbf{s}_i^{(k)}$. The search is repeated sequentially, always starting from the last immediate point in the sequence until all $\mathbf{x}_i$, $i = 1, \ldots, n$, are determined. Davies, Swann, and Campey used the linear search algorithm described in Sec. 2.6 to determine $\lambda_i^{*(k)}$. However, any effective one-dimensional search technique can be used instead.

After the kth stage has been completed by either the original Rosenbrock method or the DSC variation, the vectors for the new search directions must

[1] W. H. Swann, Report on the Development of a New Direct Search Method of Optimization, *Imperial Chemical Industries, Ltd. Central Instr. Lab. Res. Note* 6413, 1964.

be computed at the point $\mathbf{x}_0^{(k+1)} = \mathbf{x}_n^{(k)}$. In effect, the orthogonal search directions are rotated from the previous search directions so as to line up with a valley (or ridge) and eliminate the interactions between the variables. Let $\Lambda_i^{(k)}$ be the algebraic sum of all the successful steps (the net distance moved) in the direction $\mathbf{s}_i^{(k)}$ during the kth stage; $\Lambda_i^{(k)} = \lambda_i^{*(k)}$ for the DSC approach. Define the n vectors $\mathbf{A}_1, \ldots, \mathbf{A}_n$ as follows:

$$
\begin{aligned}
\mathbf{A}_1^{(k)} &= \Lambda_1^{(k)}\mathbf{s}_1^{(k)} + \Lambda_2^{(k)}\mathbf{s}_2^{(k)} + \cdots + \Lambda_n^{(k)}\mathbf{s}_n^{(k)} \\
\mathbf{A}_2^{(k)} &= \qquad\qquad \Lambda_2^{(k)}\mathbf{s}_2^{(k)} + \cdots + \Lambda_n^{(k)}\mathbf{s}_n^{(k)} \\
&\cdots\cdots\cdots\cdots\cdots\cdots\cdots\cdots \\
\mathbf{A}_n^{(k)} &= \qquad\qquad\qquad\qquad\qquad \Lambda_n^{(k)}\mathbf{s}_n^{(k)}
\end{aligned}
\tag{4.3-1}
$$

Thus $\mathbf{A}_1^{(k)}$ is the vector from $\mathbf{x}_0^{(k)}$ to $\mathbf{x}_0^{(k+1)}$, $\mathbf{A}_2^{(k)}$ is the vector from $\mathbf{x}_1^{(k)}$ to $\mathbf{x}_0^{(k+1)}$, and so on. $\mathbf{A}_1^{(k)}$ represents the overall move from stage k to stage $(k + 1)$, $\mathbf{A}_2^{(k)}$ represents the overall move less the progress made during the search in direction $\mathbf{s}_1^{(k)}$, etc.

In the DSC variation of Rosenbrock's method, to avoid any one of the $\mathbf{s}_i^{(k)}$ from becoming zero (in which case the procedure breaks down—a situation avoided by Rosenbrock's original method), the subscripts associated with Λ and $\mathbf{s}$ in Eq. (4.3–1) are not those of the directions of search in stage k, but represent the directions reordered so that $|\Lambda_1^{(k)}| > |\Lambda_2^{(k)}| > \cdots > |\Lambda_n^{(k)}|$. If any m of the $\Lambda_i^{(k)}$ are zero, new directions are found, as described below only for those $(n - m)$ directions for which $\Lambda_i^{(k)} \neq 0$; the remaining m directions remain unaltered.

$$\mathbf{s}_i^{(k+1)} = \mathbf{s}_i^{(k)} \qquad i = (n - m) + 1, \ldots, n$$

Thus, in the DSC method, the vectors with the nonzero Λ's are assigned the first $(n - m)$ numbers. The first $(n - m)$ vectors are mutually orthogonal, and because $\Lambda_i = 0$ for $i = n - m + 1, \ldots, n$, the first $(n - m)$ vectors will have no components in the directions $\mathbf{s}_i^{(k+1)}$, $i = n - m + 1, \ldots, n$. Because these latter directions themselves are mutually orthogonal, all the directions are mutually orthogonal.

Swann states that, in practice, it was more satisfactory to change the criterion for reordering the directions from $\Lambda_i^{(k)} = 0$ to $|\Lambda_i^{(k)}| < \varepsilon$, where ε is the accuracy desired in $\mathbf{x}$ or $f(\mathbf{x})$. This modification affected the orthogonality of the vectors $\mathbf{s}_i^{(k)}$ very slightly, but insignificantly. Reduction of the step length by 0.1 in the linear search was demonstrated to reduce the number of functional evaluations and was incorporated in the DSC code each time that the distance between $\mathbf{x}_0^{(k)}$ and $\mathbf{x}_1^{(k+1)}$ was less than the step length for the kth stage.

In both methods the new directions are determined as follows. The first unit vector $\hat{\mathbf{s}}_1^{(k+1)}$ of the new set of directions on the $(k + 1)$st stage is aligned with the direction of the net progress on the previous stage, $\mathbf{A}_1^{(k)}$. The remaining directions of search are constructed as mutually orthogonal unit vectors (orthonormal vectors) to $\mathbf{A}_1^{(k)}$ by the Gram-Schmidt method, the details of which can be found in texts on matrix theory and linear algebra. Thus the set of orthonormal directions $\hat{\mathbf{s}}_1^{(k+1)}, \ldots, \hat{\mathbf{s}}_n^{(k+1)}$ for the $(k + 1)$st stage are computed from the following relations:

$$
\begin{aligned}
\hat{\mathbf{s}}_1^{(k+1)} &= \frac{\mathbf{A}_1^{(k)}}{\|\mathbf{A}_1^{(k)}\|} \\
\mathbf{B}_2^{(k)} &= \mathbf{A}_2^{(k)} - [(\mathbf{A}_2^{(k)})^T \quad \hat{\mathbf{s}}_1^{(k+1)}]\hat{\mathbf{s}}_1^{(k+1)} \\
\hat{\mathbf{s}}_2^{(k+1)} &= \frac{\mathbf{B}_2^{(k)}}{\|\mathbf{B}_2^{(k)}\|} \\
&\cdots\cdots\cdots\cdots\cdots\cdots \\
\mathbf{B}_n^{(k)} &= \mathbf{A}_n^{(k)} - \sum_{i=1}^{n-1} [(\mathbf{A}_n^{(k)})^T \quad \hat{\mathbf{s}}_i^{(k+1)}]\hat{\mathbf{s}}_i^{(k+1)} \\
\hat{\mathbf{s}}_n^{(k+1)} &= \frac{\mathbf{B}_n^{(k)}}{\|\mathbf{B}_n^{(k)}\|}
\end{aligned}
\qquad (4.3\text{–}2)
$$

where $\|\mathbf{A}_i\|$ is the normal of $\mathbf{A}_i$. The same search procedure carried out on the kth stage is now repeated for the $(k + 1)$st stage, starting at the point $\mathbf{x}_0^{(k+1)} = \mathbf{x}_n^{(k)}$.

Palmer[1] pointed out that $\mathbf{B}_{j+1}^{(k)}$ and $\|\mathbf{B}_{j+1}^{(k)}\|$ are both proportional to $\Lambda_j^{(k)}$ $\left[\text{provided that } \sum_{i=j}^{n} (\Lambda_i^{(k)})^2 \neq 0\right]$. Consequently, in evaluating $\hat{\mathbf{s}}_j^{(k+1)} = \dfrac{\mathbf{B}_j^{(k)}}{\|\mathbf{B}_j^{(k)}\|}$, the quantity $\Lambda_j^{(k)}$ would cancel, leaving $\hat{\mathbf{s}}_j^{(k+1)}$ determinate even if $\Lambda_j^{(k)} = 0$. Hence Palmer suggested that use of the following relations to compute $\mathbf{s}_i^{(k+1)}$ would save both a considerable number of arithmetic operations and storage space [the proof of the validity of Eq. (4.3–3) is given in Palmer's article]:

$$
\begin{aligned}
\mathbf{A}_i^{(k)} &= \sum_{j=i}^{n} \Lambda_j^{(k)}\hat{\mathbf{s}}_j^{(k)} && 1 \le i \le n \\
\hat{\mathbf{s}}_i^{(k+1)} &= \frac{\mathbf{A}_i^{(k)}\|\mathbf{A}_{i-1}^{(k)}\|^2 - \mathbf{A}_{i-1}^{(k)}\|\mathbf{A}_i^{(k)}\|^2}{\|\mathbf{A}_{i-1}^{(k)}\| \; \|\mathbf{A}_i^{(k)}\| \; [\|\mathbf{A}_{i-1}^{(k)}\|^2 - \|\mathbf{A}_i^{(k)}\|^2]^{1/2}} && 2 \le i \le n \qquad (4.3\text{–}3) \\
\hat{\mathbf{s}}_1^{(k+1)} &= \frac{\mathbf{A}_1^{(k)}}{\|\mathbf{A}_1^{(k)}\|}
\end{aligned}
$$

The elements $\Lambda_i^{(k)}$ do not have to be reordered. If $\Lambda_{i=1}^{(k)} = 0$, then $\hat{\mathbf{s}}_i^{(k+1)} = \hat{\mathbf{s}}_{i-1}^{(k)}$ unless $\sum (\Lambda_i^{(k)})^2 = 0$.

[1] J. R. Palmer, *Computer J.*, **12**:69 (1969).

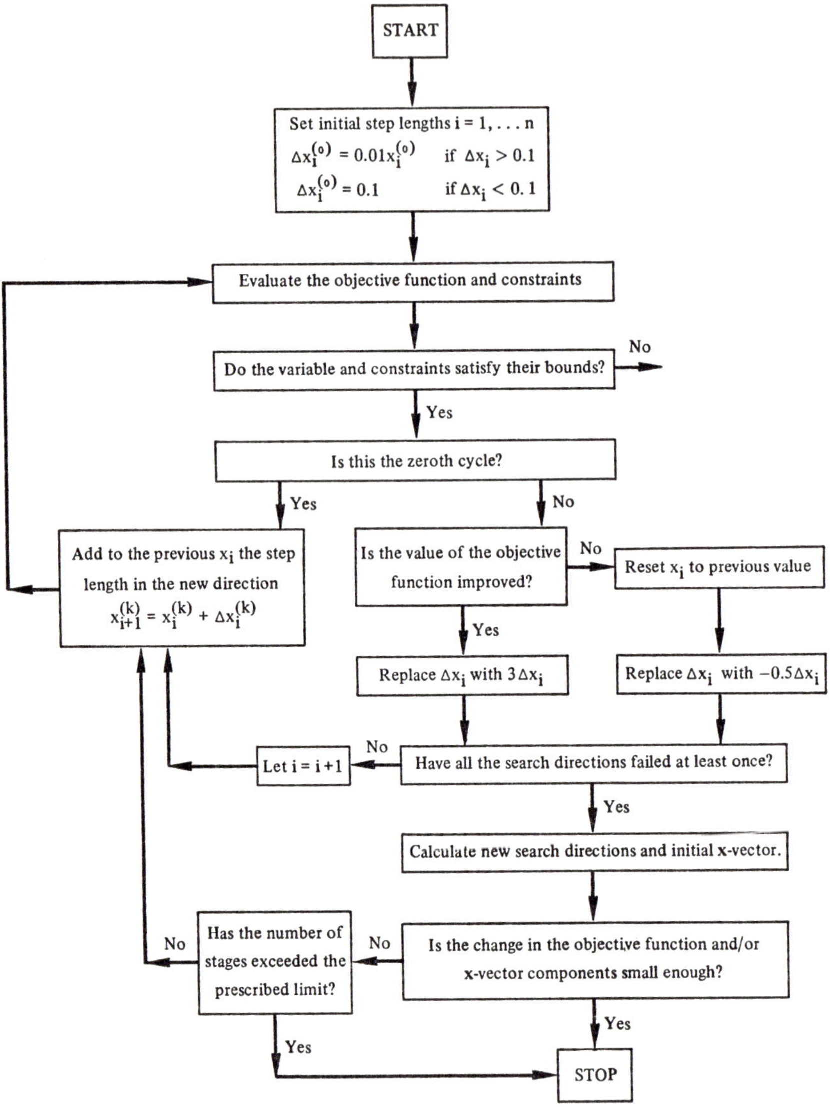

Fig. 4.3-1 Information flow diagram for Rosenbrock's algorithm (omitting the logic used to satisfy constraints).

The original method of Rosenbrock did not make provisions for automatic termination of the search when the extremum of $f(\mathbf{x})$ was found. Either the search was carried out for a specified number of stages k, or else the search was terminated whenever the magnitude of $\mathbf{A}_1$ was less than a specified value for several successive stages. In the DSC version, after each stage, the dis-

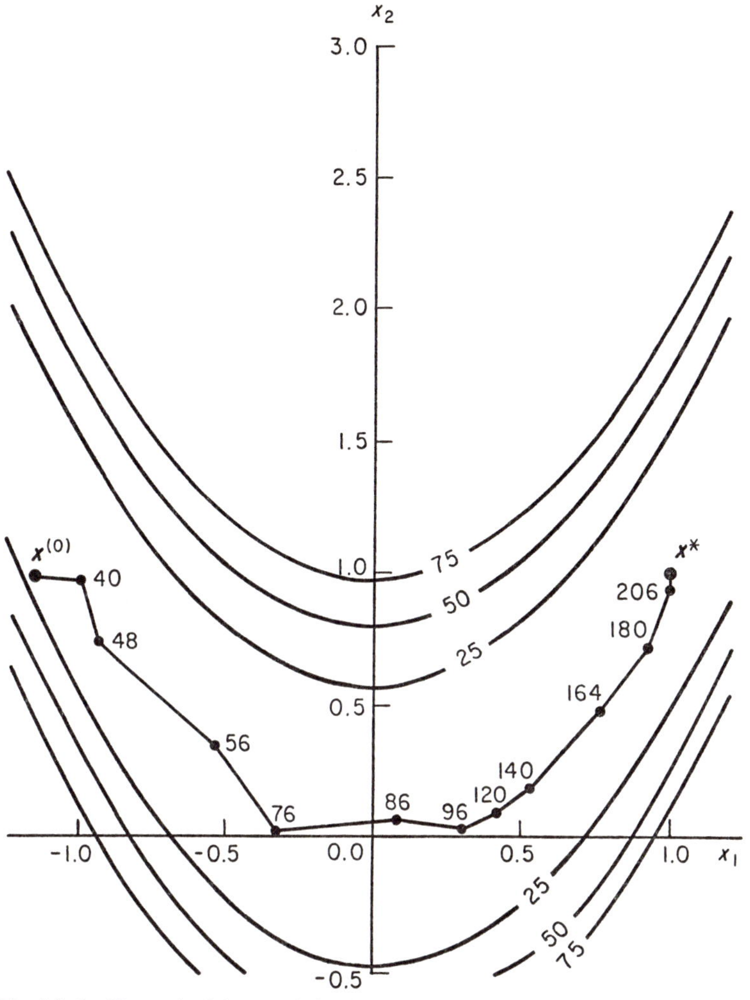

Fig. 4.3–2 The path of the search for the minimization of Rosenbrock's function by the Rosenbrock method (the numbers designate the function evaluation sequence number).

tance $\Lambda_i^{(k)}$ is compared with the step size $\delta_i^{(k)}$ used to obtain $\Lambda_i^{(k)}$ in the linear search. If $\Lambda_i^{(k)} < \delta_i^{(k)}$, $\delta_i^{(k)}$ is divided by 10, and a further search performed in the k old directions with the new δ_i. If $\Lambda_i^{(k)} > \delta_i^{(k)}$, the search starts again on the $(k + 1)$st stage, as described above.

Figure 4.3–1 is an information flow chart for the Rosenbrock algorithm, and Fig. 4.3–2 illustrates the path of the search in the minimization of Rosenbrock's function by the algorithm.

Example 4.3–1 Rosenbrock's method

The Rosenbrock algorithm is illustrated for the problem of Example 3.4–1.

Minimize: $f(\mathbf{x}) = 4(x_1 - 5)^2 + (x_2 - 6)^2$

that has a minimum at $\mathbf{x}^* = [5 \quad 6]^T$, where $f(\mathbf{x}^*) = 0$. (The numbers will be truncated to save space.) We start at $\mathbf{x}^{(0)} = [8 \quad 9]^T$, where $f(\mathbf{x}^{(0)}) = 45.000$, with $\lambda_1 = 0.10$. The initial search ($k = 0$) directions line up with the x_1 and x_2 coordinate directions.

$$\hat{\mathbf{s}}_1^{(0)} = \begin{bmatrix} 1 \\ 0 \end{bmatrix} \qquad \hat{\mathbf{s}}_2^{(0)} = \begin{bmatrix} 0 \\ 1 \end{bmatrix}$$

First $f(\mathbf{x})$ is evaluated at

$$\mathbf{x} = \begin{bmatrix} 8.00 + 0.10(1) \\ 9.00 + 0.10(0) \end{bmatrix} = \begin{bmatrix} 8.10 \\ 9.00 \end{bmatrix}$$

where $f(\mathbf{x}) = 47.44$, yielding a failure. Then $f(\mathbf{x})$ is evaluated at

$$\mathbf{x} = \begin{bmatrix} 8.00 + 0.10(0) \\ 9.00 + 0.10(1) \end{bmatrix} = \begin{bmatrix} 8.00 \\ 9.10 \end{bmatrix}$$

where $f(\mathbf{x}) = 45.61$, yielding another failure. Thus, on the next cycle, both λ_1 and λ_2 will be multiplied by $\beta = -0.5$, or $\lambda_3 = \lambda_4 = -0.50(0.10) = -0.05$. The perturbation starts from the last successful $\mathbf{x}$, or $\mathbf{x} = [8.00 \quad 9.00]^T$.

First $f(\mathbf{x})$ is evaluated at

$$\mathbf{x} = \begin{bmatrix} 8.00 - 0.05(1) \\ 9.00 - 0.05(0) \end{bmatrix} = \begin{bmatrix} 7.95 \\ 9.00 \end{bmatrix}$$

where $f(\mathbf{x}) = 43.81$, giving a success. Then $f(\mathbf{x})$ is evaluated at

$$\mathbf{x} = \begin{bmatrix} 7.95 - 0.05(0) \\ 9.00 - 0.05(1) \end{bmatrix} = \begin{bmatrix} 7.95 \\ 8.95 \end{bmatrix}$$

where $f(\mathbf{x}) = 43.125$, giving another success. On the next cycle each λ is multiplied by 3, $\lambda_5 = \lambda_6 = 3(-0.05) = -0.15$.

Several subsequent cycles of the first stage are as follows:

Search no.	λ	x_1	x_2	$f(\mathbf{x})$	*Success* (S) *or failure* (F)
5	−0.15	7.80	8.95	40.06	S
6	−0.15	7.80	8.80	39.20	S
7	−0.45	7.35	8.80	29.93	S
8	−0.45	7.35	8.35	27.61	S
9	−1.35	6.00	8.35	9.522	S
10	−1.35	6.00	7.00	5.000	S
11	−4.05	1.95	7.00	32.21	F
12	−4.05	6.00	2.95	13.30	F

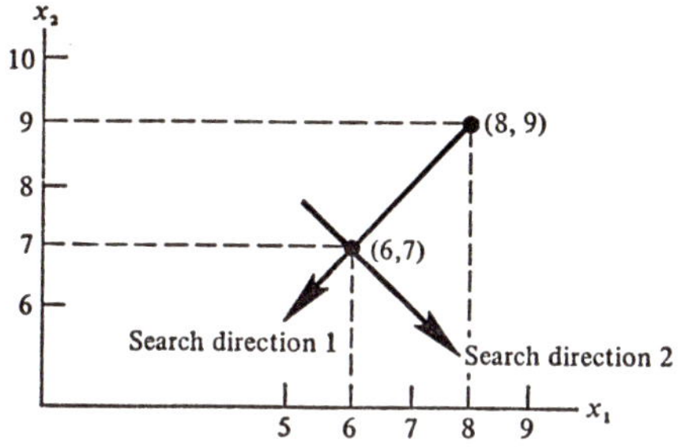

Fig. E4.3-1*a*

A success has now been followed by a failure in each search direction, and the zeroth stage of the search is terminated. New search directions are now computed, with $\hat{\mathbf{s}}_1^{(1)}$ lined up with the vector from $\mathbf{x}_0^{(0)} = [8 \quad 9]^T$ to $\mathbf{x}_0^{(1)} = [6 \quad 7]^T$, the latter point corresponding to the best $f(\mathbf{x})$ obtained in the zeroth stage; $\hat{\mathbf{s}}_2^{(1)}$ is orthonormal to $\hat{\mathbf{s}}_1^{(1)}$; see Fig. E4.3-1*a*. The vectors $\mathbf{A}_1^{(0)}$ and $\mathbf{A}_2^{(0)}$ are computed from Eqs. (4.3-1), and $\hat{\mathbf{s}}_1^{(1)}$ and $\hat{\mathbf{s}}_2^{(1)}$ from Eqs. (4.3-2).

$$\mathbf{A}_1^{(0)} = \begin{bmatrix} -2 \\ -2 \end{bmatrix} \qquad \mathbf{A}_2^{(0)} = \begin{bmatrix} 0 \\ -2 \end{bmatrix}$$

$$\hat{\mathbf{s}}_1^{(1)} = \frac{[-2 \quad -2]^T}{[(-2)^2 + (-2)^2]^{\frac{1}{2}}} = \left[-\frac{1}{\sqrt{2}} \quad -\frac{1}{\sqrt{2}}\right]^T$$

$$\mathbf{B}_2^{(0)} = \begin{bmatrix} 0 \\ -2 \end{bmatrix} - [0 \quad -2] \begin{bmatrix} -1/\sqrt{2} \\ -1/\sqrt{2} \end{bmatrix} \begin{bmatrix} -1/\sqrt{2} \\ -1/\sqrt{2} \end{bmatrix} = \begin{bmatrix} 1 \\ -1 \end{bmatrix}$$

$$\hat{\mathbf{s}}_2^{(1)} = \frac{[1 \quad -1]^T}{[(1)^2 + (-1)^2]^{\frac{1}{2}}} = \begin{bmatrix} 1/\sqrt{2} \\ -1/\sqrt{2} \end{bmatrix}$$

The first cycle on the first stage of the search ($k = 1$) employs a $\lambda_1 = \lambda_2 = -4.05(-0.5) = 2.025$. First $f(\mathbf{x})$ is evaluated in search direction 1 at

$$\mathbf{x} = \begin{bmatrix} 6.000 + (2.025)(-0.706) \\ 7.000 + (2.025)(-0.706) \end{bmatrix} = \begin{bmatrix} 4.568 \\ 5.568 \end{bmatrix}$$

where $f(\mathbf{x}) = 0.9327$, giving a success. Then $f(\mathbf{x})$ is evaluated in search direction 2 at

$$\mathbf{x} = \begin{bmatrix} 4.568 + (2.025) \quad (0.706) \\ 5.688 + (2.025)(-0.706) \end{bmatrix} = \begin{bmatrix} 6.000 \\ 4.136 \end{bmatrix}$$

where $f(\mathbf{x}) = 7.474$, yielding a failure. The remaining data for the first stage are:

Search no.	λ	x_1	x_2	$f(\mathbf{x})$	*Success* (S) *or failure* (F)
3	6.075	0.272	1.272	11.175	F
4	−1.125	3.852	6.284	5.351	F
5	−3.038	6.716	7.716	14.722	F
6	0.506	4.926	5.210	0.646	S
7	1.518	3.852	4.136	8.743	F
8	1.518	6.000	4.136	7.473	F

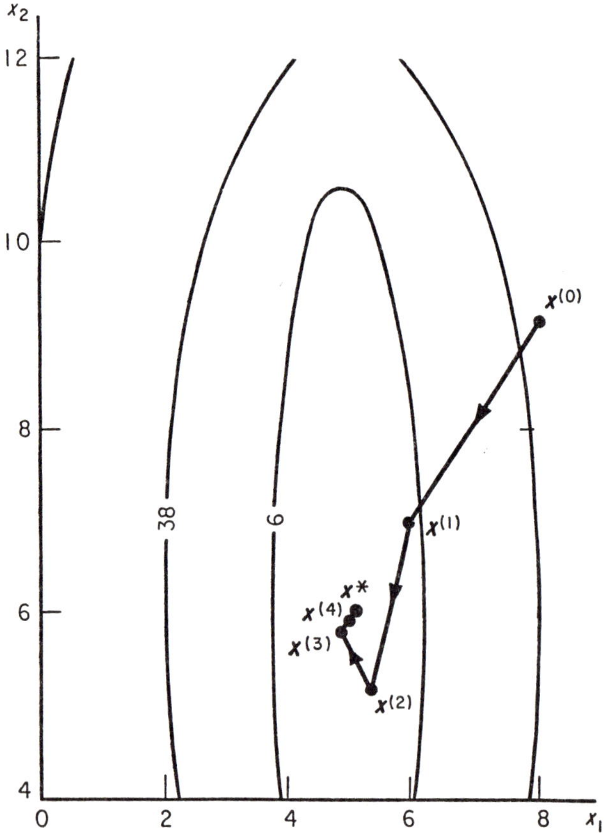

Fig. E4.3-1*b* Trajectory by Rosenbrock's algorithm.

Because the search in direction 1 is a success and that in direction 2 a failure in the first two searches, on searches 3 and 4, $\lambda_3 = 3(2.025) = 6.075$ and $\lambda_4 = -0.5(2.025) = -1.0125$, respectively. Note that after the failure of searches 3 and 4, $\mathbf{x} = 6.075$ is multiplied by -0.5 and $\lambda_4 = -1.0125$ is also multiplied by -0.5 to give λ_5 and λ_6, respectively. After search 6 a success has been obtained in each direction of search, and after search 8 two subsequent failures occurred, so that stage 1 is terminated. A new search direction must now be computed. We shall terminate the example here, but the above procedure is continued until the convergence criterion is satisfied (at 111 functional evaluations, where the fractional deviation in $f(\mathbf{x}^k)$ from the correct value of 0 was 5.5×10^{-11} and the fractional deviation in x_1 was 3.0×10^{-6} and in x_2 was 4.4×10^{-6}).

Figure E4.3-1*b* illustrates how the bulk of the minimization was achieved in the first four stages (34 function evaluations), by which time $\mathbf{x}^{(4)} = [5.036 \quad 5.938]^T$ and $f(\mathbf{x}^{(4)}) = 9.46 \times 10^{-3}$. The remaining 77 function evaluations were used to increase the precision in $\mathbf{x}$ and $f(\mathbf{x})$.

4.4 POWELL'S METHOD

Powell's method,[1] which evolved from that of Smith,[2] locates the minimum of $f(\mathbf{x})$ of a quadratic function with $\mathbf{H} > \mathbf{0}$ by successive unidimensional searches from an initial point $\mathbf{x}_0^{(k)}$ along a set of *conjugate directions* generated by the procedure. Recall from Sec. 3.3-1 that two directions of search, $\mathbf{s}_j$ and $\mathbf{s}_i$, are said to be conjugate if

$$(\mathbf{s}_j)^T\mathbf{Q}\mathbf{s}_i = 0 \qquad i \neq j$$

$$(\mathbf{s}_j)^T\mathbf{Q}\mathbf{s}_i \geq 0 \qquad i = j$$

where $\mathbf{Q} = \nabla^2 f(\mathbf{x}^{(k)})$ is a positive definite square matrix.

We use subscripts here to distinguish among the vectors on one stage (the latter denoted by the superscript). The motivation for Powell's algorithm rests essentially on the idea that if the minimum of the quadratic function $f(\mathbf{x})$ is found along each of $p(p < n)$ conjugate directions in one stage of the search, and if a step is accordingly made in each direction, the overall step from the start to the pth step is conjugate to all the p subdirections of search. Thus the method is analogous to the Partan method described in Sec. 3.3-3.

The transition from a point $\mathbf{x}_0^{(k)}$ to a point $\mathbf{x}_m^{(k)}$ is given by

$$\mathbf{x}_m^{(k)} = \mathbf{x}_0^{(k)} + \sum_{i=0}^{m-1} \lambda_i^{(k)}\mathbf{s}_i^{(k)} \qquad i = 1, \ldots, m-1 \tag{4.4-1}$$

[1] M. J. D. Powell, *Computer J.*, **7**:155 (1964); **7**:303 (1965).

[2] C. S. Smith, The Automatic Computation of Maximum Likelihood Estimates, *NCB Sci. Dept. Rept.* SC846/MR/40, 1962.

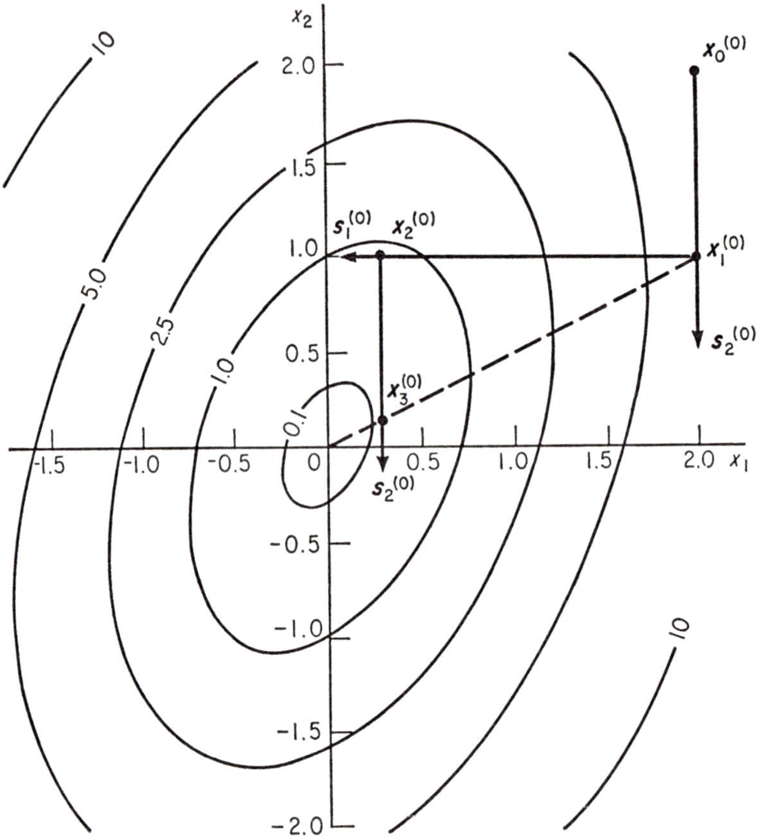

Fig. 4.4–1 Powell's method of search.

The essence of the procedure is as follows. At a vector $\mathbf{x}_0^{(0)}$ in E^n the initial $\mathbf{s}_1^{(0)}, \ldots, \mathbf{s}_n^{(0)}$ are taken to be parallel to the coordinate axis of E^n. A first step is taken in the $\mathbf{s}_n^{(0)}$ direction; that is, $f(\mathbf{x}_0^{(0)} + \lambda\mathbf{s}_n^{(0)})$ is minimized by a unidimensional search with respect to λ to evaluate $\lambda_0^{(0)}$. Then $\mathbf{x}_1^{(0)} = \mathbf{x}_0^{(0)} + \lambda_0^{(0)}\mathbf{s}_n^{(0)}$. Figure 4.4–1 indicates that $\mathbf{x}_1^{(0)}$ is the first minimum located. Next, for each of the n directions $\mathbf{s}_i^{(0)}$, $i = 1, \ldots, n$, in turn $f(\mathbf{x}_i^{(0)} + \lambda\mathbf{s}_i^{(0)})$ is minimized to find $\lambda_i^{(0)}$, and Eq. (4.4–1) applied to compute successively new values of $\mathbf{x}_i^{(0)}$. Figure 4.4–1 demonstrates the location of $x_0^{(0)}$, $x_1^{(0)}$, $x_2^{(0)}$, and $x_3^{(0)}$ for an objective function of two independent variables:

$$f(\mathbf{x}) = 2x_1^2 + x_2^2 - x_1x_2$$

The coordinates of E^n have the directions

$$\mathbf{s}_1^{(0)} = \begin{bmatrix} 1 \\ 0 \end{bmatrix} \qquad \mathbf{s}_2^{(0)} = \begin{bmatrix} 0 \\ 1 \end{bmatrix}$$

and are orthogonal, that is, $(\mathbf{s}_1^{(0)})^T\mathbf{s}_2^{(0)} = 0$, but are not conjugate because $(\mathbf{s}_1^{(0)})^T\mathbf{H}\mathbf{s}_2^{(0)} = 4 \neq 0$. The respective minima of $f(\mathbf{x})$ are located as indicated in the following data:

Iteration	$(\mathbf{s}_i^{(0)})^T$	$\lambda_i^{(0)}$		$(\mathbf{x}_{i+1}^{(0)})^T$	$f(\mathbf{x}_{i+1}^{(0)})$ *at minimum*
0	[0 1]	−1		[2 1]	7
1	[1 0]	−1.75		[0.25 1]	0.875
2	[0 1]	−0.875		[0.25 0.125]	0.109

To see how conjugate directions are involved in Powell's algorithm, we make use of the following theorem for quadratic objective functions:

Theorem

If, starting at $\mathbf{x}^{(0)}$, the point $\mathbf{x}^{(a)}$ is located in the direction $\mathbf{s}$ at the minimum of $f(\mathbf{x})$, and if, starting from the point $\mathbf{x}^{(1)} \neq \mathbf{x}^{(0)}$, the point $\mathbf{x}^{(b)}$ is located in the same direction $\mathbf{s}$ at the minimum of $f(\mathbf{x})$, then, if $f(\mathbf{x}^{(b)}) < f(\mathbf{x}^{a})$, the direction $(\mathbf{x}^{(b)} - \mathbf{x}^{(a)})$ is conjugate to $\mathbf{s}$.

Proof of the theorem is as follows. Equation (3.3–7) has shown that, for the first search,

$$\mathbf{s}^T\nabla f(\mathbf{x}^{(a)}) = \mathbf{s}^T(\mathbf{H}\mathbf{x}^{(a)} + \mathbf{b}) = 0$$

and for the second,

$$\mathbf{s}^T\nabla f(\mathbf{x}^{(b)}) = \mathbf{s}^T(\mathbf{H}\mathbf{x}^{(b)} + \mathbf{b}) = 0$$

By subtraction,

$$\mathbf{s}^T\mathbf{H}(\mathbf{x}^{(b)} - \mathbf{x}^{(a)}) = 0$$

Hence $\mathbf{s}$ and $(\mathbf{x}^{(b)} - \mathbf{x}^{(a)})$ are conjugate. Figure 4.4–1 indicates that

$$(\mathbf{x}_3^{(0)} - \mathbf{x}_2^{(0)})^T\mathbf{H}(\mathbf{x}_3^{(0)} - \mathbf{x}_1^{(0)}) = 0$$

where $\mathbf{x}_0^{(0)}$ corresponds to $\mathbf{x}^{(0)}$ in the theorem, and any point on the line $(\mathbf{x}_3^{(0)} - \mathbf{x}_2^{(0)})$ corresponds to $\mathbf{x}^{(1)}$ in the theorem, or specifically,

$$[(0.25 - 0.25)(0.125 - 1.000)]\begin{bmatrix} 4 & -1 \\ -1 & 2 \end{bmatrix}\begin{bmatrix} (0.25 - 2.00) \\ (0.125 - 1.000) \end{bmatrix} = 0$$

The theorem can be directly extended to several conjugate directions so that if, from $\mathbf{x}^{(0)}$, $\mathbf{x}^{(a)}$ is found after p conjugate directions are employed $(p < n)$, and similarly, from $\mathbf{x}^{(1)}$, $\mathbf{x}^{(b)}$ is found using the same directions, and on each individual step $f(\mathbf{x})$ is minimized, the vector $(\mathbf{x}^{(b)} - \mathbf{x}^{(a)})$ is conjugate to all the p directions.

We now have located two conjugate directions in which to search; hence direction $\mathbf{s}_1^{(0)}$ will be replaced by the direction $(\mathbf{x}_3^{(0)} - \mathbf{x}_1^{(0)})$, the overall progress from the first minimum, and the direction $\mathbf{s}_1^{(0)}$ is not used on the next stage. On the next stage the search directions will be

$$\mathbf{s}_1^1 = \mathbf{s}_2^{(0)}$$

$$\mathbf{s}_2^1 = (\mathbf{x}_3^{(0)} - \mathbf{x}_1^{(0)})$$

The search starts over by minimizing along the $\mathbf{s}_2^{(1)}$ direction, and then the steps in the $\mathbf{s}_1^{(1)}$ and $\mathbf{s}_2^{(1)}$ directions are executed, if necessary. (However, recall that after two *conjugate* directions are employed, the minimum is reached for a quadratic objective function of two variables, as in Fig. 4.4–1.)

Powell's algorithm is slightly different from the simple initial steps outlined above and will be described next.

In general, the kth stage of Powell's method employs n linearly independent search directions and can be considered to be initiated at $\mathbf{x}_0^{(k)} = \mathbf{x}_{n+1}^{(k-1)}$ as follows.

Step 1: From $\mathbf{x}_0^{(k)}$ determine $\lambda_1^{(k)}$ by a unidimensional search so that $f(\mathbf{x}_0^{(k)} + \lambda_1 \mathbf{s}_1^{(k)})$ is a minimum and let $\mathbf{x}_1^{(k)} = \mathbf{x}_0^{(k)} + \lambda_1^{(k)}\mathbf{s}_1^{(k)}$. From $\mathbf{x}_1^{(k)}$ determine $\lambda_2^{(k)}$ so that $f(\mathbf{x}_1^{(k)} + \lambda_2 \mathbf{s}_2^{(k)})$ is a minimum and let $\mathbf{x}_2^{(k)} = \mathbf{x}_1^{(k)} + \lambda_2^{(k)}\mathbf{s}_2^{(k)}$. The search is continued sequentially in each direction, starting always from the last immediate point in the sequence until all the $\lambda_i^{(k)}$, $i = 1, \ldots, n$, are determined. The search for $\lambda_0^{(k)}$ to minimize $f(\mathbf{x})$ in the direction $\mathbf{s}_n^{(k-1)}$ is taken into account in step 4 below.

Step 2: Powell pointed out that the search described in step 1—as noted in Sec. 4.3—can lead to linearly dependent search directions, as, for example, when one of the components of $\mathbf{s}^{(k)}$ becomes essentially zero because no progress was made in that particular direction. Two search directions thus might become essentially colinear. Hence it might be unwise to replace an old direction with a new one if by doing so the new set of directions became linearly dependent. Also, he demonstrated (for a quadratic function) that in scaling the search directions by

$$(\mathbf{s}_i^{(k)})^T \mathbf{H} \mathbf{s}_i^{(k)} = 1 \qquad i = 1, \ldots, n$$

the determinant of the matrix whose columns comprise the search directions takes on its maximum value if and only if the $\mathbf{s}_i^{(k)}$ are mutually conjugate with respect to $\mathbf{H}$. He concluded that the overall direction of progress for the kth stage, $\mathbf{s}^{(k)}$, should replace an existing search direction only if the replacement vector increased the determinant of the matrix of search directions, for then the set of directions would be more effective. Hence, after minimizing $f(\mathbf{x})$ in each of the n directions as described in step 1, one additional step of size $(\mathbf{x}_k^{(k)} - \mathbf{x}_0^{(k)})$ is taken corresponding to the total progress on the kth stage to yield the point $(2\mathbf{x}_n^{(k)} - \mathbf{x}_0^{(k)})$. A test is then made—see step 3 below—to ascertain whether or not adding the new direction and dropping one old one decreases the determinant of the search directions.

Step 3: Let the largest reduction in $f(\mathbf{x})$ in any search direction on the kth stage be denoted by

$$\Delta^{(k)} = \max_{i=1,\ldots,n} \{f(\mathbf{x}_{i-1}^{(k)}) - f(\mathbf{x}_i^{(k)})\}$$

The search direction corresponding to this maximum change in $f(\mathbf{x})$ will be designated $\mathbf{s}_m^{(k)}$. To make the notation more compact, let $f_1 = f(\mathbf{x}_0^{(k)})$, $f_2 = f(\mathbf{x}_n^{(k)})$, and $f_3 = f(2\mathbf{x}_n^{(k)} - \mathbf{x}_0^{(k)})$, where $\mathbf{x}_0^{(k)} = \mathbf{x}_n^{(k-1)}$ and $\mathbf{x}_n^{(k)} = \mathbf{x}_{n-1}^{(k)} + \lambda_n^{(k)}\mathbf{s}_n^{(k)} = \mathbf{x}_0^{(k)} + \sum_{i=1}^{n} \lambda_i^{(k)}\mathbf{s}_i^{(k)}$.

If either $f_3 \geq f_1$ and/or $(f_1 - 2f_2 + f_3)(f_1 - f_2 - \Delta^{(k)})^2 \geq 0.5\Delta^{(k)}(f_1 - f_3)^2$, use exactly the same directions $\mathbf{s}_1^{(k)}, \ldots, \mathbf{s}_n^{(k)}$ in the $(k+1)$st stage as in the kth stage, that is, $\mathbf{s}_i^{(k+1)} = \mathbf{s}_i^{(k)}$ for $i = 1, \ldots, n$, and start at $\mathbf{x}_0^{(k+1)} = \mathbf{x}_n^{(k)}$ [or from $\mathbf{x}_0^{(k+1)} = 2\mathbf{x}_n^{(k)} - \mathbf{x}_0^{(k)} = \mathbf{x}_{n+1}^{(k)}$, whichever $\mathbf{x}$ vector yields the lowest value of $f(\mathbf{x})$].

Step 4: If the test in step 3 is not satisfied, the direction $\mathbf{s}^{(k)}$ from $\mathbf{x}_0^{(k)}$ to $\mathbf{x}_n^{(k)}$ is searched for the minimum of $f(\mathbf{x})$, which will be used as the starting point for the next stage, $(k+1)$. The set of directions to be used in the $(k+1)$st stage are the same as the kth stage, with the exception of the direction $\mathbf{s}_m^{(k)}$, which is replaced by $\mathbf{s}^{(k)}$. However, $\mathbf{s}^{(k)}$ is placed in the last column of the matrix of directions instead of in the location of $\mathbf{s}_m^{(k)}$. Consequently, the directions to be used in the $(k+1)$st stage are

$$[\mathbf{s}_1^{(k+1)} \quad \mathbf{s}_2^{(k+1)} \quad \cdots \quad \mathbf{s}_n^{(k+1)}] = [\mathbf{s}_1^{(k)} \quad \mathbf{s}_2^{(k)} \quad \cdots \quad \mathbf{s}_{m-1}^{(k)} \quad \mathbf{s}_{m+1}^{(k)} \quad \cdots \quad \mathbf{s}_n^{(k)} \quad \mathbf{s}^{(k)}]$$

Step 5: A satisfactory convergence criterion for Powell's method is to terminate the search at the end of any stage in which the change in each independent variable is less than the required accuracy ε_i, for $i = 1, \ldots, n$, or for $\|\mathbf{x}_n^{(k)} - \mathbf{x}_0^{(k)}\| \leq 0.1\varepsilon$.

Zangwill[1] showed that Powell's procedure (slightly modified) will converge to a point at which the gradient of $f(\mathbf{x})$ is zero if $f(\mathbf{x})$ is a strictly convex function. Such a point would be a local extremum.

[1] W. I. Zangwill, *Computer J.*, **10**:293 (1967).

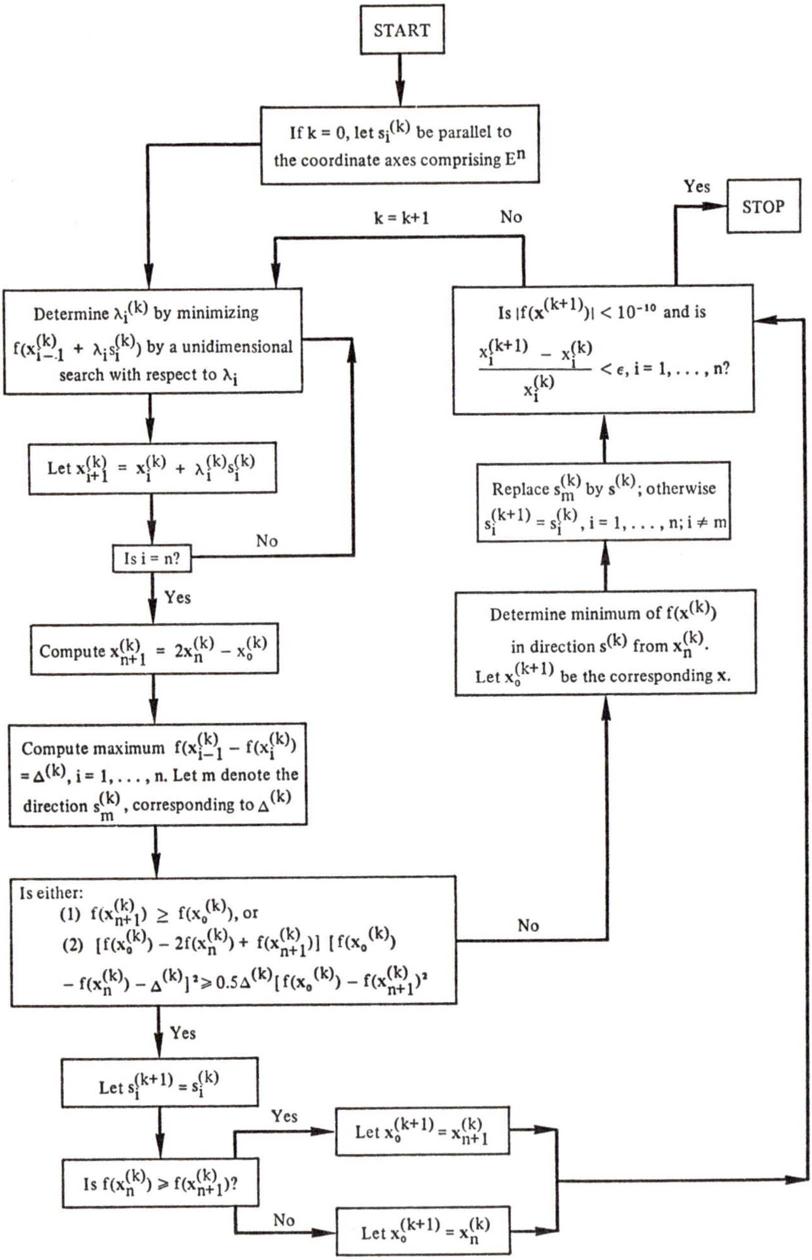

START
If k = 0, let $s_i^{(k)}$ be parallel to the coordinate axes comprising E^n
k = k+1
No
Yes
STOP
Determine $\lambda_i^{(k)}$ by minimizing $f(x_{i-1}^{(k)} + \lambda_i s_i^{(k)})$ by a unidimensional search with respect to λ_i
Let $x_{i+1}^{(k)} = x_i^{(k)} + \lambda_i^{(k)} s_i^{(k)}$
Is i = n?
No
Yes
Compute $x_{n+1}^{(k)} = 2x_n^{(k)} - x_0^{(k)}$
Compute maximum $f(x_{i-1}^{(k)}) - f(x_i^{(k)}) = \Delta^{(k)}$, i = 1, . . . , n. Let m denote the direction $s_m^{(k)}$, corresponding to $\Delta^{(k)}$
Is either:
(1) $f(x_{n+1}^{(k)}) \geq f(x_0^{(k)})$, or
(2) $[f(x_0^{(k)}) - 2f(x_n^{(k)}) + f(x_{n+1}^{(k)})] [f(x_0^{(k)}) - f(x_n^{(k)}) - \Delta^{(k)}]^2 \geq 0.5\Delta^{(k)}[f(x_0^{(k)}) - f(x_{n+1}^{(k)})^2$
No
Yes
Let $s_i^{(k+1)} = s_i^{(k)}$
Is $f(x_n^{(k)}) \geq f(x_{n+1}^{(k)})$?
Yes
Let $x_0^{(k+1)} = x_{n+1}^{(k)}$
No
Let $x_0^{(k+1)} = x_n^{(k)}$
Determine minimum of $f(x^{(k)})$ in direction $s^{(k)}$ from $x_n^{(k)}$. Let $x_0^{(k+1)}$ be the corresponding **x**.
Replace $s_m^{(k)}$ by $s^{(k)}$; otherwise $s_i^{(k+1)} = s_i^{(k)}$, i = 1, . . . , n; i ≠ m
Is $|f(\mathbf{x}^{(k+1)})| < 10^{-10}$ and is $\dfrac{x_i^{(k+1)} - x_i^{(k)}}{x_i^{(k)}} < \epsilon$, i = 1, . . . , n?

Fig. 4.4–2 Information flow chart for Powell's method.

Figure 4.4–2 is an information flow chart for Powell's algorithm, and Fig. E4.4–2 illustrates the path of the search in minimizing Rosenbrock's function.

Example 4.4–1 Powell's method

Powell's method is now illustrated for the problem

$$\text{Minimize:} \quad f(\mathbf{x}) = 4(x_1 - 5)^2 + (x_2 - 6)^2$$

starting from $\mathbf{x}^{(0)} = [8 \quad 9]^T$. At $\mathbf{x}^{(0)}$, $f(\mathbf{x}^{(0)}) = 45.000$. First, $f(\mathbf{x}^{(0)},\lambda)$ is minimized with respect to λ by a unidimensional search in the x_1 coordinate direction (x_2 remains at 9.000).

	$f(\mathbf{x})$
8.000	45.000
7.992	44.808
7.952	43.857
7.752	39.294
6.752	21.278
1.752	51.198
5.460	9.847
4.043	12.657
6.335	16.135
4.919	9.026
.	.
.	.
.	.
5.000	9.000 [minimum $f(\mathbf{x}^{(0)})$]

Next, a unidimensional search is executed in the x_2 direction, starting from $x_1^{(1)} = 5.000$ (and remaining constant) and $x_2^{(1)} = 9.000$, with the following results:

x_2	$f(\mathbf{x})$
9.000	9.000
8.991	8.946
8.946	8.678
8.721	7.403
7.596	2.547
1.971	16.232
6.142	0.024
4.549	2.104
7.127	1.271
5.534	0.217
.	.
.	.
.	.
6.000	5.44×10^{-15}

The step $\mathbf{x}_{n+1}^{(0)} = 2\mathbf{x}_n^{(0)} - \mathbf{x}_0^{(0)}$ yields

$$2\begin{bmatrix}5.000\\6.000\end{bmatrix} - \begin{bmatrix}8.000\\9.000\end{bmatrix} = \begin{bmatrix}2.000\\3.000\end{bmatrix}$$

at which point $f(\mathbf{x}_{n+1}^{(0)}) = 45.000$. The value of $\Delta^{(0)}$ is

$$\Delta^{(0)} = \text{maximum}\,\{[f(8,9) - f(5,9)], [f(5,9) - f(5,6)]\} = 36$$

We note also that

$$f(2,3) = 45.000 \geq f(8,9) = 45.000$$

and that

$$[f(8,9) - 2f(5,6) + f(2,3)][f(8,9) - f(5,6) - 36]^2 \geq 0.5(36)[f(8,9) - f(2,3)]^2$$

$$729 \geq 0$$

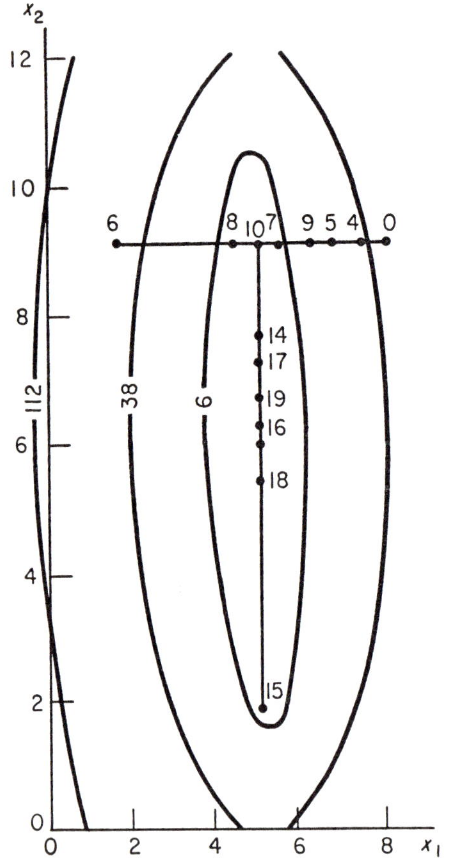

Fig. E4.4-1 Trajectory of search using Powell's algorithm (the numbers designate the function evaluation sequence number).

Hence, on the next stage, the search vector would be the same as on the preceding stage. However, the search is terminated at $\mathbf{x}^* = [5 \quad 6]^T$ because the convergence criterion is satisfied. Figure E4.4-1 illustrates the trajectory of the search.

Example 4.4-2 Powell's method for Rosenbrock's function

The application of Powell's algorithm to Rosenbrock's function

$$f(\mathbf{x}) = 100(x_2 - x_1^2)^2 + (1 - x_1)^2$$

illustrates what happens in the minimization of a nonquadratic function. We start at $\mathbf{x}^{(0)} = [-1.2 \quad 1.0]^T$, where $f(\mathbf{x}^{(0)}) = 24.2$. The initial search directions are

$$\mathbf{s}_1^{(0)} = \begin{bmatrix} 1 \\ 0 \end{bmatrix} \qquad \mathbf{s}_2^{(0)} = \begin{bmatrix} 0 \\ 1 \end{bmatrix}$$

An initial minimization of $f(\mathbf{x})$ is made using the search direction $\mathbf{s}_1^{(0)}$, that is, in the x_1 direction (the details of which are omitted) to reach the point $\mathbf{x}_1^{(0)} = [-0.995 \quad 1.000]^T$, where $f(\mathbf{x}_1^{(0)}) = 3.990$. Then a search is made using the vector $\mathbf{s}_2^{(0)}$, that is, in the x_2 direction, yielding $\mathbf{x}_2^{(0)} = [-0.995 \quad 0.990]^T$, where $f(\mathbf{x}_2^{(0)}) = 3.980$. Following a step of

$$\mathbf{x}_3^{(0)} = 2\begin{bmatrix} -0.995 \\ 0.990 \end{bmatrix} - \begin{bmatrix} -1.200 \\ 1.000 \end{bmatrix} = \begin{bmatrix} -0.790 \\ 0.980 \end{bmatrix}$$

where $f(\mathbf{x}_3^{(0)}) = 15.872$, new directions of search are computed as follows:

$$\mathbf{s}_1^{(1)} = \mathbf{s}_2^{(0)} = \begin{bmatrix} 0 \\ 1 \end{bmatrix}$$

$$\mathbf{s}_2^{(1)} = \mathbf{x}_2^{(0)} - \mathbf{x}_0^{(0)} = \begin{bmatrix} -0.995 \\ 0.990 \end{bmatrix} - \begin{bmatrix} -1.200 \\ 1.000 \end{bmatrix} = \begin{bmatrix} 0.205 \\ -0.010 \end{bmatrix}$$

$$\sqrt{(s_2^{(1)})_1^2 + (s_2^{(1)})_2^2} = \sqrt{4.21 \times 10^{-2}} = 0.206$$

$$\mathbf{s}_2^{(1)} = \begin{bmatrix} 0.999 \\ -0.0488 \end{bmatrix}$$

because the criteria listed in step 3 are not satisfied ($\Delta^{(0)} = 24.2 - 3.99 = 20.21$),

$$f(\mathbf{x}_3^{(0)}) = 15.872 < f(\mathbf{x}^{(0)}) = 24.2 \qquad (a)$$

and

$$[24.2 - 2(3.980) + 15{,}372][24.2 - 2.980 - 20.21]^2 < 0.5(20.21)(24.2 - 15.872)^2 \qquad (b)$$

The results of several additional stages of search are given on p. 176, starting from $\mathbf{x}_0^{(1)} = [-0.990 \quad 0.990]^T$:

Figure E4.4-2 illustrates the trajectory of the search. In total, the objective function was evaluated 1562 times to reach the minimum of $f(\mathbf{x})$ at $\mathbf{x}^* = [1.000 \quad 1.000]^T$ and $f(\mathbf{x}^*) = 1.338 \times 10^{-16} \approx 0$.

Stage	$(\mathbf{s}_1^{(k)})^T$	$(\mathbf{s}_2^{(k)})^T$	$\mathbf{x}^{(k)}$	$f(\mathbf{x}^{(k)})$
1	[0 1]	[0.205 −0.010]	$x_0^{(1)} = [-0.990 \quad 0.990]^T$	3.969
			$x_1^{(1)} = [-0.990 \quad 0.990]^T$	3.959
			$x_2^{(1)} = [-0.984 \quad 0.979]^T$	3.948
2	[0 1]	[0.453 −0.892]	$x_0^{(2)} = [-0.761 \quad 0.540]^T$	3.257
			$x_1^{(2)} = [-0.761 \quad 0.579]^T$	3.101
			$x_2^{(2)} = [-0.702 \quad 0.462]^T$	2.986
3	[0.453 −0.892]	[0.608 −0.794]	$x_0^{(3)} = [-0.503 \quad 0.203]^T$	2.510
			$x_1^{(3)} = [-0.538 \quad 0.273]^T$	2.396
			$x_2^{(3)} = [-0.466 \quad 0.178]^T$	2.301

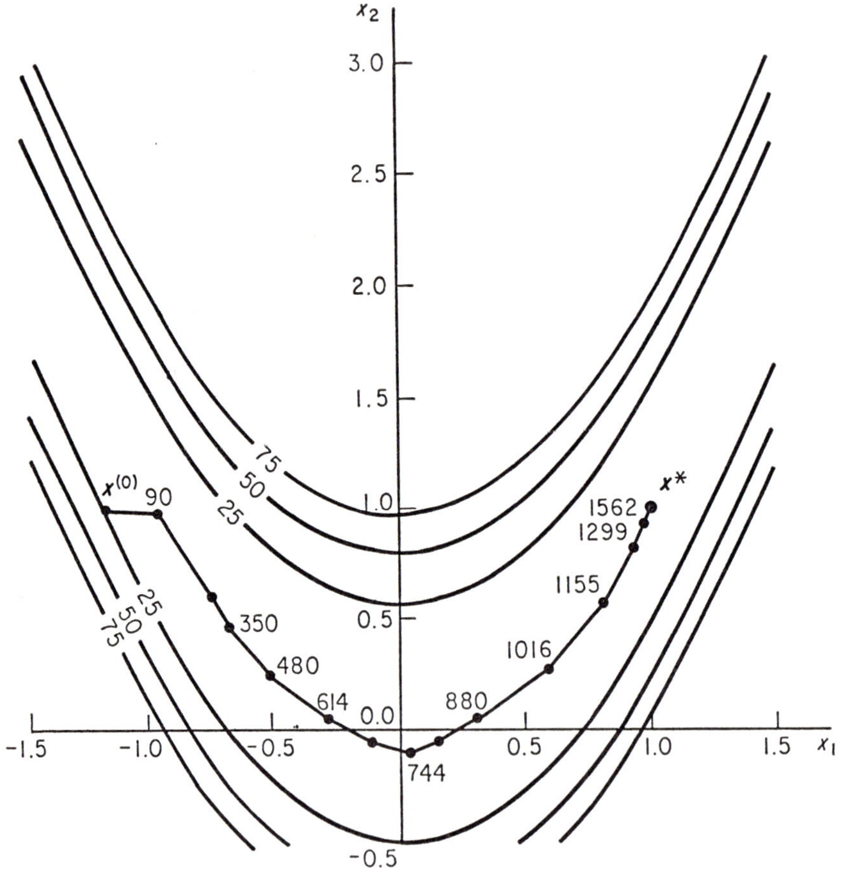

Fig. E4.4-2 Search trajectory for the Powell algorithm (the numbers designate the function evaluation sequence number).

4.5 RANDOM SEARCH METHODS

Random search methods are the least elegant and efficient of all the search techniques, but they are feasible on high-speed digital and hybrid computers. Brooks[1] reviewed various types of random search methods, and Favreau[2] and Munson presented techniques for implementing random search on the analog computer. A hybrid computer technique was presented by Mitchell[3] which employed digital logic to implement different random search strategies and step-size changes. We will describe briefly a few random search procedures.

4.5-1 The Complex Method

Although the complex method was designed by Box[4] to be applied to nonlinear programming problems with inequality constraints, we include the method in this section because of its use of random search directions. The method evolved from the simplex method of Spendley *et al.*, described in Sec. 4.2. Vertices are deleted and added as in the simplex method, but no attempt is made to preserve the regular figure so characteristic of the simplex method.

The difficulty with the methods of Spendley and Nelder and Mead on repetitively encountering a constraint is that it is necessary to withdraw the nonfeasible vertex until it becomes feasible. After many such withdrawals the polyhedron will collapse into $(n - 1)$ or fewer dimensions, and the search will be quite slow. Furthermore, if the constraint ceases to be active, the collapsed polyhedron cannot readily expand back into the full n-dimensional space again. To avoid these difficulties, Box selected a polyhedron with more than $(n + 1)$ vertices, which he termed a *complex*. (Mitchell and Kaplan—listed in the references at the end of this chapter—describe a nonrandom complex method.)

The complex method employs $(n + 1)$ or more vertices p (each of which must satisfy the constraints at all k stages). An initial $\mathbf{x}_1^{(0)}$ is chosen, and $(p - 1)$ additional vertices are selected one at a time through the use of pseudo-random numbers and the following relation:

$$\mathbf{x}_i^{(0)} = \mathbf{L}_i + \mathbf{r}_i^{(0)}(\mathbf{U}_i - \mathbf{L}_i) \qquad i = 2, \ldots, p$$

[1] *J. Operations Res.*, **6**:244 (1958).

[2] R. R. Favreau and R. G. E. Franks, Statistical Optimization, *Proc. 2d Intl. Conf. for Analog Computation*, Strasbourg, 1958, Presses Académiques Européenes, Brussels, 1959, p. 437.

[3] B. A. Mitchell, *Simulation*, **4**:399 (1965).

[4] M. J. Box, *Computer J.*, **8**:42 (1965).

where $\mathbf{L}_i$ and $\mathbf{U}_i$ are, respectively, the lower and upper bounds on $\mathbf{x}_i$, and $\mathbf{r}_i^{(0)}$ is a diagonal matrix of pseudo-random numbers uniformly distributed over the interval (0,1). If no bounds are known, the initial polyhedron should be chosen to cover the search region.

Next, the objective function is evaluated at each vertex, and the vertex having the worst value of $f(\mathbf{x})$ is replaced by a new vertex located along the line joining the rejected point and the centroid of the remaining points at a distance equal to or greater than the distance from the rejected point to the centroid. If a new vertex turns out to give the worst value of $f(\mathbf{x})$ of all the vertices in the new polyhedron, it is replaced by another vertex located half the distance from the new vertex to the centroid. (If a constraint is violated, the new vertex is also moved halfway in toward the centroid.) Box recommended from empirical studies that the overexpansion be a factor of 1.3 and that $(p = 2n)$ vertices be used in the search. The overexpansion in the reflection stage of the polyhedron and the use of more than $(n + 1)$ vertices are features of the procedure designed to prevent the polyhedron from flattening near constraints. The search will continue until the polyhedron is reduced essentially to the centroid to within a given precision.

Numerical results by Hilleary[1] demonstrated that the rate of convergence of the complex method depends on the character of the initial polyhedron. Box concluded that Rosenbrock's method is more efficient than the simplex or complex methods for unconstrained problems, and that the number of functional evaluations increased twice as rapidly for the simplex and complex methods as they did for Rosenbrock's method as the dimensionality (n) of $f(\mathbf{x})$ increased.

4.5-2 Repetitive Random Search

A completely random search at each stage of the minimization has been programmed by Kelly and Wheeling.[2] Given a starting point $\mathbf{x}^{(0)}$, the code generates a random path by constructing a sequence of steps, a step being taken from the $\mathbf{x}$ vector yielding the lowest value of $f(\mathbf{x})$ discovered in the random search to another yielding a lower value. Thus, starting at $\mathbf{x}_0$, a random $\mathbf{x}^{(1)}$ is generated from the following relation:

$$\mathbf{x}^{(k+1)} = \mathbf{x}^{(k)} + \lambda^{(k)}\left[\beta \frac{z^{(k)}}{\|z^{(k)}\|} + (1 - \beta)\mathbf{r}^{(k)}\right] \tag{4.5-1}$$

[1] R. R. Hilleary, *U.S. Naval Postgraduate School Tech. Rept./Res. Paper* 59, March, 1966.

[2] R. J. Kelly, and R. F. Wheeling, "A Digital Computer Program for Optimizing Nonlinear Functions," Mobil Oil Corp., Research Dept., Central Research Div., Princeton, N.J., July, 1962.

where

$\lambda^{(k)}$ = step size, a scalar that is increased after a successful step and decreased after an unsuccessful step;

$\mathbf{z}^{(k)}$ = a "history vector" indicating the average direction of the search in prior steps

$$\mathbf{z}^{(k+1)} = \gamma\mathbf{z}^{(k)} + (1 - \gamma)(\mathbf{x}^{(k+1)} - \mathbf{x}^{(k)})\mathbf{S}^{(k)}$$

$\mathbf{r}^{(k)}$ = a unit vector of normal deviates generated in a pseudo-random number generator;

β = an adjustable coefficient changed in the search;

γ = a constant weighting factor;

$\mathbf{S}^{(k)}$ = a vector of scale factors to scale the $\mathbf{x}$ space "suitably"

On the kth stage the random vector $\mathbf{r}^{(k)}$ and the history vector $\mathbf{z}^{(k)}$ are averaged, as indicated by Eq. (4.5–1), to yield $\mathbf{x}^{(k+1)}$. The vector $\mathbf{x}^{(k+1)}$ will be accepted or rejected according to whether or not $f(\mathbf{x}^{(k+1)}) < f(\mathbf{x}^{(k)})$. After $\mathbf{x}^{(k+1)}$ is accepted (or rejected), $\lambda^{(k)}$ is increased (or decreased) by a factor roughly depending upon whether the search has been easy or difficult. Figure 4.5–1 illustrates a hypothetical search path in two dimensions.

Tests of this program for a number of problems indicate that its general performance is less satisfactory than that of several other algorithms described previously in Chap. 3 and this chapter, and we will not discuss it further (however, see Tables 9.3–3 and 9.3–4).

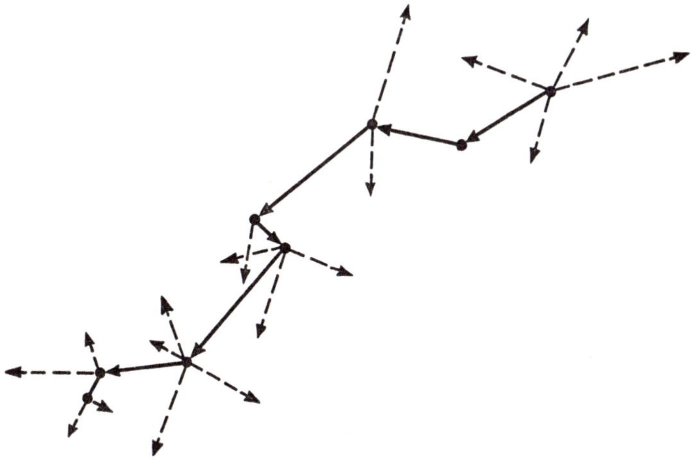

Fig. 4.5–1 A typical path in random search. The dashed arrows designate exploratory steps that were rejected, and the solid arrows represent steps that reduced the objective function.

4.5-3 Random Search with Uniform Search Radius but Random Direction

Figure 4.5–2 illustrates a search technique in which the search radius in any direction is uniform but the direction of search is random. In two dimensions, a circle is drawn with an initial vector $\mathbf{x}^{(0)}$ as center. In n dimensions a hypersphere is used. Random points on the circle are used to evaluate $f(\mathbf{x})$, and the best point is selected as $\tilde{\mathbf{x}}^{(0)}$. A search along a line through $\mathbf{x}^{(0)}$ and $\tilde{\mathbf{x}}^{(0)}$ reaches a minimum of $f(\mathbf{x})$ at $\mathbf{x}^{(1)}$, and the sequence is repeated starting from $\mathbf{x}^{(1)}$. As the circle gets larger, but not too large of course, the corresponding $\mathbf{x}^{(1)}$ will tend to be closer to $\mathbf{x}^*$. Any point on the circle segment between the broken lines in Fig. 4.5–2 will yield a more favorable $\mathbf{x}^{(1)}$ than that determined by a steepest descent minimization, but not as favorable an $\mathbf{x}^{(1)}$ as obtained by a second-derivative type of method. To have satisfactory convergence the sequence of radii of the circles (or hyperspheres) is reduced periodically. Also, the search can be accelerated if the points on the hypersphere are chosen at random but constrained to lie at least at a minimum angle from each other and from the previous direction of search. The minimum angle can be changed during the search, as well.

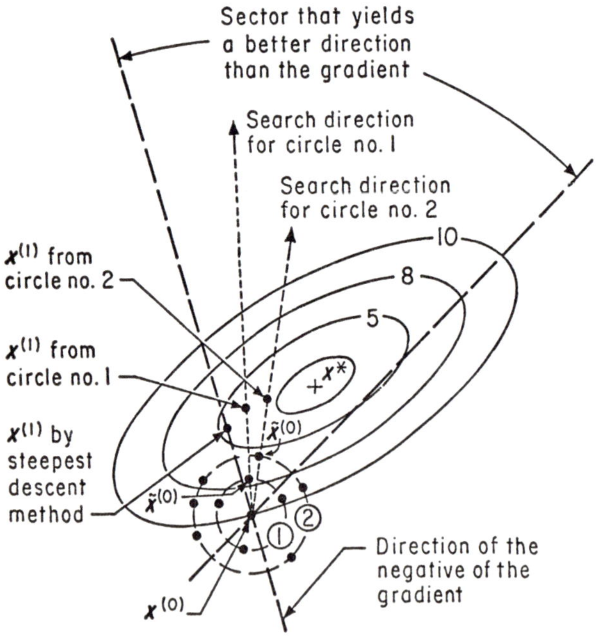

Fig. 4.5–2 Random search illustrating the effect of changing the uniform search radius.

It can be shown that if the direction cosines D_i are chosen in a certain way, the random directions selected for search point to all parts of the **x** space with equal probability. Define the direction cosines as

$$D_i = \frac{d_i}{(d_1^2 + \cdots + d_n^2)^{\frac{1}{2}}}$$

where d_i is a normal random variable with a mean of 0 and a standard deviation of σ^2. In two dimensions we have the search angle

$$\phi = \tan^{-1}\frac{D_1}{D_2} = \tan^{-1}\frac{d_1}{d_2}$$

The variable ϕ can be shown to be uniformly distributed in the interval $(-\pi/2,\pi/2)$. If the dimensionality of the problem is n, the angles ϕ_k projected onto any coordinate plane are likewise uniformly distributed.

To compare the random search described above with a nonrandom search, let the relative increment, or "gain," in $f(\mathbf{x})$ during one stage be defined as

$$E(k) = \frac{f(\mathbf{x}^{(k)}) - f(\mathbf{x}^{(k+1)})}{f(\mathbf{x}^{(k)})}$$

If M **x** vectors are selected on the surface of a hypersphere about $\mathbf{x}^{(k)}$ and if

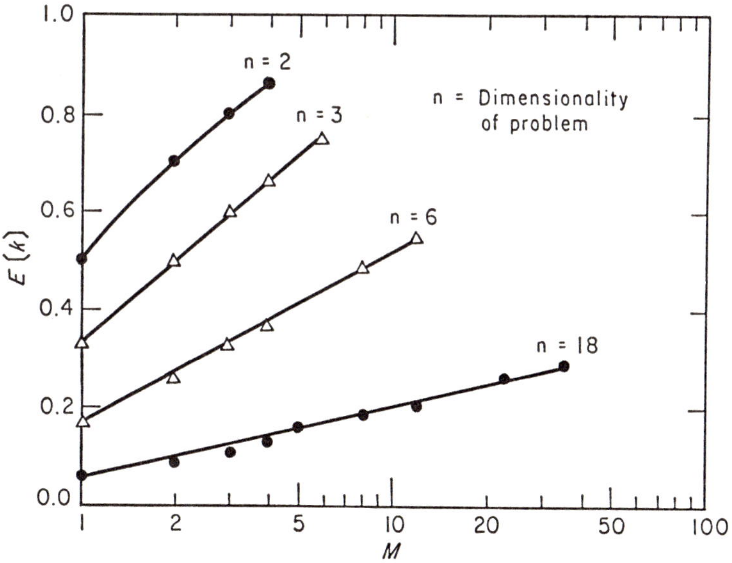

Fig. 4.5-3 Gain per cycle vs. number of **x** vectors (M) used to determine the direction of search (the objective function is spheroidal). [H. Kushner, Efficient Iterative Methods for Optimizing the Performance of Multi-parameter Noisy Systems, *MIT Lincoln Lab. Rept.* 22G-0043 (AD 245802), October, 1960.]

the direction of search is taken in the direction of $\tilde{\mathbf{x}}^{(k)}$, Fig. 4.5–3 shows the expected value of $E(k)$ as a function of M and the dimensionality of the problem for a spheroid objective function. The figure can be interpreted as follows. Compare $n = 18$ and $M = 3$, which give $E(3) \approx 0.12$, with $n = 18$ and $M = 6$, which give $E(6) \approx 0.17$. On two cycles with $M = 3$, the gain would be about 0.24 versus 0.17 for the same number of functional evaluations with $M = 6$. Consequently, it is more efficient to use fewer $\mathbf{x}$ vectors on the hypersphere and to iterate more often for $n = 18$.

The general principle that for well-scaled functions an orderly procedure of minimization is more effective than a completely random procedure can be seen from Fig. 4.5–4, in which three strategies are compared:

1. Gradient method (Sec. 3.1–1)
2. Sequence of random directions (Sec. 4.5–2)
3. Direction determined from random points on a hypersphere (Sec. 4.5–3)

Minimization methods 2 and 3 are approximately the same and both less favorable than method 1. In general, random methods and "one variable at a time" methods without rotation of axes are less efficient than the nonrandom methods of demonstrated effectiveness described in earlier sections.

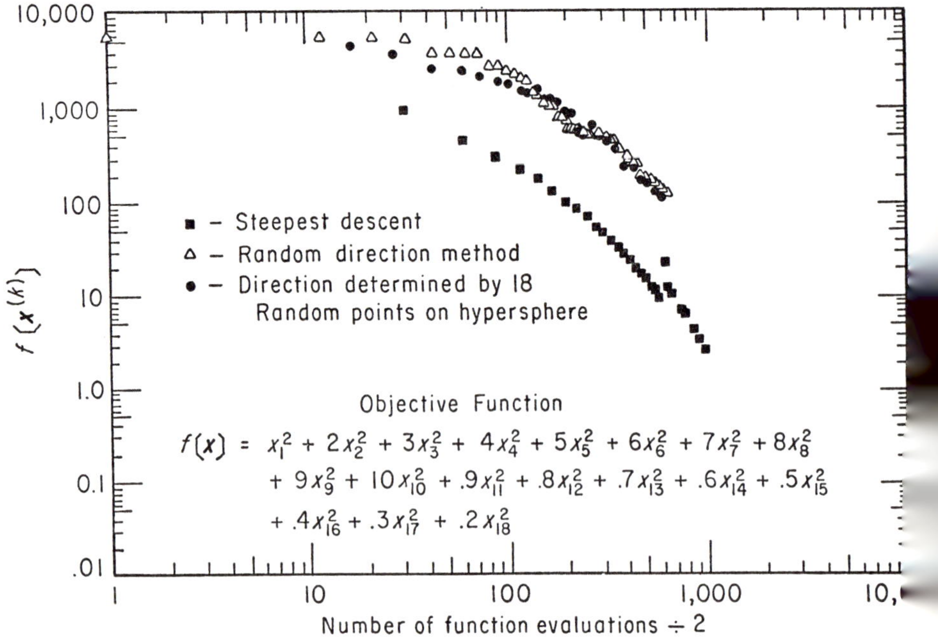

Fig. 4.5–4 Three methods compared for 18-dimensional problem.

SUPPLEMENTARY REFERENCES

General References

Box, M. J.: A Comparison of Several Current Optimization Methods, and the Use of Transformations in Constrained Problems, *Computer J.*, **9**:67 (1966).

Dorn, W. S.: Nonlinear Programming: A Survey, *Management Sci.*, **9**:171 (1963).

Kowalik, J., and M. R. Osborne: "Methods for Unconstrained Optimization Problems," American Elsevier, 1968.

Powell, M. J. D.: A Survey of Numerical Methods for Unconstrained Optimization, *SIAM Rev.*, **12**:79 (1970).

Schechter, R. S., and G. S. G. Beveridge: "Optimization: Theory and Practice," McGraw-Hill, New York, 1970.

Spang, H. A., III: A Review of Minimization Techniques for Nonlinear Functions, *SIAM Rev.*, **4**:343 (1962).

Wilde, D. J.: "Optimum Seeking Methods," Prentice-Hall, Englewood Cliffs, N.J., 1964.

———, and C. S. Beightler: "Foundations of Optimization," Prentice-Hall, Englewood Cliffs, N.J., 1967.

Wolfe, P.: Recent Developments in Nonlinear Programming, *Advan. Computers*, **3**:155–187 (1962).

Additional Methods of Unconstrained Nonlinear Programming without Using Derivatives

Nonrandom Search

Berman, G.: Minimization by Successive Approximations, *SIAM Numerical Analysis*, **3**:123 (1966).

———: Lattice Approximations to the Minima of Functions of Several Variables, *J. Assoc. Computer Mach.*, **16**:286 (1969).

Campey, I. G., and D. G. Nickols: "Simplex Minimization," Imperial Chemical Industries, Ltd., August, 1961.

Fletcher, R.: Functional Minimization without Evaluating Derivatives, *Computer J.*, **8**:33 (April, 1965).

Kiefer, J.: Sequential Minimax Search for a Minimum, *Proc. Am. Math. Soc.*, **4**:502 (1953).

———: Optimum Sequential Search and Approximation Methods under Minimum Regularity Assumptions, *SIAM J.*, **5**:105 (1957).

Mitchell, R. A., and J. L. Kaplan: Nonlinear Constraint Optimization by a Nonrandom Complex Method, *J. Res. Natl. Bur. Std.*, **72C**:249 (1968).

Spendley, W., G. R. Hext, and F. R. Himsworth: The Sequential Application of Simplex Designs in Optimization and Evolutionary Operation, *Technometrics*, **4**:441 (1962).

Swann, W. H.: Report on the Development of a New Direct Search Method of Optimization, *Imperial Chemical Industries, Ltd., Central Instr. Lab. Res. Note* 64/3, 1964.

Vignes, J.: Algorithme pour la détermination d'un extremum local d'une fonction de plusiers variables, *Rev. Inst. Franç. Pétrole*, **23**:537 (1968).

Whitte, B. F. W.: Two New Direct Minimum Search Procedures for Functions of Several Variables, paper presented at the 1964 Spring Joint Computer Conference, Washington, D.C., April, 1964.

Wood, C. F.: Application of "Direct Search" to the Solution of Engineering Problems, *Westinghouse Res. Lab. Sci. Paper* 6–41210–1–P1, 1960.

Random Search

Bekey, G. A., M. H. Gran, A. E. Sabroff, and A. Wong: Parameter Optimization by Random Search Using Hybrid Computer Techniques, *Proc. Fall Joint Computer Conf.*, 1966, p. 191.

Brooks, S. H.: A Discussion of Random Methods for Seeking Maxims, *J. Operations Res.*, **6**:244 (1958).

———: A Comparison of Maximum Seeking Methods, *J. Operations Res. Soc. Am.*, vol. 7, 1959.

Favreau, R. R., and R. G. E. Franks: "Random Optimization by Analog Techniques," *Proc. 2d Intl. Conf. for Analog Computation*, Strasbourg, France, September, 1958, Presses Académiques Européenes, Brussels, 1959, pp. 437, 443.

Gallagher, P. J.: MOP-1: An Optimizing Routine for the IBM 650, *Can. G.E. Civilian Atomic Power Dept. Rept.* R60cAP35, 1960.

McArthur, D.S.: Strategy in Research: Alternative Methods for the Design of Experiments, *IRE Trans.*, **EM-8**:34 (1961).

Matyas, J.: "Random Optimization" (English transl.), *Automatic and Remote Control*, **26**:244 (1965).

Mitchell, B. A.: A Hybrid Analog-Digital Parameter Optimizer for ASTRAC II, *Simulation*, **4**:398 (1965).

Munson, J. K., and A. I. Rubin: Optimization by Random Search on the Analog Computer, *IRE Trans.*, **EC-8**:200 (1959).

Schumer, M. A., and K. Steiglitz: *IEEE Trans. Autom. Control*, **AC-13**:270 (1968).

Shimuzu, T.: A Stochastic Approximation Method for Optimization Problems, *J. Assoc. Computer Mach.*, **16**:511 (1969).

Zellnik, H. E., N. E. Sondak, and R. S. Davis: Gradient Search Optimization, *Chem. Eng. Progr.*, **58**(8):35 (1962).

PROBLEMS[1]

4.1 For the objective function

$$f(\mathbf{x}) = 3x_1^2 + 5x_2^2$$

carry out three stages of a Hooke-Jeeves search. Use $\Delta\mathbf{x}^{(0)} = [0.5 \quad 0.5]^T$, starting from the base point $\mathbf{x}^{(0)} = [2 \quad 1]^T$. (A stage consists of a local exploration followed by an acceleration move.)

4.2 Continue the Hooke-Jeeves search from $x^{(7)}$ in Example 4.4–1 for ——— stages.

4.3 Determine a regular simplex figure in a three-dimensional space such that the distance between vertices is 0.2 unit and one vertex is at the point $(-1, 2, -2)$.

[1] Additional problems suitable for this chapter can be found in the problem set at the end of Chap. 3.

4.4 Use the simplex figure generated in Prob. 4.3 to carry out eight cycles of vertex rejection and regeneration in searching for a minimum of the objective function

$$f(\mathbf{x}) = x_1^2 + 3x_2^2 + 5x_3^2$$

4.5 A three-dimensional simplex optimal search for a minimum provides the following intermediate results:

x *vector*	*Value of objective function*
$[0 \quad 0 \quad 0]^T$	4
$[-1/3 \quad -1/3 \quad -1/3]^T$	7
$[-1/3 \quad -4/3 \quad -1/3]^T$	10
$[-1/3 \quad -1/3 \quad -4/3]^T$	5

What is the next point to be evaluated in the search? What point is dropped? What is the centroid of the new simplex?

4.6 Consider the function

$$f(\mathbf{x}) = 4x_1^2 + x_2^2 - 40x_1 - 12x_2 + 136$$

Start at the point $\mathbf{x}^{(0)} = [4 \quad 8]^T$, and carry out ——— stages of the Nelder and Mead search, including reflection, expansion, or contraction, etc., until the three original vertices of the simplex have been deleted.

4.7 For the function $f(\mathbf{x}) = 2x_1^2 + x_2^4$, what is the initial simplex for the Nelder and Mead search? Which of the three vertices is deleted first? second?

4.8 Adjust the values of β and γ in the Nelder and Mead algorithm so as to determine the optimal values for Problems 26 through 32 in Appendix A.

4.9 Change the parameters α and β in the Rosenbrock method to various other values and determine the most effective values for the quadratic function

$$f(\mathbf{x}) = 10x_1^2 + 0.1x_2^2$$

Repeat for

$$f(\mathbf{x}) = 0.1x_1^2 + 10x_2^2$$

4.10 At the end of one stage of the Rosenbrock method, the following values exist in the search for a minimum of $f(\mathbf{x})$:

Result			
x_1	x_2	x_1	x_2
Start	Start	3	7
Failure	Failure	4	8
Success	Success	2	8
Success	Success	1.5	7.5
Failure	Failure	−1.5	10.5
Failure			

(*a*) What were the two directions of search used in the stage?
(*b*) What should the next two new directions be?

4.11 Use the Rosenbrock search to find the minimum of the objective function

$$f(\mathbf{x}) = 3x_1^2 + x_2^2$$

with $\beta = 1/2$ and $\alpha = 3$ until no further improvement is possible.

4.12 After evaluating the function $f(\mathbf{x}) = 4(x_1 - 5)^2 + (x_2 - 6)^2$ at $\mathbf{x} = [7.35 \quad 8.80]^T$, what are the next two stages by Rosenbrock's method? Assume that a new search direction must be obtained, and $\mathbf{s}_1 = [1 \quad 0]^T$, $\mathbf{s}_2 = [0 \quad 1]^T$.

4.13 After minimizing the function $f(\mathbf{x}) = 2x_1^2 + x_2^2 + x_1x_2$ by Powell's method, the $\mathbf{x}$ vector was $\mathbf{x} = [0.371 \quad 0.116]^T$ and $f(\mathbf{x}) = 0.443$. Then the new search direction was computed and the point $\mathbf{x} = [0.574 \quad 0.308]^T$ reached. What is the next search direction?

4.14 List the search directions for Powell's method to minimize $f(\mathbf{x}) = 2x_1^2 + x_2^2 - x_1x_2$, starting from $\mathbf{x}^{(0)} = [2 \quad 2]^T$.

4.15 Find a direction orthogonal to the vector

$$\mathbf{s} = \left[\frac{1}{\sqrt{3}} \; -\frac{1}{\sqrt{3}} \; -\frac{1}{\sqrt{3}}\right]^T$$

at the point

$$\mathbf{x} = [0 \quad 0 \quad 0]^T$$

Find a direction conjugate to $\mathbf{s}$ with respect to the objective function $f(\mathbf{x}) = \mathbf{x}_1 + 2x_2^2 - x_1x_2$ at the same point.

4.16 Because Powell's method uses conjugate directions, can one guarantee to find the minimum of a quadratic objective function of *n* variables in *n* steps?

4.17 List the first four search directions for Powell's method to minimize $f(\mathbf{x}) = x_1^2 + \exp(x_1^2 + x_2^2)$, starting at the point $\mathbf{x}^{(0)} = [2 \quad 2]^T$.

4.18 Explain how Powell's method obtains a set of conjugate search directions for a three-dimensional problem. After proceeding in two of the search directions, give the details of determining the third direction. After two stages, are all the search directions conjugate?

4.19 Will Powell's method give the same set of search directions as Rosenbrock's method if you start at the same initial $\mathbf{x}$ vector?

4.20 The pair of equations $x_1^2 + x_2^2 = 1$ and $x_1 + x_2 = 1$ have the solutions (1,0) and (0,1). The contours of

$$f(\mathbf{x}) = (x_1^2 + x_2^2 - 1)^2 + (x_1 + x_2 - 1)^2$$

indicate minima at (1,0) and (0,1) and a saddle point at $(4^{-1/3}, 4^{-1/3})$. Can the search techniques find both minima or only a single minimum? Explain.

4.21 Starting from the point $\mathbf{x} = [3 \quad 3]^T$, plot the trajectory [$f(\mathbf{x})$ versus iteration number] of the following search techniques in solving Prob. 4.20:

(*a*) Hooke-Jeeves

(*b*) Nelder-Mead

(*c*) Rosenbrock

(*d*) Powell

What happens if you start at the saddle point?

4.22 Consider the function

$$f(\mathbf{x}) = (x_1^2 + x_2^2) + \frac{0.9x_1}{\sqrt{x_1^2 + x_2^2}}$$

$$\times \left[\tfrac{3}{2}(x_1^2 - x_2^2) - x_1x_2 + \sqrt{x_1^2 + x_2^2} + 0.25x_1 - \frac{x_1x_2}{\sqrt{x_1^2 + x_2^2}} \right]$$

(*a*) Plot the contour of $f(\mathbf{x})$ for $f(\mathbf{x}) = 1$ using a contour plotter.

(*b*) Steepest descent in eight iterations reached the following points:

		x_1	x_2	$f(\mathbf{x})$
(1)	$\mathbf{x}^{(0)}$	0.119	0.677	1.000
	$\mathbf{x}^{(8)}$	0.007	0.006	0.006
(2)	$\mathbf{x}^{(0)}$	−0.598	−0.502	1.000
	$\mathbf{x}^{(8)}$	−0.012	−0.005	0.005

Compare these with results of several of the search methods. Which method appears to be the more favorable?

4.23 Find the best estimates of the parameters b_0, b_1, and c in the following model:

$$\hat{y} = b_0 + b_1e^{-cx}$$

given the data

y_{exptl}	x
51.6	0.4
53.4	1.4
20.0	5.4
−4.2	19.5
−3.0	48.2
−4.8	95.9

by minimizing the sum of the square of the residuals $\sum (\hat{y}_i - y_{\text{exptl}})^2$. Use the method of

(*a*) Hooke-Jeeves

(*b*) Nelder-Mead

(*c*) Powell

(*d*) Rosenbrock

(*e*) Random search

4.24 Minimize the present total value of costs for expansion, P (in \$), given

$$P = 4900k_0^{0.88} + \sum_{i=1}^{n=1} k_i^{0.88}\left(\frac{10}{\sum_{j=0}^{i-1} k_j}\right)^{0.559} + \left(60 - \sum_{j=0}^{n-1} k_j\right)^{0.88}\left(\frac{10}{\sum_{j=0}^{n-1} k_j}\right)^{0.559}$$

where k_0 is the starting size of installed capacity, and k_i is the size of additional capacity, in integers, that is, $k_i = 1, 2, 3, \ldots$. Find the minimum n, $n = 1, 2, 3, \ldots$, and related k's, given $k_0 = 1$.

4.25 Find the minimum and the maximum of the function

$$f(\mathbf{x}) = 20 + 0.3x_1 - 4x_2 + 0.3x_1^2 + 0.3x_2^2 + 0.4x_1x_2$$

by one of the search methods. Start from

(*a*) $\mathbf{x}^{(0)} = [0.25 \quad 2.5]^T$
(*b*) $\mathbf{x}^{(0)} = [25 \quad 2.5]^T$
(*c*) $\mathbf{x}^{(0)} = [-0.25 \quad -2.5]^T$

4.26 The function

$$f(\mathbf{x}) = (1 + 8x_1 - 7x_1^2 + \tfrac{7}{3}x_1^3 - \tfrac{1}{4}x_1^4)(x_2^2e^{-x_2})F(\mathbf{x}_3)$$

has two maxima and a saddle point. For (*a*) $F(\mathbf{x}_3) = 1$ and (*b*) $F(\mathbf{x}_3) = x_3e^{-(x_3+1)}$, locate the global optimum by a search technique. [Ans.: (*a*) $\mathbf{x}^* = [4 \quad 2]^T$ and (*b*) $\mathbf{x}^* = [4 \quad 2 \quad 1]^T$.]

4.27 By starting with (*a*) $\mathbf{x}^{(0)} = [2 \quad 1]^T$ and (*b*) $\mathbf{x}^{(0)} = [2 \quad 1 \quad 1]^T$, can you reach the solution for Prob. 4.26? Repeat for (*a*) $\mathbf{x}^{(0)} = [2 \quad 2]^T$ and (*b*) $\mathbf{x}^{(0)} = [2 \quad 2 \quad 1]^T$. (*Hint*: [2 2 1] is a saddle point.)

4.28 Does the following function have a minimum? a maximum?

$$f(\mathbf{x}) = 1 + t + t^2 + t^3$$

4.29 Minimize

(*a*) $f(\mathbf{x}) = 1 + x_1 + x_2 + x_3 + x_4 + x_1x_2 + x_1x_3 + x_1x_4 + x_2x_3$
$x_2x_4 + x_3x_4 + x_1^2 + x_2^2 + x_3^2 + x_4^2$

starting from $\mathbf{x}^{(0)} = [-3 \quad -30 \quad -4 \quad -0.1]^T$ and also $\mathbf{x}^{(0)} = [0.5 \quad 1.0 \quad 8.0 \quad -0.7]^T$.

(*b*) $f(\mathbf{x}) = x_1x_2^2x_3^3x_4^4\,[\exp -(x_1 + x_2 + x_3 + x_4)]$, starting from $\mathbf{x}^{(0)} = [3 \quad 4 \quad 0.5 \quad 1]^T$.

4.30 Estimate the coefficients in the correlation

$$y = ax_1^{b_1}x_2^{b_2}$$

from the following experimental data by minimizing the sum of the square of the deviations between the experimental and predicted values of y.

y_{exptl}	x_1	x_2
46.5	2.0	36.0
591	6.0	8.0
1285	9.0	3.0
36.8	2.5	6.25
241	4.5	7.84
1075	9.5	1.44
1024	8.0	4.0
151	4.0	7.0
80	3.0	9.0
485	7.0	2.0
632	6.5	5.0

4.31 The cost of refined oil when shipped via the Malacca Straits to Japan in dollars per kiloliter was given as the linear sum of the crude oil cost, the insurance, customs, freight cost for the oil, loading and unloading cost, sea berth cost, submarine pipe cost, storage cost, tank area cost, refining cost, and freight cost of products as[1]

$$c = c_c + c_i + c_x + \frac{2.09 \times 10^4 t^{-0.3017}}{360} + \frac{1.064 \times 10^6 a t^{0.4925}}{52.47q(360)}$$

$$+ \frac{4.242 \times 10^4 a t^{0.7952} + 1.813 ip(nt + 1.2q)}{52.47q(360)}$$

$$+ \frac{4.25 \times 10^3 a(nt + 1.2q)}{52.47q(360)} + \frac{5.042 \times 10^3 q^{-0.1899}}{360}$$

$$+ \frac{0.1049 q^{0.671}}{360}$$

where a = annual fixed charges, fraction (0.20)
c_c = crude oil price, \$/kl (12.50)
c_i = insurance cost, \$/kl (0.50)
c_x = customs cost, \$/kl (0.90)
i = interest rate (0.10)
n = number of ports (2)
p = land price, \$/m^2 (7000)
q = refinery capacity, bbl/day
t = tanker size, kl

Given the values indicated in parentheses, compute the minimum cost of oil and the optimum tanker size and refinery size by the following methods (note that 1 kl = 6.29 bbl):

(*a*) Hooke-Jeeves
(*b*) Nelder-Mead
(*c*) Rosenbrock
(*d*) Powell
(*e*) Random search

[1] T. Uchiyama, *Hydrocarbon Process.*, **47**(12):85 (1968).

5

Evaluation of algorithms for unconstrained nonlinear programming

In this chapter we compare the performance of most of the algorithms described in Chaps. 3 and 4. Of particular interest are answers to the following questions:

1. Which are the better and which are the poorer algorithms?
2. How does the nature of the problem, that is, the degree of nonlinearity, the number of variables, and so forth, affect the performance of an algorithm?
3. How do the derivative-free algorithms compare with those that use derivatives?
4. Why do specific algorithms founder?

To compare successfully the performance of different algorithms, it is necessary first to establish equitable criteria for evaluation. We describe certain criteria first, and then rate the algorithms, using two of the criteria.

5.1 CRITERIA FOR EVALUATION

Before evaluating the relative effectiveness of the various unconstrained algorithms, some remarks are appropriate concerning the criteria to use in evaluating their effectiveness. Algorithms can be examined from a theoretical viewpoint, as well as by experimentation. The former method can be applied only to a rather restricted class of problems; hence we will be concerned here with the evaluation of the effectiveness of algorithms by experimentation, i.e., by solving test problems. Algorithms can be tested on problems with both a small and large number of variables, on problems with varying degrees of nonlinearity, and on problems evolving from practical applications, such as least squares, solution of sets of nonlinear equations, and the like. By examining the effectiveness of an algorithm in treating a variety of problems, one can hope to predict the general effectiveness of an algorithm in solving other problems.

One matter of primary concern is that of *robustness*, or reliability: can an algorithm be expected to solve most problems? Of course, any algorithm can be defeated by a suitably designed (pathological) problem. Even for other than pathological problems we cannot realistically ask that an algorithm solve *all* possible problems, for it is easy to pose an unconstrained nonlinear programming problem that leads to negative arguments, division by zero, discontinuities, and the like. Furthermore, we cannot expect that an algorithm will pick out the global minimum if the problem has more than one minimum, but it should at least reach a local minimum to be considered successful. However, one man's concept of success may be another man's concept of failure. For example, consider Problem 31 in Appendix A, illustrated by Fig. 5.2–7 (a penalty function), in which the global minimum is at $-\infty$ whereas a local minimum exists near (1.7,1.3). If a minimization technique proceeds toward the global minimum, should it be deemed a success or a failure? If the technique is used as a subroutine in a penalty function algorithm, then it is the local minimum that is sought rather than the global minimum.

Any experimental comparison of algorithms depends to a considerable extent on how the algorithms are programmed for the computer. Small details of the programming can exert a considerable influence on the effectiveness of an algorithm. Slight changes in the termination criteria, the unidimensional search technique, tests of matrices for singularity, matrix inversion procedures, reset, and the like, make a big difference in the performance of an algorithm. Just a simple change in the initial step in the unidimensional search was shown in Sec. 3.4 to have quite an impact on the search trajectory in minimizing Rosenbrock's function. Many of these factors have been ignored by authors in reporting their test results for an algorithm because the factors were deemed to be unrelated to the basic algorithm, yet their contribution to the workability of an algorithm should never go unrecognized. Many algorithms, to be successful, also require that heuristic logic be introduced into the algorithm. Such logic is devised from experimental experience with failure and has little to do with the fundamental concept underlying the algorithm, but makes it work.

The criteria to be considered in the evaluation of the unconstrained algorithms in this chapter are:

1. Robustness—success in obtaining an optimal solution (to within a certain precision) for a wide range of problems
2. Number of functional evaluations
3. Computer time to termination (to within the desired degree of precision)

Some comments concerning the choice among these criteria and their vague character follow.

It is generally accepted that the primary criterion in evaluating general-purpose algorithms must be whether or not the algorithm can solve most of the problems posed. Associated with this concept is that of the acceptable degree of precision in the solution, that is, in the value of the objective function $f(\mathbf{x}^*)$ and of the elements of the vector of variables $\mathbf{x}^*$. Usually, the degree of precision in the solution depends upon the termination criteria used to end the computation.

To provide for uniform criteria for termination, in all the unpublished work described here, the algorithms were modified so that the same relative precision in the optimal $\mathbf{x}$ vector $\mathbf{x}^*$ and also in $f(\mathbf{x}^*)$ was the joint base for stopping the search in each code. Figure 5.1–1 indicates why both criteria must be satisfied. If the algorithm is set up to terminate solely on the fractional change in $f(\mathbf{x})$ being less than some small number, a flat plateau can cause premature termination. Alternatively, if the algorithm is set up to terminate solely on the fractional change in the elements of $\mathbf{x}$, a steep slope can cause premature termination. Use of only the components of the gradient can lead to termination at a saddle point, and in minimizing penalty functions the gradient components can be small and yet the $\mathbf{x}$ vector can change significantly. One feature that should be mentioned concerning the termination criteria is that when $f(\mathbf{x})$ and/or $\mathbf{x} \rightarrow 0$, the termination criteria must be the fractional change rather than relative change in $f(\mathbf{x})$

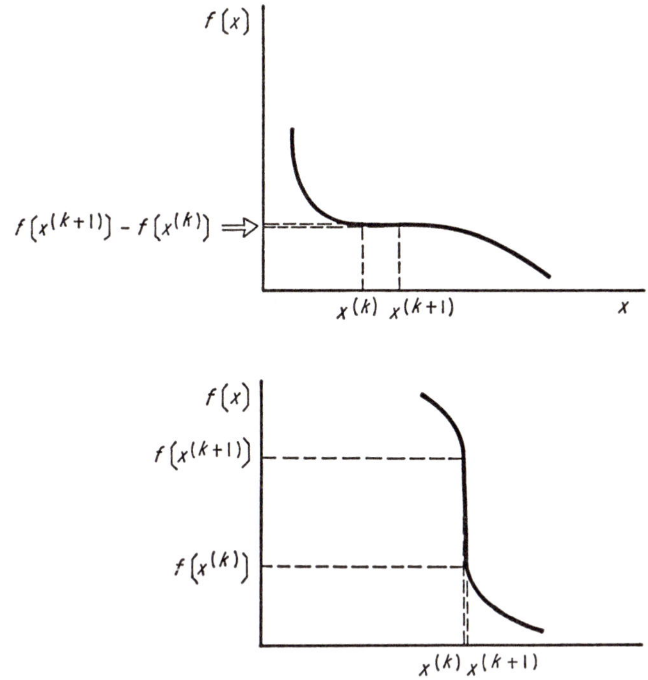

Fig. 5.1–1 Joint criteria for termination in minimizing $f(\mathbf{x})$ illustrated in two dimensions. A criterion based solely on

$$\frac{f(\mathbf{x}^{(k+1)}) - f(\mathbf{x}^{(k)})}{f(\mathbf{x}^{(k)})} > \varepsilon$$

will terminate prematurely on a flat plateau; a criterion based solely on

$$\frac{\mathbf{x}^{(k+1)} - \mathbf{x}^{(k)}}{\mathbf{x}^{(k)}} < \varepsilon$$

will terminate prematurely on a very steep slope.

and/or $\mathbf{x}$ to avoid dividing by a very small number. Some authors have used as termination criteria the norm of $\nabla f(\mathbf{x})$, the norm of $\mathbf{x}$, or the norm of $\mathbf{s}$, and although these are perfectly adequate criteria under most circumstances, they do suffer from the same deficiencies identified in Fig. 5.1–1.

If a problem can be solved, the second criterion, one that is widely employed, comes into play: a measure of the effectiveness of an algorithm is the number of functional evaluations of $f(\mathbf{x})$ to reach a certain precision in $f(\mathbf{x})$ and $\mathbf{x}$. Certainly, this criterion is better than the number of stages, for the latter varies quite widely from algorithm to algorithm and in many algorithms means something quite different from the selection of a new search direction. Nevertheless, the number of function evaluations itself is not too satisfactory a measure of efficiency for algorithms with widely differing strategies because the number of functional evaluations to devise a search direction relative to the number of functional evaluations to move in a given direction differs widely from strategy to strategy. Furthermore, how should the evaluation of the derivatives be weighted relative to the evaluation of the objective function itself so that the derivative methods include both objective function and derivative evaluations? Finally, one can reduce the number of function evaluations by all sorts of time-consuming tests, special heuristic operations, matrix operations, and so forth, so that a comparison based solely on function evaluations can easily be misleading.

Consequently, a third criterion, the computation time to execute an algorithm, is alternatively cited as a measure of the effectiveness of an algorithm. Although the relative time to termination is not a particularly desirable measure of the effectiveness of an unconstrained nonlinear programming algorithm, in lieu of a better measure it often has to serve. Section 9.1 contains some specific comments on the hazards of using time alone as a criterion. For simple test problems the time required to read the data and execute the print commands (not the printing itself) in a code with a modestly detailed printout—say $\mathbf{x}$ and $f(\mathbf{x})$ for each stage—may be two or three times the computation time experienced when these phases of the code are bypassed. In computers in which the central processing unit operates on several programs in a time-sharing recycling mode, the input-output times when added up may easily exceed by a factor of 2 or 3 the single pass time for execution. Thus the type of computer, the care in the coding of the algorithm, and the character of the measured time, all have an important bearing on the use of time of execution as a criterion. Such information is usually missing from reports in the literature describing the behavior of a specific algorithm.

5.2 TEST PROBLEMS

A number of test problems have been used by various authors of nonlinear programming algorithms. Some of the test problems have been used so often that they have assumed the role of "classics," being repetitively used to compare the performance of algorithms, usually to demonstrate that a new algorithm is as good or better than its predecessor. Table 5.2–1 lists 10 functions that have been reported quite often in the literature as test functions, and Problems 25 through 35 in Appendix A constitute an additional set,

Table 5.2-1 Unconstrained objective functions used as test functions

Function	Ref.	Starting vector $(\mathbf{x}^0)^T$	Values at minimum of $f(\mathbf{x})$: $f(\mathbf{x}^*)$	$(\mathbf{x}^*)$
I: $100(x_2 - x_1^2)^2 + (1 - x_1)^2$	[1]	(−1.2,1)	0	(1,1)
II: $(x_2 - x_1^2)^2 + (1 - x_1)^2$	[2]	(−1.2,1)	0	(1,1)
III: $(x_2 - x_1^2)^2 + 100(1 - x_1)^2$	[2]	(−1.2,1)	0	(1,1)
IV: $100(x_2 - x_1^3)^2 + (1 - x_1)^2$	[2]	(−1.2,1)	0	(1,1)
V: $[1.5 - x_1(1 - x_2)]^2 + [2.25 - x_1(1 - x_2^2)]^2 + [2.625 - x_1(1 - x_2^3)]^2$	[3]		0	$(3,\frac{1}{2})$
VI: $100(x_2 - x_1^2)^2 + (1 - x_1)^2 + 90(x_4 - x_3^2)^2 + (1 - x_3)^3 + 10.1(x_2 - 1)^2 + (x_4 - 1)^2 + 19.8(x_2 - 1)(x_4 - 1)$	[4]	(−3,−1,−3,−1)	0	(1,1,1,1)
VII: $(x_1 + 10x_2) + 5(x_3 - x_4)^2 + (x_2 - 2x_3)^4 + 10(x_1 - x_4)^4$	[6]	(−3,−1,0,1)	0	(0,0,0,0)
VIII: $(e^{x}_1 - x_2)^4 + 100(x_2 - x_3)^6 + \tan^4(x_3 - x_4) + x_1^8 + (x_4 - 1)^2$	[7]	(1,2,2,2)	0	$[0,1,1,(1 \pm n\pi)]$
IX: *P* function for Problem 10 in Appendix A	[5]	See Appendix A for details; Chap. 7 for *P*	See Appendix A for details; Chap. 7 for *P*	
X: *P* function for Problem 18 in Appendix A	[5]	See Appendix A for details; Chap. 7 for *P*	See Appendix A for details; Chap. 7 for *P*	

[1] H. H. Rosenbrock, *Computer J.*, **3**:175 (1960).
[2] B. F. Whitte and W. R. Holst, paper submitted at the 1964 Spring Joint Computer Conference, Washington, D.C., 1964.
[3] E. M. L. Beale, On an Iterative Method of Finding a Local Minimum of a Function of More Than One Variable, *Princeton Univ. Stat. Tech. Res. Group Tech. Rept.* 25, November, 1958.
[4] Ascribed to C. F. Wood, Westinghouse Research Laboratories; the function has several local minima that can cause premature termination.
[5] Reference is in Appendix A.
[6] M. J. D. Powell, *Computer J.*, **7**:155 (1964). Note that the hessian matrix of this function at its minimum is singular.
[7] E. E. Cragg and A. V. Levy, *Rice Univ. Aero-Astronautics Rept.* 58, Houston, Tex., 1969.

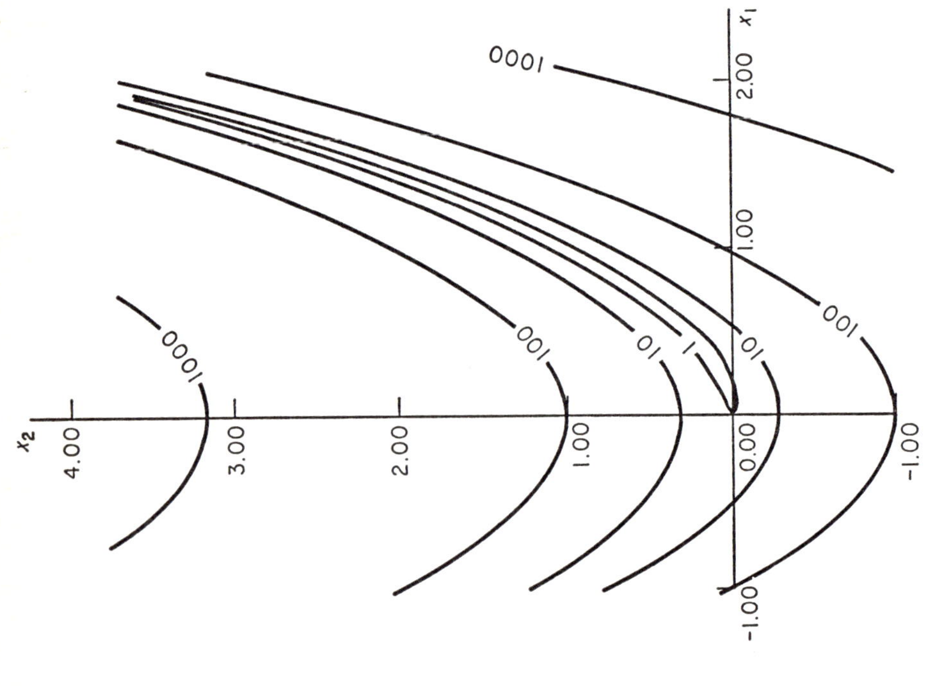

Fig. 5.2-1 Function I: $f(\mathbf{x}) = 100(x_2 - x_1^2)^2 + (1 - x_1)^2$.

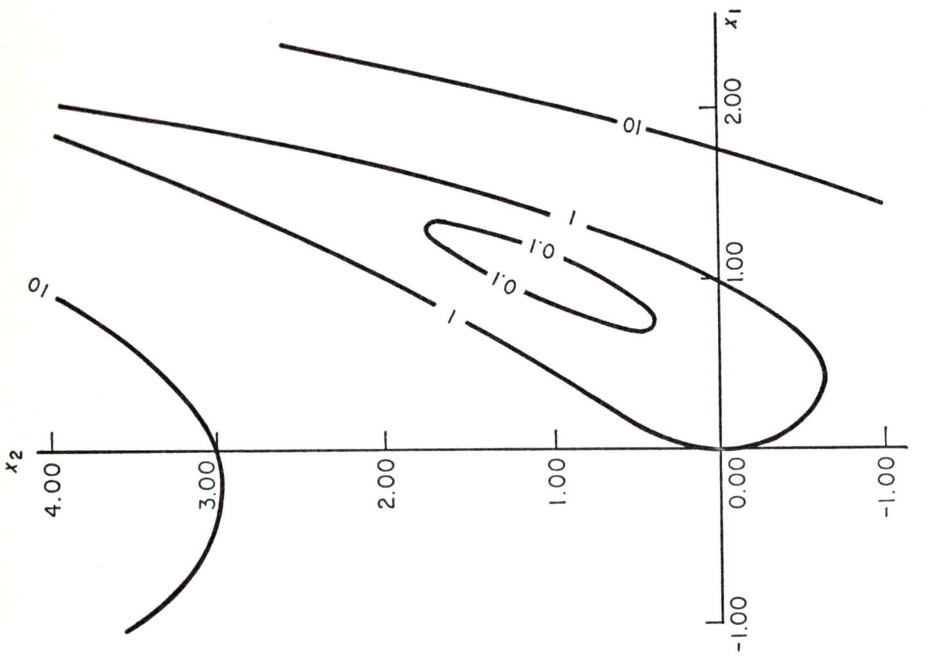

Fig. 5.2-2 Function II: $f(\mathbf{x}) = (x_2 - x_1^2)^2 + (1 - x_1)^2$.

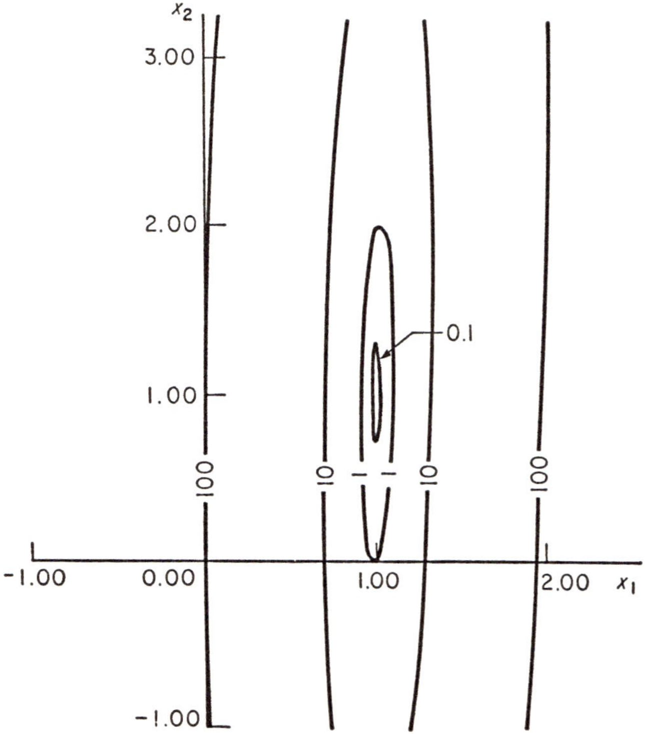

Fig. 5.2-3 Function III: $f(\mathbf{x}) = (x_2 - x_1^2)^2 + 100\,(1 - x_1)^2$

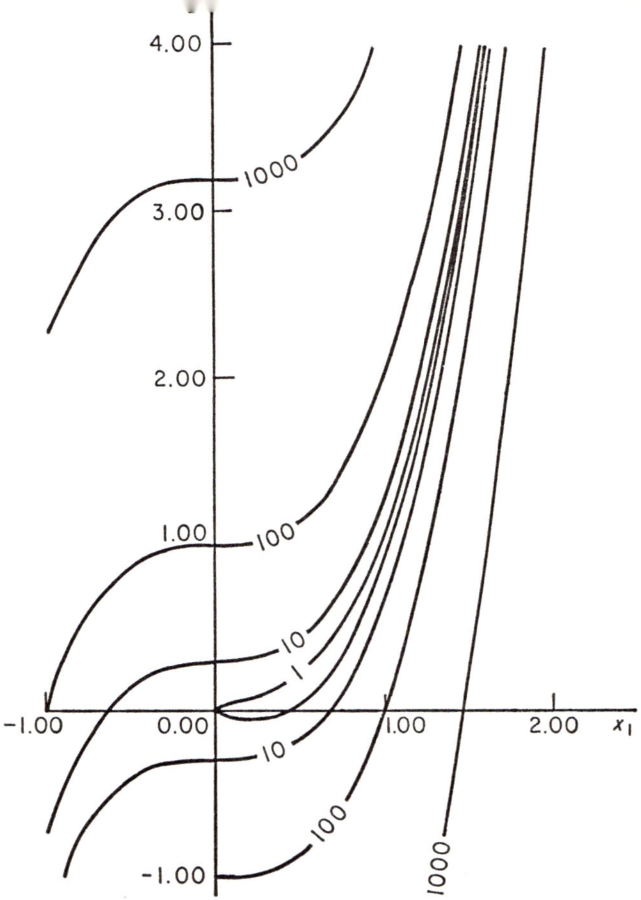

Fig. 5.2-4 Function IV: $f(\mathbf{x}) = (x_2 - x_1^3) + (1 - x_1)^2$.

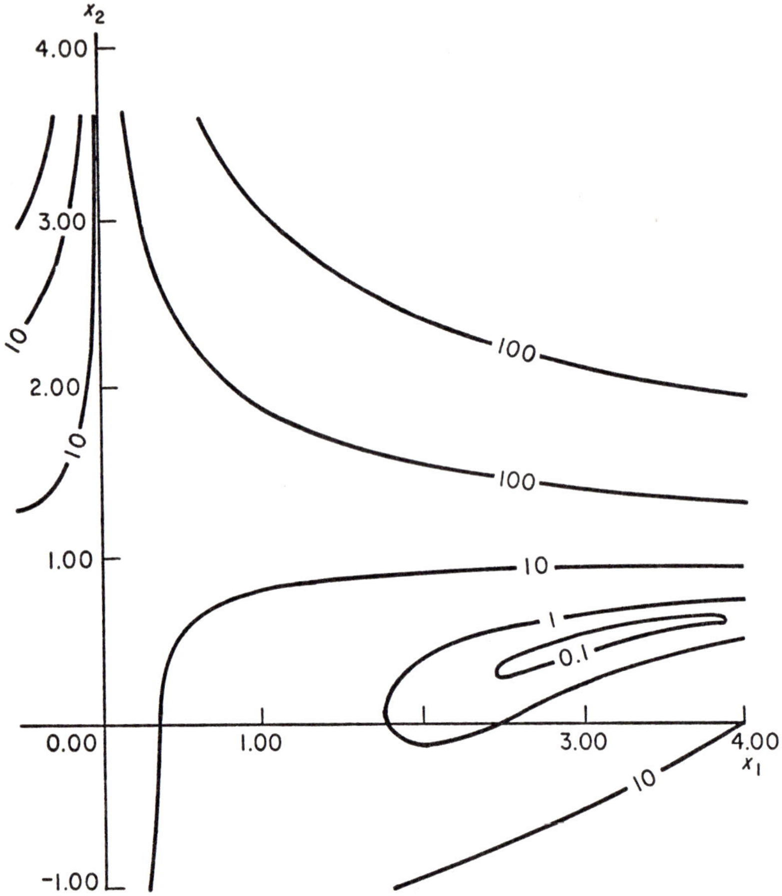

Fig. 5.2-5 Function V: $f(\mathbf{x}) = [1.5 - x_1(1 - x_2)]^2 + [2.25 - x_1(1 - x_2^2)]^2 + [2.625 - x_1(1 - x_2^3)]^2$.

some of which have not been used before. Figures 5.2-1 through 5.2-8 illustrate the contours of the two-dimensional objective functions, demonstrating how complex they can be. Rosenbrock's function (function I in Table 5.2, and Problem 2 in Appendix A), a function that has been illustrated many times in Chaps. 3 and 4, has a steep curved valley along the curve $x_2 = x_1^2$, whereas function II has a shallower valley. Function III has a steep valley along $x_1 = 1$. Function IV has a steep valley along the curve $x_2 = x_1^3$, and Beale's function, V, has a narrow curving valley approaching the line $x_2 = 1$. Functions IX and X are penalty functions (to be described in Chap. 7).

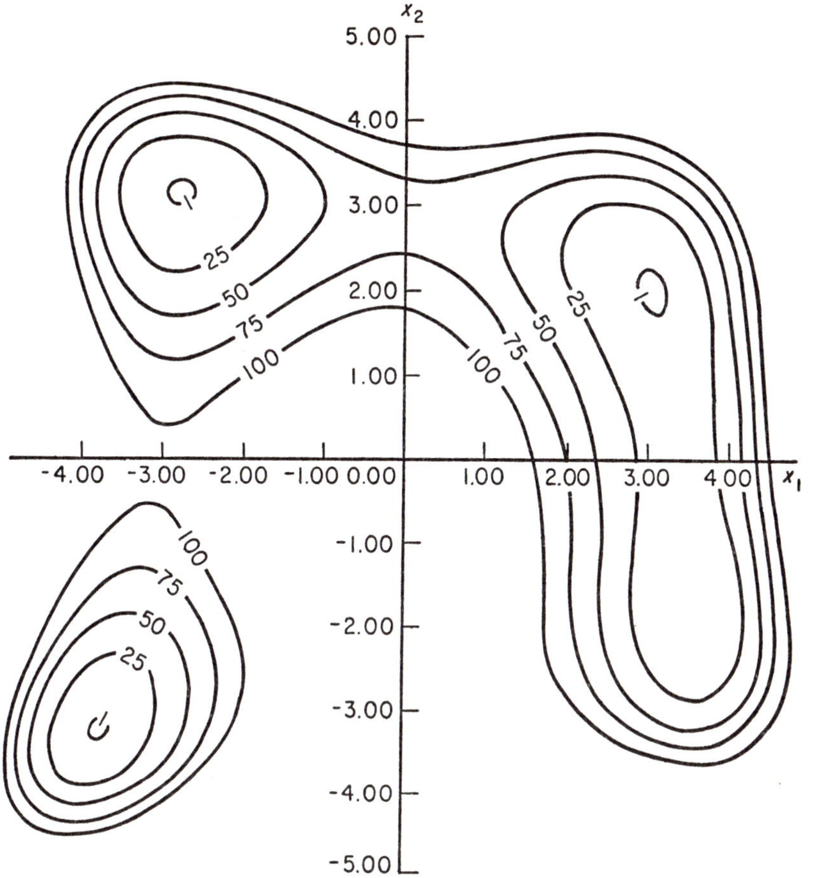

Fig. 5.2-6 Function 28, Appendix A: $f(\mathbf{x}) = (x_1^2 + x_2 - 11)^2 + (x_1 + x_2^2 - 7)^2$.

5.3 EVALUATION OF UNCONSTRAINED ALGORITHMS

We will first examine some studies reported in the literature and then look at some unpublished results, comparing most of the algorithms in Chaps. 3 and 4 on a uniform basis.

A study by Leon[1] compared, among others:

1. The Davidon method as programmed by Stevens[2]

[1]Alberto Leon, A Comparison among Eight Known Optimizing Procedures, in A. Lavi and T. P. Vogl (eds.), "Recent Advances in Optimization Techniques," John Wiley & Sons, Inc., New York, 1966.

[2]D. F. Stevens, "Instructions for the Use of VARMINT," University of California, Lawrence Radiation Laboratory, Berkeley, June, 1961.

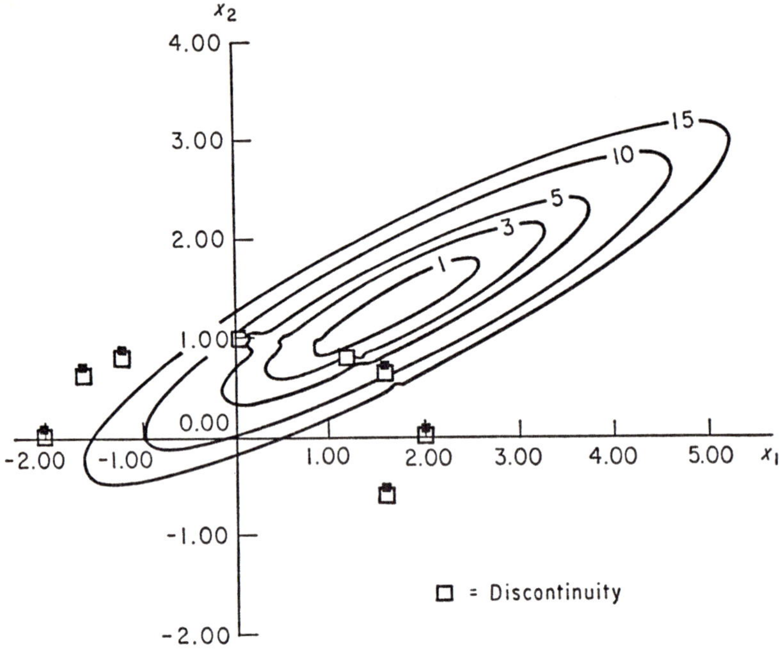

Fig. 5.2–7 Function 31, Appendix A:

$$f(\mathbf{x}) = (x_1 - 2)^2 + (x_2 - 1)^2 + \frac{0.04}{-(x_1^2/4) - x_2^2 + 1} + \frac{1}{0.2}(x_1 - 2x_2 + 1)^2$$

2. A program by Baer[1] that generated sequences of restricted minima, and interpolates between them in the vicinity of $f(\mathbf{x})$
3. Steepest descent Partan
4. Continued Partan[2]
5. Iterated Partan

using the first five objective functions listed in Table 5.2–1. Table 5.3–1 lists several of the starting vectors, the final $\mathbf{x}$ vector, the value of $f(\mathbf{x})$ at the final $\mathbf{x}$ vector, and the relative time to the termination of the minimization. All values except the relative times are rounded to the third decimal place. Steepest descent Partan and iterated Partan are not included in Table 5.3–1 inasmuch as these algorithms performed very poorly, in the sense that the final $\mathbf{x}$ vectors deviated from the known $\mathbf{x}^*$ vectors at the minima by more

[1] R. M. Baer, *Computer J.*, **5**:193 (1962).

[2] T. E. Doerfler, "PARTAN Minimization by Method of Parallel Tangents," Iowa State University, Ames, Iowa, April, 1964.

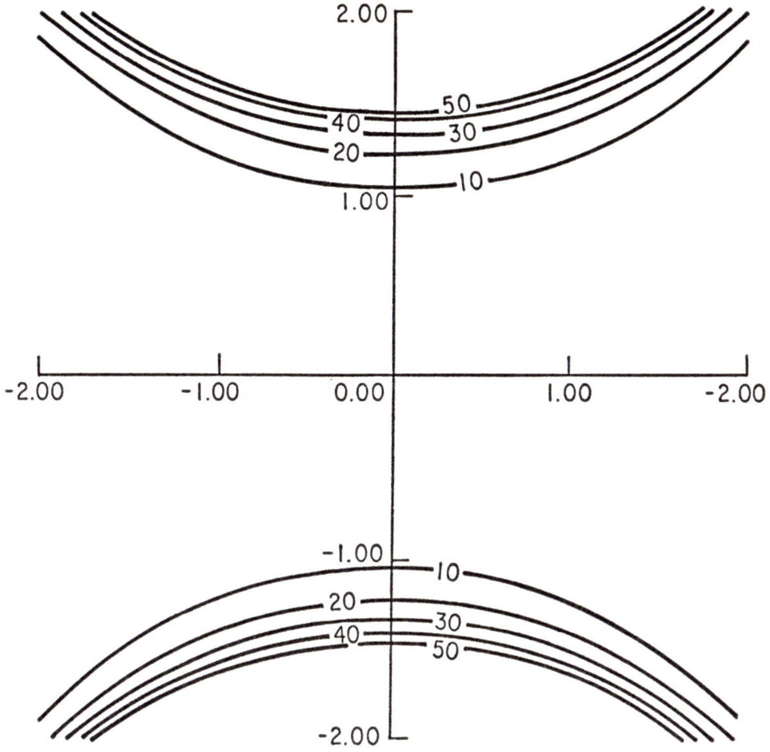

Fig. 5.2–8 Function 33, Appendix A: $f(\mathbf{x}) = e^{-(x_1^2 - x_2^2)}[2x_1^2 + 3x_2^2]$.

than 5 percent in a large fraction of the trials, and in many cases deviated by more than 100 percent.

Table 5.3–1 demonstrates that the Davidon-Fletcher-Powell procedure was superior as a general unconstrained nonlinear programming tool for obtaining correct values of the **x** vector at the minimum of the objective function. Baer's procedure stumbled in minimizing Beale's objective function from certain starting vectors, while continued Partan was unable to deal with Rosenbrock's function. Inasmuch as the relative execution times for the algorithms were roughly the same, the Davidon-Fletcher-Powell method was preferred.

Another study, one by Wortman,[1] employed the Davidon-Fletcher-Powell and Newton methods along with the Hooke-Jeeves and Powell search methods (described in Chap. 4) as subroutines in a larger computer program.

[1]J. D. Wortman, NLPROG, *Ballistic Res. Lab. Mem. Rept.* 1958, Aberdeen Proving Grounds, Md., January, 1969.

Table 5.3-1 Results from the minimization of five functions

Function	Initial values			Davidon				Baer				Continued Partan			
				Final values			Relative* time	Final values			Relative* time	Final values			Relative* time
	x_1	x_2	$f(\mathbf{x})$	x_1	x_2	$f(\mathbf{x})$		x_1	x_2	$f(\mathbf{x})$		x_1	x_2	$f(\mathbf{x})$	
I	−1.200	1.000	24.200	1.000	1.000	3.4×10^{-11}	1.00	1.000	1.000	2.7×10^{-12}	0.50	0.939	0.882	3.7×10^{-2}	0.50
	−2.000	−2.000	3609.0	1.000	1.000	6.5×10^{-11}	0.64	1.000	1.000	4.3×10^{-12}	1.71	1.002	1.003	4.0×10^{-6}	0.35
	5.621	−3.635	1.24×10^{5}	1.000	1.000	9.3×10^{-13}	0.78	1.000	1.000	1.0×10^{-12}	1.62	1.000	1.000	9.6×10^{-3}	0.41
	−0.221	0.639	36.320	1.000	1.000	7.5×10^{-15}	0.66	1.000	1.000	1.7×10^{-12}	0.92	0.940	0.883	3.6×10^{-3}	0.50
II	−2.000	−2.000	45.000	1.000	1.000	1.4×10^{-12}	0.51	1.000	1.000	7.2×10^{-16}	1.77	0.999	1.000	1.0×10^{-6}	0.34
	0.803	−0.251	0.840	1.000	1.000	5.8×10^{-15}	0.26	1.000	1.000	9.7×10^{-11}	1.11	0.991	0.979	9.2×10^{-5}	0.19
	0.211	3.505	12.600	1.000	1.000	1.5×10^{-14}	0.30	1.000	1.000	2.9×10^{-15}	0.29	1.000	1.000	2.2×10^{-16}	0.27
III	2.000	−2.000	136.00	1.000	1.000	5.5×10^{-12}	0.44	1.000	1.000	5.6×10^{-15}	0.50	1.000	1.000	4.7×10^{-11}	0.17
	1.992	−3.222	150.10	1.000	1.000	1.1×10^{-12}	0.34	1.000	1.000	2.6×10^{-10}	0.20	1.000	1.000	1.1×10^{-12}	0.16
	1.986	5.227	98.86	1.000	1.000	2.7×10^{-12}	0.23	1.000	1.000	2.2×10^{-12}	0.32	1.000	1.000	1.0×10^{-12}	0.12
IV	1.200	−2.000	1389.8	1.000	1.000	2.3×10^{-13}	0.95	1.000	1.000	2.1×10^{-13}	1.05	1.000	0.999	9.8×10^{-7}	0.94
	0.248	−3.082	964.54	1.000	1.000	5.6×10^{-13}	0.92	1.000	1.000	1.0×10^{-8}	0.90	1.000	1.000	9.9×10^{-13}	1.16
	−1.200	−1.000	57.840	1.000	1.000	9.2×10^{-13}	1.00	1.000	1.000	5.2×10^{-14}	0.98	1.000	1.000	1.1×10^{-13}	1.15
V	0.000	0.000	14.200	3.000	0.500	1.8×10^{-15}	0.54	3.000	0.500	2.3×10^{-12}	0.37	2.999	0.500	3.3×10^{-7}	1.07
	8.000	0.200	81.700	3.000	0.500	1.0×10^{-11}	0.67	2.045	0.075	5.4×10^{-1}	1.21	3.002	0.501	8.7×10^{-7}	0.40
	5.000	0.800	0.490	3.000	0.500	2.2×10^{-13}	0.42	3.000	0.500	3.6×10^{-14}	0.94	3.000	0.500	3.7×10^{-13}	0.43
	8.000	0.800	2.042	3.000	0.500	2.8×10^{-12}	0.62	7.996	0.874	3.8×10^{-1}	0.10	3.000	0.500	1×10^{0}	0.37

*All times are relative to the time for function I by the Davidon method from $\mathbf{x}^0 = [-1.2 \quad 1.0]^T$.

Functions I, II, IV, and VII in Table 5.2–1 were tested. Table 5.3–2 lists Wortman's results in terms of the number of function evaluations, together with some data collected by others. (Table 7.2–1 details some related results for function IX in Table 5.2–1.) In Table 5.3–2 the column head "Stages" refers to the number of successive search directions set up (the same as the number of minima found in the linear searches), and "Evals." refers to the number of function evaluations. In the linear searches a mixture of sequential search and curve fitting was employed.

As executed by Wortman, the Hooke and Jeeves procedure was slightly modified from that described in Sec. 4.1, in that on a successful step, the next x_i was twice the previous x_i, whereas on a failure, the next x_i was one-half the previous x_i. In the Hooke and Jeeves search, the column headed "Stages" refers to an exploratory search plus, possibly, a pattern move, while in the Powell search, a stage consists of finding a minimum by a linear search in each of the N independent coordinate directions plus, possibly, a minimum in the composite direction.

All the final values of the elements of the vector of independent variables were within 10^{-5} (10^{-4} for Hooke-Jeeves) of the true values of the elements of $\mathbf{x}^*$ except as indicated by the footnote. The number of function evaluations is somewhat larger than would be obtained if the particular computer code were removed as a subroutine and used alone. Nevertheless, the Davidon-Fletcher-Powell algorithm appears to be nearly as satisfactory as Newton's method. (In this instance, in the Newton algorithm, when the hessian matrix was not positive definite, the direction matrix was replaced by the identity matrix; i.e., the negative of the gradient was chosen as the search direction.)

Table 5.3–3 lists for several algorithms the number of stages reported by Pearson to reduce $f(\mathbf{x}^*)$ below 10^{-13}. These numbers are not the number of functional evaluations, because during each stage a one-dimensional Fibonacci search was executed to find the minimum of $f(\mathbf{x})$. Changing the termination criterion for the one-dimensional search would change the number of iterations; hence the data reported in the table must be viewed as relative rather than absolute data. The column headed "Reset" indicates that after $(n + 1)$ steps, $\boldsymbol{\eta}^{(n+1)}$ was reset to $\mathbf{R}^{(0)}$, and the algorithm repeated; in the Fletcher-Reeves and projection methods, the starting point *must* be reset.

Newton's method always was the best, and the other methods, exclusive of the Fletcher-Reeves method, which failed in some tests, were roughly of the same effectiveness. Table 5.3–3 demonstrates that the resetting of $\boldsymbol{\eta}$ has merit for objective functions evolving from the penalty function concept—as the active constraints are approached by $\mathbf{x}$, the hessian matrix of the

Table 5.3-2 Comparison of several unconstrained minimization techniques

	Davidon-Fletcher-Powell method						*Newton method by Wortman* [1]		
	By Wortman [1]			*By Fletcher-Powell* [2]					
Function and $\mathbf{x}^{(0)}$	$f(\mathbf{x}^*)$	*Stages*	*Evals.*	$f(\mathbf{x}^*)$	*Stages*	*Evals.*	$f(\mathbf{x}^*)$	*Stages*	*E*[illegible]
I(−1.2,1.0)	1×10^{-12}	23	120	1×10^{-8}	18	—	3×10^{-13}	17	
I(−2.547,1.489)	6×10^{-16}	16	87				6×10^{-16}	20	[illegible]
II(0.211,3.505)	1×10^{-11}	9	36				2×10^{-18}	8	
IV(−1.2,1.0)	3×10^{-12}	21	120				4×10^{-15}	25	[illegible]
IV(0.248,−3.082)	7×10^{-15}	23	115				2×10^{-19}	16	
V(0,0)	7×10^{-14}	12	39				2×10^{-17}	9	
V(8,0.8)	7×10^{-14}	21	119				0.25†	400	1[illegible]
VI(3,−1,0,1)	5×10^{-10}	32	149	2.5×10^{-8}	6	—	8×10^{-12}	26	

†Hessian matrix not positive definite so that a steepest descent search was used; $\mathbf{x}_{\text{final}} = [7.94 \quad 0.858$[illegible]

[1] J. D. Wortman, NLPROG, *Ballistic Res. Lab.* MR 1958, Aberdeen Proving Grounds, January, 19[illegible]

[2] R. Fletcher and M. J. D. Powell, *Computer J.*, **6**:163 (1963).

[3] R. Fletcher, *Computer J.*, **8**:33 (1965).

penalty function becomes quite ill-conditioned. For the other functions the resetting of $\boldsymbol{\eta}$ has no advantage. McCormick and Pearson[1] concluded that the use of reset variable metric methods is the most advantageous in the early stages of the optimization, whereas the absence of reset is preferable in later stages, when $\mathbf{x}$ is close enough to $\mathbf{x}^*$ so that the conjugate properties of the variable metric algorithms become effective.

Examination of the test results presented so far can give only a fragmentary picture of the relative effectiveness of the unconstrained algorithms because each study used different unidimensional search methods, different termination criteria, and different methods of counting function evaluations. A more desirable state of affairs would be to conduct the evaluation using a uniform set of standards and test problems. To reduce the mass of data that can be generated by solving test problems to some reasonably comprehensible size, we will take advantage of the fact that all the algorithms reduce (at least are supposed to reduce) the objective function monotonically from stage to stage. Hence, if we plot $[f(\mathbf{x}) - f(\mathbf{x}^*)]$, $\|f(\mathbf{x})\|$, or even better, $\log_{10}[f(\mathbf{x}) - f(\mathbf{x}^*)]$ versus number of function evaluations or time, we obtain figures such as Fig. 5.3–1 and 5.3–2. We could plot $\|\mathbf{x} - \mathbf{x}^*\|$ or another criterion for comparison, but these functions may not be reduced monotonically. Such figures provide an empirical measure of the

[1] G. P. McCormick and J. D. Pearson, Chap. 21 in R. Fletcher (ed.), "Optimization," Academic Press, Inc., London, 1969.

avies-Swann-Campey ethod by Fletcher [3]			*Hooke and Jeeves method*			*Powell method*					
			By Wortman [1]			*By Wortman* [1]			*By Powell* [2]		
(x^*)	*Stages*	*Evals.*	$f(x^*)$	*Stages*	*Evals.*	$f(x^*)$	*Stages*	*Evals.*	$f(x^*)$	*Stages*	*Evals.*
$\times 10^{-12}$	21	187	2×10^{-7}	87	353	4×10^{-14}	15	192	7×10^{-10}	13	151
			2×10^{-9}	142	588	9×10^{-14}	17	216			
			2×10^{-10}	40	168	6×10^{-16}	7	66			
			3×10^{-9}	106	458	5×10^{-13}	17	202			
			3×10^{-7}	44	181	9×10^{-16}	24	333			
			1×10^{-11}	43	181	1×10^{-15}	7	77			
			4×10^{-10}	56	230	1×10^{-17}	9	119			
10^{-11}	12	196	2×10^{-8}	100	769	3×10^{-9}	19	89	5×10^{-9}	16	235

rate of convergence of the respective algorithms. Observe that if we arbitrarily terminate the optimization at a reasonable degree of precision in $[f(\mathbf{x}) - f(\mathbf{x}^*)]$, say 10^{-10}, we can use the corresponding number of function evaluations or time at that cutoff level for each algorithm as a single measure of the degree of effectiveness of the algorithm. Although the absolute values of the function evaluations or times may have little meaning, the relative ranking of the algorithms proves to be a reasonable quantitative mechanism for evaluation.

Attempts to compare quite different algorithms on the basis of the number of function evaluations can be less satisfactory than on the basis of the use of execution times, particularly if the times can be determined on the same computer, using common subroutines, and the problems are solved to the same degree of precision. For example, to cite one obstacle to the use of the number of function evaluations from Fig. 5.3–1, the equivalent number of function evaluations for Powell's method represents just objective function evaluations; in the Fletcher-Reeves method it represents calls of the function subroutine adjusted so that one gradient call (comprising two derivatives) is equivalent to one objective function call; and in the Goldstein-Price algorithm the calculation of two components of the gradient is also treated as equivalent to one objective function evaluation. In Fig. 5.3–2, one gradient call is equivalent to two objective function calls. However, the gradient components are evaluated much more often in the Goldstein-Price algorithm than in the Fletcher-Reeves algorithm, leading to some relative distortion between these algorithms because of the arbitrary assignment of equivalent function count. Consequently, times to reach a given value of

Table 5.3-3 Number of stages to reduce $f(x)$ to $<10^{-13}$

Algorithm	*Sec. ref.*	*Function I in Table 5.2-1 (Rosenbrock's function)*		*Function VI in Table 5.2-1 (Wood's function)*		*Function IX in Table 5.2-1**		*Function X in Table 5.2-1†*	
		Normal	*Reset*	*Normal*	*Reset*	*Normal*	*Reset*	*Normal*	*Reset*
Pearson No. 2	3.4-3	18	31	36	47	27(62)	22(60)	134(221)	98(187)
Pearson No. 3	3.4-3	21	37	46	47	33(67)	22(54)	136(246)	100(168)
Davidon-Fletcher-Powell	3.4-2	19	35	40	49	27(60)	22(56)	406(500)	97(169)
Newton	3.2-1	12		23	—	11(22)	—	30(48)	—
Fletcher-Reeves	3.3-2	—	16	—	30	—	34(F)	—	>489(F)
Projected Newton (Pearson)	3.4-3	36	21	58	55	31(20)	67(54)	166(230)	113(186)
Projection (Zoutendijk)	3.3-4	—	42	—	65	(26)	(70)	(120)	(211)

*Numbers without parentheses are for $r = 1$; with parentheses, for $r = 2.44 \times 10^{-4}$ (see Chap. 7).
†Numbers without parentheses are for $r = 1$; with parentheses, for $r = 0.0625$ (see Chap. 7).
F = failure.
Source: J. D. Pearson, *Computer J.*, **13**:171 (1969).

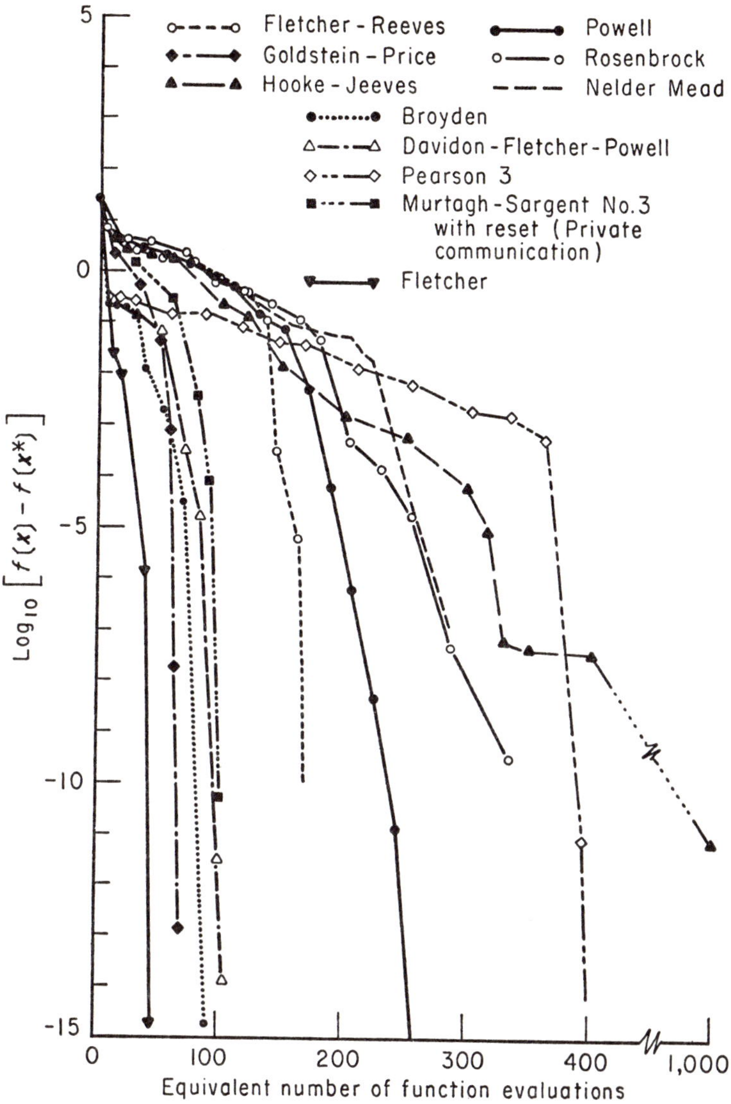

Fig. 5.3-1 Comparison of unconstrained algorithms for Rosenbrock's function.

$\log_{10}[f(\mathbf{x}) - f(\mathbf{x}^*)]$ rather than equivalent function evaluations have been selected for the subsequent analysis as being the single most suitable measure of effectiveness.

Two unidimensional searches have been employed, where appropriate, the golden section and the DSC-Powell search, both of which have been de-

Table 5.3-4 Comparison of execution times (in seconds) for eleven test problems by eleven algorithms

		Problems in Appendix A or Table 5.2-1										
Algorithm	*Sec.*	*2(I[a])*	*VI[a]*	*26(VII[a])*	*28*	*29*	*30*	*31*	*32*	*33*	*34*	*35(V[a])*
Broyden	3.4-1											
DSC		0.013[b]	0.089	0.060	0.040	0.031	0.024	0.010	0.125	0.015	0.037	0.013
G		0.016[b]	0.092	0.046	0.012	0.018	0.021	0.006	0.109	0.016	0.132	0.012
Davidon-Fletcher-Powell	3.4-2											
DSC		0.014[b]	0.088	0.104	0.027	0.099	0.027	0.008	0.052	0.015	0.056	0.015
G		0.016[b]	0.113	0.088	0.010	0.046	0.025	0.019	0.121	0.016	0.134	0.010
Pearson 2	3.4-3											
DSC		>1.00	F	F	>1.00	F	F	0.008	F	0.022	F	F
G		>1.00	F	F	>1.00	F	F	0.011	F	F	—	F
Pearson 3	3.4-3											
DSC		0.058	2.900 (0.314)[c]	>100	0.028	0.059	0.046	0.008	>10	0.024	>10	0.016
G		0.051	3.012 (1.199)[c]	2.763	0.011	0.106	0.065	0.010	>10	0.016	>10	0.013
Goldstein-Price	3.4-6											
DSC		0.016[b]	0.079	0.100	0.052	0.026	0.021	0.096	0.066	0.035	0.158	0.014
G		0.013	0.089	0.057	0.014	0.044	0.029	0.145	0.149	0.020	0.097	0.016
GP		—	—	—	0.081	—	—	—	0.094	—	0.043	—

Table 5.3–4 (continued)

Algorithm	*Sec.*	*2(I[a])*	*VI[a]*	*26(VII[a])*	*28*	*29*	*30*	*31*	*32*	*33*	*34*	*35(V[a])*
		Problems in Appendix A or Table 5.2–1										
Fletcher-Reeves	3.3–2											
DSC		0.027	25.0[d]	0.144	0.055	0.069	0.019	0.015	F	0.013[e]	0.064	0.012
G		—	0.330	2.330	—	—	—	—	F	—	0.975	—
Fletcher	3.4–5	0.022	0.024	0.050	0.006	0.018	0.012	0.004	0.050	0.010	0.028	0.011
Hooke-Jeeves	4.1	0.100	0.152	0.067	0.008	0.167	0.018	0.012	0.127[f]	0.054	F	0.009
Nelder-Mead	4.2	0.097	0.154	0.072	0.024	0.036	0.148	[g]	0.685[f]	0.019	0.531	0.014
Rosenbrock	4.3	0.058	0.378	0.097	0.035	0.125	0.131	0.025	0.202[f]	0.027	0.148	0.025
Powell	4.4											
DSC		0.035	0.041	0.084	0.006	0.014	0.014	0.005	0.178	0.017	0.025	0.012
G		0.050	0.098	0.174	0.021	0.106	0.028	0.015	0.857	0.018	0.108	0.027

[a]Roman number indicates problem number in Table 5.2–1.
[b]Times are 70 to 100 percent greater if search is forced to follow the curved valley.
[c] = with reset.
[d] = reset at $(n + 1)$ stages.
[e]Works only with scaling (see computer program in Appendix B).
[f] = terminated before reaching minimum in a flat plateau.
[g] = moved to global minimum at $-\infty$.
Abbreviations: DSC = DSC-Powell search; G = golden section search; F = failure; GP = Goldstein-Price search.

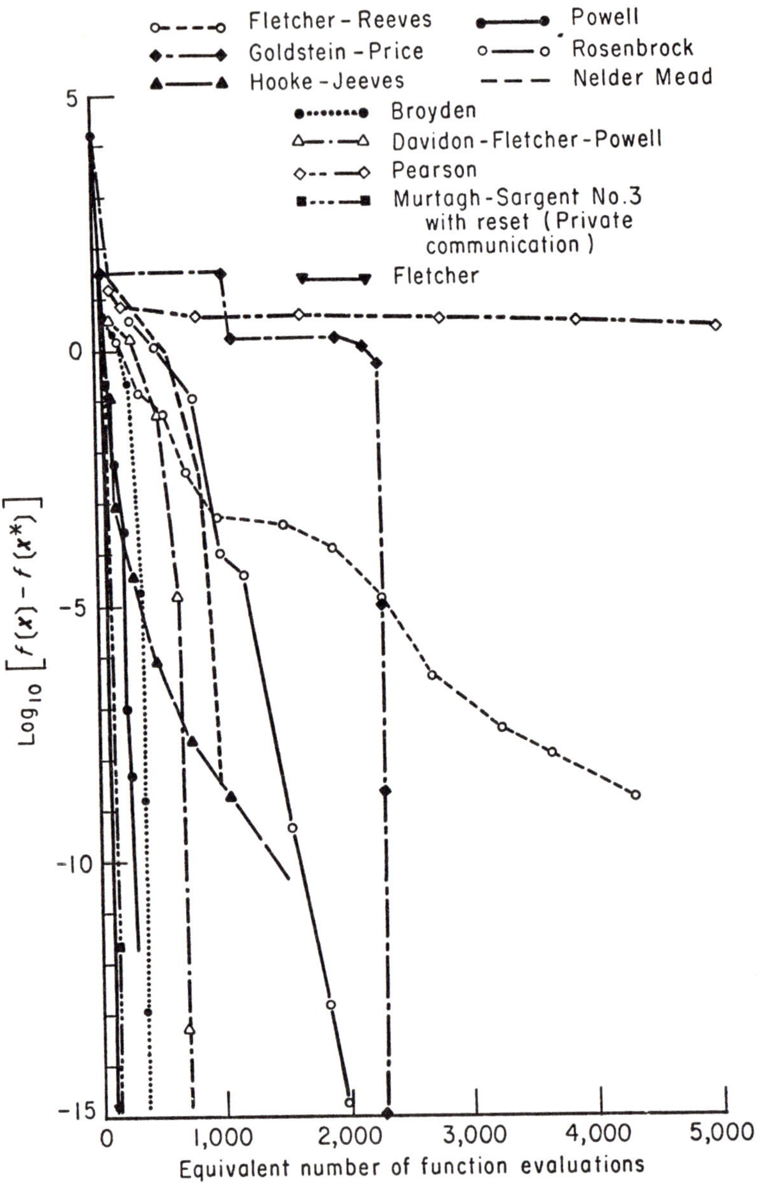

Fig. 5.3-2 Comparison of unconstrained algorithms for Wood's function

scribed in Sec. 2.6. Computer codes for these searches and many of the algorithms can be found in Appendix B. The termination criteria for the unidimensional searches were all the same, and the termination criteria for the algorithms were all essentially the same. A CDC 6600 computer was used to determine the execution times. All printing, peripheral processing, and system manipulation times are specifically excluded from the times listed in Table 5.3–4, so that the times indeed represent the number of seconds required to execute the algorithms without interruption of any sort.

Table 5.3–5 was prepared to yield an overall rating for the algorithms based on the data in Table 5.3–4. Each algorithm with accompanying subroutine was ranked in order of increasing times from 1 (fastest) to 11. The Pearson No. 2 algorithm was ignored because of repeated failures. (Some other nonrobust algorithms have been described in Chaps. 3 and 4.) After the rankings had been completed, they were averaged for the 11 problems, with each problem weighted equally. It could be argued that the more difficult problems should be weighted more than the easier problems, but this was not done. However, the distinction between the two unidimensional search subroutines was obliterated by merging the rankings to give one ranking for each algorithm.

A surprising result of the ranking was that the algorithms tended to cluster into groups. Consequently, Table 5.3–5 lists the algorithms in decreasing rank order according to execution times, classed by the qualitative terms "Superior," "Good," and "Fair," a procedure that seems to be more meaningful for the limited set of test problems used than a continuous classification. Within each classification the order is that of the computed ranking.

Table 5.3–5 Evaluation of unconstrained algorithms from execution times

Classification	*Algorithm*
Superior	Fletcher
	Davidon-Fletcher-Powell
	Broyden
	Powell
Good	Goldstein-Price
Fair	Nelder-Mead
	Rosenbrock
	Fletcher-Reeves
	Hooke-Jeeves
	Pearson No. 3
Not robust	Pearson No. 2

As expected, the search algorithms were slower than the algorithms that used derivatives, but what is of interest is the high ranking of Powell's algorithm. Broyden's algorithm and Powell's algorithm seemed to perform better in the more difficult problems (such as Problems 26 and 32) than did the Davidon-Fletcher-Powell algorithm, whereas the reverse was true for some of the simpler problems.

Five algorithms fall in the class of "Fair" algorithms. Each of these methods generally required more time than those in the "Superior" class. Further, each of these algorithms is less robust than the "Superior" group in that they can terminate prematurely or can be ineffective because of unduly excessive use of computer time. In the derivative methods, slow oscillations in the search indicate that the direction matrix becomes nearly singular. Perhaps incorporation of an appropriate restart procedure, restoring the direction matrix to a positive definite form, can improve some of the variable metric methods.

The Hooke-Jeeves, Nelder-Mead, and Rosenbrock algorithms performed rather poorly on Problem 32, a statistical estimation problem. In the vicinity of the minimum the objective function was insensitive to changes in the variables; i.e., the shape of the objective function was a plateau.

All the test problems used in developing Table 5.3–5 contained only a few variables. It is important to inquire into how the algorithms perform as the dimensionality of the problem increases. Unfortunately, very few data exist on this topic. Fletcher and Powell (1963) introduced a function to be minimized containing an adjustable number of variables.

$$f(\mathbf{x}) = \sum_{i=1}^{n} \left[E_i - \sum_{j=1}^{n} (A_{ij} \sin x_j + B_{ij} \cos x_j) \right]^2 \qquad (5.3\text{–}1)$$

Equation (5.3–1) corresponds to the solution of a simultaneous set of transcendental equations

$$\sum_{j=1}^{n} (A_{ij} \sin x_j + B_{ij} \cos x_j) = E_i \qquad i = 1, \ldots, n$$

by minimizing the sum of the squares of the residuals. The coefficients A_{ij} and B_{ij} were generated as pseudo-random integers with a uniform (rectangular) probability distribution over the interval $-100 \leq A_{ij} \leq 100$ and $-100 \leq B_{ij} \leq 100$. Values of E_i were simulated by generating various-size groups of x_j from n equal to 5 to n equal to 100 as pseudo-random real numbers in the interval $-\pi$ to π.

The objective function $f(\mathbf{x})$ was minimized with respect to the vector $\mathbf{x} = [x_1, \ldots, x_n]^T$, starting from the vector $\mathbf{x}^{(0)} = [x_1 + 0.1\delta, \ldots, x_n$

$+ 0.1\delta_n]^T$, in which the δ_j's were random numbers generated in the interval $-\pi$ to π. Table 5.3-6 lists the number of equivalent function evaluations in order to reduce the change in each x_j to less than 10^{-4}. In some trials different minima can be reached, but of course many minima exist for a function such as (5.3-1); in other trials a true local minimum may not be found.

Table 5.3-6 Influence of dimensionality on the minimization algorithm*
(Average values of equivalent function evaluations compiled from Box*)

Algorithm	*Section*	*Number of variables, n*		
		5	*10*	*20*
Fletcher-Reeves	3.3-2	286	1925	8150
Davidon-Fletcher-Powell	3.4-2	126	358	1910
Nelder-Mead	4.2	241	890	9760
Rosenbrock	4.3	426	1258	7770
Davies-Swann-Campey	4.3	298	1530	6450
Powell (1964)	4.4	103	399	1863
Powell (1965)	†	22	35	56

*M. J. Box, *Computer J.*, **9**:67 (1966). Equivalent function evaluations for the derivative methods means that 1 function evaluation plus n derivative evaluations are counted as $(n + 1)$ equivalent function evaluations.

†Least-squares method by M. J. D. Powell, *Computer J.*, **7**:303 (1965).

Although Table 5.3-6 can provide only qualitative evidence concerning the effectiveness of the respective algorithms when applied to higher-dimensional problems, it does seem as if the Davidon-Fletcher-Powell and Powell (1964) methods are roughly equivalent and distinctly superior to the other methods, except that of Powell (1965). The remarkable performance of Powell's least-squares algorithm for the problems generated by Eq. (5.3-1) leads to the question: How effective are the algorithms when applied to the special case of the least-squares problem, and in particular how do they compare with the Gauss least-squares method?

For the special case of a sum-of-squares objective function

$$f(\mathbf{x}) = \sum_{l=1}^{q} \phi_l^2(\mathbf{x}) = \boldsymbol{\phi}^T(\mathbf{x})\boldsymbol{\phi}(\mathbf{x})$$

as used in statistical analysis, $\nabla f(\mathbf{x}) = 2\mathbf{J}^T(\mathbf{x})\boldsymbol{\phi}(\mathbf{x})$, where $J(\mathbf{x})$ is the $q \times n$

jacobian matrix

$$J(\mathbf{x}) = \begin{bmatrix} \dfrac{\partial \phi_1}{\partial x_1} & \cdots & \dfrac{\partial \phi_1}{\partial x_n} \\ \cdots & \cdots & \cdots \\ \dfrac{\partial \phi_q}{\partial x_1} & \cdots & \dfrac{\partial \phi_q}{\partial x_n} \end{bmatrix}$$

and $\boldsymbol{\phi}$ is a column vector of q functions. If the gradient at $\mathbf{x}^{(k+1)}$ is approximated by

$$\nabla f(\mathbf{x}^{(k+1)}) \approx 2\mathbf{J}^T(\mathbf{x}^{(k)})\boldsymbol{\phi}(\mathbf{x}^{(k+1)}) \tag{5.3-2}$$

and $\boldsymbol{\phi}(\mathbf{x}^{(k+1)})$ is approximated by a first-order Taylor series

$$\boldsymbol{\phi}(\mathbf{x}^{(k+1)}) = \boldsymbol{\phi}(\mathbf{x}^{(k)}) + \mathbf{J}(\mathbf{x}^{(k)})(\mathbf{x}^{(k+1)} - \mathbf{x}^{(k)}) \tag{5.3-3}$$

then the introduction of Eq. (5.3–3) into Eq. (5.3–2) gives an approximation for the gradient of the objective function at the new point. The necessary conditions for a minimum to exist at $\mathbf{x}^{(k+1)}$ are $\nabla f(\mathbf{x}^{(k+1)}) = \mathbf{0}$, leading to the Gauss least-squares method for the computation of $\mathbf{x}^{(k+1)}$.

$$\mathbf{x}^{(k+1)} = \mathbf{x}^{(k)} - [\mathbf{J}^T(\mathbf{x}^{(k)})\mathbf{J}(\mathbf{x}^{(k)})]^{-1}\mathbf{J}^T(\mathbf{x}^{(k)})\boldsymbol{\phi}(\mathbf{x}^{(k)}) \tag{5.3-4}$$

{The Levenburg-Marquardt correction mentioned in Sec. 3.2 was to change $[\mathbf{J}^T(\mathbf{x}^{(k)})\mathbf{J}(\mathbf{x}^{(k)})]$ to $[\mathbf{J}^T(\mathbf{x}^{(k)})\mathbf{J}(\mathbf{x}^{(k)}) + \beta\mathbf{I}]$.} In using the Gauss or Marquardt methods, the matrix inversion technique should be one that guarantees a positive definite inverse from a positive definite matrix, an operation deficient in many commonly used digital computer methods.

The Gauss algorithm is executed as follows, starting at $\mathbf{x}^{(k)}$:

1. Evaluate $\mathbf{J}(\mathbf{x}^{(k)})$ and compute $[\mathbf{J}^T(\mathbf{x}^{(k)})\mathbf{J}(\mathbf{x}^{(k)})]^{-1}$ and $\boldsymbol{\phi}(\mathbf{x}^{(k)})$.
2. Compute $\mathbf{x}^{(k+1)}$ from Eq. (5.3–4).
3. Iterate from steps 1 to 2 until the termination criterion is satisfied.

Figure 5.3–3 compares the application of Gauss least squares to the solution of sets of equations, but is not too revealing because one stage in least squares is not the same as one stage in the other methods. Similarly, it is difficult to compare the number of function and derivative evaluations. Table 5.3–7 lists the times (on a CDC 6600 computer) to solve seven problems by least squares and also lists the corresponding best time obtained by any of the algorithms in Table 5.3–4. Problem 29 in Appendix A was not

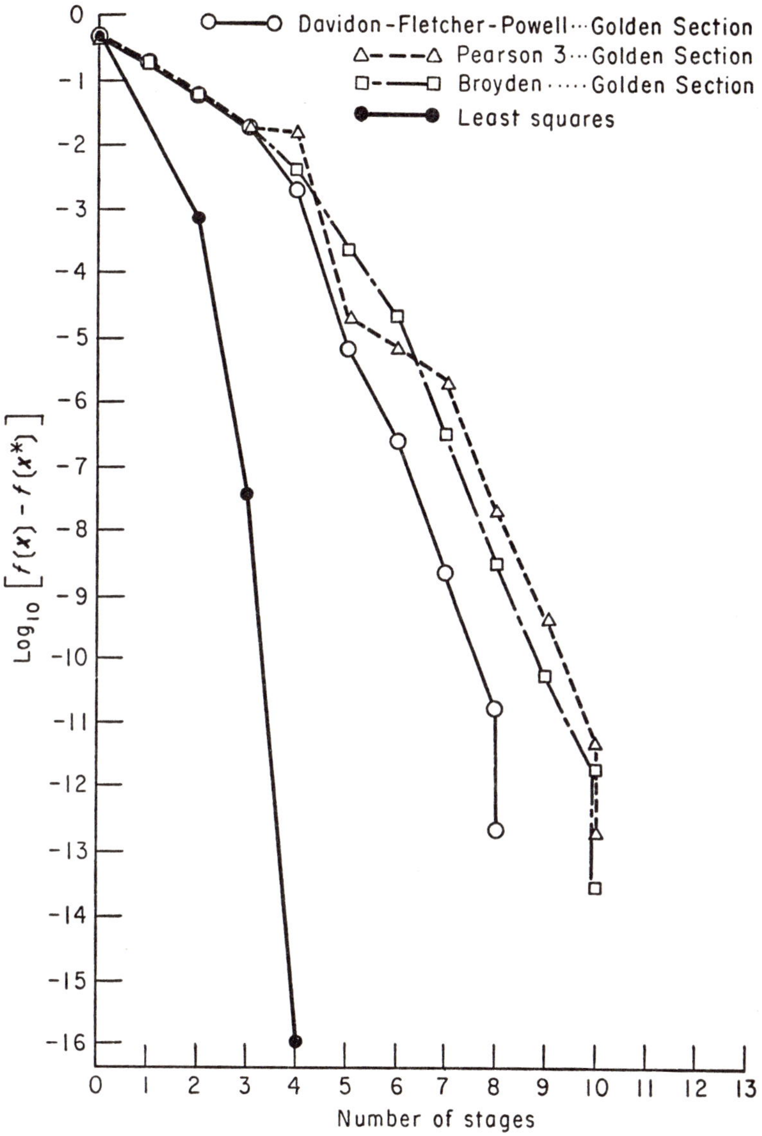

Fig. 5.3-3 Comparison of minimization methods for least-squares problems for Problem 35 of Appendix A.

solved because the $(\mathbf{J}^T\mathbf{J})$ matrix became ill-conditioned. (Problem 32 in Appendix A, a statistical problem, is included for information.)

Table 5.3-7 demonstrates that the Gauss method can compete on an equal footing with the best of the unconstrained algorithms for this special

Table 5.3-7 Comparison of least squares with best time by other methods for sum-of-squares functions

Problem (Appendix A)	*Least-squares time, sec*	*Best other time, sec*	*By algorithm*
Problem 2	0.012	0.013	Broyden
Problem 26	0.058	0.046	Broyden
Problem 28	0.013	0.006	Powell; Fletcher
Problem 30	0.015	0.012	Fletcher
Problem 32	0.061	0.050	Fletcher
Problem 34	0.020	0.025	Powell
Problem 35	0.017	0.010	Davidon-Fletcher-Powell

type of problem. Other references[1] treating the special case of the solution of sets of simultaneous nonlinear equations by minimizing the residuals of the equations indicate that the variable metric methods may not generally be suitable because the latter may not be robust.

In an investigation of nonlinear estimation algorithms for statistics, Bard[2] tested five quite nonlinear models containing three to ten parameters, ranked the performance of each algorithm for each problem (rank 1 being the best), and then classified the results of the algorithms as follows:

Class I: Best results
Class II: Not as good as class I but still acceptable results
Class III: Unacceptable results and/or lack of convergence

Table 5.3-8 lists the average sum of rankings for the particular algorithm and the number of times each algorithm appeared in classes II and III. As the number of parameters estimated increases, the rankings in column 2 of Table 5.3-8 shift only slightly, as indicated by Table 5.3-9. Although the Gauss and Marquardt methods still appear to be best, the Davidon-Fletcher-Powell technique becomes relatively more favorable.

[1] M. J. Box, *Computer J.*, **9**:67 (1966); J. G. P. Barnes, *Computer J.*, **8**:66 (1965); M. J. D. Powell, *Computer J.*, **7**:303 (1965); W. Spendley, Chap. 16 in R. Fletcher (ed.), "Optimization," Academic Press Inc., London, 1969.

[2] Y. Bard, Comparison of Gradient Methods for the Solution of Nonlinear Parameter Estimation Problems, *IBM N.Y. Sci. Center Rept.* 320–2955, 1968; *SIAM J. Numerical Anal.*, 7:157 (1970).

Table 5.3-8 Experience with least-squares algorithms

Group	*Overall ranking*	*Algorithm*	*Average sum of ranks*	*No. of appearances in class* *II*	*III*
A	1	Gauss	26	0	0
	2	Marquardt (Sec. 3.2)	32	0	0
B	3	Broyden (Sec. 3.4–1)*	73	2	2
	4	(Sec. 3.4–6)	77	3	1
C	5	DFP† (Sec. 3.4–2)	97	3	3

*Eigenvalues adjusted to use absolute values by Greenstadt's procedure of Sec. 3.2.
†Davidon-Fletcher-Powell.

Table 5.3-9 Effect of number of parameters estimated on performance of least-squares algorithm

Algorithm	*Rank for the indicated number of parameters* 3	5	6	8	10
Gauss	1	2	1	2	1
Marquardt (Sec. 3.2)	2	1	2	1	2
Broyden (Sec. 3.4–1)	3	3	3	5	5
DFP* (Sec. 3.4–2)	5	5	5	4	3

*Davidon-Fletcher-Powell.

Part Three

Constrained nonlinear programming methods

The state of the art with respect to the general constrained nonlinear programming problem [Eqs. (2.2–1) through (2.2–3)] is in less satisfactory shape than for unconstrained problems. Constrained nonlinear programming problems are much harder to solve than unconstrained problems with a comparable number of independent variables and degree of nonlinearity because of the additional requirement that the solution must satisfy the constraints. The majority of constrained nonlinear optimization procedures that have been proposed in the literature to date are centered around one of three basic concepts:

1. Extension of linear methodology to nonlinear programming problems by means of repeated linear approximations
2. Transformation of the constrained nonlinear problem into a sequence of unconstrained problems through the use of penalty functions
3. Use of flexible tolerances to accommodate both feasible and nonfeasible $\mathbf{x}$ vectors.

Table A classifies the main characteristics and capabilities of the constrained nonlinear programming methods to be discussed in Chaps. 6 through 8. The methods selected for inclusion in Table A have been chosen from the viewpoint of:

1. Relative effectiveness in solving nonlinear programming problems
2. Simplicity of computational logic
3. Availability of digital computer codes to execute the algorithm.

Table A Characteristics of selected constrained nonlinear programming techniques

General technique	*Chapter 6 Linear approximation*								*Chapter 7 Transformation of objective function (penalty function)*			*Chapter 8 Flexible tolerance*
Method [*Sec. no.*]	*Approximate programming* [*6.1–1*]	*POP* [*6.1–2*]	*NLP* [*6.2*]	*Rosen gradient projection* [*6.3–1*]	*Generalized gradient search* [*6.3–2*]	*Projected DFP* [*6.3–3*]	*Feasible directions* [*6.4*]	*Reduced gradient* [*6.5*]	*Rosenbrock* [*7.1–2*]	*Davidon-CRST* [*7.1–3*]	*SUMT* [*7.2*]	
Characteristics: Objective function	L and NL	L and NL	L and NL	L and NL	L and NL	L and NL	L and NL	L and NL	L and NL	L and NL	L and NL	L and NL
Can accommodate equality constraints	No	No	L and NL	L	L and NL	L	No	L and NL	No	No	L	L and NL
Can accommodate inequality constraints	NL*	L and NL	L and NL	L and NL†	L and NL	L and NL	L and NL	L and NL	L and NL	L and NL	L and NL	L and NL
Starting point	F	F and NF	F and N	F	F and NF	F	F	F and NF	Interior	Interior	Interior	F and N
Solves nonconvex problems	Yes	Yes	Yes	Yes	Yes	Yes	Yes	Yes	Yes	Yes	Yes	Yes
Speed of convergence	Slow	Slow	Slow	Fast‡	Slow	Average	Fast	Average	Average	Average	Fast	Slow
Intermediate solutions	F	F	F and N	F	F and N	F	F	F	F	F	Interior	F and N

Notation: L = linear; NL = nonlinear; F = feasible; N = nonfeasible.

*Inefficient for problems with linear constraints.

†Rather inefficient for problems with nonlinear constraints.

‡For problems with linear constraints only.

6

Constrained minimization procedures: linear approximation methods

Because linear programming methods have been successfully applied to large-dimensional problems containing both equality and inequality constraints (linear, of course), the linearization of nonlinear programming problems to meet the requirements for the iterative application of linear programming methods is one of the most obvious approaches to solving nonlinear programming problems. Two probably somewhat more effective methods that we will discuss involve linearization of only the constraints, leaving the objective function nonlinear. One of the methods employs projection matrices to project the search direction onto a reduced set of active constraints; the other makes use of the reduced gradient (defined in Sec. 6.5).

Linear approximation of nonlinear functions is accomplished by replacing the nonlinear functions in the problem given by Eqs. (2.2–1) through (2.2–3) with their first-order Taylor series approximates expanded at the point of interest $\mathbf{x}^{(k)}$. By repeated linearization of the nonlinear functions at each intermediate solution, a sequence $\mathbf{x}^{(0)}, \mathbf{x}^{(1)}, \ldots, \mathbf{x}^{(k)}$ is generated which, under suitable circumstances, converges to optimal solution $\mathbf{x}^*$ of the original nonlinear programming problem. To illustrate, we restate the original nonlinear problem described in Sec. 2.2 [Eqs. (2.2–1) through (2.2–3)]:

$$\begin{aligned} \text{Minimize:} \quad & f(\mathbf{x}) && \mathbf{x} \in E^n \\ \text{Subject to:} \quad & h_i(\mathbf{x}) = 0 && i = 1, \dots, m \\ & g_i(\mathbf{x}) \geq 0 && i = m+1, \dots, p \end{aligned} \tag{6.0–1}$$

This problem can be modified by replacing the nonlinear functions of problem (6.0–1) by their first-order Taylor series approximates at $\mathbf{x}^{(k)}$ to yield

$$\begin{aligned} \text{Minimize:} \quad & f(\mathbf{x}^{(k)}) + \nabla^T f(\mathbf{x}^{(k)})(\mathbf{x} - \mathbf{x}^{(k)}) && \mathbf{x} \in E^n \\ \text{Subject to:} \quad & h_i(\mathbf{x}^{(k)}) + \nabla^T h_i(\mathbf{x}^{(k)})(\mathbf{x} - \mathbf{x}^{(k)}) = 0 && i = 1, \dots, m \\ & g_i(\mathbf{x}^{(k)}) + \nabla^T \mathbf{g}_i(\mathbf{x}^{(k)})(\mathbf{x} - \mathbf{x}^{(k)}) \geq 0 && i = m+1, \dots, p \end{aligned} \tag{6.0–2}$$

Inasmuch as $f(\mathbf{x}^{(k)})$, $\nabla f(\mathbf{x}^{(k)})$, $h_i(\mathbf{x}^{(k)})$, $\nabla h_i(\mathbf{x}^{(k)})$, $g_i(\mathbf{x}^{(k)})$, and $\nabla g_i(\mathbf{x}^{(k)})$ are all constant vectors or scalars evaluated at $\mathbf{x}^{(k)}$, problem (6.0–2) is a linear programming problem.

As a numerical example of approximating a nonlinear programming problem locally at some point $\mathbf{x}^{(k)}$ by a linearized approximation, consider the following:

$$\begin{aligned} \text{Minimize:} \quad & f(\mathbf{x}) = 4x_1 - x_2^2 - 12 \qquad \mathbf{x} \in E^n \\ \text{Subject to:} \quad & h_1(\mathbf{x}) = 25 - x_1^2 - x_2^2 = 0 \\ & g_2(\mathbf{x}) = 10x_1 - x_1^2 + 10x_2 - x_2^2 - 34 \geq 0 \\ & g_3(\mathbf{x}) = x_1 \geq 0 \\ & g_4(\mathbf{x}) = x_2 \geq 0 \end{aligned}$$

Let $\mathbf{x}^{(k)} = [2 \quad 4]^T$. Replacement of the nonlinear functions by their linear approximates at $\mathbf{x}^{(k)}$ gives the linear programming problem

$$\begin{aligned} \text{Minimize:} \quad & \tilde{f}(\mathbf{x}^{(k)}) = 4x_1 - 8x_2 + 4 \qquad \mathbf{x} \in E^n \\ \text{Subject to:} \quad & \tilde{h}_1(\mathbf{x}^{(k)}) = 45 - 4x_1 - 8x_2 = 0 \\ & \tilde{g}_2(\mathbf{x}^{(k)}) = -14 + 6x_1 + 2x_2 \geq 0 \\ & \tilde{g}_3(\mathbf{x}^{(k)}) = x_1 \geq 0 \\ & \tilde{g}_4(\mathbf{x}^{(k)}) = x_2 \geq 0 \end{aligned}$$

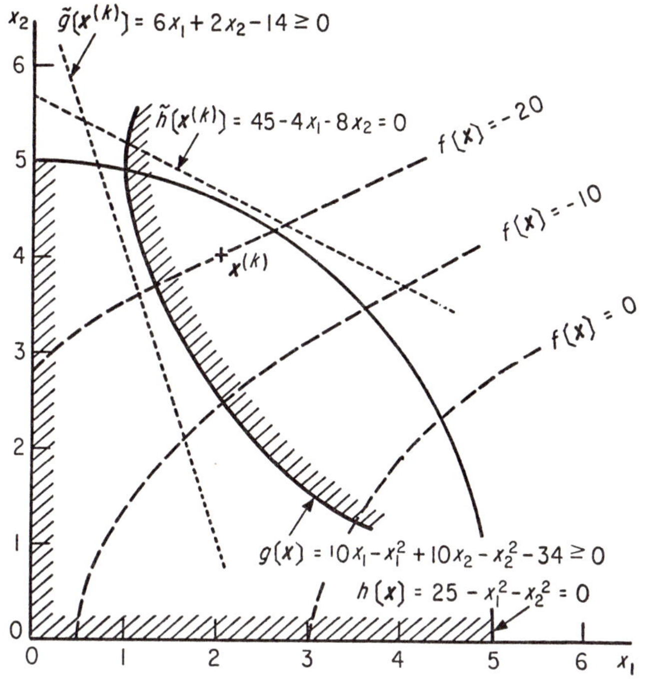

Fig. 6.0–1 Example of local linearization of the constraints at $\mathbf{x}^{(k)} = [2 \quad 4]^T$.

where the overlay tilde (˜) denotes linearized approximate. Figure 6.0–1 illustrates the programming problem in which the constraints are linearized but the objective function is not.

Table 6.0–1, listing the major algorithms described in this chapter and the section in which they appear, serves as a guide to the main characteristics of the respective algorithms. A number of other algorithms which are not generally as effective as those listed in Table 6.0–1, that work only for special types of problems (such as convex problems or problems with linear constraints only), or whose performance has not been reported in the open literature, are not described but can be found in the references at the end of this chapter. The methods described in this chapter can be said to range from poor to excellent in their speed and effectiveness.

The conditions under which convergence to the solution of problem (6.0–1) is guaranteed are:

1. $f(\mathbf{x})$, $h_1(\mathbf{x}), \ldots, h_m(\mathbf{x})$, $g_{m+1}(\mathbf{x}), \ldots, g_p(\mathbf{x})$ are continuous and differentiable functions.
2. $f(\mathbf{x})$ is convex; $\sum h_j^2(\mathbf{x})$ is convex in R.

3. $g_{m+1}(\mathbf{x}), \ldots, g_p(\mathbf{x})$ are concave.
4. The feasible region is nonempty; that is, values for $\mathbf{x}$ do exist which satisfy the constraints; i.e., the problem has a solution.
5. R is closed and convex.
6. There exists an $\varepsilon > 0$ such that $|h_j(\mathbf{x})| \leq \varepsilon$, $j = 1, \ldots, m$, and $g_j(\mathbf{x}) \geq -\varepsilon$, $j = m + 1, \ldots, p$; that is, the constraint functions are bounded.

Table 6.0-1 Characteristics of the linear approximation methods of nonlinear programming

*Method**	*Section*	*Objective function*	*Equality constraints*	*Inequality constraints*	*Starting vector†*
Linear programming:					
MAP	6.1-1	L and NL	L and NL	L and NL	F
POP	6.1-2	L and NL	None	L and NL	F and N
NLP	6.2	L and NL	L and NL	L and NL	F and N
Projection:					
Rosen (gradient projection)	6.3-1	L and NL	L‡	L‡	F
Generalized gradient search	6.3-2	L and NL	L and NL	L and NL	F and N
Davidon-Goldfarb-Davies	6.3-3	L and NL	L	L and NL	F
Zoutendijk (feasible directions)	6.4	L and NL	None	L and NL	F
Reduced gradient:					
Generalized reduced gradient	6.5	L and NL	L and NL	L and NL	F and N

Notation: F = feasible; N = nonfeasible; L = linear; NL = nonlinear.

*References can be found in the corresponding section.

†An interior vector can be obtained without difficulty by minimizing the sum of the squares of the violated inequality constraints.

‡Existing computer programs can handle only linear constraints.

In practice any of the algorithms can reach a local optimum even if conditions 1 through 6 are not met, depending, of course, on the nature of the problem. Specific details concerning the performance of most of the algorithms described in this chapter will be found in Chap. 9.

6.1 REPETITIVE APPROXIMATE LINEAR PROGRAMMING

6.1-1 Method of Approximation Programming (MAP)

Griffith and Stewart[1] described the Shell Oil Company method of approximation programming (MAP), which uses a linear programming algorithm repetitively in such a way that in the limit the successive solutions of the linear programming problems converge to the solution of the nonlinear programming problem (6.0–1). (On occasion this type of algorithm is called a *small-step gradient* method, in contrast to the method of Sec. 6.3, sometimes termed a *large-step gradient* method.) The linearized problem is:

Minimize: $f(\mathbf{x}) - f(\mathbf{x}^{(k)}) = \sum_{j=1}^{n} \frac{\partial f(\mathbf{x}^{(k)})}{\partial x_j} \Delta x_j^{(k)}$

Subject to:

Equality constraints

$$\sum_{j=1}^{n} \frac{\partial h_i(\mathbf{x}^{(k)})}{\partial x_j} \Delta x_j^{(k)} = -h_i(\mathbf{x}^{(k)}) \qquad i = 1, \ldots, m \qquad (6.1\text{–}1)$$

Inequality constraints

$$\sum_{j=1}^{n} \frac{\partial g_i(\mathbf{x}^{(k)})}{\partial x_j} \Delta x_j^{(k)} \geq -g_i(\mathbf{x}^{(k)}) \qquad i = m + 1, \ldots, p$$

where $\Delta x_j^{(k)} = (x_j - x_j^{(k)})$. Approximation programming takes into account all the inequality constraints, in contrast to some of the methods we will describe in subsequent sections that act on only the active inequality constraints. [In the Glass and Cooper[2] method, which we will not consider in detail, even though the linearized inequality is satisfied when an inequality of problem (6.0–1) is violated, leading to a nonfeasible $\mathbf{x}$, the search is forced into the feasible region by adding a constant to the right-hand side of the linearized inequality.]

One stage of Griffith and Stewart's method is carried out as follows. Let $\mathbf{x}^{(k)}$ be a feasible point of R. Replace the nonlinear functions in problem (6.0–1) by their linear approximates at $\mathbf{x}^{(k)}$ as in Eqs. (6.1–1) [≡ (6.0–2)] and solve the resulting linear programming problem with the added constraint.

[1] R. E. Griffith and R. A. Stewart, *Management Sci.*, **7**:379 (1961).

[2] H. Glass and L. Cooper, *J. Assoc. Computer Mach.*, **12**:71 (1965).

$$\delta_j^k - \left|x_j^{(k+1)} - x_j^{(k)}\right| \geq 0 \qquad j = 1, \ldots, n \tag{6.1–2}$$

where $\left|x_j^{(k+1)} - x_j^{(k)}\right|$ is the absolute value of the change in x_j, and $\delta_j^{(k)} > 0$, for $j = 1, \ldots, n$, is a small number which limits the size of the step in the various directions so as to restrict the $\mathbf{x}$ vector to the feasible region of problem (6.1–1). The solution of problem (6.1–1), together with (6.1–2) for $(\mathbf{x} - \mathbf{x}^{(k)})$, say $(\tilde{\mathbf{x}} - \mathbf{x}^{(k)})$, gives $\mathbf{x}^{(k+1)}$.

$$\mathbf{x}^{(k+1)} = \mathbf{x}^{(k)} + (\tilde{\mathbf{x}} - \mathbf{x}^{(k)})$$

Once $\mathbf{x}^{(k+1)}$ is calculated, the entire sequence is repeated with gradually decreasing $\delta^{(k)}$ (in order to reduce the nonfeasible elements in $\mathbf{x}$ to within an acceptable tolerance) until the improvement in the value of $f(\mathbf{x})$ is less than some prespecified small number.

Constraints on $\mathbf{x}$ can be added to Eq. (6.1–1) in a slightly different way. Let $\Delta^+\mathbf{x}^{(k)} = \mathbf{x} - \mathbf{x}^{(k)}$ when $(\mathbf{x} - \mathbf{x}^{(k)}) \geq 0$ and $\Delta^-\mathbf{x}^{(k)} = (\mathbf{x} - \mathbf{x}^{(k)})$ when $(\mathbf{x} - \mathbf{x}^{(k)}) \leq 0$. Then the following restrictions are imposed on the admissible step in any coordinate direction before reapproximating the nonlinear problem:

$$p_j^{(k)}\,\Delta^+x_j^{(k)} + q_j^{(k)}\,\Delta^-x_j^{(k)} \leq m_j^{(k)} \qquad j = 1, \ldots, n \tag{6.1–3}$$

where
$$p_j^{(k)} = \max\left\{1, \frac{m_j^{(k)}}{U_j - x_j^{(k)}}\right\}$$

$$q_j^{(k)} = \max\left\{1, \frac{m_j^{(k)}}{x_j^{(k)} - L_j}\right\}$$

$m_j^{(k)}$ = maximum permissible change in j^{th} coordinate direction on k^{th} stage

L_j = lower bound on x_j

U_j = upper bound on x_j

If $\Delta^-x_j^{(k)} = 0$, then $p_j^{(k)}\Delta^+x_j^{(k)} \leq m_j^{(k)}$. When $\mathbf{x}_j^{(k)}$ is near its upper limit, $(U_j - x_j^{(k)}) \approx 0$ and the maximum term in $\{1, m_j^{(k)}/(U_j - x_j^{(k)})\}$ is $(m_j^{(k)}/(U_j - x_j^{(k)}))$. Consequently, $x_j - x_j^{(k)} \leq U_j - x_j^{(k)}$, or $x_j \leq U_j$; that is, x_j is prevented from violating its upper bound. A similar analysis for $\Delta^+x^{(k)} = 0$ indicates x_j cannot violate its lower bound.

Equations (6.1–1) and (6.1–3) form the linearized equations for the linear programming phase. Two additional sets of variables, known as *slack* and *artificial* variables, are introduced into Eqs. (6.1–1) and (6.1–3) as the first step in the linear programming solution by the revised simplex method. Slack variables transform the inequality constraints into equality constraints. Representing the slack variables by the symbol u_i, we can rewrite the inequality constraints as

$$\sum_{j=1}^{n} \frac{\partial g_i(\mathbf{x}^{(k)})}{\partial x_j} \Delta^+ x_j^{(k)} - \sum_{j=1}^{n} \frac{\partial g_i(\mathbf{x}^{(k)})}{\partial x_j} \Delta^- x_j^{(k)} - u_i^{(k)} = -g_i(\mathbf{x}^{(k)}) \qquad i = m+1, \ldots, p$$

where $u_i^{(k)} \geq 0$. Slack variables v_j are also added to the set of equations (6.1–3) to form equality constraints thus:

$$p_j^{(k)} \Delta^+ x_j^{(k)} + q_j^{(k)} \Delta^- x_j^{(k)} + v_j^{(k)} = m_j \qquad j = 1, \ldots, n$$

Artificial variables w_i are incorporated solely to obtain an initial feasible point in the event that the initial **x** vector is nonfeasible. Adding the artificial variables to the equality and inequality constraints yields

$$\sum_{j=1}^{n} \frac{\partial h_i(\mathbf{x}^{(k)})}{\partial x_j} \Delta^+ x_j^{(k)} - \sum_{j=1}^{n} \frac{\partial h_i(\mathbf{x}^{(k)})}{\partial x_j} \Delta^- x_j^{(k)} + w_j^{(k)} = -h_i(\mathbf{x}^{(k)}) \qquad i = 1, \ldots, m$$

$$\sum_{j=1}^{n} \frac{\partial g_i(\mathbf{x}^{(k)})}{\partial x_j} \Delta^+ x_j^{(k)} - \sum_{j=1}^{n} \frac{\partial g_i(\mathbf{x}^{(k)})}{\partial x_j} \Delta^- x_j^{(k)} - u_i^{(k)} + w_i^{(k)} = -g_i(\mathbf{x}^{(k)}) \qquad i = m+1, \ldots, p$$

where $w_i \geq 0$. The artificial variables are nonzero for any constraint that is violated. The revised simplex method itself is used to drive the artificial variables to zero by minimizing $\sum w_i$.

As long as on each stage k a feasible solution is found, the MAP method proceeds rapidly. But when a nonfeasible **x** vector is reached that yields a decreased value of $f(\mathbf{x})$, the progress becomes quite slow. Linear programming operates first to satisfy the constraints causing the infeasibilities and then to improve the objective function. As a result, it is likely that a solution to (6.1–1) and (6.1–3) on the next stage will yield a still nonfeasible **x** vector but with a decreased value of $f(\mathbf{x})$. Thus, once several constraints become active, MAP proceeds rather slowly. Because a complete relinearization of the problem takes place at each stage, all old information is discarded; hence MAP can be used to solve nonconvex problems. Intermediate solutions are feasible or near-feasible.

Olson[1] described how the oscillation history of the algorithm is used to

[1] F. A. Olson, paper presented at the ACM SIGMAP Workshop, IBM Data Processing Div., June 14–15, 1966.

Table 6.1-1 Application of MAP to the Wood River Refinery runs

Stage	*1*	2	3	...	16	17	18	...	27	28	29
Value of objective function	100.0	107.9	116.9	...	122.0	122.1	122.1	...	122.0	122.1	122.0
No. of variables changing	22	22	21	...	8	5	4	...	4	4	5
Variables (initial value in parentheses):											
Feed (17.00)	18.00	19.00	20.00	...	21.67	21.67	21.67	...	21.69	21.69	21.70
Temperature (920.0)	930.0	925.1	924.9	...	915.4	915.4	915.4	...	916.4	917.2	915.7
Antiknock gasoline (104.0)	92.8	104.3	108.1	...	103.4	103.5	103.9	...	103.8	103.7	103.8
Regular gasoline (156.0)	172.8	172.8	173.0	...	162.2	162.7	162.1	...	161.1	160.4	161.5
. . .											
Times, min:											
Matrix writer	10.4	5.6	4.1	...	4.3	4.2	4.1	...	4.2	4.5	4.4
LP/90	3.1	2.1	2.8	...	2.0	2.0	1.9	...	4.2	2.1	3.4

expand or contract the maximum step size m_j. Some typical empirical rules are:

Plan	*Stage k*	*Variable-movement history*	*Change in* m_j
I	≥ 4	$+, -, +, -, +, -$	$m_j^{(k+1)} = \alpha_1 m_j^{(k)}$
		$-, -, -, +, +, +$	$m_j^{(k+1)} = \alpha_2 m_j^{(k)}$
II	≥ 5	$+, -, +, -, +, -$	$m_j^{(k+1)} = 0.5 m_j^{(k)}$
	< 8	$-, -, -, +, +, +$	$m_j^{(k+1)} = 0.8\lvert x_j^{(k)} - x_{jb}\rvert$

where α_1 = a contraction coefficient in range 0.5 to 0.8
α_2 = an expansion coefficient in range 1.2 to 1.5
x_{jb} = limiting upper or lower bound on x_i in direction of movement on k^{th} stage.

Figure 6.1-1 is a very general information flow diagram of the MAP algorithm. Griffith and Stewart reported solving a problem with approxi-

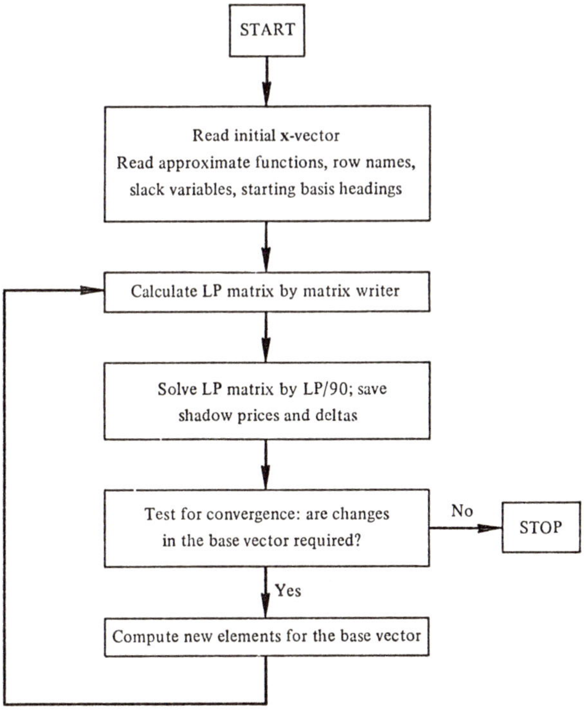

Fig. 6.1-1 Information flow diagram for the MAP algorithm.

mately 30 variables and over 100 nonlinear constraints, and Olson reported the breakdown of times in minutes on an IBM 7094 computer between the matrix writer and the linear programming phase as listed in Table 6.1-1. Twenty-seven variables were involved in the nonlinear functions, and the linear programming matrix had 205 rows. The total time through stage 29 was 229 min. The method of Griffith and Stewart is relatively inefficient (1) for unconstrained problems relative to methods which are designed to apply only to unconstrained problems and (2) for linear or quadratic programming problems.

Example 6.1-1 Approximation programming

The method of Griffith and Stewart can be illustrated by means of the following example.

$$\begin{aligned} \text{Minimize:} \quad & f(\mathbf{x}) = x_1^2 + x_2^2 - 16x_1 - 10x_2 \\ \text{Subject to:} \quad & g_1(\mathbf{x}) = 11 - x_1^2 + 6x_1 - 4x_2 \geq 0 \\ & g_2(\mathbf{x}) = x_1 x_2 - 3x_2 - e^{x_1 - 3} + 1 \geq 0 \qquad (a) \\ & g_3(\mathbf{x}) = x_1 \geq 0 \\ & g_4(\mathbf{x}) = x_2 \geq 0 \end{aligned}$$

Figure E6.1-1 illustrates the topography associated with problem (a); the dashed lines represent the contours of $f(\mathbf{x})$, and the curved solid lines represent the nonlinear con-

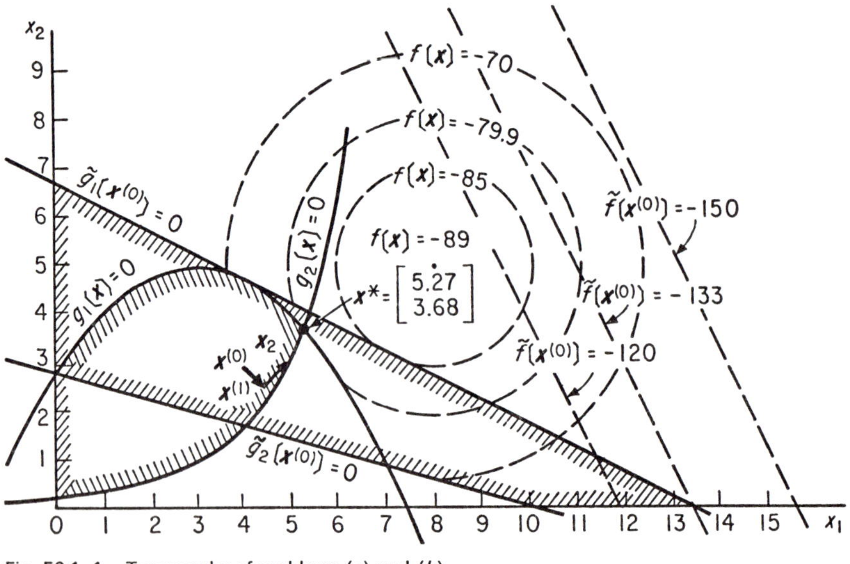

Fig. E6.1-1 Topography of problems (a) and (b).

straints $g_1(\mathbf{x})$ and $g_2(\mathbf{x})$ at the locus of points for which $g_i(\mathbf{x}) = 0$. The axes represent $g_3(\mathbf{x}) = 0$ and $g_4(\mathbf{x}) = 0$. The solution to problem (a) is at $\mathbf{x}^* = [5.27 \quad 3.68]^T$, at which $f(\mathbf{x}) = -79.9$. The initial steps in the procedure are as follows:

1. Let $\mathbf{x}^{(0)} = [4 \quad 3]^T$, at which $f(\mathbf{x}^{(0)}) = -69$, be the (feasible) initial point.
2. The linear approximation to problem (a) at $\mathbf{x}^{(0)} = [4 \quad 3]^T$ is obtained by replacing the nonlinear functions in (a) with their linear approximates to yield

$$
\begin{aligned}
\text{Minimize:} \quad & \tilde{f}(\mathbf{x}^{(0)}) = -8x_1 - 4x_2 - 25 \\
\text{Subject to:} \quad & \tilde{g}_1(\mathbf{x}^{(0)}) = -2x_1 - 4x_2 + 27 \geq 0 \\
& \tilde{g}_2(\mathbf{x}^{(0)}) = 0.28x_1 + x_2 - 2.84 \geq 0 \\
& \tilde{g}_3(\mathbf{x}^{(0)}) = x_1 \geq 0 \\
& \tilde{g}_4(\mathbf{x}^{(0)}) = x_2 \geq 0
\end{aligned}
\qquad (b)
$$

The tilde (˜) over the function symbol refers to the linearized approximate of the function. The feasible region resulting from the linearized constraints of problem (a) at $\mathbf{x}^{(0)} = [4 \quad 3]^T$ is shown in Fig. E6.1-1 by the heavy solid straight lines. The linearized objective function $f(\mathbf{x}^{(0)})$ is represented by the heavy dashed lines. The solution of problem (b) is at $\mathbf{x}^{(1)} = [13.5 \quad 0]^T$, a vector which is feasible with regard to problem (b) and not with respect to (a).

To prevent the $\mathbf{x}$ vector from leaving the feasible region of problem (a), constraints are placed upon $\mathbf{x}$ as indicated in equality (6.1-2), that is,

$$|x_j^{(1)} - x_j^{(0)}| \leq \delta_j^{(0)} \qquad j = 1, \ldots, n \qquad (c)$$

An arbitrary initial value of $\delta^{(0)} = [0.5 \quad 0.5]^T$ is suitable for problem (a). Note that the move from $\mathbf{x}^{(0)} = [4 \quad 3]^T$ to $\mathbf{x}^{(1)} = [13.5 \quad 0]^T$ causes x_1 to increase and x_2 to decrease substantially. Therefore, from the condition imposed by Eq. (c), $\mathbf{x}^{(1)}$ is located at $\mathbf{x}^{(1)} = [(4 + 0.5) \quad (3 - 0.5)]^T = [4.5 \quad 2.5]^T$, for which $f(\mathbf{x}^{(1)}) = -70.65$.

For the next stage, $k = 1$, let $\boldsymbol{\delta}^{(1)} = 0.8\boldsymbol{\delta}^{(0)} = [0.4 \quad 0.4]^T$. The linear version of problem (a) at $\mathbf{x}^{(1)} = [4.5 \quad 2.5]^T$ is

$$
\begin{aligned}
\text{Minimize:} \quad & \tilde{f}(\mathbf{x}^{(1)}) = -7x_1 - 5x_2 - 36 \\
\text{Subject to:} \quad & \tilde{g}_1(\mathbf{x}^{(1)}) = 31.4 - 3x_1 - 4x_2 \geq 0 \\
& \tilde{g}_2(\mathbf{x}^{(1)}) = 5.42 - 1.98x_1 + 1.5x_2 \geq 0 \\
& \tilde{g}_3(\mathbf{x}^{(1)}) = x_2 \geq 0 \\
& \tilde{g}_4(\mathbf{x}^{(1)}) = x_2 \geq 0
\end{aligned}
\qquad (d)
$$

The solution of problem (d) is at $\mathbf{x}^{(2)} = [5.45 \quad 3.58]^T$, which is fairly close to the feasible region of problem (a). After imposing the additional condition $|x_j^{(2)} - x_j^{(1)}| \leq \delta_j^{(1)}, j = 1, \ldots, n$, the feasible $\mathbf{x}^{(2)}$ is at $\mathbf{x}^{(2)} = [4.9 \quad 2.9]^T$, for which $f(\mathbf{x}^2) = -75.1$. The next stage $(k = 2)$ is computed in the same manner with $\boldsymbol{\delta}^{(2)} < \boldsymbol{\delta}^{(1)}$, say $\boldsymbol{\delta}^{(2)} = 0.8\boldsymbol{\delta}^{(1)}$. The iterative procedure is terminated when $\boldsymbol{\delta}^{(k)} \leq \varepsilon$ (where ε is a sufficiently small number) and the nonfeasible elements in $\mathbf{x}^{(k+1)}$ are acceptable. At any stage in which the $\mathbf{x}$ vector becomes nonfeasible, linear programming is used to obtain a feasible solution before proceeding.

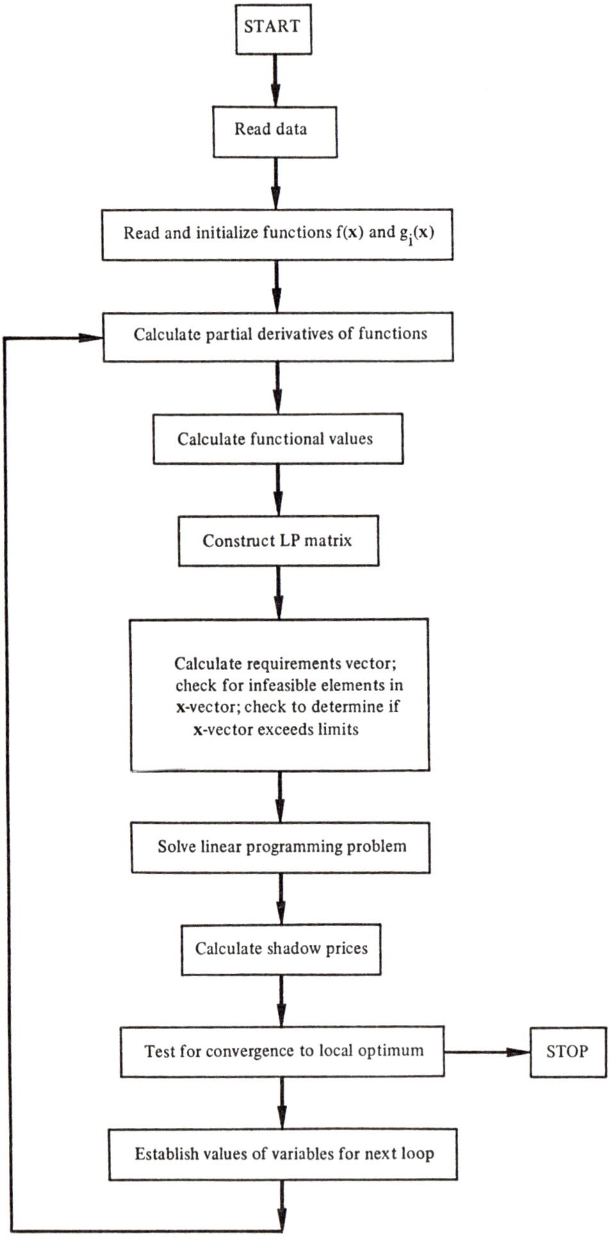

Fig. 6.1-2. Information flow diagram for POP II.

6.1-2 POP

POP (standing for process optimization program) was developed by Smith[1] as a general purpose nonlinear optimization code similar to that described in Sec. 6.1-1. Linearization of the problem takes place at each step, followed by optimization, using a modified simplex algorithm. Relinearization takes place at the solution point, and step-size limits are imposed to restrict the range over which the linearized approximates can apply. Equality constraints cannot be accommodated except insofar as they are split up into two inequalities; i.e.,

$$h(\mathbf{x}) = 0$$

becomes

$$h_1(\mathbf{x}) + \xi \geq 0 \qquad \text{and} \qquad h_2(\mathbf{x}) - \xi \leq 0$$

ξ being reduced as the optimization continues. However, this treatment of equality constraints rarely proves satisfactory in practice. Consequently, POP II is in general restricted to solving the following problem.

$$\begin{aligned} &\text{Minimize:} && f(\mathbf{x}) && \mathbf{x} \in E^n \\ &\text{Subject to:} && g_i(\mathbf{x}) \geq 0 && i = 1, \ldots, p \\ &&& L_j \leq x_j \leq U_j && j = 1, \ldots, n \end{aligned} \tag{6.1-4}$$

Linear programming is applied repetitively to the sectionally linearized nonlinear programming problem in such a way that the solutions to the linearized subproblems can converge to the solution of the nonlinear problem (6.1-4). Successive $\mathbf{x}$ vectors can be feasible or nonfeasible. Figure 6.1-2 is a general information flow diagram of the POP II algorithm.

POP II automatically builds an *incremental* linear programming (LP) matrix illustrated by Fig. 6.1-3 from the coefficients of the linearized model. The elements of the matrix, starting with the $(n + 1)$st row, are the values of the first partial derivatives of the objective function and the constraints with respect to each independent variable x_j. The first partial derivatives are calculated numerically at the current $\mathbf{x}$ vector. It should be noted that a separate matrix row exists for each independent variable x_j. In addition, there is a row for each active constraint.

The linear programming matrix includes several additional rows and columns:

[1] H. V. Smith, A Process Optimization Program for Nonlinear Systems: POP II, *IBM Gen. Program Library* 7090 H9 IBM 0021, 1965.

	Row No. \ Column No.	1 2 . . . n	n+1 Force Vector	n+2 Requirement Vector	n+3 Working Space
x_j	1 2 . . . n	1 . . . 1 (diagonal), 0 (off-diagonal)			
$\frac{\partial f(x)}{\partial x_j}$	n+1				
$-\frac{\partial g_i(x)}{\partial x_j}$	n+2 n+3 . . . n+m+1				
	n+m+2	Force Eqn.	1	100	
	n+m+3	Functional Eqn.	−500		
	n+m+4	Move Penalty			

Fig. 6.1-3 Layout of portions of the linear programming matrix.

1. *Requirements vector column:* Elements in the rows corresponding to the independent variables are the smaller of the move limit on the variable or the incremental distance to the nearest bound. Elements in the columns opposite the rows corresponding to the derivatives contain the incremental values between the constraint at its current value and (*a*) zero or (*b*) the nearest limit on the constraint.
2. *Force vector column:* Used to handle implicit calculations and initial infeasibilities.

If an x_i is infeasible, the infeasibility is eliminated by changing the value of x_i by the smaller of the differences between x_i and its two limits. This step also requires a change in the requirements vector. Infeasibilities with respect to the constraints are temporarily eliminated by combining the elements with the arbitrary elements of value 100 and -500 shown in Fig. 6.1-3.

Solution of the linear programming problem is accomplished by the revised simplex algorithm. The computer program calculates from the linear programming solution the change in the $\mathbf{x}$ vector, $\Delta\mathbf{x}$, verifying that the objective function evaluated at $(\mathbf{x}^{(k)} + \Delta\mathbf{x})$ is an improvement over the objective function evaluated at the previous $\mathbf{x}$ vector, $\mathbf{x}^{(k)}$, with only a minor linearity error [defined below by Eq. (6.1–5)]. Each such cycle of buildup of the linear programming matrix and solution of the linear programming problem is called a *loop*. These loops are automatically repeated until an optimum is detected, or until the number of loops executed exceeds the maximum number permitted by the user.

1. Computation of numerical partial derivatives. The linear programming matrix described above includes in its elements the values of the first partial derivatives of the objective function and the constraints with respect to each independent variable x_j. POP II uses the numerical technique of "centered differences" to approximate these derivatives. To calculate the value of the first partial derivatives of the objective function with respect to the independent variable x_j at the current $\mathbf{x}$ vector $\mathbf{x}^{(k)}$, the code evaluates the objective function at $(\mathbf{x}^{(k)} + \boldsymbol{\delta}_j)$ and at $(\mathbf{x}^{(k)} - \boldsymbol{\delta}_j)$, where $\boldsymbol{\delta}_j$ is a vector of user-supplied parameters. On the kth stage the numerical first partial derivative of the objective function with respect to x_j is thus computed from

$$\frac{\partial f(\mathbf{x}^{(k)})}{\partial x_j} = \frac{f(\mathbf{x}^{(k)} + \boldsymbol{\delta}_j) - f(\mathbf{x}^{(k)} - \boldsymbol{\delta}_j)}{2\delta_j} \qquad j = 1, \ldots, n$$

where $\mathbf{x}^{(k)} + \boldsymbol{\delta}_j = [x_1^{(k)}, x_2^{(k)}, \ldots, x_j^{(k)} + \delta_j, \ldots, x_n^{(k)}]^T$ and $\mathbf{x}^{(k)} - \boldsymbol{\delta}_j = [x_1^{(k)}, x_2^{(k)}, \ldots, x_j^{(k)} - \delta_j, \ldots, x_n^{(k)}]^T$. The numerical first partial derivatives of the constraints with respect to x_j are computed from

$$\frac{\partial g_i(\mathbf{x}^{(k)})}{\partial x_j} = \frac{g_i(\mathbf{x}^{(k)} + \boldsymbol{\delta}_j) - g_i(\mathbf{x}^{(k)} - \boldsymbol{\delta}_j)}{2\delta_j} \qquad i = 1, \ldots, p, j = 1, \ldots, n$$

The chosen values of the δ_j's remain unchanged throughout the optimization, and their choice can seriously affect the precision of the estimated value of the derivatives.

2. Adaptive move limits. The values which POP II uses as the move or step limits on the independent variables x_j can be obtained in one of two ways, the choice being left to the discretion of the user. First, they may be entered by the user as data (as approximately 10 percent of the range of the x_j) and the code instructed to use these fixed values after appropriate scaling (see below). Alternatively, the user can let the code calculate values for the move limits during each loop. The evaluation of "adaptive move limits" is performed as the numerical first derivatives are calculated. The code calculates the maximum change in each x_j which can be made without incurring a linearity error (described below) greater than that specified in the data for the objective function or any of the constraints. The code evaluates the objective function and the constraints at the current $\mathbf{x}$ vector $\mathbf{x}^{(k)}$, and also at $(\mathbf{x}^{(k)} + \boldsymbol{\delta}_j)$ and $(\mathbf{x}^{(k)} - \boldsymbol{\delta}_j)$. Because the calculation of adaptive move limits is executed concurrently with the evaluation of the numerical first derivatives, the values of the objective function and constraints at $(\mathbf{x} - \boldsymbol{\delta}_j)$, $\mathbf{x}$, and $(\mathbf{x} + \boldsymbol{\delta}_j)$ are computed only once for both purposes. The code then calculates the linearity error $E_{j,i}$ as follows both for the objective function

$$E_{j,0} = f(\mathbf{x}) - \frac{f(\mathbf{x} + \delta_j) + f(\mathbf{x} - \delta_j)}{2} \qquad j = 1, \ldots, n \tag{6.1–5a}$$

and for the constraints

$$E_{j,i} = g_i(\mathbf{x}) - \frac{g_i(\mathbf{x} + \boldsymbol{\delta}_j) + g_i(\mathbf{x} - \boldsymbol{\delta}_j)}{2} \qquad j = 1, \ldots, n, i = 1, \ldots, p \tag{6.1–5b}$$

Each of the resulting linearity errors is then used in Eq. (6.1–6) below to calculate a move limit on the x_j. For the objective function, the limit is

$$\Delta x_{j,0,\max} = \delta_j \left(\frac{\text{maximum linearity error permitted for the objective function}}{E_{j,0}} \right)^{\frac{1}{2}} \qquad j = 1, \ldots, n \tag{6.1–6a}$$

and for the constraints,

$$\Delta x_{j,i,\max} = \delta_j \left(\frac{\text{maximum linearity error permitted for constraint } g_i(\mathbf{x})}{E_{j,i}} \right)^{\frac{1}{2}} \qquad j = 1, \ldots, n, i = 1, \ldots, m \tag{6.1–6b}$$

For each x_j, the move limit used for the solution to the linear programming problem at $\mathbf{x}^{(k)}$ is *either* (1) the minimum of the $\Delta x_{j,i}$ $(i = 0, \ldots, m)$ or (2) twice the move limit furnished as data, whichever is smaller. Alternative

(2) can be included only if the objective function and constraints are linear in x_j. The technique of calculating adaptive move limits on the independent variables allows the move limits to vary with the curvature of the model. On the other hand, the move limits may become too small and greatly slow down the progress of the optimization. However they are chosen, the move limits are multiplied by a variable ζ initially of value 1, that is, decreased when an optimum is detected, as described next, under termination.

3. Termination. Two separate criteria for detecting an optimum are included in the POP II algorithm. If the unconstrained optimum is an exterior point to the constraint set, the constrained optimum is detected at the end of the linear programming phase from the fact that none of the elements of $(\mathbf{x}^{(k+1)} - \mathbf{x}^{(k)})$ were larger than their respective move limits. If the unconstrained optimum lies interior to or on the boundary of the constraint set, the optimum is detected because either (1) $\mathbf{x}$ oscillates around the optimum or (2) a series of moves with very small improvements in $f(\mathbf{x})$ causes ζ to be reduced below the limit prespecified by the user. Figure 6.1–4 outlines the logic of the termination tests.

If any change in the x_j is as large as its move limit, then further moves are very likely possible. A test is executed to see if the positive improvement in the value of the objective function can be classified "large" or "small." An improvement is classified "large" if it is greater than a user-supplied constant (Smith suggests 0.25 as a typical value, but it should be noted that the units of the constant are those of the objective function), and "small" if not. This classification is used in connection with a "large" move counter L and a "small" move counter S in the program. In Fig. 6.1–4, $S = +1$ and $L = +1$ indicate that the small or large move counters are increased by $+1$; $S = 0$ and $L = 0$ indicate that the counters are reset to 0. Smith recommended that the move-limit multiplier ζ be multiplied by 2 to increase it and divided by 2 to reduce it.

The computer program to execute POP II requires that the user supply a separately written subroutine, named Model, the purpose of which is to evaluate the objective function $f(\mathbf{x})$ and the constraints $g_i(\mathbf{x})$ when provided with the $\mathbf{x}^{(k)}$ vector. The subroutine Model is called after every linear programming phase to revise the functional values. In addition, the user must supply a complete set of data, including the initial $\mathbf{x}$ vector, the upper and lower bounds on the independent variables, and a large number of other optimization parameters and controls. So many adjustments can be made in the code that it is rarely clear what independent effect an individual parameter has on the progress of the optimization.

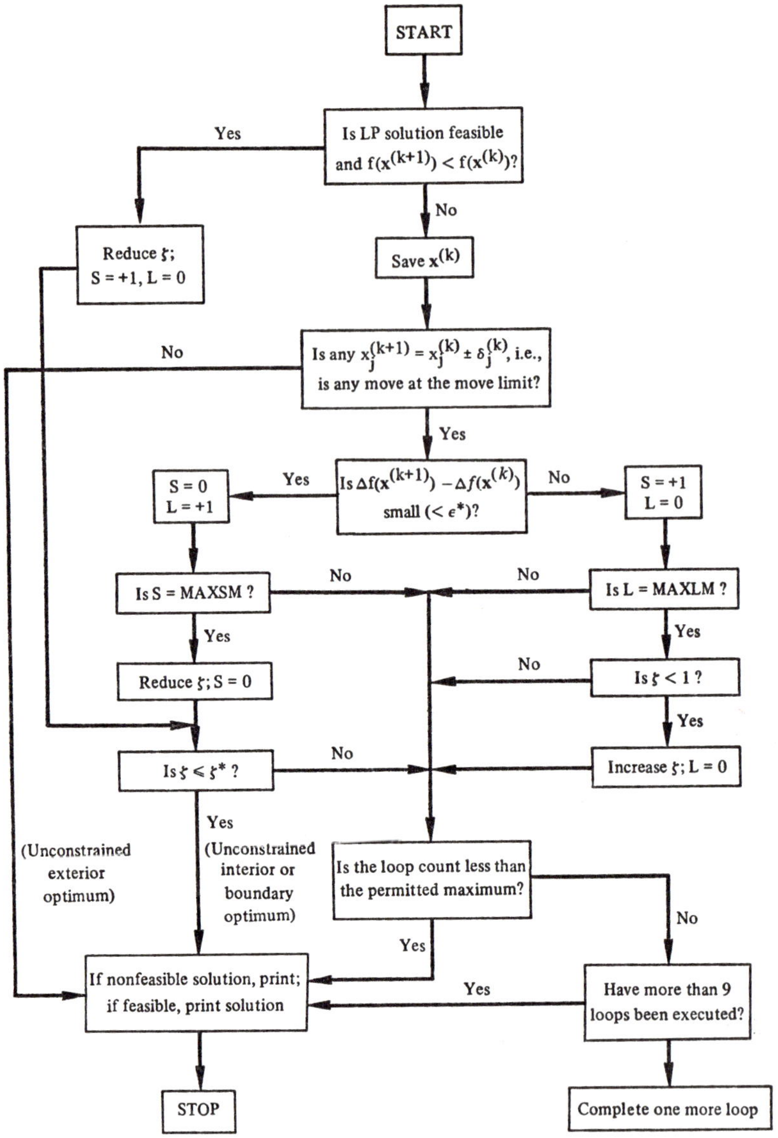

Fig. 6.1-4 Information flow diagram of convergence criteria in POP II. MAXLM = maximum number of consecutive 'large' moves permitted before increasing ζ. (Typical value = 3.) MAXSM = maximum number of consecutive 'small' moves permitted before reducing ζ. (Typical value = 2.) ζ^* = minimum permissible value of ζ. (Typical value = 0.05.)

The POP II algorithm is compared with other algorithms in Chap. 9, but no detailed example will be given because of the large choice of options available to the user, each of which requires considerable explanation to tie into the main structure of the algorithm.

6.1-3 Difficulties with Linear Approximation Programming

Zwart[1] called attention to the four main deficiencies of the linear programming approach to solving nonlinear programming problems.

1. The progress of the optimization is slow if the points $\mathbf{x}^{(k-1)}$, $\mathbf{x}^{(k)}$, $\mathbf{x}^{(k+1)}$, . . . are forced to be feasible or extremely near-feasible. Figure 6.1-5 illustrates how a narrow tolerance for constraint violation forces the search to progress in small steps. A greater tolerance may leave the solution to the nonlinear programming problem nonfeasible if the computer operation is interrupted because of a time limit.

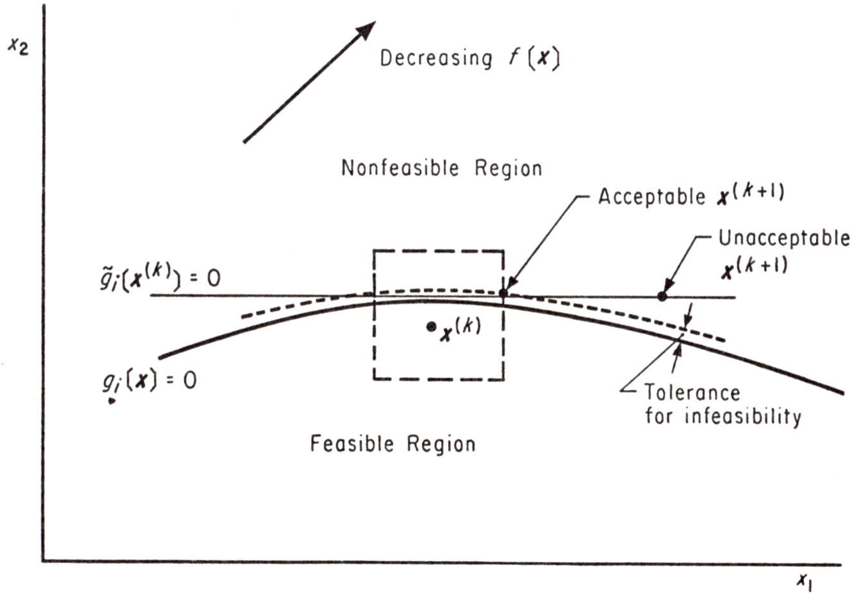

Fig. 6.1-5 Effect of feasibility tolerance on step size in a two-dimensional problem. The dashed box represents the δ's in Eq. (6.1-2); $g(\mathbf{x}^{(k)})$ is the linearized constraint.

[1] P. B. Zwart, paper presented at the SIGMAP Workshop on Nonlinear Programming, Yorktown Heights, N.Y., 1967.

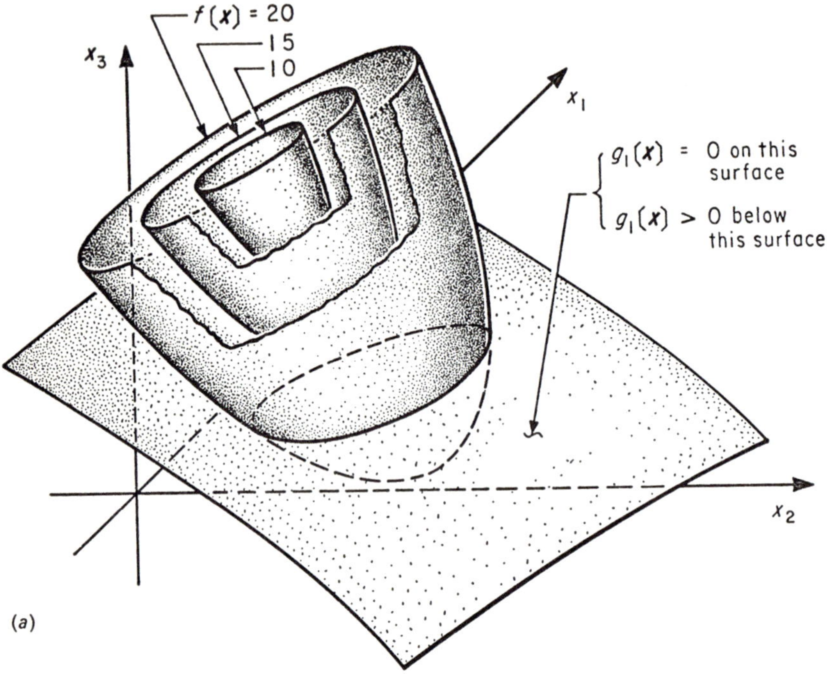

(a)

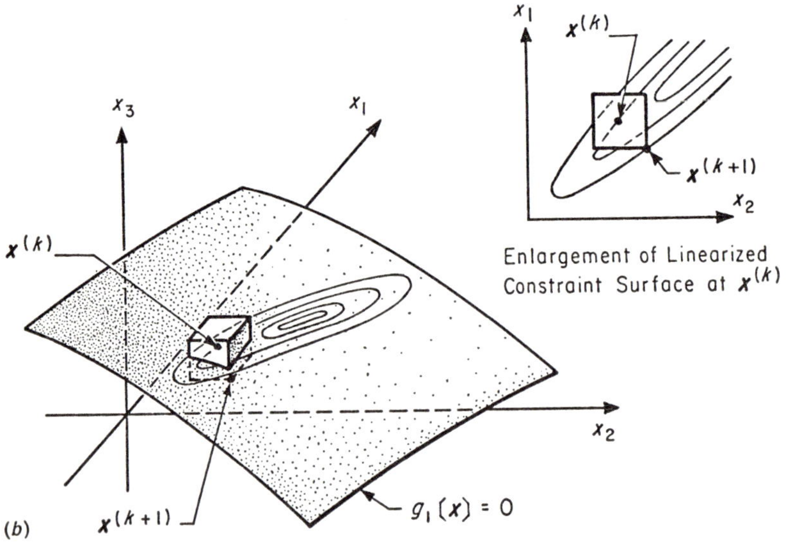

(b)

Fig. 6.1-6 (a) Intersection of objective function (illustrated by surfaces of constant value) with active constraint surface; (b) contours produced on linearized constraint surface.

2. It is difficult to compare two successive $\mathbf{x}$ vectors that give different values of $f(\mathbf{x})$ but violate one or more constraints by different amounts. Is the point $\mathbf{x}^{(k)}$ with the smaller value of $f(\mathbf{x}^{(k)})$ but with a larger deviation from constraint $g_1(\mathbf{x}^{(k)})$ better than the point $\mathbf{x}^{(k+1)}$ with a larger value of $f(\mathbf{x}^{(k+1)})$ but a smaller deviation from constraint $g_1(\mathbf{x}^{(k+1)})$, or perhaps from another constraint, $g_2(\mathbf{x}^{(k+1)})$?
3. The linear programming solution may give rise to a poor search direction if the objective function, or constrained objective function, is highly nonlinear. Recall that one of the difficulties of the gradient method mentioned in Chap. 3 was that the gradient points toward the minimum only if the problem variables are suitably scaled so that the objective function contours are hyperspheres. Linear programming also yields a poor search direction if the response surface is elongated. Figure 6.1–6*a* illustrates the objective function and a constraining surface $g_1(\mathbf{x})$, and Fig. 6.1–6*b* illustrates the search direction on the constraint (from $\mathbf{x}^{(k)}$ to $\mathbf{x}^{(k+1)}$) determined by linear programming for a δ_j corresponding to the dashed cube. The insert gives details of the search direction in the linearized hypersurface of the constraint $\tilde{g}_1(\mathbf{x}^{(k)}) = 0$. A similar difficulty arises when the constraint surface takes the form of a ridge, even though the objective function is reasonably linear.
4. In addition, a suitable acceleration procedure to make use of prior information and make the progress of the optimization more rapid is hard to devise for linear approximate programming methods.

6.1–4 Quadratic Programming and Other Approximation Methods

Instead of approximating the objective function as a linear function, it can equally well be approximated as a quadratic one. Wilson[1] and others[2] have developed algorithms to implement such an approach, but there is some question as to whether any computation time is saved in view of the more complicated algorithms for quadratic programming relative to linear programming. Very little computational experience has been reported except for Wilson's Solver, which has not performed well.

Graves and Whinston,[3] recognizing that the second-order methods in

[1] R. B. Wilson, Ph.D. dissertation, Harvard University Graduate School of Business Administration, Boston, 1963.

[2] Refer to E. M. L. Beale, Numerical Methods, in J. Abadie (ed.), "Nonlinear Programming," Interscience Publishers, Inc., New York, 1967.

[3] G. W. Graves and A. B. Whinston, *Univ. Calif. Western Management Sci. Inst. Paper* 108, Los Angeles, September, 1966.

unconstrained optimization speed convergence, extended the linear approximation to make a second-order expansion of the general nonlinear programming problem. First-order conditions for a local stationary point were introduced. For an unconstrained problem their algorithm stepped in the usual second-order direction of descent. With linear constraints and a quadratic objective function their procedure reduced to that of Frank and Wolfe.[1] Graves and Whinston reported from their computational experience in solving Problems 8, 10, 11, and 18 in Appendix A that the second-order method required far fewer iterations than a first-order method to reach the same precision. Starting from $\mathbf{x}^{(0)} = [3 \quad 3 \quad 3 \quad 3]^T$:

	Using first-order derivatives		*Using second-order derivatives*	
Problem no.	*No. of iterations*	$f(\mathbf{x}^*)$	*No. of iterations*	$f(\mathbf{x}^*)$
10	>200	−32.3163	9	−32.3487
18	>200	−32.8153	16	−32.3478
11	7	−30665.29		
8	50	2.25×10^{-6}	32	0

Also, the computer times to carry out the optimization (using the hessian matrix) were 60 to 90 percent of the times obtained for the linear approximation method. Because the termination criteria were different for the two methods, the second-order technique is probably somewhat more efficient than it appears to be from the data presented.

6.2 ALGORITHM NLP

The nonlinear programming method entitled NLP was devised by Barnes[2] to extend the algorithm proposed by DiBella and Stevens.[3] DiBella and Stevens' algorithm was designed to solve nonlinear programming problems with only equality constraints (plus upper and lower bounds on the independent variables) by using the linear approximates of the nonlinear functions at some feasible or near-feasible point $\mathbf{x}^{(k)}$. DiBella's suggestion to minimize $f(\mathbf{x})$ by a combination of gradient and linear programming

[1] M. Frank and P. Wolfe, *Naval Res. Logistics Quart.*, **3**:95 (1956).
[2] G. K. Barnes, M.S. thesis, University of Texas, Austin, Tex., 1967.
[3] C. W. DiBella and W. F. Stevens, *Ind. Eng. Chem. Process Design Develop.*, **4**:16 (1965).

phases was extended by Barnes to include the capability of handling a set of general inequality constraints in addition to the equality constraints. Thus NLP can handle the nonlinear programming problem (6.0–1).

Both nonfeasible and feasible starting $\mathbf{x}$ vectors can be employed. If $\mathbf{x}^{(0)}$ is nonfeasible, the algorithm executes a steepest descent phase to bring the $\mathbf{x}$ vector "close" to satisfying the set of constraints. The algorithm then operates on the linearized nonlinear programming problem and sets up a linear programming matrix of the values of the first partial derivatives of objective function and constraints with respect to the independent variables. The linear programming problem is solved by the revised simplex method, and the value of the objective function improved in a small region about the current $\mathbf{x}$ vector. The linear programming procedure is then repeated. At any stage in which a nonfeasible $\mathbf{x}$ vector is obtained as a linear programming solution that exceeds a prespecified limit, the steepest descent phase is reapplied.

The discussion of the NLP algorithm is conveniently divided into the steepest descent phase and the linear programming phase.

The steepest descent phase of the NLP algorithm is concerned only with improving the feasibility of the $\mathbf{x}$ vector with regard to the constraint sets $h_i(\mathbf{x}) = 0$ and $g_i(\mathbf{x}) \geq 0$; improvement of the objective function is disregarded in this phase. The steepest descent routine minimizes the unconstrained sum of the squares of the residual errors defined as

$$T(\mathbf{x}) = \sum_{i=1}^{m} h_i^2(\mathbf{x}) + \sum_{i=m+1}^{p} \mathcal{U}_i g_i^2(\mathbf{x}) \tag{6.2–1}$$

where, for the equality constraints, the residual error is $h_i(\mathbf{x})$, $i = 1, \ldots, m$, and for the inequality constraints, the residual error is $g_i(\mathbf{x})$ if $g_i(\mathbf{x}) < 0$, but made zero by the Heaviside operator if $g_i(\mathbf{x}) \geq 0$, $i = m + 1, \ldots, p$; that is, $\mathcal{U}_i = 0$ if $g_i(\mathbf{x}) \geq 0$. The sum of the squares of the residual errors is calculated before each steepest descent and linear programming phase regardless of whether or not the previous $\mathbf{x}$ vector was in the feasible region.

After calculating $T(\mathbf{x})$, the code makes tests devised after considerable computational experience with a variety of test problems that ascertain whether or not the $\mathbf{x}$ vector is close enough to the feasible region. If the $\mathbf{x}$ vector is close enough, the linear programming phase is initiated following the technique proposed by Griffith and Stewart (see Sec. 6.1); otherwise the steepest descent phase is continued.

Acceleration or deceleration of the linear programming phase is achieved by varying the maximum value that Δx_j can attain. When the $\mathbf{x}$ vector is oscillating about a "ridge" or valley, the oscillation is indicated by a parameter ρ_j that changes sign when two successive steps Δx_j are of opposite sign. The parameter ρ_j actuates a counter λ_j (which has an initial value of 1) that is used to indicate if the limiting step size m_j should be changed. The value of λ_j is determined by the number of times that a move for variable x_j has been in the same direction. Thus the numerical value of λ_j is a measure of the number of successful moves that variable x_j has made in the same direction; it is reset to unity when the step direction in the variable x_j is reversed. If ρ_i changes sign, the value of m_j used in the previous move is divided by 2. If ρ_j does not change sign and the numerical value of λ_j is greater than 4, the value of m_j used in the previous move is doubled. Although the acceleration may cause the **x** vector to become unfeasible, it must be remembered that the sum of the squares of the residual errors, $T(\mathbf{x})$, is evaluated after *every* change in **x**, and a highly nonfeasible point causes the steepest descent phase to come into play.

After each linear programming move, a test is conducted to determine if the absolute value of each Δx_j used is less than an arbitrary constant ε supplied by the user (the constant is the same for all the independent variables).

$$|x_j^{(k)} - x_j^{(k-1)}| \leq \varepsilon$$

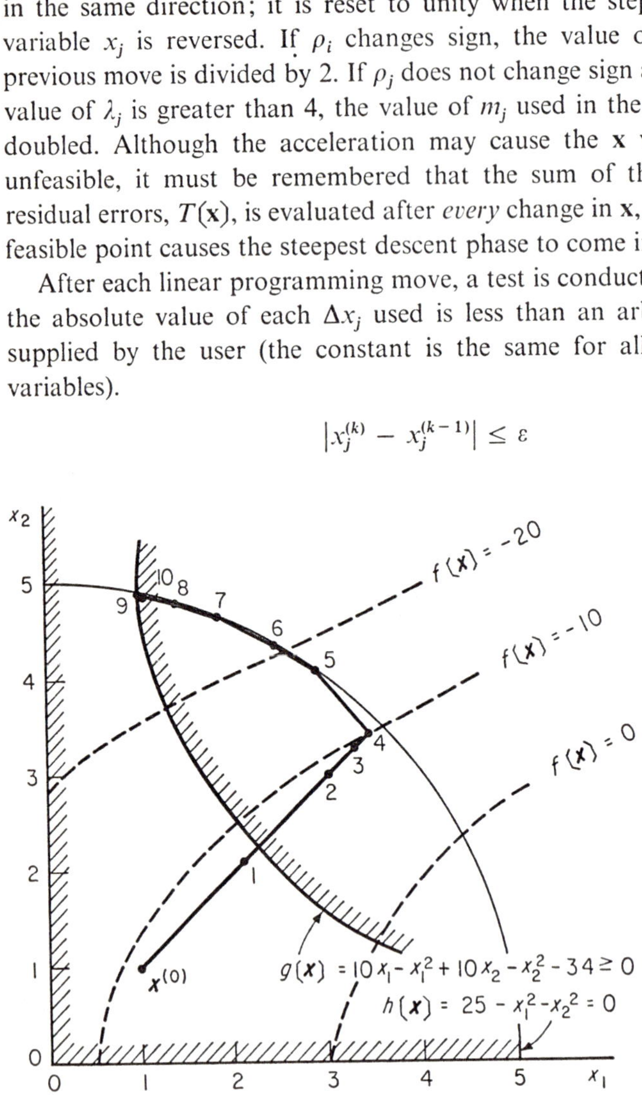

Fig. 6.2-1 Trajectory of NLP search for the problem illustrated in Fig. 6.0-1.

If the criterion is satisfied, the search is terminated; if not, the search for an optimum is continued.

Figure 6.2–1 illustrates the trajectory of the search for the problem illustrated in Fig. 6.0–1.

6.3 PROJECTION METHODS

A number of related methods are included in the classification of projection methods; they are sometimes termed methods of "feasible directions" or "large-step gradient" methods, the latter in contrast to the algorithms of Sec. 6.1, which can alternatively be named small-step gradient methods. In essence, linear constraints, or linearized constraints, form a linear manifold (defined by the intersection of the constraints), and an appropriate search direction **s** can be projected onto this manifold (Secs. 6.3–1 and 6.3–2). Of the early methods described in the literature,[1] the method of Rosen is perhaps the best-known, because commercial computer codes exist to execute the algorithm.

All the projection or feasible direction methods execute the following general sequence of steps at any stage k:

1. The algorithm begins at a feasible point $\mathbf{x}^{(k)}$.
2. A feasible direction is determined (to be precisely defined later on), $\mathbf{s}^{(k)}$.
3. A step of length $\lambda^{(k)}$ is taken in the feasible direction that minimizes $f(\mathbf{x})$ but yields an $\mathbf{x}^{(k+1)} = \mathbf{x}^{(k)} + \lambda^{(k)}s^{(k)}$ still feasible.

The algorithms differ primarily in how the direction $\mathbf{s}^{(k)}$ is computed, but they all have the common characteristic that they start at a feasible solution and (for linear constraints) progress in a direction such that the value of the objective function is reduced and the **x** vector never leaves the feasible region.

Most algorithms for solving linear programming problems represent adaptations of algorithms for matrix inversion. For example, the simplex method of linear programming corresponds to the Gauss-Jordan method of inverting a matrix. The methods of Frisch and Rosen are based on alternative methods of inverting a symmetric matrix $\mathbf{A}^T\mathbf{A}$ (where **A** is the matrix of coefficients in the constraints). However, the projection method

[1] R. Frisch, The Multiple Method for Linear Programming, *Mem. Univ. Socialokøn Inst.*, Oslo, October, 1955; G. Zoutendijk, "Methods of Feasible Directions," Elsevier Publishing Company, Amsterdam, 1960; J. B. Rosen, *J. Soc. Ind. Appl. Math.*, **8**:181 (1960), **9**:514 (1961); J. B. Rosen and R. P. Merrill, Gradient Projection—GP90, Share Program 7090–H2–3430GP90; B. A. Murtagh and R. W. H. Sargent, Chap. 14 in R. Fletcher (ed.), "Optimization," Academic Press Inc., London, 1969.

does not require that at each stage *all* the inequality constraints be treated as equalities with the aid of slack variables as in linear programming; projection methods include as few inequality constraints as possible in the computations at each $\mathbf{x}^{(k)}$—just the active constraints. Before presenting Rosen's algorithm, the concept of projection will be described.

The connotation "projection" comes from the concept of a projection of a vector—a vector that expresses the local variation of a function in a designated direction.

Let $\mathbf{A}^T = [\mathbf{a}_1 \quad \mathbf{a}_2 \quad \ldots \quad \mathbf{a}_n]$, a rectangular matrix whose column vectors are linearly independent and span the space R, be partitioned into two matrices, a set of column vectors $\mathbf{A}_\ell^T = [\mathbf{a}_1 \quad \ldots \quad \mathbf{a}_\ell]$ and the remaining $\mathbf{a}_j$'s, $\mathbf{A}_{n-\ell}^T = [\mathbf{a}_{\ell+1} \quad \ldots \quad \mathbf{a}_n]$. The vectors constituting $\mathbf{A}^T$ span a space of dimension n, and any $n \times 1$ vector $\mathbf{x}$ in R can be uniquely expressed as a linear combination of the $\mathbf{a}_j$'s.

$$\mathbf{x} = \sum_{j=1}^{n} \tau_j \mathbf{a}_j \qquad \text{or} \qquad \mathbf{x} = \mathbf{A}^T \boldsymbol{\tau} \tag{6.3–1a}$$

(The τ_j's are the unit coordinates with respect to the basis $\mathbf{A}$.) On the other hand, the vectors constituting $\mathbf{A}_\ell^T$ span a space of dimension ℓ only, and only a subset of the $\mathbf{x}$ vectors in R can be expressed as

$$\mathbf{x} = \sum_{j=1}^{\ell} \tau_j \mathbf{a}_j \qquad \text{or} \qquad \mathbf{x} = \mathbf{A}_\ell^T \boldsymbol{\tau} \tag{6.3–1b}$$

The equation $\mathbf{a}_j^T\mathbf{x} = 0$ is a hyperplane in R passing through the origin. Let the intersection of the set of all such hyperplanes $j = 1, 2, \ldots, \ell$, that is, $\mathbf{A}_\ell \mathbf{x} = \mathbf{0}$, that form a linear manifold[1] of dimension $(n - \ell)$ be designated $\mathcal{M}$. The orthogonal *projection* of $\mathbf{x}$ on $\mathcal{M}$, to be denoted by $\mathbf{x}_\mathcal{M}$, has the projection property that $\mathbf{x}_\mathcal{M}$ and $(\mathbf{x} - \mathbf{x}_\mathcal{M})$ are orthogonal, or

$$\mathbf{x}_\mathcal{M}^T(\mathbf{x} - \mathbf{x}_\mathcal{M}) = 0$$

The $n \times n$ projection matrix $\mathbf{P}_\ell$, defined from

$$\mathbf{x}_\mathcal{M} = \mathbf{P}_\ell \mathbf{x} \tag{6.3–2}$$

[1] A manifold in E^n is almost the same as a subspace in E^n except that the manifold need not go through the origin as does a subspace. The dimension $(n - \ell)$ of a linear manifold is related to the solution of a set of linear equations $\mathbf{A}^T\mathbf{x} = \mathbf{b}$ in that the dimension $(n - \ell)$ is the largest number of linearly independent vectors that constitute the solution. For example, if $\mathbf{A}^T$ is an $\ell \times n$ matrix $(n > \ell)$ and each of the ℓ rows represents an independent equation, then $(n - \ell)$ represents the number of independent variables in the system of equations and ℓ corresponds to the number of constraints (or dependent variables). In E^n a point has the dimension $\ell = 0$, so that $(n - \ell) = n$, a hyperplane has the dimension $\ell = 1$, so that $(n - \ell) = n - 1$, and so forth. Thus, adding an independent equation to a given set of independent equations reduces the dimensionality of the manifold by 1.

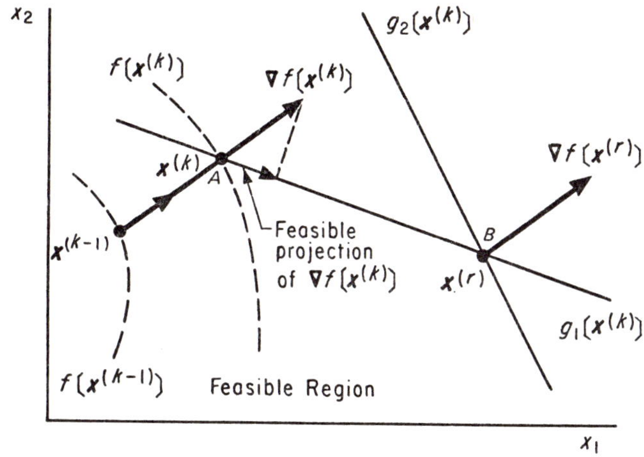

Fig. 6.3-1 Gradient projection onto the active constraints illustrated for inequality constraints. At A one constraint is active, hence $(n - l) = 2 - 1 = 1$, while at B two constraints are active, hence $(n - l) = 2 - 2 = 0$. At $\mathbf{x}^{(k-1)}$, an interior feasible point, no constraints are active and $\mathbf{P}_0 \equiv \mathbf{I}$ so that the projection of $\nabla f(\mathbf{x}^{(k-1)})$ is $\nabla f(\mathbf{x}^{(k-1)})$ itself. At the intersection of two active constraints $\mathbf{x}^{(r)}$, note that $\mathbf{P}_2 \equiv \mathbf{O}$ and the only feasible projection of $\nabla f(\mathbf{x}^{(r)})$ is the point itself.

and computed using the equation[1]

$$\mathbf{P}_\ell = \mathbf{I} - \mathbf{A}_\ell^T(\mathbf{A}_\ell\mathbf{A}_\ell^T)^{-1}\mathbf{A}_\ell \tag{6.3-3}$$

can be used to determine $\mathbf{x}_{\mathcal{M}}$. At one extreme $\mathbf{P}_0 \equiv \mathbf{I}$; that is, when the subset of ℓ vectors is empty so that $\ell = 0$, $\mathbf{x}_{\mathcal{M}} = \mathbf{x}$; the vector $\mathbf{x}$ and its projection are the same. At the other extreme, $P_n \equiv \mathbf{0}$; that is, the subset of vectors in R is full, so that $\ell = n$, $\mathbf{x}_{\mathcal{M}} = \mathbf{0}$; a projection on a point is a zero vector as illustrated in Fig. 6.3-1. It is when the gradient of the objective function at $\mathbf{x}^{(k)}$, $\nabla f(\mathbf{x}^{(k)})$, is projected onto the intersection of a subset of constraints that the optimization method is termed a *gradient projection method.*

6.3-1 Rosen's Gradient Projection Method

We turn now to the method of Rosen. In essence, the method for minimization is one of steepest descent coupled with orthogonal projection of the negative gradient onto a linear manifold of constraints or their

[1]A. S. Householder, "The Theory of Matrices in Numerical Analysis," Blaisdell Publishing Company, Waltham, Mass., 1964, p. 8.

approximates. At a feasible point $\mathbf{x}^{(k)}$, the constraints that are satisfied as equalities (the active constraints) are linearized (if nonlinear) and replaced temporarily by their respective tangent hyperplanes at $\mathbf{x}^{(k)}$. It is assumed that the hyperplanes are independent and thus the normals to the hyperplanes are independent. (As described by Rosen, the technique cannot handle constraints that are linear combinations of other constraints.) These normals (the components of both $\nabla g_i(\mathbf{x}^{(k)})$ and $\nabla h_i(\mathbf{x}^{(k)})$ will be designated $\partial g_i(\mathbf{x}^{(k)})/\partial x_j$) are used to form a projection matrix that projects the gradient of the objective function evaluated at $\mathbf{x}^{(k)}$, $\nabla f(\mathbf{x}^{(k)})$, onto the intersection of the tangent hyperplanes. In an unconstrained space, n variables constitute the n-dimensional domain. However, if ℓ equality constraints (equality constraints plus active inequalities) are satisfied at $\mathbf{x}^{(k)}$, the dimension of the space of independent vectors is reduced by ℓ to $(n - \ell)$. The term *constraint basis* refers to the set of linearly independent hyperplanes in whose intersection $\mathscr{M}$ the search is restricted. The main characteristic of the gradient projection method is that it modifies (projects) the gradient of the objective function so that its components lie in the $(n - \ell)$ dimensional

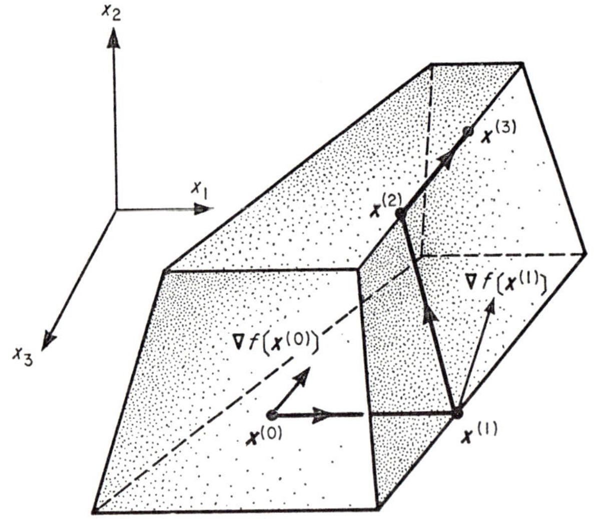

Fig. 6.3-2 Projected gradient method applied to active constraints in three dimensions. The feasible domain is a polyhedron consisting of faces (two-dimensional manifolds), edges (one-dimensional manifolds), and vertices (zero-dimensional manifolds). → indicates direction of projected gradient. $\mathbf{x}^{(0)}$ is the initial starting point, $\mathbf{x}^{(1)}$ is the minimum of the search in the $(\mathbf{x}^{(1)} - \mathbf{x}^{(0)})$ direction, and so on.

manifold which defines the feasible region in which the ℓ equality constraints are satisfied. Examine Fig. 6.3–2.

Let $\mathbf{A}_\ell$ be the $\ell \times n$ matrix of partial derivatives of the active constraints (the dependence of $\mathbf{A}_\ell$ on $\mathbf{x}^{(k)}$ will be suppressed to save space).

$$\mathbf{A}_\ell = \begin{bmatrix} \dfrac{\partial g_1(\mathbf{x}^{(k)})}{\partial x_1} & \cdots & \dfrac{\partial g_1(\mathbf{x}^{(k)})}{\partial x_n} \\ \cdots & \cdots & \cdots \\ \dfrac{\partial g_\ell(\mathbf{x}^{(k)})}{\partial x_1} & \cdots & \dfrac{\partial g_\ell(\mathbf{x}^{(k)})}{\partial x_n} \end{bmatrix} = \begin{bmatrix} a_{11} & \cdots & a_{1n} \\ \cdots & \cdots & \cdots \\ a_{\ell 1} & \cdots & a_{\ell n} \end{bmatrix}$$

From Eqs. (6.3–2) and (6.3–3), the projection of $\nabla f(\mathbf{x}^k)$ onto the active constraints defines the new direction of search $\mathbf{s}^{(k+1)}$.

$$\begin{aligned} \mathbf{s}^{(k+1)} &= P_\ell \nabla f(\mathbf{x}^{(k)}) \\ &= \nabla f(\mathbf{x}^{(k)}) - \mathbf{A}_\ell^T(\mathbf{A}_\ell \mathbf{A}_\ell^T)^{-1}\mathbf{A}_\ell \nabla f(\mathbf{x}^{(k)}) \end{aligned} \tag{6.3–4}$$

The expression $(\mathbf{A}_\ell \mathbf{A}_\ell^T)^{-1}\mathbf{A}_\ell \nabla f(\mathbf{x}^{(k)}) = \mathbf{u}$ can be regarded as a column vector of Lagrange multipliers (so-called "shadow prices") that can be used to compute a new direction

$$\mathbf{s}^{(k+1)} = \nabla f(\mathbf{x}^{(k)}) - \mathbf{A}_\ell^T \mathbf{u}$$

and the elements u_j of $\mathbf{u}$ indicate whether or not additional progress can be made in the search. If any element u_j is negative, the corresponding inequality constraint could be removed from the constraint basis before the search continues. Because of the interaction among the constraints, it is not practical to remove more than one constraint at a time, the one with the most negative value of u_j being selected.

If the active constraints are linear, the new direction $\mathbf{s}^{(k+1)}$ will lie along the constraints themselves, as illustrated in Fig. 6.3–2. On the other hand, if the active constraints are nonlinear as in Fig. 6.3–3, the components of the new direction will lie along the hyperplanes tangent to the constraints at $\mathbf{x}^{(k)}$. Thus, at a boundary point where following the gradient of the objective function would lead to a nonfeasible point, a step is taken instead in each of the components of the projected gradient rather than along the components of the gradient itself. If the problem includes nonlinear constraints and $\mathbf{x}^{(k+1)}$ proves to be nonfeasible, a form of the gradient projection algorithm is used to move to the closest feasible point. Then the algorithm is repeated. The optimization proceeds in large steps (with linear constraints), and at the end of any stage each $\mathbf{x}$ vector is always feasible and located on one or more of the constraints. For an unconstrained problem, Rosen's method reduces to that of steepest descent, described in Chap. 3.

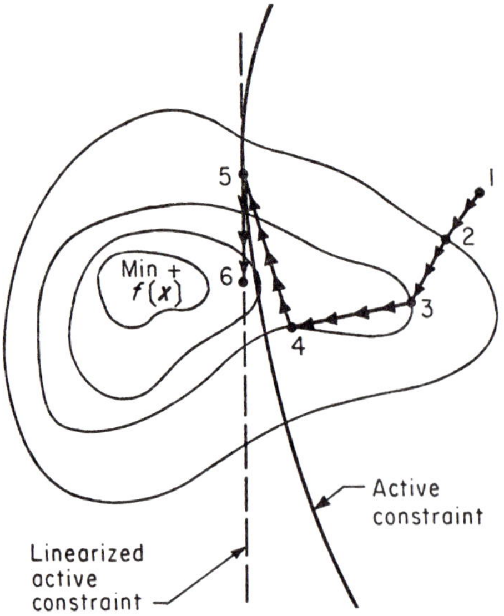

Fig. 6.3–3 Gradient projection method applied at an active constraint. If the active constraint at $\mathbf{x}^{(5)}$ is nonlinear, $\mathbf{x}^{(6)}$ may be a nonfeasible point.

The detailed explanation of Rosen's algorithm which follows will encompass only the nonlinear programming problem with linear constraints instead of the more general problem (6.0–1), inasmuch as no computational experience has been reported for the general problem (6.0–1). Section 6.3–3 discusses a method of accommodating nonlinear constraints that has been tested. The algorithm is initiated at a feasible point and continues (effectively) by the method of steepest descent until a point is reached at which one or more of the constraints become active. If equality constraints form part of the problem, there are always active constraints at each stage, but if only inequality constraints are in the problem, a boundary point eventually must be reached (if the solution to the problem is not at an interior point). At the boundary point $\mathbf{x}^{(k)}$, $g_i(\mathbf{x}^{(k)}) = 0$ and $h_i(\mathbf{x}^{(k)}) = 0$ for $i = 1, \ldots, \ell$, where $\ell \leq n$ (n = number of variables). The method of Rosen projects $\nabla f(\mathbf{x}^{(k)})$ onto the intersection of the ℓ constraints $\{\mathbf{x}^{(k)} | g_i(\mathbf{x}^{(k)}) = 0 \text{ and } h_i(\mathbf{x}^{(k)}) = 0 \text{ for } i = 1, \ldots, \ell\}$. Let $\mathbf{P}_\ell = \mathbf{I} - \mathbf{A}_\ell^T(\mathbf{A}_\ell \mathbf{A}_\ell^T)^{-1}\mathbf{A}_\ell$ be the projection matrix. If $\ell = 0$ (in which case $\mathbf{x}^{(k)}$ is an interior point), $\mathbf{P}_0 = \mathbf{I}$, the identity matrix. The projection of $\nabla f(\mathbf{x}^{(k)})$ onto the intersection of all the $g_i(\mathbf{x}^{(k)}) = 0$ and $h_i(\mathbf{x}^{(k)}) = 0$ for $i = 1, \ldots, \ell$ is obtained from Eq. (6.3–4). From Sec. 2.5 we know that $\mathbf{x}^{(k)}$

is a solution of the nonlinear programming problem if and only if $\mathbf{P}_\ell \nabla f(\mathbf{x}^{(k)}) = \mathbf{0}$ and $\mathbf{u} = (\mathbf{A}_\ell \mathbf{A}_\ell^T)^{-1}\mathbf{A}_\ell \nabla f(\mathbf{x}^{(k)}) \geq \mathbf{0}$. Thus we consider two cases, first when $\mathbf{P}_\ell \nabla f(\mathbf{x}^{(k)}) \neq \mathbf{0}$ and second when $\mathbf{P}_\ell \nabla f(\mathbf{x}^{(k)}) = \mathbf{0}$. (If the solution is an interior point, $\mathbf{P}_0 \nabla f(\mathbf{x}^{(k)}) = \nabla f(\mathbf{x}^{(k)}) = \mathbf{0}$.)

Condition 1. $\mathbf{P}_\ell \nabla f(\mathbf{x}^{(k)}) \neq \mathbf{0}$

Let $\hat{\mathbf{s}}^{(k)}$ be the unit vector in the direction of the projection of $\nabla f(\mathbf{x}^{(k)})$ onto the intersection of all the $g_i(\mathbf{x}^{(k)}) = 0$ and $h_i(\mathbf{x}^{(k)}) = 0$.

$$^{(k)} = \frac{\mathbf{P}_\ell \nabla f(\mathbf{x}^{(k)})}{\|\mathbf{P}_\ell \nabla f(\mathbf{x}^{(k)})\|} \tag{6.3-5}$$

As usual, we apply the relationship

$$\mathbf{x}^{(k+1)} = \mathbf{x}^{(k)} + \lambda^{(k)}\hat{\mathbf{s}}^{(k)}$$

By moving from $\mathbf{x}^{(k)}$ along the projected gradient with a unidimensional search, it is possible to find a λ that yields the minimum value of $f(\mathbf{x})$ and yet keeps $\mathbf{x}^{(k+1)}$ in the feasible region. More precisely, by unidimensional search in the direction of $\mathbf{s}^{(k)}$, determine $\lambda^* = \max\{\lambda | \mathbf{x}^{(k)} + \lambda\hat{\mathbf{s}}^{(k)} \in R\}$, where $R = \{\mathbf{x} | g_i(\mathbf{x}) \geq 0 \text{ and } h_i(\mathbf{x}) = 0,\ i = 1, \ldots, p\}$ and then determine $\lambda^{(k)}$, $0 \leq \lambda^{(k)} \leq \lambda^*$, so that $f(\mathbf{x}^{(k)} + \lambda^{(k)}\hat{\mathbf{s}}^{(k)})$ is a minimum in the direction of $\hat{\mathbf{s}}^{(k)}$. The value of λ^* is then the maximum step length that can be taken in the direction $\hat{\mathbf{s}}^{(k)}$ for $\mathbf{x}^{(k)}$ to remain in the feasible domain of R.

If $\lambda^{(k)} < \lambda^*$, there is no change in the number of constraints that are satisfied as equalities at $\mathbf{x}^{(k+1)}$; that is, $g_i(\mathbf{x}^{(k+1)}) = 0$ and $h_i(\mathbf{x}^{(k+1)}) = 0$ for $i = 1, \ldots, \ell$, and consequently there is no change in the elements a_{ij} of $\mathbf{A}_\ell$ to be used on the $(k + 1)$st stage. On the other hand, if $\lambda^{(k)} = \lambda^*$, one or more inequality constraints must be satisfied as equalities at $\mathbf{x}^{(k+1)}$ in addition to the ℓ constraints that were satisfied as equalities at $\mathbf{x}^{(k)}$ and remained as equalities in the transition from $\mathbf{x}^{(k)}$ to $\mathbf{x}^{(k+1)}$. Examine the transition from $\mathbf{x}^{(0)}$ to $\mathbf{x}^{(1)}$ in Fig. 6.3–2. In this latter case, a new matrix $\mathbf{A}$ is computed that includes all the constraints satisfied as equalities at $\mathbf{x}^{(k+1)}$. Then the algorithm is repeated.

Condition 2. $\mathbf{P}_\ell \nabla f(\mathbf{x}^{(k)}) = \mathbf{0}$

From Eq. (6.3–1*a*), we know that $\nabla f(\mathbf{x}^{(k)})$ can be expressed in terms of $\mathbf{A}_\ell^T$ and $\mathbf{u}$.

$$\nabla f(\mathbf{x}^{(k)}) = \mathbf{A}_\ell^T \mathbf{u} \tag{6.3-6}$$

Multiplication of Eq. (6.3–6) from the left by $(\mathbf{A}_\ell \mathbf{A}_\ell^T)^{-1}\mathbf{A}_\ell$ yields

$$(\mathbf{A}_\ell \mathbf{A}_\ell^T)^{-1}\mathbf{A}_\ell \nabla f(\mathbf{x}^k) = \mathbf{u}$$

If $u_i \geq 0$ for all $i = 1, \ldots, \ell$, then $\mathbf{x}^{(k)}$ is the solution. Otherwise, choose the $u_m < 0$ for which $\|\mathbf{a}_m\| u_m$ is the most negative, disregard the corresponding hyperplane, delete from the matrix $\mathbf{A}_\ell$ the mth row, and return to Eq. (6.3–5). (The $\|\ \|$ here stands for the norm of $\mathbf{a}_m$.) The new projection matrix is $\mathbf{P}_{\ell-1}$, and

$$\mathbf{P}_{\ell-1}\nabla f(\mathbf{x}^{(k)}) = \mathbf{P}_{\ell-1}\mathbf{A}_\ell^T\mathbf{u} \neq \mathbf{0}$$

Thus, at each stage, the active constraint set can remain the same, or a constraint can be added, or a constraint can be removed from the set of active constraints. The case in which by chance two or more active constraints qualify under condition 2 is termed *degeneracy*. Refer to Künzi[1] or Fletcher[2] for a detailed treatment of degeneracy. Efficient ways of computing $(\mathbf{A}_{\ell+1}\mathbf{A}_{\ell+1}^T)^{-1}$ or $(\mathbf{A}_{\ell-1}\mathbf{A}_{\ell-1}^T)^{-1}$ from $(\mathbf{A}_\ell\mathbf{A}_\ell^T)^{-1}$ are described in these references as well as in Sec. 6.3–3.

6.3–2 Generalized Gradient Search

The *generalized gradient search* (GGS) program, developed by K. E. Cross and W. L. Kephart, Union Carbide Corp., Oak Ridge, Tenn., can accommodate both linear and nonlinear equality and inequality constraints and is available as Share Release SDA 3541. The program follows a steepest descent search in the interior of the feasible region where the numerical approximation of the partial derivatives of the objective function (by a forward-difference formula) and the step size in a given direction at stage $(k + 1)$ are functions of the number of successful steps on the kth stage. A gradient projection with linearized constraints is employed for the nontrivial constraints (constraints other than $L_j \leq x_j \leq U_j$). Analytical partial derivatives of the nontrivial constraints must be provided. A parabolic approximation of the gradient vector is used in the vicinity of a constraint to determine the approximate point of tangency of the bounding hyperplane of a constraint. Also, several special strategies are incorporated in the computer program to handle the ridges and the trivial constraints, as well as to accelerate the optimization. A projection technique is used to reach a feasible point from a nonfeasible starting point.

Figure 6.3–4 illustrates the trajectory of the gradient method in a valley (the equivalent of a ridge in a maximization problem). The presence of the valley can be detected by noting the change in sign of the components of the gradient of the objective function, such as the alternation in sign of the x_2

[1] H. P. Künzi and W. Krelle, "Nonlinear Programming," Blaisdell Publishing Company, Waltham, Mass., 1966.

[2] R. Fletcher, *J. Inst. Math. Appl.*, **5**:2 (1969).

Fig. 6.3-4 Adjustment of the trajectory of the gradient phase.

component. To speed up the search in the valley, at $\mathbf{x}^{(4)}$ the step in the x_2 direction is reduced to 0.64 of its original value, so that the trajectory follows the dashed line instead of the solid line. If, after the first reduction is effected, the sign of the partial derivative continues to oscillate, further reductions are made. On the other hand, if the oscillation ceases, the step length in the x_2 direction is increased by 1.25.

Another type of acceleration used to speed up the gradient phase of the search is to use the method of parallel tangents (discussed in Sec. 3.3-3) to pass a vector through points 2 and 4, as illustrated in Fig. 6.3-5, to reach point A, eliminating points 5 through 8.

When a trivial constraint is violated, the step size is reduced by multiplying the current step length by the ratio of the distance between $x_j^{(k)}$ and its bound, divided by the step length actually taken in the x_j direction. Should more than one variable violate a bound, the step length is reduced to satisfy the nearest constraint. If a projection is to be made onto the bounding constraint as an inequality constraint, a different procedure is used. The component $\partial f(\mathbf{x}^{(k)})/\partial x_j$ is set equal to zero, and the variable x_j is removed from consideration in the projection of the gradient of the objective

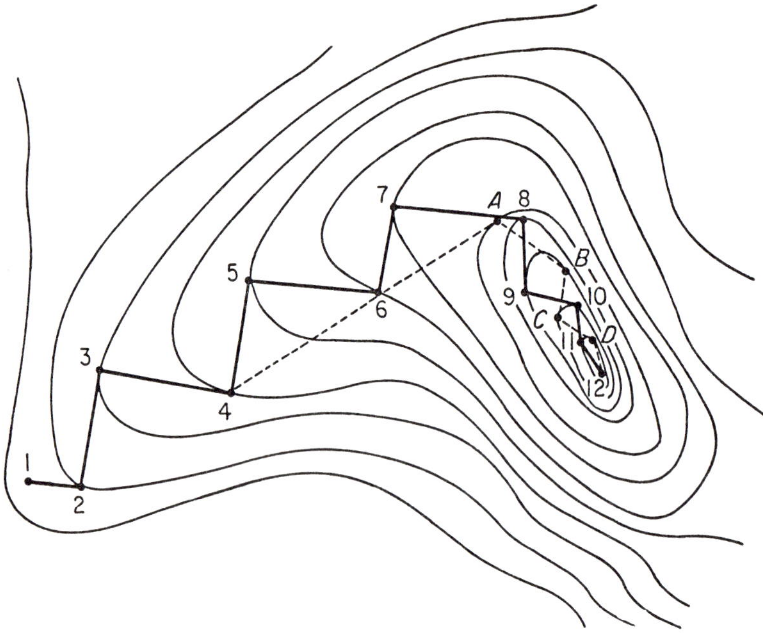

Fig. 6.3-5 Application of Partan steps in the gradient phase.

function by setting $\partial g_i(\mathbf{x}^{(k)})/\partial x_j$ equal to zero for each constraint j being considered as an equality constraint during the gradient projection. Thus the projection is carried out on a subspace in which x_j has been eliminated.

When constraints other than the trivial constraints are violated, and the constraints are nonlinear, several successive iterations may be required to obtain the next feasible point. Let $\Delta\mathbf{x}$ represent the n-dimensional column vector which takes a nonfeasible $\mathbf{x}$ into a feasible $\mathbf{x}^{(k+1)}$, and let $\Delta\mathbf{b}$ be a p-dimensional column vector representing the required change in the value of the constraints so that they are satisfied. To the first order,

$$\Delta\mathbf{b} = \mathbf{A}\,\Delta\mathbf{x} \tag{6.3-7}$$

where $\mathbf{A}$ is the matrix of first partial derivatives of the constraints with respect to x_j. The change in $\mathbf{x}$, $\Delta\mathbf{x}$, is computed by multiplying $\mathbf{A}^T$ by a p-dimensional vector γ, $\Delta\mathbf{x} = \mathbf{A}^T\gamma$, so that $\Delta\mathbf{b} = \mathbf{A}\mathbf{A}^T\gamma$. Consequently, since $\Delta\mathbf{b}$ and $\mathbf{A}$ are known,

$$\gamma = (\mathbf{A}\mathbf{A}^T)^{-1}\,\Delta\mathbf{b} \tag{6.3-8}$$

The actual step taken is calculated from

$$x_j^{(k+1)} = x_j^{(k)} + (\Delta\mathbf{x})^T\left(\frac{\partial\mathbf{h}}{\partial x_j}\right) \tag{6.3-9}$$

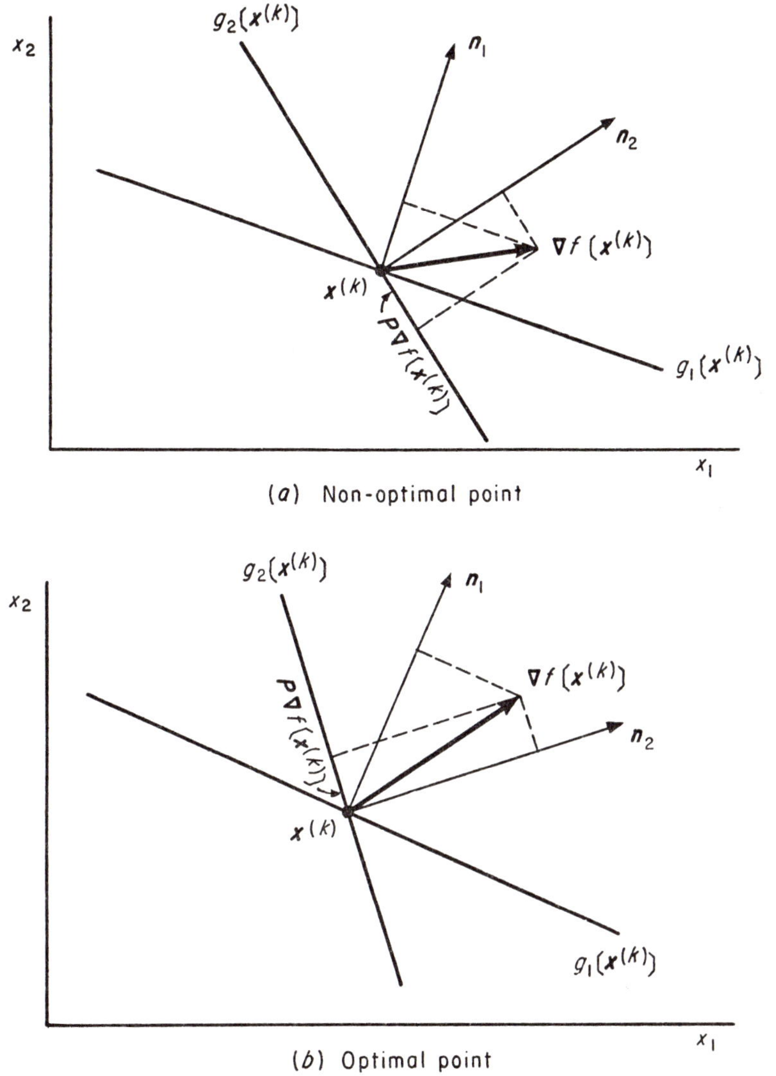

Fig. 6.3-6 Adding inequality constraints to the active constraint set in the generalized gradient search and subsequent gradient projection. (*a*) Nonoptimal point; (*b*) optimal point.

where **h** includes in the matrix the active constraints.

To keep track of which inequalities must be treated as equalities at any point, in addition to the original set of equalities, the dot product of the gradient (or its negative for minimization) of the objective function and the unit normal $\mathbf{n}_i$,

$$\nabla^T f(\mathbf{x}^{(k)})\mathbf{n}_i = \nabla^T f(\mathbf{x}^{(k)}) \frac{\nabla g_i(\mathbf{x}^{(k)})}{\|\nabla g_i(\mathbf{x}^{(k)})\|}$$

is calculated for each inequality constraint. The constraint corresponding to the largest dot product is added to the original set of equality constraints, $\nabla f(\mathbf{x}^{(k)})$ is projected onto the constraint set, and the cycle repeated until the gradient projection onto the constraint intersection yields a feasible direction. In Fig. 6.3–6*a* the dot product of $\nabla f(\mathbf{x}^{(k)})$ and the unit normal at $\mathbf{x}^{(k)}$ indicate that $g_2(\mathbf{x}^{(k)})$ would be added to the active constraint set first. Because the projection of $\nabla f(\mathbf{x}^{(k)})$ on $g_2(\mathbf{x}^{(k)}) = 0$ gives a feasible direction, $g_1(\mathbf{x}^{(k)})$ would not be added to the active constraint set. Thus, although $\nabla f(\mathbf{x}^{(k)})$ may violate several inequality constraints, it is not always necessary to project $\nabla f(\mathbf{x}^{(k)})$ onto *all* the violated constraints. If while moving in the feasible direction another constraint is encountered, it is added to the constraint set, and $\nabla f(\mathbf{x})$ is projected again. Removal of constraints from the group considered as equalities takes place before a new gradient of the objective function is calculated.

Figure 6.3–6*b* illustrates what happens at an optimal $\mathbf{x}^{(k)}$. As in Fig. 6.3–6*a*, $g_2(\mathbf{x}^{(k)})$ is added to the active constraint set since

$$\nabla^T f(\mathbf{x}^{(k)}) \frac{\nabla g_2(\mathbf{x}^{(k)})}{\|\nabla g_2(\mathbf{x}^{(k)})\|} > \nabla^T f(\mathbf{x}^{(k)}) \frac{\nabla g_1(\mathbf{x}^{(k)})}{\|\nabla g_1(\mathbf{x}^{(k)})\|}$$

However, the projection of $\nabla f(\mathbf{x}^{(k)})$ on $g_2(\mathbf{x}^{(k)})$ now violates $g_1(\mathbf{x}^{(k)})$, and hence is not a feasible vector. Then $g_1(\mathbf{x}^{(k)})$ is added to the constraint set and $\nabla f(\mathbf{x}^{(k)})$ projected onto the intersection of $g_1(\mathbf{x}^{(k)})$ and $g_2(\mathbf{x}^{(k)})$, yielding a zero vector. Termination of the search takes place when, on two consecutive stages, no successful steps have been found.

The generalized gradient search, as outlined in Fig. 6.3–7, is compared with other algorithms, in Chap. 9. One version[1] has been reported to solve problems with as many as 50 constraints and 50 variables.

One difficulty with the above approach is that the values of the elements of $\mathbf{A}$ are approximations to the desired values because the partial derivatives are evaluated at nonfeasible points. Consequently, in cases in which the iteration fails to yield a feasible point to within a prespecified tolerance because a constraint was violated by a very large amount, after a preset number of iterations have been exceeded, the algorithm calculates a new gradient and reduces the step size to obtain a feasible point. Another difficulty with nonlinear constraints is that a linearized constraint may coincide with a boundary at some point. Then the matrix $\mathbf{A}\mathbf{A}^T$ will become

[1] K. E. Cross, *AEC Doc.* K–1746, May 30, 1968.

START

Initialize constants and variables (A)

Obtain a feasible starting point if $x^{(o)}$ is nonfeasible

Fit parabola to 3 previous values of f(x) and find minimum (omitted if constraints are present).

Compute for $i = 1, \ldots, n$

$$\frac{\partial f}{\partial x_i} = -(x_i^{(m_2)} - x_i^{(m_1)})$$

$x_i^{(m_1)}$ = value of x_i on last successful step

$x_i^{(m_2)}$ = value of x_i on last successful step prior to $x_i^{(m_1)}$

Determine whether or not to use the acceleration procedure

Yes ← | → No

Calculate partial derivatives of f(x) by forward differences, $i = 1, \ldots, n$

$$\frac{\partial f}{\partial x_i} = \frac{f(x_1, \ldots, x_i + \Delta x_i, \ldots, x_n) - f(x)}{\Delta x_i}$$

$(\Delta x_i^{(o)})$ is difference between lower and upper bounds on x_i

For each variable held on a boundary, the number of variables is reduced by one for the next direction change

Are there constraints present? Check for partial derivatives oscillating in sign

Yes | No

Project the gradient to obtain a feasible search direction

Compute Δx_i, $i = 1, \ldots, n$, from the scaled elements of the search direction

Yes

Are constraints present?

No

Compute a new x-vector: $x^{(k+1)} = x^{(k)} + \Delta x^{(k)}$
If it violates the bounding value on a variable, reduce the Δx_i (omit latter if constraints are present).

Continue moving along search direction. Accelerate step size if progress is too slow.

Evaluate $f(x^{(k+1)})$

Yes

Is $f(x^{(k+1)}) < f(x^{(k)})$?

No

Go to (A)

Has limit on number of passes through block (A) been exceeded?

3d pass

Is this the 1st, 2nd, or 3d pass through this block?

1st pass

Is the number of previous successful steps since block (A) > 0?

No

2nd pass

Yes

Minimization has been completed unless a variable was held on a bound. If so, go to (A)

No

Is the number of previous successful steps since block (A) > 1?

Yes → Are constraints present? → No

Yes

Is the number of previous steps since block (A) > 1?

Yes

Carry out a parabolic fit for last 3 values of f(x) and determine new minimum for testing.

No

Go to (A)

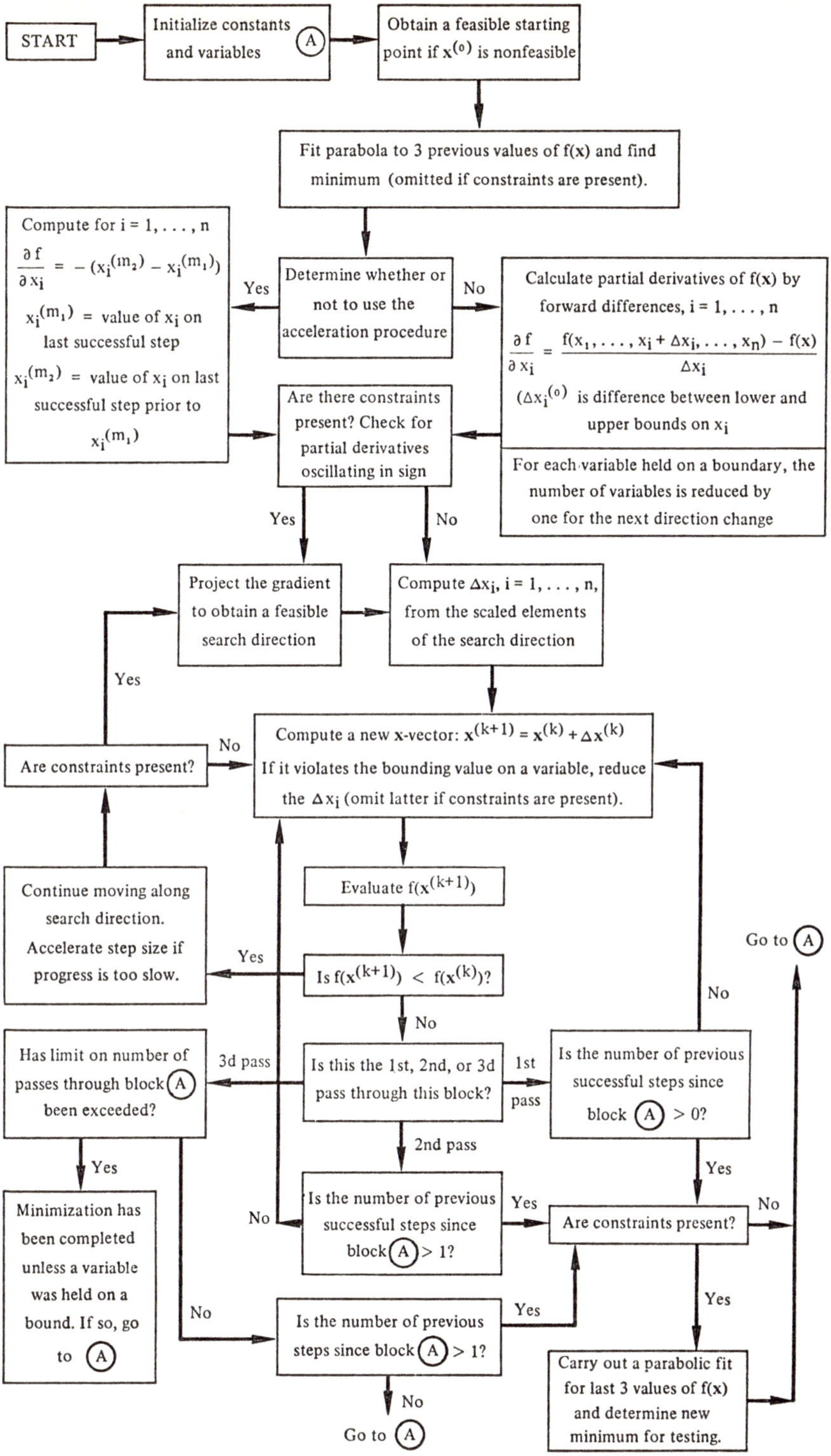

Fig. 6.3-7 Information flow diagram for generalized gradient search (GRS).

singular. Singularity can also be caused by adding too many bounds to an existing set of constraints so that the local point is "overconstrained." The singularity is removed by replacing the jth diagonal element of $\mathbf{A}\mathbf{A}^T$ by 1 whenever it is 0. Because the jth element of the vector $\mathbf{A}\,\Delta f(\mathbf{x})$ is also zero, λ_j will prove to be zero, in effect disregarding the jth constraint. If a step in the new direction does not improve $f(\mathbf{x})$ or if $\mathbf{P}\nabla f(\mathbf{x}) = 0$, a new $\nabla f(\mathbf{x})$ is computed and projected.

Example 6.3-1 Generalized gradient search (GGS)

The example problem is

$$
\begin{aligned}
\text{Minimize:} \quad & f(\mathbf{x}) = 4x_1 - x_2^2 - 12 \\
\text{Subject to:} \quad & h_1(\mathbf{x}) = 25 - x_1^2 - x_2^2 = 0 \\
& g_2(\mathbf{x}) = 10x_1 - x_1^2 + 10x_2 - x_2^2 - 34 \ge 0 \\
& g_3(\mathbf{x}) = x_1 \ge 0 \\
& g_4(\mathbf{x}) = x_2 \ge 0
\end{aligned}
$$

Figure 6.0-1 illustrates the functions.

We start from the nonfeasible but interior vector $\mathbf{x}^{(0)} = [2 \quad 4]^T$ and place lower bounds of (0,0), respectively, on x_1 and x_2, and arbitrary upper bounds of $(10^6, 10^6)$. The partial derivatives of the objective function and nontrivial constraints are

$$
\frac{\partial f(\mathbf{x})}{\partial x_1} = 4 \qquad \frac{\partial f(\mathbf{x})}{\partial x_2} = -2x_2
$$

$$
\frac{\partial h_1(\mathbf{x})}{\partial x_1} = -2x_1 \qquad \frac{\partial h_1(\mathbf{x})}{\partial x_2} = -2x_2
$$

$$
\frac{\partial g_2(\mathbf{x})}{\partial x_1} = 10 - 2x_1 \qquad \frac{\partial g_2(\mathbf{x})}{\partial x_2} = 10 - 2x_2
$$

The values of the partial derivatives at the initial point are (in the order given above)

$$
\begin{bmatrix} 4 & -8 \\ -4 & -8 \\ 6 & 2 \end{bmatrix}
$$

First the matrix $\mathbf{A}$ is computed (only the constraint $h_1(\mathbf{x})$ is considered active at the point $\mathbf{x}^{(0)} = [2 \quad 4]^T$) from the relation

$$
a_{ik}^{(k)} = \sum_{j=1}^{n} \left(\frac{\partial h_i(\mathbf{x}^{(k)})}{\partial x_j}\right)\left(\frac{\partial h_k(\mathbf{x}^{(k)})}{\partial x_j}\right) \qquad i,k = 1, \ldots, n^*
$$

where n^* is the number of active inequality constraints plus the equality constraints.

Here (with $n^* = 1$)

$$\mathbf{A}^{(0)} = a_{11}^{(0)} = -4\,(-4) + -8\,(-8) = 80$$

Next the matrix $\Delta\mathbf{b}$, composed of the required changes in the values of all the constraints (equality plus active inequality) so that they are satisfied from the point $\mathbf{x}^{(0)} = [2 \quad 4]^T$, is calculated; $\Delta\mathbf{b}$ comprises just one element here,

$$b_1^{(0)} = -5$$

because the value of $h_1(\mathbf{x}) = 5$ at $x = [2 \quad 5]^T$. From Eq. (6.3–7)

$$\Delta\mathbf{x} = \mathbf{A}^{-1}\Delta\mathbf{b}$$

or

$$\Delta\mathbf{x} = \frac{1}{80}(-5) = -0.0625$$

For the stage ($k = 1$), the vector $\mathbf{x}^{(1)}$ is computed from Eq. (6.3–9).

$$x_j^{(1)} = x_j^{(0)} + (\Delta x)\frac{\partial h_1(\mathbf{x}^0)}{\partial x_j}$$

$$x_1^{(1)} = 2.00 - 0.0625\,(-4) = 2.25$$

$$x_2^{(1)} = 4.00 - 0.0625\,(-8) = 4.50$$

Successive stages of the search are (the numbers are truncated):

Stage k	x_1	x_2	$\frac{\partial h_1(\mathbf{x}^{(k)})}{\partial x_1}$	$\frac{\partial h_1(\mathbf{x}^{(k)})}{\partial x_2}$	$h(\mathbf{x}^{(k)})$	Δx
1	2.250	4.500	−4.500	−9.000	-3.125×10^{-1}	3.083×10^{-3}
2	2.236	4.472	−4.472	−8.944	-9.645×10^{-4}	9.644×10^{-6}
3	2.236	4.472	−4.472	−8.944	-9.302×10^{-9}	

After three stages the tolerance criterion for $h(\mathbf{x}^{(k)})$ is satisfied and the independent variables are sequentially perturbed by the large quantity $\alpha(U_j - L_j)$, where $\alpha = 0.005$, an arbitrary constant, and U_j and L_j are the upper and lower bounds on x_j, respectively. In the example, $\alpha(U_j - L_j) = 0.005(10^6) = 5 \times 10^3$ for x_1 and x_2, so that the following perturbations are made:

$x_1^{(3)} + \delta x_1$	$x_2^{(3)} + \delta x_2$	$f(\mathbf{x})$ *or* $f(\mathbf{x} + \delta\mathbf{x})$
$2.236 + 0$	$4.472 + 0$	-23.05
$2.236 + 5 \times 10^3$	$4.472 + 0$	1.99×10^4
$2.236 + 0$	$4.472 + 5 \times 10^3$	-2.50×10^7

These perturbations are used to compute new components of the gradient of $f(\mathbf{x})$ as follows:

$$\frac{\partial f(\mathbf{x})}{\partial x_j} \approx \frac{f(x_1, x_2, \ldots, x_j + \delta x_j, \ldots, x_n) - f(\mathbf{x})}{\delta x_j}$$

$$\frac{\partial f(\mathbf{x}^{(3)'})}{\partial x_1} \approx \frac{1.99 \times 10^4 - (-23.05)}{5 \times 10^3} = 4.00$$

$$\frac{\partial f(\mathbf{x}^{(3)'})}{\partial x_2} \approx \frac{-2.50 \times 10^{-7} - (-23.05)}{5 \times 10^3} = -5.009 \times 10^3$$

that replace the previous components. Consequently, on stage $k = 4$, the search takes relatively large steps and by stage 6 reaches the vector $\mathbf{x}^{(6)} = [0 \quad 5.590]^T$, where $h_1(\mathbf{x}) = -6.250$ and $g_2(\mathbf{x}) = -9.348$.

Now, because $g_2(\mathbf{x}) \geq 0$ is not satisfied, both $h_1(\mathbf{x})$ and $g_2(\mathbf{x})$ must be taken into account. The matrices are

$$\mathbf{A} = \begin{bmatrix} 1.250 \times 10^2 & 1.319 \times 10^1 \\ 1.319 \times 10^1 & 1.393 \end{bmatrix} \qquad \Delta\mathbf{b} = \begin{bmatrix} 6.250 \\ 9.348 \end{bmatrix}$$

and

$$\Delta\mathbf{x} = \begin{bmatrix} -6.545 \times 10^{13} \\ 6.113 \times 10^{14} \end{bmatrix}$$

On the next stage the matrix **A** becomes the identity matrix. After a few more stages,

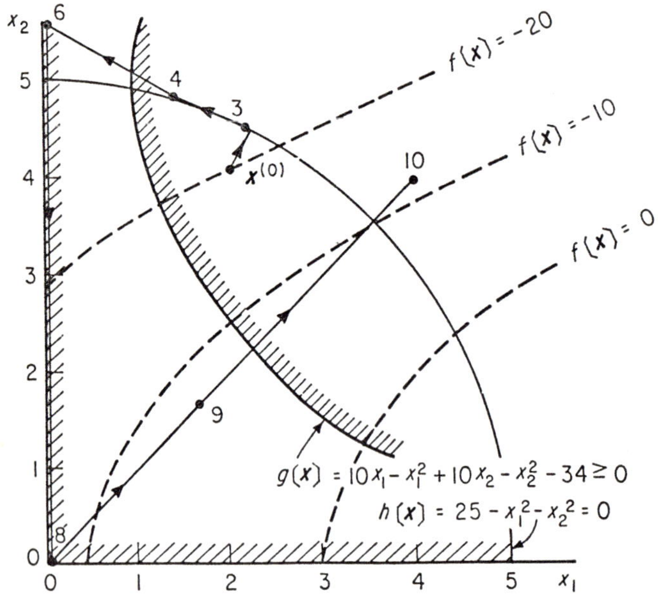

Fig. E6.3-1 Trajectory of the generalized gradient search.

k stage	$x_1^{(k)}$	$x_2^{(k)}$
7	0	0
8	0	0
9	1.70	1.70
10	4.00	4.00

On the stage $k = 10$ the matrix **A** unfortunately becomes exactly singular:

$$\mathbf{A} = \begin{bmatrix} 128 & -32 \\ -32 & 8 \end{bmatrix}$$

so that the execution of the algorithm terminates prematurely. Figure E6.3–1 illustrates the search trajectory.

6.3–3 Extension of Davidon's Method to Accommodate Constraints

We will first describe the extension of conjugate methods and variable metric methods to accommodate linear constraints, and then indicate what might be done to accommodate nonlinear constraints. This subsection is based primarily on the work of Davidon,[1] who originally suggested the approach, Goldfarb,[2] who provided many of the details of the matrix manipulations, Davies[3] and Murtagh and Sargent,[4] who modified the method and prepared a computer code to execute it. Although the Davidon-Fletcher-Powell or Broyden's algorithm will be the one assumed operating to determine the search directions at each stage of the optimization, almost any of the methods described in Chap. 3 could be substituted instead.

Davidon, in his original paper, suggested that his method could be extended to nonlinear programming problems with *linear* equality and inequality constraints by reducing the rank of $\boldsymbol{\eta}^{(k)}$ by 1 for each active constraint and modifying $\boldsymbol{\eta}^{(k)}$ so that each of the components of $\mathbf{x}^{(k+1)} = \mathbf{x}^{(k)} + \Delta\mathbf{x}^{(k)}$ satisfied all the active constraints [refer to Eq. (3.4–1)]. To so modify $\boldsymbol{\eta}$ in practice, following the ideas underlying Eqs. (6.3–2) and (6.3–3), we can define a *generalized projection matrix*; $\mathbf{x}_{\mathcal{M}}$ is the orthogonal

[1] W. C. Davidon, *AEC Doc.* ANL–5990 (rev.), 1959.

[2] D. Goldfarb, Ph.D. dissertation, Princeton University, Princeton, N.J., 1966; D. Goldfarb and L. Lapidus, *Ind. Eng. Chem. Fundamentals*, 7:142 (1968).

[3] D. Davies, The Use of Davidon's Method in Nonlinear Programming, *ICI Ltd. Rept.* MSDH/68/110, August, 1968; *Doc.* N69–33235 available from CFSTI, Springfield, Va.

[4] B. A. Murtagh and R. W. H. Sargent, Chap. 14 in R. Fletcher (ed.), "Optimization," Academic Press Inc., London, 1969.

projection with respect to the matrix $\mathbf{Q}$ of the vector $\mathbf{x}$†

$$\mathbf{x}_{\mathscr{M}} = \hat{\mathbf{P}}_\ell \mathbf{x} \tag{6.3–10}$$

where $\hat{\mathbf{P}}_\ell$ is defined as

$$\hat{\mathbf{P}}_\ell = \mathbf{I} - \mathbf{A}_\ell^T(\mathbf{A}_\ell \mathbf{Q} \mathbf{A}_\ell^T)^{-1}\mathbf{A}_\ell \mathbf{Q} \tag{6.3–11}$$

From this viewpoint, $\mathbf{Q} = \mathbf{I}$ in Eqs. (6.3–2) and (6.3–3); also,

$$\mathbf{x}_{\mathscr{M}}^T \mathbf{Q}(\mathbf{x} - \mathbf{x}_{\mathscr{M}}) = 0$$

Thus $\mathbf{P}_\ell$ is a generalized projection matrix that projects $\mathbf{x}$ onto the manifold $\mathscr{M}$ according to the metric $\mathbf{Q}$. Subsequently we will let $\mathbf{Q} = \boldsymbol{\eta}^{(k)}$, where $\boldsymbol{\eta}^{(k)}$ is the estimate of the inverse of the hessian matrix described in Sec. 3.4 for unconstrained optimization.

Recall that the search direction for an unconstrained nonlinear programming problem by the Davidon method described in Sec. 3.4 was determined from

$$\mathbf{s}^{(k)} = -\boldsymbol{\eta}_0^{(k)} \nabla f(\mathbf{x}^{(k)})$$

where $\boldsymbol{\eta}_0^{(k)}$ here means $\boldsymbol{\eta}$ evaluated at $\mathbf{x}^{(k)}$ in the absence of constraints. If ℓ active constraints are present, $\mathbf{A}_\ell \mathbf{x} = \mathbf{b}$, we have seen from Eq. (6.3–4) that

$$\mathbf{s}^{(k)} = -\mathbf{P}_\ell \nabla f(\mathbf{x}^{(k)})$$

One way of combining the idea of the projection matrix with the Davidon method gives a search direction of

$$\mathbf{s}^{(k)} = -\boldsymbol{\eta}_0^{(k)}[\hat{\mathbf{P}}_\ell \nabla f(\mathbf{x}^{(k)})] = -\boldsymbol{\eta}_\ell^{(k)} \nabla f(\mathbf{x}^{(k)}) \tag{6.3–12}$$

where $\hat{\mathbf{P}}_\ell$ is given by Eq. (6.3–11)* with $\mathbf{Q} = \boldsymbol{\eta}_0^{(k)}$ and

$$\boldsymbol{\eta}_\ell^{(k)} = \boldsymbol{\eta}_0^{(k)} \hat{\mathbf{P}}_\ell = \boldsymbol{\eta}_0^{(k)} - \boldsymbol{\eta}_0^{(k)} \mathbf{A}_\ell^T (\mathbf{A}_\ell \boldsymbol{\eta}_0^{(k)} \mathbf{A}_\ell^T)^{-1} \mathbf{A}_\ell \boldsymbol{\eta}_0^{(k)} \tag{6.3–13}$$

The notation of $\boldsymbol{\eta}_\ell^{(k)}$ will designate the matrix $\boldsymbol{\eta}$ evaluated at $\mathbf{x}^{(k)}$ with ℓ active constraints existing at $\mathbf{x}^{(k)}$. For example, to add one constraint $\mathbf{a}_j^T \mathbf{x} = \mathbf{b}$ to an unconstrained problem, Eq. (6.3–13) becomes

$$\boldsymbol{\eta}_1^{(k)} = \boldsymbol{\eta}_0^{(k)} - \frac{\boldsymbol{\eta}_0^{(k)} \mathbf{a}_j \mathbf{a}_j^T \boldsymbol{\eta}_0^{(k)}}{\mathbf{a}_j^T \boldsymbol{\eta}_0^{(k)} \mathbf{a}_j} \tag{6.3–13a}$$

†A. S. Householder, "The Theory of Matrices in Numerical Analysis," Blaisdell Publishing Company, Waltham, Mass., 1964, p. 10.

*If $\mathbf{s}^{(k)}$ is defined as $\mathbf{s}^{(k)} = -\hat{\mathbf{P}}_\ell^*[\boldsymbol{\eta}_0^{(k)} \nabla f(\mathbf{x}^{(k)})]$, wherein the projection matrix is viewed as projecting the unconstrained step onto the constraint surface, then $\hat{\mathbf{P}}_\ell^*$ is defined as (Goldfarb, *op. cit.*).

$$\hat{\mathbf{P}}_\ell^* = \mathbf{I} - \mathbf{Q}\mathbf{A}_\ell^T(\mathbf{A}_\ell \mathbf{Q} A_\ell^T)^{-1}\mathbf{A}_\ell$$

Goldfarb has demonstrated that the use of Eq. (6.3–12) to establish the search directions plus a minimization by a linear search will converge in $(n - \ell)$ iterations for a quadratic function of n variables subject to ℓ equality constraints. One updates the $\boldsymbol{\eta}$ matrix by using Broyden's (rank 1 algorithm) correction, but the efficiency of the algorithm depends on not computing the projection matrix $\hat{\mathbf{P}}_\ell$ (or $\hat{\mathbf{P}}_\ell^*$) explicitly on each stage but updating $\hat{\mathbf{P}}_\ell$ from the previous stage.

If one or more linear inequality constraints exist that would be violated during a search in a given direction, these constraints must be added to the set of equality constraints in forming $\boldsymbol{\eta}_\ell^{(k)}$. On the other hand, it may be possible to eliminate one (or more) of the inequality constraints from the set of active constraints because the search direction is such that one of the group of m inequality constraints

$$\mathbf{B}_m\mathbf{x} \geq \mathbf{c}$$

is no longer violated. Goldfarb gave the following relation to remove one inequality constraint from the group of ℓ active constraints:

$$\boldsymbol{\eta}_{\ell-1}^{(k)} = \boldsymbol{\eta}_\ell^{(k)} + \frac{\mathbf{P}_{m-1}\mathbf{b}_j^T\mathbf{b}_j\hat{\mathbf{P}}_{m-1}}{\mathbf{b}_j\mathbf{P}_{m-1}\mathbf{b}_j^T} \tag{6.3–14}$$

where $\mathbf{b}_j = [b_{j1} \quad b_{j2} \quad \ldots \quad b_{jn}]$, that is, $\mathbf{b}_j$ is the row of $\mathbf{B}_m$ corresponding to the jth constraint to be eliminated from the set of active constraints, and $\mathbf{P}_{m-1}$ is obtained from Eq. (6.3–3), with the inequality constraint j removed from the set of m inequality constraints

$$\mathbf{P}_{m-1} = \mathbf{I} - \mathbf{B}_{m-1}^T(\mathbf{B}_{m-1}\mathbf{B}_{m-1}^T)^{-1}\mathbf{B}_{m-1} \tag{6.3–15}$$

One matter that remains to be discussed is how to determine which of the inequality constraints are going to be the active ones at $\mathbf{x}^{(k)}$. As explained in Sec. 6.3–1, the so-called shadow prices, that is, the elements in the vector $\mathbf{u}$ defined in connection with Eq. (6.3–4),

$$\mathbf{u} = (\mathbf{A}_\ell\mathbf{A}_\ell^T)^{-1}\mathbf{A}_\ell\nabla f(\mathbf{x}^{(k)})$$

indicate whether or not a constraint will be active. A negative u_j corresponds to a constraint that can be removed from the constraint basis, and the constraint corresponding to the most negative u_j is the one selected for deletion. Because the inequalities in the set of active constraints are the only relations that may possibly be eliminated from the constraint basis (the equalities are always active), it is only necessary to compute

$$\tilde{\mathbf{u}} = (\mathbf{B}_m\mathbf{B}_m^T)^{-1}\mathbf{B}_m\nabla f(\mathbf{x}^{(k)}) \tag{6.3–16}$$

instead of $\mathbf{u}$. Furthermore, as mentioned in Sec. 6.3–1, there are more efficient ways of obtaining $(\mathbf{B}_m\mathbf{B}_m^T)^{-1}$ from $(\mathbf{B}_{m+1}\mathbf{B}_{m+1}^T)^{-1}$ and $(\mathbf{B}_{m-1}\mathbf{B}_{m-1}^T)^{-1}$ than by matrix multiplication followed by matrix inversion.

With $\boldsymbol{\eta}_\ell^{(k)}$, $\hat{\mathbf{P}}_\ell$, and $\tilde{\mathbf{u}}$ now defined, we can summarize the Davidon method as applied to nonlinear programming problems with linear constraints. An initial feasible point $\mathbf{x}^{(0)}$ is assumed known, or must be found, so that the algorithm can commence. If $\mathbf{x}^{(0)}$ is an interior point of R and if there are no equality constraints, $\boldsymbol{\eta}_0^{(0)}$ is chosen to be $\mathbf{I}$. However, if $\mathbf{x}^{(0)}$ lies on ℓ linearly independent hyperplanes, i.e., satisfies ℓ equality constraints, $\boldsymbol{\eta}_\ell^{(0)}$ is computed from $\boldsymbol{\eta}_0^{(0)} = \mathbf{I}$ by application of Eq. (6.3–13*a*) ℓ times. Thus the set of (independent) equality constraints is included in the initial constraint basis, and only inequality constraints are subsequently added or removed from the constraint basis.

On the kth stage of the search we assume we know $\mathbf{x}^{(k)}$, $f(\mathbf{x}^{(k)})$, $\nabla f(\mathbf{x}^{(k)})$, and $\boldsymbol{\eta}_\ell^{(k)}$ and that $\mathbf{x}^{(k)}$ lies in R and in the manifold $\mathscr{M}$ determined by the intersection of ℓ linearly independent hyperplanes that constitute the active constraints (the constraint basis). The steps listed below follow those recommended by Davies.

1. *Determine the active inequality constraints.* Compute $\mathbf{s}^{(k)} = -\boldsymbol{\eta}_\ell^{(k)} \nabla f(\mathbf{x}^{(k)})$ and $\tilde{\mathbf{u}}$ from Eq. (6.3–16). If $\|\mathbf{s}^{(k)}\| = 0$ and each $\tilde{u}_j \geq 0$, the optimum, $\mathbf{x}^*$, has been found, and the algorithm terminates; otherwise continue.
2. *Alteration of constraint basis.* Remove from the constraint basis that inequality constraint corresponding to the largest negative value of $\tilde{u}_j$; removal is by application of Eq. (6.3–14). Compute $\mathbf{s}^{(k)} = -\boldsymbol{\eta}_{\ell-1}^{(k)}\nabla f(\mathbf{x}^{(k)})$ and ascertain as in the Rosen gradient projection algorithm that the new $\mathbf{s}^{(k)}$ yields a feasible point with respect to each of the inactive constraints. If $\mathbf{s}^{(k)}$ does not yield a feasible point, use Eq. (6.3–13*a*) to add to the basis the inequality constraint that will be violated, recompute $\mathbf{s}^{(k)}$ from Eq. (6.3–12), and repeat from the start of this step until a feasible direction is obtained. Return to step 1 if $\|\mathbf{s}_{\text{feasible}}^{(k)}\| = 0$; otherwise continue.
3. *Univariate search.* Carry out a univariate search in the feasible direction as described in Secs. 3.4 and 2.6. If a step in the univariate search reaches a constraint, go to step 5. Otherwise, locate the minimum of $f(\mathbf{x})$.
4. *Matrix update.* If no new constraints are encountered during the linear search, update $\boldsymbol{\eta}_\ell^{(k)}$ to $\boldsymbol{\eta}_\ell^{(k+1)}$ by the Davidon-Fletcher-Powell or Broyden method (refer to Sec. 3.4). Go back to step 1.

5. *Alteration of constraint basis.* Add the new constraint encountered in step 3 to the basis. Go back to step 1.

Murtagh and Sargent used the projection matrix $\hat{\mathbf{P}}_\ell^*$ in determining the search direction

$$\begin{aligned}\Delta\mathbf{x}^{(k)} &= -\lambda^{(k)}\hat{\mathbf{P}}_\ell^{*(k)}\boldsymbol{\eta}_0^{(k)}\nabla f(\mathbf{x}^{(k)}) \\ &= -\lambda^{(k)}[\mathbf{I} - \boldsymbol{\eta}_0^{(k)}\mathbf{A}_\ell^T(\mathbf{A}_\ell\boldsymbol{\eta}_0^{(k)}\mathbf{A}_\ell^T)^{-1}\mathbf{A}_\ell]\boldsymbol{\eta}_0^{(k)}\nabla f(\mathbf{x}^{(k)}) \\ &= -\lambda^{(k)}\boldsymbol{\eta}_0^{(k)}[\nabla f(\mathbf{x}^{(k)}) - \mathbf{A}_\ell^T\mathbf{u}_\ell^{(k)}]\end{aligned}$$

where $\mathbf{u}_\ell^{(k)} \equiv (\mathbf{A}_\ell\boldsymbol{\eta}_0^{(k)}\mathbf{A}_\ell^T)^{-1}\mathbf{A}_\ell\boldsymbol{\eta}_0^{(k)}\nabla f(\mathbf{x}^{(k)})$ can be regarded as a vector of Lagrange multipliers associated with the active constraints that can be used to determine which constraints to drop from the constraint basis when the need arises. The expression $[\nabla f(\mathbf{x}^{(k)}) - \boldsymbol{\eta}_0^{(k)}\mathbf{u}_\ell^{(k)}]$ can be viewed as the difference between the gradient of $f(\mathbf{x})$ at $\mathbf{x}^{(k)}$ and the gradient at the estimated stationary point, $\boldsymbol{\eta}_0^{(k)}\mathbf{u}_\ell^{(k)}$.

The Murtagh-Sargent algorithm is quite similar to that of Davies. On the kth stage, the steps are as follows:

1. Compute
$$\mathbf{u}_\ell^{(k)} = \mathbf{M}_\ell^{(k)}\mathbf{A}_\ell\boldsymbol{\eta}_0^{(k)}\nabla f(\mathbf{x}^{(k)})$$
where $\mathbf{M}_\ell^{(k)}$ is the estimate of $(\mathbf{A}_\ell\boldsymbol{\eta}^{(k)}\mathbf{A}_\ell^T)^{-1}$.
2. Compute $\Delta\mathbf{x}^{(k)} = -\boldsymbol{\eta}_0^{(k)}[\nabla f(\mathbf{x}^{(k)}) - \mathbf{A}_\ell^T\mathbf{u}_\ell^{(k)}]$.
3. Compute
$$\beta = \max_{\substack{j|u_j>0 \\ j=1,\ldots,\ell}} \left\{\frac{\frac{1}{2}u_j}{m_{jj}}\right\}$$
where m_{jj} is the jth diagonal element of $\mathbf{M}_\ell^{(k)}$.
4. Terminate if $\|\Delta\mathbf{x}^{(k)}\| < \varepsilon$ and $\beta < \varepsilon$; otherwise continue.
5. Change the constraint basis if needed.
   a. Add a constraint. If $\mathbf{x}^{(k)}$ is on the boundary of a new constraint, $g_{\ell+1}(\mathbf{x}^{(k)}) = 0$, and if $(\Delta\mathbf{x}^{(k)})^T\nabla g_{\ell+1}(\mathbf{x}^{(k)}) > 0$, add $g_{\ell+1}(\mathbf{x}^{(k)})$ to the constraint basis and go back to step 1.
   b. Delete a constraint. If $\|\Delta\mathbf{x}^{(k)}\| < \beta$, delete constraint j from the basis and go back to step 1.

   In adding a constraint, $\mathbf{M}_\ell^{(k)}$ is updated as follows:

$$\mathbf{M}_{\ell+1}^{(k)} = \begin{bmatrix}\mathbf{M}_{11} & \mathbf{M}_{12} \\ \mathbf{M}_{21} & \mathbf{M}_{22}\end{bmatrix}$$

where $\mathbf{M}_{11} = \mathbf{A}_{11}^{-1} + \mathbf{A}_{11}^{-1}\mathbf{A}_{12}\mathbf{A}_0^{-1}\mathbf{A}_{21}\mathbf{A}_{11}^{-1} = \dfrac{\mathbf{M}_{12}\mathbf{M}_{12}^T}{\mathbf{M}_{22}}$

$$\mathbf{M}_{12} = \mathbf{M}_{21}^T = -\mathbf{A}_{11}^{-1}\mathbf{A}_{12}\mathbf{A}_0^{-1}$$

$$\mathbf{M}_{22} = \mathbf{A}_0^{-1} \qquad \text{(a scalar)}$$

$$\mathbf{A}_{11}^{-1} = \mathbf{M}_\ell^{(k)}$$

$$\mathbf{A}_{12} = \mathbf{A}_{21}^T = \mathbf{A}_\ell \boldsymbol{\eta}_0^{(k)} \nabla g_{\ell+1}(\mathbf{x}^{(k)})$$

$$\mathbf{A}_{22} = \nabla g_{\ell+1}^T(\mathbf{x}^{(k)}) \boldsymbol{\eta}_0^{(k)} \nabla g_{\ell+1}(\mathbf{x}^{(k)})$$

$$\mathbf{A}_0 = \mathbf{A}_{22} - \mathbf{A}_{21}\mathbf{A}_{11}^{-1}\mathbf{A}_{12} \qquad \text{(a scalar)}$$

In dropping a constraint, $\mathbf{M}_\ell^{(k)}$ is updated as follows:

$$\mathbf{M}_{\ell-1}^{(k)} = \mathbf{M}_{11} - \mathbf{M}_{12}\mathbf{M}_{22}^{-1}\mathbf{M}_{21}$$

6. Search in the projected direction.

$$\Delta\mathbf{x}^{(k)} = -\lambda \boldsymbol{\eta}_0^{(k)}[\nabla f(\mathbf{x}^{(k)}) - \mathbf{A}_\ell^T \mathbf{u}_\ell^{(k)}]$$

Adjust λ to reduce $f(\mathbf{x})$ but keep $\mathbf{x}$ feasible; use a unidimensional search.

7. Compute $\Delta\mathbf{g}^{(k)} = \nabla f(\mathbf{x}^{(k+1)}) - \nabla f(\mathbf{x}^{(k)})$.
8. Update the direction matrix $\boldsymbol{\eta}$ by Broyden's method.

$$\boldsymbol{\eta}_0^{(k+1)} = \boldsymbol{\eta}_0^{(k)} + \frac{(\Delta\mathbf{x}^{(k)} - \boldsymbol{\eta}_0^{(k)}\Delta\mathbf{g}^{(k)})(\Delta\mathbf{x}^{(k)} - \boldsymbol{\eta}_0^{(k)}\Delta\mathbf{g}^{(k)})^T}{(\Delta\mathbf{x}^{(k)} - \boldsymbol{\eta}_0^{(k)}\Delta\mathbf{g}^{(k)})^T\Delta\mathbf{g}^{(k)}}$$

Check to make sure that $\boldsymbol{\eta}^{(k+1)}$ is positive definite. If not, let $\boldsymbol{\eta}_0^{(k+1)} = \boldsymbol{\eta}_0^{(k)}$.
9. Update $\mathbf{M}_\ell^{(k)}$.

$$\mathbf{M}_\ell^{(k+1)} = \mathbf{M}_\ell^{(k)}$$
$$+ \frac{[\mathbf{M}_\ell^{(k)}\mathbf{A}_\ell(\Delta\mathbf{x}^{(k)} - \boldsymbol{\eta}_0^{(k)}\Delta\mathbf{g}^{(k)})][\mathbf{M}_\ell^{(k)}\mathbf{A}_\ell(\Delta\mathbf{x}^{(k)} - \boldsymbol{\eta}_0^{(k)}\Delta\mathbf{g}^{(k)})]^T}{(\Delta\mathbf{x}^{(k)} - \boldsymbol{\eta}_0^{(k)}\Delta\mathbf{g}^{(k)})^T\Delta\mathbf{g}^{(k)} + [\Delta\mathbf{x}^{(k)} - \boldsymbol{\eta}_0^{(k)}\Delta\mathbf{g}^{(k)}]^T\mathbf{A}_\ell^T[\mathbf{M}_\ell^{(k)}\mathbf{A}_\ell(\Delta\mathbf{x}^{(k)} - \boldsymbol{\eta}_0^{(k)}\Delta\mathbf{g}^{(k)})]}$$

Return to step 1.

How can the Davidon method be extended to accommodate *nonlinear constraints*? If the constraints are locally linearized, a practical method of minimization must return to the feasible region from a nonfeasible point, such as $\mathbf{x}^{(6)}$ in Fig. 6.3–3, and ensure that the point so located does in fact improve the value of $f(\mathbf{x})$. What follows has been recommended by Davies[1]

[1] *Op. cit.*

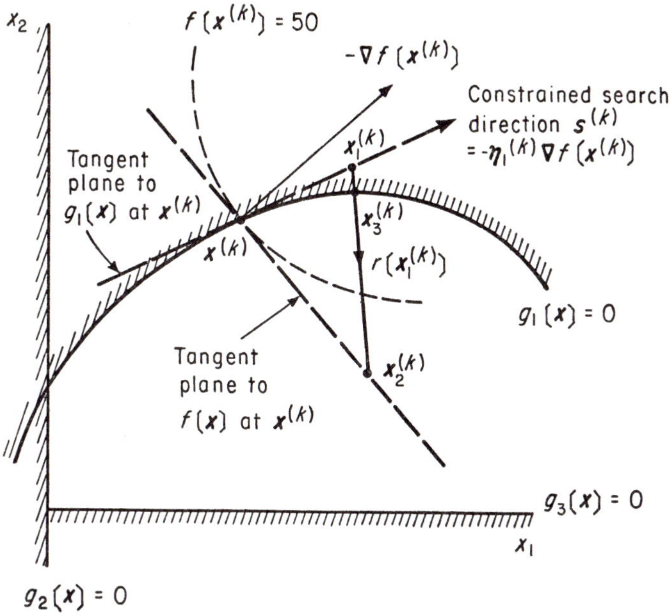

Fig. 6.3–8 Davidon method modified to apply to nonlinear constraints.

and is based on the work of Rosen.[1] Figure 6.3–8 illustrates an active constraint $g_1(\mathbf{x})$, two inactive constraints $g_2(\mathbf{x})$ and $g_3(\mathbf{x})$, the contour of $f(\mathbf{x})$ at $\mathbf{x}^{(k)}$, the tangent plane to $f(\mathbf{x}^{(k)})$ at $\mathbf{x}^{(k)}$, and the tangent plane to $g_1(\mathbf{x}^{(k)})$ at $\mathbf{x}^{(k)}$, the latter representing the linearized constraint $\tilde{g}_1(\mathbf{x}^{(k)})$. An active nonlinear inequality constraint will be one for which the corresponding linearized constraint is deemed active when introduced into Eq. (6.3–15). The return vector $\mathbf{r}(\mathbf{x}^{(k)})$ points into the feasible region from a nonfeasible point,

$$\mathbf{r}(\mathbf{x}^{(k)}) = \mathbf{B}^T(\mathbf{B}\mathbf{B}^T)^{-1}\boldsymbol{\phi}^{(k)} \tag{6.3–17}$$

where $\mathbf{B}$ is the matrix whose rows are composed of elements consisting of the partial derivative of the active inequality constraints with respect to each of the variables evaluated at $\mathbf{x}^{(k)}$, and $\boldsymbol{\phi}$ is a column vector whose elements are the absolute values of the active constraints evaluated at points along $\mathbf{s}^{(k)}$ in the vicinity of $\mathbf{x}^{(k)}$. Finally, the search direction $\mathbf{s}^{(k)}$ is the projection of $-\boldsymbol{\eta}^{(k)}\nabla f(\mathbf{x}^{(k)})$ onto the intersection of all the active linear constraints and the active linearized nonlinear constraints, i.e., onto their tangent hyperplanes.

[1] J. B. Rosen, *J. Soc. Ind. Appl. Math.*, **8**:181 (1960), **9**:514 (1961).

The method proposed by Davies is as follows (presumably equality constraints can be accommodated but no specific rules have been given):

Step 1: Determine the active inequality constraints as in step 1 for the linear constraint algorithm but with constraints linearized at $\mathbf{x}^{(k)}$ substituted for the respective nonlinear ones.

Step 2: Because the approximations involved cause the constraint basis to change on each iteration, rather than using the time-consuming Eqs. (6.3–13*a*) and (6.3–14) to reduce and raise the rank of $\boldsymbol{\eta}$ to accommodate the changing active (linearized) constraints, instead compute the matrix $\boldsymbol{\eta}_j^{(k)}$ for the j active linear inequality constraints. Store the matrix $\boldsymbol{\eta}_j^{(k)}$, and then reduce a duplicate of $\boldsymbol{\eta}_j^{(k)}$ in rank, using Eq. (6.3–13*a*) successively for each active linearized constraint to get the matrix $\boldsymbol{\eta}_\ell^{(k)}$, where ℓ is the total number of active constraints. Finally, compute

$$\mathbf{s}^{(k)} = -\boldsymbol{\eta}_\ell^{(k)}\nabla f(\mathbf{x}^{(k)})$$

Follow the procedure for step 2 for linear constraints.

Step 3: To initiate the search for $\mathbf{x}^{(k+1)}$, a step is taken in a univariate search along the direction $\mathbf{s}^{(k)}$ as follows. A step length $\lambda^{(k)}$ is fixed at the minimum of either (*a*) 2 (twice the Newton step to the minimum) or (*b*) the distance to the nearest linearized constraint along $\mathbf{s}^{(k)}$. This ensures that an unconstrained minimization can be executed and that unreasonable step sizes are avoided.

Compute $\mathbf{x}_1^{(k)} = \mathbf{x}^{(k)} + \lambda^{(k)}\mathbf{s}^{(k)}$ (see Fig. 6.3–8) and evaluate the nonlinear constraints to see if they are all satisfied. If any $g_i(\mathbf{x}_1^{(k)})$ is violated, a step is taken along the return vector $\mathbf{r}(\mathbf{x}^{(k)})$ from $\mathbf{x}_1^{(k)}$ toward the interior region. To avoid excessive constraint evaluations, a step is made all the way to the intersection of $\mathbf{r}(\mathbf{x}^{(k)})$ with the tangent to $f(\mathbf{x}^{(k)})$, that is, to $\mathbf{x}_2^{(k)}$, for it is in the region between the tangent plane to $f(\mathbf{x}^{(k)})$ and the constraints that an interior point will be found. Once the bracket $\mathbf{x}_1^{(k)} \ldots \mathbf{x}_2^{(k)}$ is established, an interpolation can be carried out until the point $\mathbf{x}_3^{(k)}$ is established on the boundary (to within some tolerance) representing the nearest constraint to $\mathbf{x}_2^{(k)}$.

If the point $\mathbf{x}_2^{(k)}$ does not satisfy the active constraints, a new step is taken from $\mathbf{x}^{(k)}$ but with a reduced step length, and a new $\mathbf{x}_2^{(k)}$ is determined.

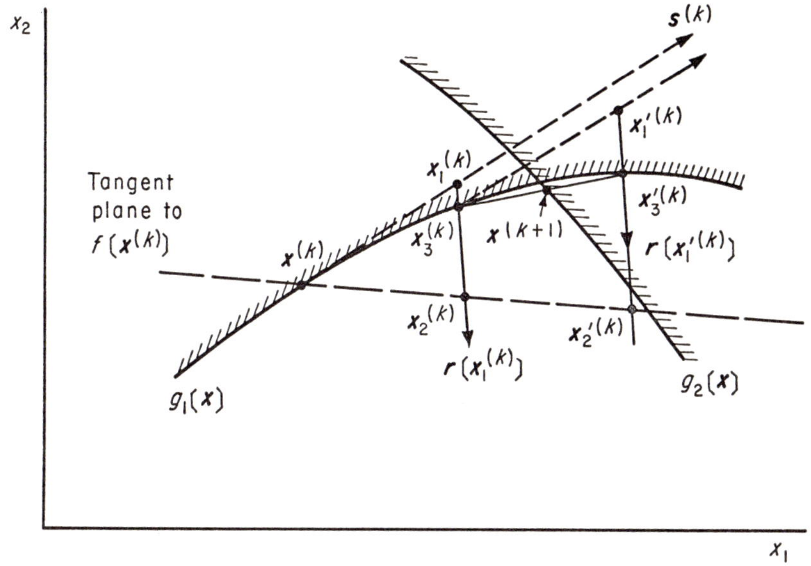

Fig. 6.3-9 Extrapolation to find a boundary point when a new constraint is violated.

After a boundary point $\mathbf{x}_3^{(k)}$ is located, a check is made to determine if a minimum of $f(\mathbf{x})$ exists along the arc between $\mathbf{x}^{(k)}$ and $\mathbf{x}_3^{(k)}$ as described in step 4. If a minimum is located, an interpolation is carried out to locate the minimum more accurately. This minimum becomes $\mathbf{x}^{(k+1)}$. If a minimum is not located, a step of length λ is taken from $\mathbf{x}_3^{(k)}$ in the direction $\mathbf{s}^{(k)}$, and step 1 is repeated, to obtain the point $\mathbf{x}_3'^{(k)}$; see Fig. 6.3-9.

If a *new* nonlinear constraint is encountered that is violated at $\mathbf{x}_3'^{(k)}$, as illustrated in Fig. 6.3-9 by $g_2(\mathbf{x})$, a boundary point $\mathbf{x}^{(k+1)}$ is determined by extrapolation along a line between the most recent $\mathbf{x}_3^{(k)}$ (designated $\mathbf{x}_3'^{(k)}$) and the immediately preceding $\mathbf{x}_3^{(k)}$ as in step 4. Then proceed to step 5.

Step 4: Termination of the search for $\mathbf{x}^{(k+1)}$ can take place in several ways. Except when one or more new constraints are violated, termination usually takes place following the indication that $f(\mathbf{x}_3'^{(k)}) \geq f(\mathbf{x}_3^{(k)})$ or $\nabla^T f(\mathbf{x}_3'^{(k)})\mathbf{s}^{(k)} \geq 0$ because a minimum in $f(\mathbf{x})$ has been bracketed along the line $\mathbf{x}_3'^{(k)} \ldots \mathbf{x}_3^{(k)}$. An interpolation is carried out to locate the minimum of $f(\mathbf{x})$ at $\mathbf{x}_4^{(k)}$ on the line more precisely. Subsequently, a step is taken in the direction of steepest descent from $\mathbf{x}_4^{(k)}$ to the nearest constraint to yield $\mathbf{x}^{(k+1)}$. Davies suggested for convex constraints that $\mathbf{x}^{(k+1)}$ be located by determining the intersection between $-\nabla f(\mathbf{x}_4^{(k)})$ and $\mathbf{s}^{(k)}$ at $\mathbf{x}_5^{(k)}$, a nonfeasible point, and subsequently interpolating and extrapolating (for concave constraints) be-

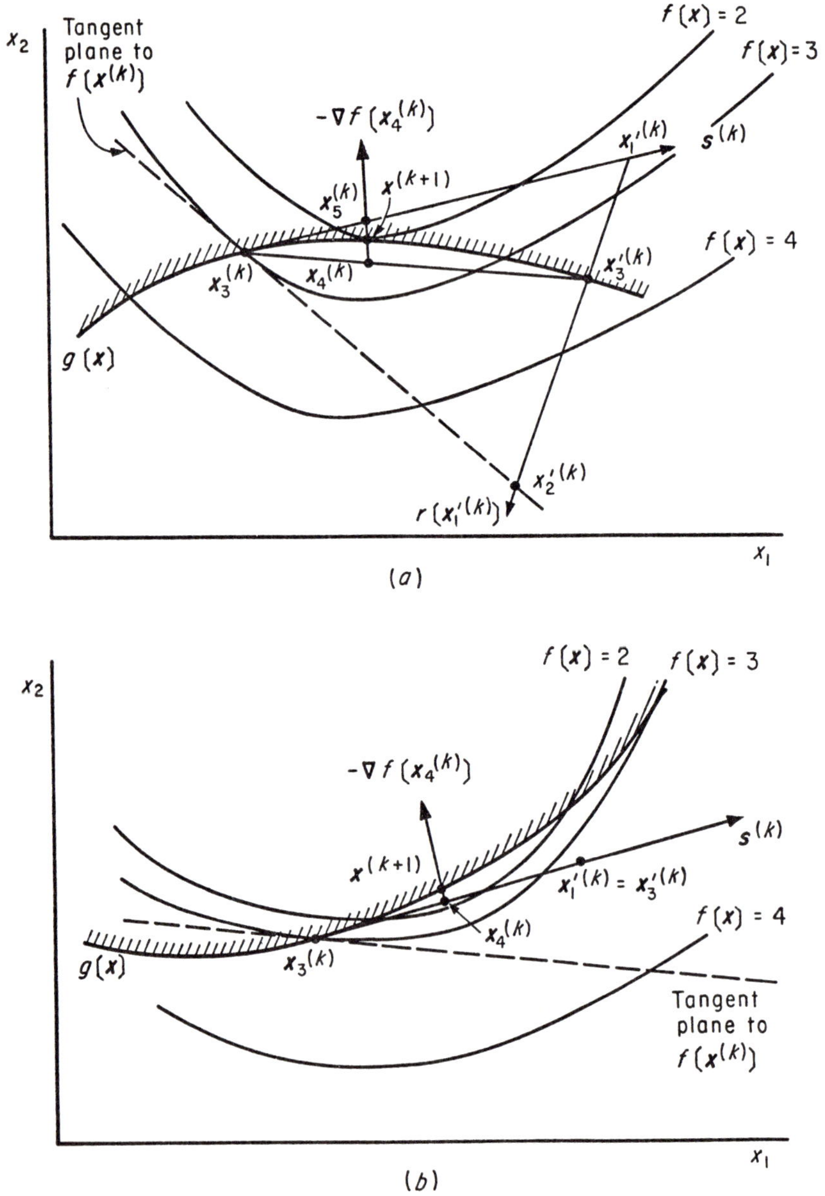

Fig. 6.3-10 Determination of $\mathbf{x}^{(k+1)}$.

tween $\mathbf{x}_4^{(k)}$ and $\mathbf{x}_5^{(k)}$ to yield $\mathbf{x}^{(k+1)}$. Figure 6.3–10 illustrates the procedure in two dimensions. Note that for a concave constraint, $\mathbf{x}^{(k+1)}$ must be found by a linear search along $-\nabla f(\mathbf{x}_4^{(k)})$ because $\mathbf{x}_4^{(k)}$ and $\mathbf{x}_5^{(k)}$ coincide.

If the search for a minimum of $f(\mathbf{x})$ along the line $\mathbf{x}_3^{(k)} \ldots \mathbf{x}_3'^{(k)}$ does not yield an $f(\mathbf{x})$ less than $f(\mathbf{x}_3^{(k)})$, then let $\mathbf{x}^{(k+1)} = \mathbf{x}_3^{(k)}$.

Step 5: Once $\mathbf{x}^{(k+1)}$ is located, newly active linear constraints are added to $\boldsymbol{\eta}_\ell^{(k)}$ as in step 5 of the procedure for linear constraints, and the method returns to step 1.

Step 6: If no new constraints are added, update the matrix $\boldsymbol{\eta}_\ell^{(k)}$ to $\boldsymbol{\eta}_\ell^{(k+1)}$ as in step 4 of the procedure for linear constraints.

The procedure described above is essentially a form of "hemstitching." Because only little information is available on the effectiveness of Davidon's method as applied to nonlinear constraints, we will list here, in Table 6.3–1, results of Davies' method for three minimization procedures:

a. Davidon with CRST (described in Sec. 7.1–3)
b. Goldfarb with CRST
c. Davidon-Davies (this section)
d. Murtagh and Sargent (whose algorithm was similar to that of Davies).

Table 6.3–1 Comparison of Function Evaluations for Three Methods

*Problem**	*Method*	*No. of constraints active at minimum*	*No. of $f(\mathbf{x})$ evaluations*	*No. of nonlinear constraint evaluations*
10	*a*	5	120	0
	b		12	0
	c		8	0
	d		7	
11	*a*	5	109	114
	b		94	111
	c		10	22
	d		9	
18	*a*	11	712	805
	b		657	794
	c		227	421
	d		124	

*Initiated at the feasible starting point.

Problems 10, 11, and 18 in Appendix A (and some simpler ones) were tested.

For problems with linear constraints only (not shown in the table) Goldfarb with CRST was considerably better than Davidon with CRST, but for problems involving nonlinear constraints, the two methods were about equally effective. Neither was as good by a considerable margin as the method of Davidon-Davies.

6.4 ZOUTENDIJK'S METHOD OF FEASIBLE DIRECTIONS

As mentioned previously, for each feasible point $\mathbf{x}^{(k)}$ in R there can be many feasible directions of search.[1] In essence, these methods start at a feasible solution and (for linear constraints) progress in a direction such that the optimization path improves the objective function and never leaves the feasible region. Thus Rosen's gradient projection method qualifies as a method of feasible directions. But whereas the projection of $\nabla f(\mathbf{x}^{(k)})$ onto the constraint set containing $\mathbf{x}^{(k)}$ gives a direction of search that corresponds precisely in the euclidean metric to the direction of steepest descent for the objective function, Zoutendijk's method uses another metric,

$$\|\Delta\mathbf{x}\| = \max\{|\Delta x_1|, \ldots, |\Delta x_n|\}$$

which leads to selecting as the feasible direction that direction giving the greatest improvement in $f(\mathbf{x})$ without violating any constraint.

Zoutendijk's method can handle linear as well as nonlinear inequality constraints, but cannot accommodate equality constraints. The problem to be considered here is essentially problem (6.1–1) without the equality constraints. Linearization of the problem at some feasible point $\mathbf{x}^{(k)}$ by a Taylor series expansion gives the revised problem

$$\text{Minimize:} \quad f(\mathbf{x}^{(k)}) + \nabla^T f(\mathbf{x}^{(k)})(\mathbf{x} - \mathbf{x}^{(k)}) \qquad \mathbf{x} \in E^n \qquad (6.4\text{–}1)$$

$$\text{Subject to:} \quad g_i(\mathbf{x}^{(k)}) + \nabla^T g_i(\mathbf{x}^{(k)})(\mathbf{x} - \mathbf{x}^{(k)}) \geq 0 \qquad i = 1, \ldots, p$$

Zoutendijk's procedure fixes the best (in the sense that the greatest improvement of $f(\mathbf{x})$ is obtained in moving from $\mathbf{x}^{(k)}$ to $\mathbf{x}^{(k+1)}$ without violating any of the constraints) possible direction of search from a feasible $\mathbf{x}^{(k)}$ by solving a related subproblem, problem (6.4–5) below.

The translation from $\mathbf{x}^{(k)}$ to $\mathbf{x}^{(k+1)}$ is determined as usual by $\mathbf{x}^{(k+1)} = \mathbf{x}^{(k)} + \lambda^{(k)}\mathbf{s}^{(k)}$. The replacement of $\mathbf{x}$ in problem (6.4–1) by $\mathbf{x}^{(k+1)}$

[1] G. Zoutendijk, "Methods of Feasible Directions," Elsevier Publishing Company, Amsterdam, 1960.

gives

$$\begin{aligned} &\text{Minimize:} \quad f(\mathbf{x}^{(k)}) + \lambda^{(k)}\nabla^T f(\mathbf{x}^{(k)})\mathbf{s}^{(k)} \\ &\text{Subject to:} \quad g_i(\mathbf{x}^{(k)}) + \lambda^{(k)}\nabla^T g_i(\mathbf{x}^{(k)})\mathbf{s}^{(k)} \geq 0 \qquad \text{for } i = 1, \ldots, p \end{aligned} \tag{6.4–2}$$

Since $f(\mathbf{x}^{(k)})$ and $g_i(\mathbf{x}^{(k)}) \geq 0$ are constants, the necessary and sufficient conditions for the transition from $\mathbf{x}^{(k)}$ to $\mathbf{x}^{(k+1)}$ in problem (6.4–2), with $\mathbf{x}^{(k+1)}$ remaining feasible for problem (6.4–1), are that

$$\nabla^T f(\mathbf{x}^{(k)})\mathbf{s}^{(k)} < 0 \tag{6.4–3}$$

and

$$\nabla^T g_i(\mathbf{x}^{(k)})\mathbf{s}^{(k)} \geq 0 \qquad \text{for } i = 1, \ldots, p \tag{6.4–4}$$

Any vector $\mathbf{s}^{(k)}$ that satisfies inequalities (6.4–3) and (6.4–4) simultaneously is a feasible direction.

Zoutendijk's method chooses the feasible direction that produces the greatest improvement in the value of $f(\mathbf{x})$ on the step from $\mathbf{x}^{(k)}$ to $\mathbf{x}^{(k+1)}$ by solving the following linear programming problem.

$$\begin{aligned} &\text{Minimize:} \quad \nabla^T f(\mathbf{x}^{(k)})\mathbf{s}^{(k)} \qquad \mathbf{s}^k \in E^n \\ &\text{Subject to:} \quad \nabla^T g_i(\mathbf{x}^{(k)})\mathbf{s}^{(k)} \geq 0 \qquad \text{for } i = 1, \ldots, p \end{aligned} \tag{6.4–5}$$

The solution of problem (6.4–5) gives the components of the feasible direction to be used in moving from $\mathbf{x}^{(k)}$ to $\mathbf{x}^{(k+1)}$.

One stage of Zoutendijk's method of feasible directions is carried out as follows:

1. Let $\mathbf{x}^{(k)}$ be some feasible point of problem (6.0–1) without equality constraints.
2. Evaluate the gradients of $f(\mathbf{x})$ and $g_i(\mathbf{x})$, $i = 1, \ldots, p$, at $\mathbf{x}^{(k)}$ and solve the linear programming problem (6.4–5) to obtain the feasible direction $\mathbf{s}^{(k)}$. Any linear programming algorithm can be used to solve problem (6.4–5).
3. If $\nabla^T f(\mathbf{x}^{(k)})\mathbf{s}^{(k)} < 0$, determine the maximum step length λ^* to be taken in the direction of $\mathbf{s}^{(k)}$ and still remain in the feasible region of problem (6.0–1), that is, $\lambda^* = \max \{\lambda | \mathbf{x}^{(k)} + \lambda\mathbf{s}^{(k)} \in R\}$. The value of λ^* may be determined by a unidimensional search in the direction $\mathbf{s}^{(k)}$, starting at $\mathbf{x}^{(k)}$. Determine the value of $\lambda^{(k)}$, $0 \leq \lambda^{(k)} \leq \lambda^*$, so that $f(\mathbf{x}^{(k)} + \lambda^{(k)}\mathbf{s}^{(k)})$ is a minimum in the direction $\mathbf{s}^{(k)}$. The new point is $\mathbf{x}^{(k+1)} = \mathbf{x}^{(k)} + \lambda^{(k)}\mathbf{s}^{(k)}$. Return to step 2 to start the search for the $(k + 1)$st stage.
4. If $\nabla^T f(\mathbf{x}^{(k)})\mathbf{s}^{(k)} = 0$, the search is terminated since it is no longer possible to further reduce the value of $f(\mathbf{x})$.

Zoutendijk has also described a modified method of feasible directions,[1] which we need not consider here. There is not much information in the literature regarding computer routines incorporating the methods of Zoutendijk, although some results have been reported.[2] The method of Zoutendijk described above is fast in comparison with other methods under similar conditions, and it has the advantage of including nonlinear as well as linear inequality constraints. However, there is no supporting evidence to demonstrate its capability to solve problems with a large number of nonlinear inequality constraints.

6.5 GENERALIZED REDUCED GRADIENT METHOD (GRG)

The generalized reduced gradient algorithm[3] is an extension of the Wolfe algorithm[4] to accommodate both a nonlinear objective function and non-linear constraints. In essence the method employs linear, or linearized constraints, defines new variables that are normal to some of the constraints, and transforms the gradient to this new basis. (Wolfe describes the relation of the original reduced gradient method to the simplex method of linear programming.) Although the problem solved by the GRG method is

$$\begin{aligned} &\text{Minimize:} && f(\mathbf{x}) && \mathbf{x} \in E^n \\ &\text{Subject to:} && h_i(\mathbf{x}) = 0 && i = 1, \ldots, m \\ & && L_j \leq x_j \leq U_j && j = 1, \ldots, n \end{aligned} \tag{6.5-1}$$

inequality constraints can be accommodated by subtracting nonnegative slack variables from the inequality constraints thus:

$$h_i(\mathbf{x}) = g_i(\mathbf{x}) - v_i^2 = 0$$

and permitting the bounds on the v_i's to be $-\infty \leq v_i \leq \infty$. (The v_i's are added to the set of n variables.)

[1] G. Zoutendijk, *SIAM J. Control*, **4**:194 (1966).

[2] P. Wolfe, Recent Developments in Nonlinear Programming, *Rand Corp. Rept.* R-401-PR, 1962.

[3] J. Abadie and J. Carpentier, Généralization de la méthode du gradient réduit de Wolfe au cas de contraintes nonlinéaires. *Proc. IFORS Conf.*, rev. and in English in R. Fletcher (ed.), Chap. 4, "Optimization," Academic Press Inc., London, 1969; P. Faure and P. Huard, *Rev. Franç Recherche Operationelle*, **9**:167 (1965); J. Abadie and J. Guigou, Gradient réduit généralisé, *Électricité de France Note* HI 069/02, Apr. 15, 1969.

[4] P. Wolfe, *Notices Am. Math. Soc.*, **9**(4):308 (1962); Methods of Nonlinear Programming, pp. 76–77 in R. L. Graves and P. Wolfe (eds.), "Recent Advances in Mathematical Programming," McGraw-Hill Book Company, New York, 1963.

Two sets of variables are distinguished in the GRG algorithm if a nondegeneracy assumption holds, the m basic (e.g., dependent) variables comprising the set I, $\mathbf{x}_I$, and the $(n - m)$ nonbasic (e.g., independent) variables comprising the set K, $\mathbf{x}_K$. The dependent variables are implicitly determined by the independent variables; hence the objective function is a function only of the $(n - m)$ independent variables. To clarify the special notation to be used in this section, we let

$$\mathbf{h} \equiv \begin{bmatrix} h_1(\mathbf{x}) \\ \cdot \\ \cdot \\ \cdot \\ h_m(\mathbf{x}) \end{bmatrix} \quad \text{an } m \times 1 \text{ matrix}$$

$$\frac{\partial \mathbf{h}}{\partial \mathbf{x}_I} \equiv \begin{bmatrix} \dfrac{\partial h_1(\mathbf{x})}{\partial x_1} & \cdots & \dfrac{\partial h_1(\mathbf{x})}{\partial x_m} \\ \cdots\cdots & \cdots & \cdots \\ \dfrac{\partial h_m(\mathbf{x})}{\partial x_1} & \cdot & \dfrac{\partial h_m(\mathbf{x})}{\partial x_m} \end{bmatrix} \quad \text{an } m \times m \text{ matrix ("base" matrix)}$$

$$\nabla^T_{\mathbf{x}_I} f = \begin{bmatrix} \dfrac{\partial f(\mathbf{x})}{\partial x_{m+1}} & \cdots & \dfrac{\partial f(\mathbf{x})}{\partial x_n} \end{bmatrix} \quad \text{a } 1 \times (n - m) \text{ matrix}$$

$$\nabla^T_{\mathbf{x}_I} f = \begin{bmatrix} \dfrac{\partial f(\mathbf{x})}{\partial x_1} & \cdots & \dfrac{\partial f(\mathbf{x})}{\partial x_m} \end{bmatrix} \quad \text{a } 1 \times m \text{ matrix}$$

$$\frac{df(\mathbf{x})}{d\mathbf{x}_K} = \begin{bmatrix} \dfrac{df(\mathbf{x})}{dx_{m+1}} & \cdots & \dfrac{df(\mathbf{x})}{dx_n} \end{bmatrix} = \mathbf{z} \quad \text{a } 1 \times (n - m) \text{ matrix ("reduced gradient" matrix)}$$

$$\frac{d\mathbf{x}_I}{d\mathbf{x}_K} = \begin{bmatrix} \dfrac{dx_1}{dx_{m+1}} & \cdots & \dfrac{dx_1}{dx_n} \\ \cdots\cdots & \cdots & \cdots \\ \dfrac{dx_m}{dx_{m+1}} & \cdots & \dfrac{dx_m}{dx_n} \end{bmatrix} \quad \text{an } m \times (m - n) \text{ matrix}$$

$$\frac{d\mathbf{h}}{d\mathbf{x}_K} = \begin{bmatrix} \dfrac{dh_1(\mathbf{x})}{dx_{m+1}} & \cdots & \dfrac{dh_1(\mathbf{x})}{dx_n} \\ \cdot & \cdots & \cdots \\ \dfrac{dh_m(\mathbf{x})}{dx_{m+1}} & \cdots & \dfrac{dh_m(\mathbf{x})}{dx_n} \end{bmatrix} \quad \text{an } m \times (m - n) \text{ matrix}$$

6.5-1 The Reduced Gradient

Problem (6.5–1) in general cannot be directly reduced in dimensionality because the equality constraints implicitly connect the variables. Hence the equations cannot be solved for a set of dependent variables that can be substituted into the objective function, leaving only independent variables. However, the method of constrained variation permits a reduction of dimensionality to take place, and leads to the use of the reduced gradient as one of the criteria for establishing optimality. To illustrate the basic idea, consider problem (6.5–1) for an objective function of just two variables subject to one equality constraint:

Minimize: $f(x_1,x_2)$

Subject to: $h(x_1,x_2) = 0$

For differential displacements in x_1 and x_2,

$$df(\mathbf{x}) = \frac{\partial f(\mathbf{x})}{\partial x_1}\,dx_1 + \frac{\partial f(\mathbf{x})}{\partial x_2}\,dx_2$$

Furthermore,

$$dh(\mathbf{x}) = \frac{\partial h(\mathbf{x})}{\partial x_1}\,dx_1 + \frac{\partial h(\mathbf{x})}{\partial x_2}\,dx_2 = 0$$

These equations are linear in the differential displacement, so that the selected differential dependent variable can be eliminated from the differential objective function. Figure 6.5–1 shows how the only admissible displacements can be those along the constraint.

Solve $dh(\mathbf{x}) = 0$ for dx_2:

$$dx_2 = -\frac{\partial h(\mathbf{x})/\partial x_1}{\partial h(\mathbf{x})/\partial x_2}\,dx_1$$

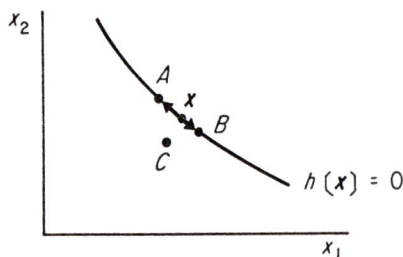

Fig. 6.5–1 Admissible displacements when $f(x)$ is subject to an equality constraint $h(\mathbf{x}) = 0$; A and B are admissible points, while C is not.

and introduce dx_2 into the differential objective function

$$df(\mathbf{x}) = \left(\frac{\partial f(\mathbf{x})}{\partial x_1} - \frac{\partial f(\mathbf{x})}{\partial x_2}\frac{\partial h(\mathbf{x})/\partial x_1}{\partial h(\mathbf{x})/\partial x_2}\right) dx_1$$

to yield the *reduced gradient*

$$\frac{df(\mathbf{x})}{dx_1} = \frac{\partial f(\mathbf{x})}{\partial x_1} - \frac{\partial f(\mathbf{x})}{\partial x_2}\left[\frac{\partial h(\mathbf{x})}{\partial x_2}\right]^{-1}\frac{\partial h(\mathbf{x})}{\partial x_1}$$

One necessary condition for $f(\mathbf{x})$ to be a minimum is that $df(\mathbf{x}) = 0$, or by analogy to the condition for an unconstrained minimum, that

$$\frac{df(\mathbf{x})}{dx_1} = 0$$

Next we shall express the (generalized) reduced gradient in terms of the elements gradient of the objective function, the inverse of the base matrix, and the jacobian of the equality constraints. For differential displacements in $\mathbf{x}$,

$$df(\mathbf{x}) = \nabla^T_{\mathbf{x}_K} f d\mathbf{x}_K + \nabla^T_{\mathbf{x}_I} f d\mathbf{x}_I$$

and it can be shown by direct multiplication of the matrix elements that the reduced gradient can be computed by

$$\frac{df(\mathbf{x})}{d\mathbf{x}_K} = \nabla^T_{\mathbf{x}_K} f + \nabla^T_{\mathbf{x}_I} f \frac{d\mathbf{x}_I}{d\mathbf{x}_K} \tag{6.5-2}$$

[Keep in mind that derivatives such as $(d\mathbf{x}_{m+1}/d\mathbf{x}_{m+2})$ and $(d\mathbf{x}_{m+1}/d\mathbf{x}_n)$ vanish, because the variables x_i, $i = m + 1, \ldots, n$, are the independent variables.] To eliminate the awkward matrix $(d\mathbf{x}_I/d\mathbf{x}_K)$ from Eq. (6.5–2), we note that

$$dh_i(\mathbf{x}) = \nabla^T_{\mathbf{x}_K} h_i(\mathbf{x}) d\mathbf{x}_K + \nabla^T_{\mathbf{x}_I} h_i(\mathbf{x}) d\mathbf{x}_I = 0 \qquad i = 1, \ldots, m$$

and

$$\frac{d\mathbf{h}}{d\mathbf{x}_K} = \frac{\partial \mathbf{h}}{\partial \mathbf{x}_K} + \left(\frac{\partial \mathbf{h}}{\partial \mathbf{x}_I}\right)\left(\frac{\partial \mathbf{x}_I}{d\mathbf{x}_K}\right) = \mathbf{0} \tag{6.5-3a}$$

so that

$$\frac{d\mathbf{x}_I}{d\mathbf{x}_K} = -\left(\frac{\partial \mathbf{h}}{\partial \mathbf{x}_I}\right)^{-1}\left(\frac{\partial \mathbf{h}}{\partial \mathbf{x}_K}\right) \tag{6.5-3b}$$

Introduction of Eq. (6.5–3*b*) into Eq. (6.5–2) gives for the generalized reduced gradient

$$\frac{df(\mathbf{x})}{d\mathbf{x}_K} = \nabla^T_{\mathbf{x}} f - \nabla^T_{\mathbf{x}_I} f \left(\frac{\partial \mathbf{h}}{\partial \mathbf{x}_I}\right)^{-1}\left(\frac{\partial \mathbf{h}}{\partial \mathbf{x}_K}\right) \tag{6.5-4}$$

Note that the reduced gradient has one element for each independent variable.

Figure 6.5–2 illustrates the reduced gradient associated for the following quadratic programming problem with one equality constraint:

Minimize: $f(\mathbf{x}) = x_1^2 + x_2^2$

Subject to: $h(\mathbf{x}) = 2x_1 + x_2 - 1 = 0$

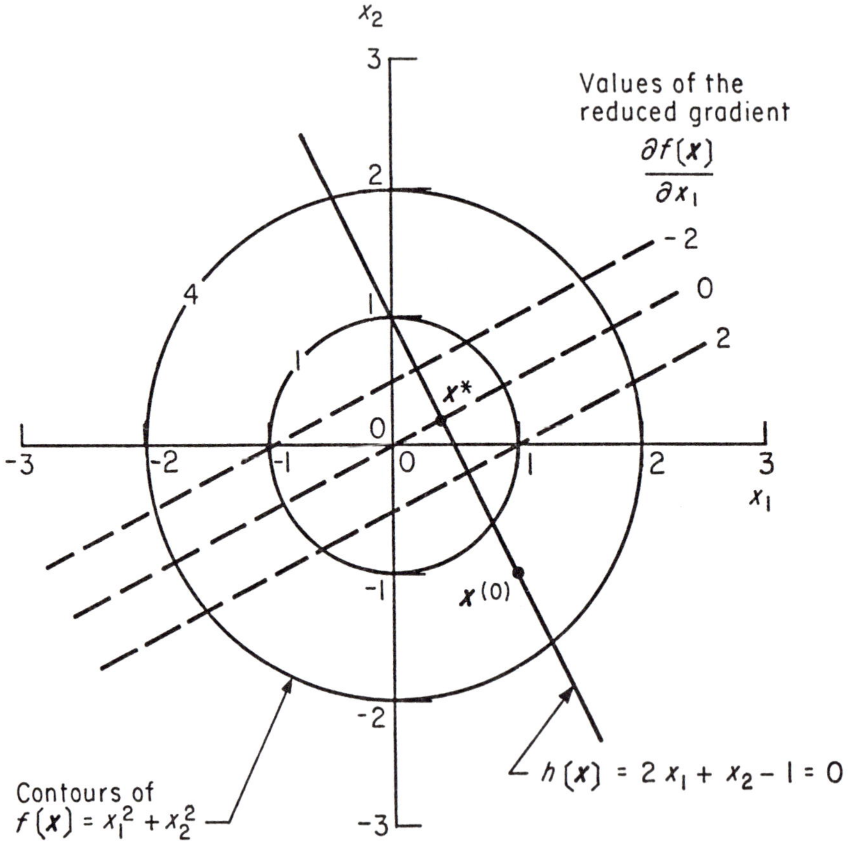

Fig. 6.5–2 The reduced gradient; the constrained minimum occurs along $h(\mathbf{x}) = 0$ at $\mathbf{x}^* = [0.4 \quad 0.2]^T$, where the reduced gradient vanishes.

Let x_1 be the independent (nonbasic) variable and let x_2 be the dependent (basic) variable. The partial derivatives are

$$\frac{\partial f(\mathbf{x})}{\partial x_1} = 2x_1$$

$$\frac{\partial h(\mathbf{x})}{\partial x_1} = 2$$

$$\frac{\partial f(\mathbf{x})}{\partial x_2} = 2x_2$$

$$\frac{\partial h(\mathbf{x})}{\partial x_2} = 1$$

and the generalized reduced gradient is

$$\frac{df(\mathbf{x})}{dx_1} = \frac{\partial f(\mathbf{x})}{\partial x_1} - \frac{\partial f(\mathbf{x})}{\partial x_2}\left[\frac{\partial h(\mathbf{x})}{\partial x_2}\right]^{-1}\frac{\partial h(\mathbf{x})}{\partial x_1}$$

$$= 2x_1 - 2x_2(1)(2) = 2x_1 - 4x_2$$

From any feasible point a search along the constraint $h(\mathbf{x}) = 0$ until $df(\mathbf{x})/dx_1 = 0$ yields the minimum of $f(\mathbf{x})$.

Another way to interpret the reduced gradient is in terms of the dual programming problem[1] associated with (6.5–1). It can be shown that the Kuhn-Tucker conditions (see Sec. 2.5–4) for the dual of (6.5–1), if (6.5–1) is a convex programming problem, are

$$\nabla_{\mathbf{x}_K} f(\mathbf{x}) - \mathbf{v}\frac{\partial \mathbf{h}(\mathbf{x})}{\partial \mathbf{x}_K} = \mathbf{z} \qquad (6.5\text{–}5a)$$

$$\nabla_{\mathbf{x}_I} f(\mathbf{x}) - \mathbf{v}\frac{\partial \mathbf{h}(\mathbf{x})}{\partial \mathbf{x}_I} = \mathbf{0} \qquad (6.5\text{–}5b)$$

$$\begin{aligned} z_j &\le 0 \quad \text{if } x_j = L_j \\ z_j &\ge 0 \quad \text{if } x_j = U_j \qquad j = m+1, \ldots, n \qquad (6.5\text{–}5c) \\ z_j &= 0 \quad \text{if } L_j \le x_j \le U_j \end{aligned}$$

where $\mathbf{z} = [z_{m+1} \quad \ldots \quad z_n]$ and $\mathbf{v} = [v_1 \quad \ldots \quad v_m]$.

[1]Duality in mathematical programming refers to the fact that if a feasible optimal $\mathbf{x}$ vector exists that solves the programming problem expressed as a minimization problem (termed the *primal* problem), then the same vector will solve an associated programming problem expressed as a maximization problem (termed the *dual* problem).

Substitution of Eq. (6.5–5*b*) in (6.5–5*a*) yields Eq. (6.5–4) if $\mathbf{z} \equiv (df(\mathbf{x})/d\mathbf{x}_K)$. Thus the values of the elements of the reduced gradient serve as a guide to the optimal $\mathbf{x}$ vector, and the vanishing of the reduced gradient is sought.

6.5–2 Direction of Search

The GRG algorithm is initiated at a feasible point. If the initial $\mathbf{x}$ vector in the problem statement is nonfeasible so that artificial variables must be introduced into the constraints, the values of the artificial variables are reduced to zero by adding a penalty to the objective function (refer to Chap. 7), thus eventually yielding a feasible $\mathbf{x}$ vector. It is also possible to use the GRG algorithm itself to the same end by minimizing (or maximizing) each artificial variable (or the sum of their absolute values). If the reduced gradient is not zero at any stage in the calculations, then the $\mathbf{x}$ vector is changed by the standard relation

$$\mathbf{x}^{(k+1)} = \mathbf{x}^{(k)} + \lambda^{(k)}\boldsymbol{\Delta}^{(k)} \tag{6.5–6}$$

where $\lambda \geq 0$ and the n elements of the column vector $\boldsymbol{\Delta}^{(k)}$ designate the direction of search for the GRG algorithm. The Δ_j for the independent (nonbasic) variables are determined differently from the Δ_j for the dependent (basic) variables, and the former will be discussed first.

We will suppress the subscript K to denote the independent variable set in what follows, except where it is needed to distinguish between $\mathbf{x}_I$ and $\mathbf{x}_K$. The search directions Δ_j, $j = m + 1, \ldots, n$, for the independent variables are defined as follows, in terms of the values of the elements of the reduced gradient:

$$\Delta_j^{(k)} = 0 \begin{cases} \text{if } x_j^{(k)} = U_j \text{ and } z_j^{(k)} > 0 \\ \text{if } x_j^{(k)} = L_j \text{ and } z_j^{(k)} < 0 \end{cases}$$

$$\Delta_j^{(k)} = -z_i^{(k)} \qquad \text{if } L_j < x_j^{(k)} < U_j$$

where z_j is defined in connection with Eq. (6.5–5*c*), namely, an element of the reduced gradient. For example, in the illustration in Fig. 6.5–2 at the point $\mathbf{x}^{(0)} = [1 \quad -1]^T$, $\Delta_1^{(0)} = -z_1^{(0)} = -(df(\mathbf{x})/dx_1) = -6$; hence $x_1^{(1)} = 1 - 6\lambda$, whereas at the point $\mathbf{x}^{(0)} = [-\frac{1}{2} \quad 2]^T$, $-z_1^{(0)} = 9$ and $x_1^{(1)} = 1 + 9\lambda$.

If the constraints are linear, Eq. (6.5–6) causes the GRG method to be the same as the reduced gradient method of Wolfe. The algorithm also causes $\Delta_j^{(k)}$ to be placed equal to zero if x_j is very close (within an arbitrarily small number ε) to a boundary, either L_j or U_j.

Two other variants of the GRG algorithm can be used to select $\Delta_j^{(k)}$ for the independent variables.

1. The GRGS method. Let

$$|z_\ell^{(k)}| = \max |z_j^{(k)}|$$

over the indexes j, for which $L_j < x_j^{(k)} < U_j$, and place

$$\Delta_j^{(k)} = \begin{cases} 0 & \text{if } j \neq \ell \\ -z_j^{(k)} & \text{if } j = \ell \end{cases}$$

If the objective function and constraints are linear, the GRGS method is equivalent to the simplex method of linear programming. This method has the advantages that it requires fewer computations to determine a direction of search $\boldsymbol{\Delta}^{(k)}$, and the search directions do not depend entirely on the units of the elements of the **x** vector.

2. The GRGC method. In this method the elements of $\boldsymbol{\Delta}^{(k)}$ are determined as follows:

Iteration no.	$\Delta_j^{(k)}$
1	$\Delta_j^{(1)} = \begin{cases} -z_1^{(1)} & j = 1 \\ 0 & j \neq 1 \end{cases}$
2	$\Delta_j^{(2)} = \begin{cases} -z_2^{(2)} & j = 2 \\ 0 & j \neq 2 \end{cases}$
etc.	

After n stages the cycle repeats. This method also does not depend on the units of **x**.

Lastly, it is also possible to introduce other directions of search for the independent variables into the GRG algorithm than those defined by Δ_j above, if desired, such as the directions given by the method of conjugate gradients (refer to Sec. 3.3–2). Tests indicate that a certain additional amount of logic and empirical experience will have to be accumulated before such directions can be said to prove better in general than those described above.

Turning now to the search directions for the dependent variables, one chooses the direction vector $\boldsymbol{\Delta}_{\mathbf{x}_I}$ for those elements of the **x** vector comprising the set $\mathbf{x}_I$ differently than for the independent variables comprising the set $\mathbf{x}_K$. Although for linear constraints the basic (dependent) variables can be solved for explicitly in terms of the independent (nonbasic) variables, this is not possible, presumably, for the case of nonlinear constraints. Instead, the search direction vector for the set $\mathbf{x}_I$ is determined essentially by linearizing the constraints, as indicated by Eq. (6.5–3*a*), or from Eq. (6.5–3*b*),

$$d\mathbf{x}_I = -\left(\frac{\partial \mathbf{h}}{\partial \mathbf{x}_I}\right)^{-1}\left(\frac{\partial \mathbf{h}}{\partial \mathbf{x}_K}\right) d\mathbf{x}_K$$

or in difference form,

$$\Delta_{\mathbf{x}_I}^{(k)} = -\left(\frac{\partial \mathbf{h}(\mathbf{x}^{(k)})}{\partial \mathbf{x}_I}\right)^{-1}\left(\frac{\partial \mathbf{h}(\mathbf{x}^{(k)})}{\partial \mathbf{x}_K}\right) \Delta_{\mathbf{x}_K}^{(k)} \tag{6.5–7}$$

For example, in the illustration in Fig. 6.5–2, from the point $\mathbf{x}^{(0)}$, $\Delta_1^{(0)} = -6$, and consequently $\Delta_2^{(0)} = -(1)(2)(-6) = 12$.

6.5–3 The Search in the Chosen Direction to Obtain the Feasible Point

We describe first the termination of the step length using both the independent and dependent variables to reduce $f(\mathbf{x})$, and then describe how the dependent variables are adjusted so as to improve the value of $f(\mathbf{x})$ yet obtain a feasible $\mathbf{x}$ vector. First we want to determine how large $\lambda^{(k)}$ should be in Eq. (6.5–6). As usual, the objective function evaluated at $(\mathbf{x}^{(k)} + \lambda\Delta^{(k)})$ is minimized, with $\lambda^{(k)}$ the parameter to be determined by a unidimensional dichotomous search. The values of $\lambda^{(k)}$ fall in the range $0 \leq \lambda^{(k)} \leq \lambda_m$, where

$$\lambda_m = \min\{\lambda_1, \lambda_2\} \tag{6.5–8}$$

and for $j = 1, \ldots, n$,

$$\lambda_1 = \min\left\{\min\left\{\frac{x_j^{(k)} - L_j}{-\Delta_j^{(k)}} \,\middle|\, \Delta_j < 0\right\}, \min\left\{\frac{U_j - x_j^{(k)}}{\Delta_j^{(k)}} \,\middle|\, \Delta_j > 0\right\}\right\}$$

$$\lambda_2 = \left\{\max \frac{\lambda_3^{(i)}}{\nabla^T f(\mathbf{x}^{(i)})\Delta^{(i)}/\|\Delta^{(i)}\|^2}\right\}\left\{\frac{\nabla^T f(\mathbf{x}^{(k)})\Delta^{(k)}}{\|\Delta^{(k)}\|^2}\right\}$$

where $\lambda_3^{(i)}$ is the largest value of λ that yielded a feasible and improved value of $f(\mathbf{x})$ without changing the set of base variables $\mathbf{x}_I$ used in the previous p iterations. The superscript index k refers to the current stage, and the superscript index i to the iteration associated with λ_3. The choice of λ_2 is supposed to take advantage of prior information at the kth stage. It may happen that the choice of λ by minimizing $f(\lambda)$ yields a change in $f(\mathbf{x})$ such that the change

$$f(\mathbf{x}^{(k+1)}) - f(\mathbf{x}^{(k)})$$

is less than some prespecified number. If so, then λ can be successively increased, say by a factor of 2, until

$$\left|\frac{f(\mathbf{x}^{(k+1)}) - f(\mathbf{x}^{(k)})}{f(\mathbf{x}^{(k)})}\right| > \varepsilon$$

These changes in λ will overcome a poor (too small) choice of λ_m but cause additional difficulties. Abadie and Guigou describe a number of other factors that influence the choice of λ. In any case, a step of length $\lambda^{(k)}\Delta_j^{(k)}$ is taken in each of the $\Delta_j^{(k)}$ directions except for instances in which the bound L_j or U_j on an independent variable is exceeded, in which case the boundary value becomes the new $x_j^{(k+1)}$ for the independent variable.

If the λ obtained by the dichotomous search when introduced into Eq. (6.5–6) together with Eq. (6.5–7) yields one or more elements of $x_I^{(k)}$ that are infeasible (to be denoted by $\tilde{\mathbf{x}}_I^{(k)}$), as is quite likely with nonlinear constraints, then the basic (dependent) variables (only) are modified to obtain a feasible $\mathbf{x}_I^{(k+1)}$. Suppose at the point $(\mathbf{x}_K^{(k+1)}, \tilde{\mathbf{x}}_I^{(k+1)})$ that $\mathbf{h}(\mathbf{x}_K^{(k+1)}, \tilde{\mathbf{x}}_I^{(k+1)}) \neq \mathbf{0}$. If the constraints are linearized by a truncated Taylor series, we can find the $\mathbf{x}_I^{(k+1)}$ that causes $\mathbf{h}(\mathbf{x}_K^{(k+1)}, \mathbf{x}_I^{(k+1)})$ to vanish.

$$\mathbf{h}(\mathbf{x}_K^{(k+1)}, \mathbf{x}_I^{(k+1)}) \approx \mathbf{h}(\mathbf{x}_K^{(k+1)}, \tilde{\mathbf{x}}_I^{(k+1)}) + \frac{\partial \mathbf{h}(\mathbf{x}_K^{(k+1)}, \tilde{\mathbf{x}}_I^{(k+1)})}{\partial \mathbf{x}_I}(\mathbf{x}_I^{(k+1)} - \tilde{\mathbf{x}}_I^{(k+1)}) = \mathbf{0}$$

or

$$\mathbf{x}_I^{(k+1)} - \tilde{\mathbf{x}}_I^{(k+1)} = -\left(\frac{\partial \mathbf{h}}{\partial \mathbf{x}_I}\right)^{-1} \mathbf{h}(\mathbf{x}_K^{(k+1)}, \tilde{\mathbf{x}}_I^{(k+1)}) \tag{6.5–9}$$

Equation (6.5–9) is termed an "iteration by Newton's method,"[1] and is continued until one of the following outcomes is obtained.

If $(\mathbf{x}_K^{(k+1)}, \tilde{\mathbf{x}}_I^{(k+1)})$ is feasible (to within a selected tolerance), as in Fig. 6.5–3*a*, then $\tilde{\mathbf{x}}_I^{(k+1)}$ becomes $\mathbf{x}_I^{(k+1)}$. (1) If $f(\mathbf{x}_K^{(k+1)}, \mathbf{x}_I^{(k+1)}) < f(\mathbf{x}_K^{(i)}, \mathbf{x}_I^{(i)})$, where the superscript i designates the most recent feasible $\mathbf{x}$ vector, the iteration by Newton's method is terminated, and the search is continued, starting again with Eq. (6.5–6). (2) If $\tilde{\mathbf{x}}_I^{(k+1)}$ is an interior or boundary point but $f(\mathbf{x}_K^{(k+1)}, \tilde{\mathbf{x}}_I^{(k+1)}) > f(\mathbf{x}_K^{(i)}, \mathbf{x}_I^{(i)})$,[2] or if the iteration by Eq. (6.5–9) fails to converge in a fixed number of iterations, say 20, then λ is reduced by some fraction (such as 1/2 or 1/10), and the iteration by Eq. (6.5–9) is repeated. (3) If neither of the first two outcomes is achieved, and if the last point obtained by Eq. (6.5–9) is not an interior or boundary point, a change in basis is carried out. The line segment between $\tilde{\mathbf{x}}_I^{(k+1)}$ and its extension

[1] If the basis contains slack variables because the problem includes inequality constraints, a slightly more efficient recursion relation (presented in the references) is used in lieu of Eq. (6.5–9).

[2] Certain other supplementary tests are also made.

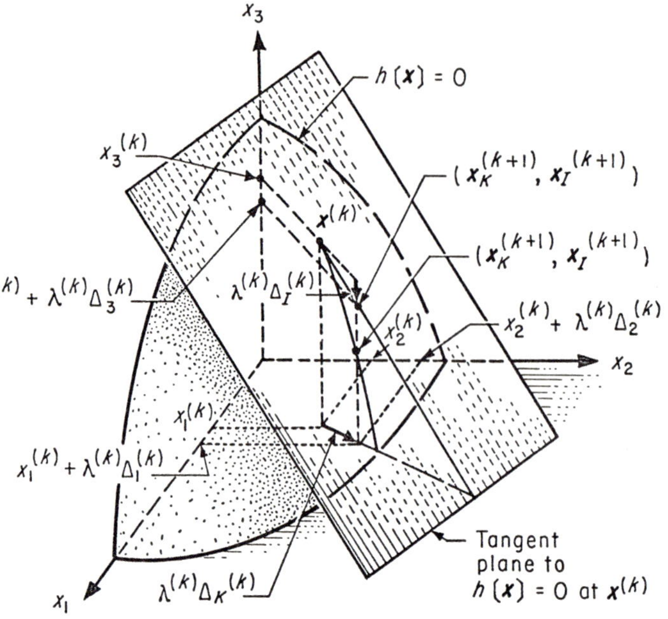

(a)

by Eq. (6.5–9) cuts the boundary of the paralleltrope defined by **L** and **U** in problem (6.5–1) at some point where one variable, x_r, of the set x_I takes on either the value at its upper bound, U_r, or the value at its lower bound, L_r. Examine Fig. 6.5–3*b*; here x_r is x_3. The variable x_r is removed from the basis, taking its boundary value, and is replaced by a variable x_s from the set $\mathbf{x}_K$. Newton's iteration is then carried out for the new set of independent variables.

Various rules can be used to choose the variable to replace x_r. The variable introduced into the base set of variables should not be one that is on its boundary, and preferably should be far from its bounds.

Let K' = set of indices of variables in K that can be added to the basis

Ω_r = rth row of matrix $(\partial\mathbf{h}/\partial\mathbf{x}_I)^{-1}$, where r designates variable to be removed from the basis

$\dfrac{\partial\mathbf{h}}{\partial x_k}$ = kth column of matrix $(\partial\mathbf{h}/\partial\mathbf{x})$

$d_k = \min\{(x_k - L_k), (U_k - x_k)\}$

$Y_j = (x_j^{(k+2)} - x_j^{(k)})$ with $x_j^{(k+2)}$ and $x_j^{(k)}$ feasible

ε = an arbitrary small number

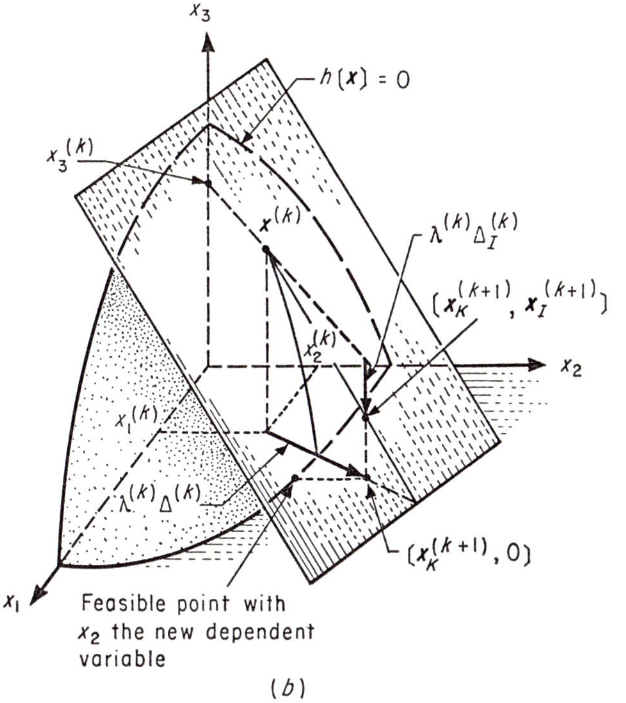

Fig. 6.5–3 GRG search and modification of the dependent variables. Here x_3 is the dependent variable and x_1 and x_2 are the independent variables. One nonlinear equality constraint, $h(\mathbf{x}) = 0$, exists, and $0 \le x_j \le 100$, $j = 1, 2, 3$. Figure *b* indicates a change in the basis, removing x_3 and adding x_2. Figure *a* indicates the location of a new feasible point.

Then, if s is designated as the index of the variable to be added to the basis, s is determined from:

Criterion 1:

$$\left|\Omega_r \frac{\partial \mathbf{h}}{\partial x_s}\right| d_s = \max_{K'} \left\{ \left|\Omega_r \frac{\partial \mathbf{h}}{\partial x_k}\right| d_k, \left|\Omega_r \frac{\partial \mathbf{h}}{\partial x_k}\right| > \varepsilon \right\} \tag{6.5–10}$$

If criterion (6.5–10) does not yield a variable x_s, because, for example, $|\Omega_r(\partial \mathbf{h}/\partial x_s)| < \varepsilon$, the following criteria apply to determine x_s.

Criteria 2:

(*a*) If $x_r = L_r$ (x_r is at its lowest bound),

$$\Omega_r \frac{\partial \mathbf{h}}{\partial x_s} = \max \left\{ \left|\Omega_r \frac{\partial \mathbf{h}}{\partial x_k}\right|, \Omega_r \frac{\partial \mathbf{h}}{\partial x_k} Y_k > 0 \right\} \tag{6.5–11a}$$

(*b*) If $x_r = U_r$ (x_r is at its upper bound),

$$\Omega_r \frac{\partial \mathbf{h}}{\partial x_s} = \max \left\{ \left| \Omega_r \frac{\partial \mathbf{h}}{\partial x_s} \right|, \Omega_r \frac{\partial \mathbf{h}}{\partial x_s} Y_k < 0 \right\} \qquad (6.5\text{–}11b)$$

If in the execution of a Newton iteration in determining x_r one finds $\lambda = 0$, then certain other criteria are used, the details of which are given by Abadie and Guigou. The performance of the Newton iteration can be improved if the elements of the base matrix from one stage to the next are not permitted to grow too large relative to one another. For example, one can determine the ratio of Δ_{x_j} to the norm of $\mathbf{\Delta}_K$, and if the ratio exceeds some preset criterion, remove x_j as a base variable and replace it with another variable. In the special case in which in the first iterations all the basic variables are the slack variables, certain special rules apply in the iteration by the method of Newton to restrict changing the base variables.

6.5-4 Termination Criteria

At an extremum the elements of $\mathbf{\Delta}$ vanish. The first test carried out in testing for convergence is to determine if

$$|\Delta_j^{(k)}| < \varepsilon |\Delta_j^{(1)}| \qquad j = m + 1, \ldots, n$$

where ε is some small number. A secondary test is to determine if $\Gamma < \Gamma_{\max}$, where

$$\Gamma = \max_K \{ \underbrace{\Delta_j^{(k)}(U_j - x_j^{(k)})}_{\Delta_j^{(k)} > 0}, \underbrace{\Delta_j^{(k)}(L_j - x_j^{(k)})}_{\Delta_j^{(k)} < 0} \}$$

$$\Gamma_{\max} = \text{an arbitrary parameter}$$

6.5-5 Methods of Reducing Computation Time

Rather than compute $(\partial \mathbf{h}/\partial \mathbf{x}_I)^{-1}$ each time it is called for, the matrix can be approximated by a method suggested originally by Beale. Suppose that the matrix $(\partial \mathbf{h}/\partial \mathbf{x}_I)^{-1}$ has been evaluated at $\mathbf{x}^{(k)}$. Then at some later stage ℓ, Abadie and Guigou suggested that

$$\left(\frac{\partial \mathbf{h}(\mathbf{x}^{(\ell)})}{\partial \mathbf{x}_I} \right)^{-1} \approx 2 \left(\frac{\partial \mathbf{h}(\mathbf{x}^{(k)})}{\partial \mathbf{x}_I} \right)^{-1} - \left(\frac{\partial \mathbf{h}(\mathbf{x}^{(k)})}{\partial \mathbf{x}_I} \right)^{-1} \left(\frac{\partial \mathbf{h}(\mathbf{x}^{(\ell)})}{\partial \mathbf{x}_I} \right) \left(\frac{\partial \mathbf{h}(\mathbf{x}^{(k)})}{\partial \mathbf{x}_I} \right)$$

This approximation has yet to be investigated thoroughly but appears promising. By a suitable check, the inverse of the reference base matrix can be recomputed when the approximation becomes too approximate. Abadie and Guigou suggest several appropriate tests to measure the extent of the approximation.

It is also possible to search (in the interior of the feasible region only) using the method of steepest descent, find several successive points $\mathbf{x}^{(k)}, \mathbf{x}^{(k+1)}, \ldots, \mathbf{x}^{(k+p)}$, and move in the direction $\mathbf{x}^{(k+p)} - \mathbf{x}^{(k)}$. Abadie and Guigou, on the basis of numerical studies, recommended that $p = 2$.

Older, coded versions of the GRG algorithm for linear constraints (only) are available from the VIM Library as E4 EDF PHIMAX and E4 EDF PHIMAQ, dated May 9, 1968. The GRG method has been reported successfully applied by Wolfe to a nonlinear objective function, 200 to 300 linear constraints, and 1000 variables.[1] The performance of the 1969 version of the GRG code on several test problems is disclosed in Chap. 9.

Example 6.5-1 Generalized reduced gradient method

The example problem is

Minimize: $f(\mathbf{x}) = 4x_1 - x_2^2 - 12$

Subject to: $h_1(\mathbf{x}) = 25 - x_1^2 - x_2^2 = 0$

$$g_2(\mathbf{x}) = 10x_1 - x_1^2 + 10x_2 - x_2^2 - 34 \geq 0$$

$$g_3(\mathbf{x}) = x_1 \geq 0$$

$$g_4(\mathbf{x}) = x_2 \geq 0$$

Figure 6.0-1 illustrates the functions.

Because the starting point $\mathbf{x}^{(0)} = [2 \quad 4]^T$ is not feasible and because one inequality constraint $g_2(\mathbf{x})$ forms part of the problem, an artificial variable x_3 is added to the equality constraint and a slack variable x_4 is subtracted from the inequality constraint. The partial derivatives of the objective function and the constraints with respect to the variables x_1 and x_2 are

$$\frac{\partial f(\mathbf{x})}{\partial x_1} = 4 \qquad \frac{\partial f(\mathbf{x})}{\partial x_2} = -2x_2$$

$$\frac{\partial h_1(\mathbf{x})}{\partial x_1} = -2x_1 \qquad \frac{\partial h_1(\mathbf{x})}{\partial x_2} = -2x_2$$

$$\frac{\partial g_2(\mathbf{x})}{\partial x_1} = 10 - 2x_1 \qquad \frac{\partial g_2(\mathbf{x})}{\partial x_2} = 10 - 2x_2$$

Four variables exist, x_1, x_2, x_3, and x_4, and two equality constraints $h_1(\mathbf{x})$ and

[1] H. P. Künzi, *Unternehmensforschung*, **12**:1 (1968).

$g_2(\mathbf{x})$; hence two variables will be independent variables and two dependent ones. We start with x_1 and x_2 as the independent variables and x_3 and x_4 as the dependent, or basic, variables. To seek a feasible solution, subtract $10^5 x_3$ from $f(\mathbf{x})$ and let $-10^{10} < x_3 < 0$ and $0 < x_4 < 10^{10}$. Then

$$\frac{\partial f(\mathbf{x})}{\partial x_1} = 4 \qquad \frac{\partial f(\mathbf{x})}{\partial x_2} = -8 \qquad \frac{\partial f(\mathbf{x})}{\partial x_3} = -10^5$$

To complete the reduced gradient we need the matrices $[\partial \mathbf{h}(\mathbf{x}^{(0)})/\partial \mathbf{x}_I]^{-1}$ and $[\partial \mathbf{h}(\mathbf{x}^{(0)})/\partial \mathbf{x}_K]$; that is, we need the jacobian matrices in terms of the two sets of variables evaluated at $\mathbf{x}^{(0)}$.

$$\frac{\partial \mathbf{h}(\mathbf{x}^{(0)})}{\partial \mathbf{x}_I} = \begin{bmatrix} \dfrac{\partial h_1(\mathbf{x}^{(0)})}{\partial x_3} & \dfrac{\partial h_1(\mathbf{x}^{(0)})}{\partial x_4} \\ \dfrac{\partial g_2(\mathbf{x}^{(0)})}{\partial x_3} & \dfrac{\partial g_2(\mathbf{x}^{(0)})}{\partial x_4} \end{bmatrix} = \begin{bmatrix} 1 & 0 \\ 0 & -1 \end{bmatrix}$$

The reduced gradient from Eq. (6.5–4) is

$$\begin{aligned} \frac{df(\mathbf{x}^{(0)})}{\partial \mathbf{x}_K} &= \begin{bmatrix} \dfrac{\partial f(\mathbf{x}^{(0)})}{\partial x_1} & \dfrac{\partial f(\mathbf{x}^{(0)})}{\partial x_2} \end{bmatrix} \\ &= [4 \quad -8] - [-10^5 \quad 0] \begin{bmatrix} 1 & 0 \\ 0 & -1 \end{bmatrix}^{-1} \begin{bmatrix} -4 & -8 \\ 6 & 2 \end{bmatrix} \\ &= [-3.99996 \times 10^5 \quad -8.00008 \times 10^5] \end{aligned}$$

A test is made on the norm of the reduced gradient, 8.944×10^5, to see if it is less than the termination criterion based on the current point and bounds of the variables, but of course it is not.

Next the search directions for the independent variables are computed from

$$\Delta_1^{(0)} = -\frac{\partial f(\mathbf{x}^{(0)})}{\partial x_1} = -3.99996 \times 10^5$$

$$\Delta_2^{(0)} = -\frac{\partial f(\mathbf{x}^{(0)})}{\partial x_2} = -8.00008 \times 10^5$$

Following this calculation comes the calculation of the search directions for the dependent variables using Eq. (6.5–7).

$$\begin{aligned} \Delta_{\mathbf{x}_I}^{(0)} &= -\left[\frac{\partial \mathbf{h}(\mathbf{x}^{(0)})}{\partial \mathbf{x}_I}\right]^{-1} \left[\frac{\partial \mathbf{h}(\mathbf{x}^{(0)})}{\partial \mathbf{x}_K}\right] \Delta_{\mathbf{x}_K}^{(0)} \\ &= -\begin{bmatrix} 1 & 0 \\ 0 & -1 \end{bmatrix} \begin{bmatrix} -4 & -8 \\ 6 & 2 \end{bmatrix} \begin{bmatrix} -3.99996 \times 10^5 \\ -8.00008 \times 10^5 \end{bmatrix} \\ &= -\begin{bmatrix} 8.000 \times 10^6 \\ 4.000 \times 10^6 \end{bmatrix} \end{aligned}$$

After the search directions are obtained, the search takes place to find the λ that minimizes $f(\mathbf{x})$; see Eq. (6.5–6).

Variable	$x^{(0)}$	Search stage 1	2	Last
x_1	2	2.250	2.125	2.250
x_2	4	4.500	4.250	4.500
x_3	-5	-2.842×10^{-14}	-2.500	0
x_4	6	8.500	7.250	8.500
$f(\mathbf{x})$	$\sim 5 \times 10^5$	-23.250	24.997×10^5	-23.250

The final λ is 6.250×10^{-7}.

Equation (6.5–9) is now applied successively to adjust the dependent variables so that $\mathbf{x}$ becomes feasible.

$$\begin{bmatrix} x_3 \\ x_4 \end{bmatrix} = \begin{bmatrix} 0 \\ 8.500 \end{bmatrix} - \begin{bmatrix} 1 & 0 \\ 0 & -1 \end{bmatrix} \begin{bmatrix} -0.3125 \\ -0.3125 \end{bmatrix} = \begin{bmatrix} 0.3125 \\ 8.1875 \end{bmatrix}$$

Because $\tilde{\mathbf{x}} = [2.250 \quad 4.500 \quad 0.3125 \quad 8.187]^T$ was not feasible, λ is changed, and five iterations of Newton's method ensue, at the end of which a feasible point is found.

$$\mathbf{x}^{(1)} = [1.568 \quad 4.748 \quad 0 \quad 4.161]^T$$

Both x_1 and x_2 are still the independent variables, and x_3 has been driven to 0.

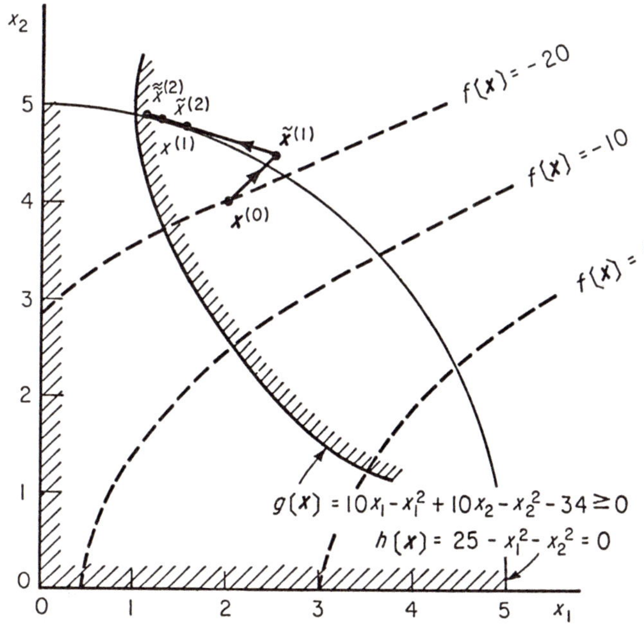

Fig. E6.5–1 Trajectory of generalized reduced gradient search.

Next, a new reduced gradient is computed, and the computations start over again. Subsequent values of the **x** vector are shown in Fig. E6.5–1. The reduced gradient itself is calculated only once more, all the remaining searches being devoted to finding a feasible vector and the termination tests. In total, the constraints were evaluated 103 times, the objective function 110 times, and the gradient of the objective function 27 times. Two changes in the base variables were carried out (actually, rearrangement of the order of the variables).

SUPPLEMENTARY REFERENCES

General

Abadie, J.: Numerical Experiments with the GRG Method, in "Integer and Nonlinear Programming" (ed. J. Abadie), North Holland Pub. Co., Amsterdam, 1970.

Bellmore, M., H. J. Greenberg, and J. J. Jarvis: Generalized Penalty-function Concepts in Mathematical Optimization, *Operations Res.*, **18**:193 (1970).

Carpentier, J., and J. Abadie: "Généralisation de la méthode du gradient réduit de Wolfe au cas de contraintes nonlinéaires," *Proc. IFORS Congr.*, Cambridge, Mass., August 29–September 2, 1966.

Charnes, A., and W. W. Cooper: Nonlinear Power of Adjacent Extreme Point Methods in Linear Programming, *Econometrica*, **25**:132 (1957).

Davies, D.: "Some Practical Methods of Optimization: Notes for the NATO Summer School, on Integer and Nonlinear Programming," June 8–20, 1969, Academic, New York (in press). (Discussion of Rosenbrock's and Davidon's methods extended to linear and nonlinear inequality constraints.)

———: Review of Constrained Optimization, Clearinghouse for Federal Scientific and Technical Information, *Document* N69-36898, September 30, 1968.

Dennis, J. B.: "Mathematical Programming and Electrical Networks," M.I.T., Cambridge, Mass., 1959.

Fauré, P., and P. Huard: Résolution de programmes mathématiques à fonction nonlinéaire par la méthode du gradient réduit, *Rev. Franç. Recherche Operationelle, no. 36*, p. 167, 1965.

Fletcher, R.: Clearinghouse for Federal Scientific and Technical Information, *Document* N69-37016, September 30, 1968.

Griffith, R. E., and R. A. Stewart: A Nonlinear Programming Technique for Optimization of Continuous Processing Systems, *Management Sci.*, **7**:379 (1961).

Kleinbohm, K.: Ein Verfahren zur approximativen Lösung von konvexen Programmen, Ph.D. dissertation, University of Zurich, 1966.

Leviton, E. S., and B. T. Polyak: Constrained Minimization Methods, *USSR Computational Math. and Math. Phys.*, **6**:1 (1966).

Rosen, J. B.: The Gradient Projection Method for Nonlinear Programming, Part I, *J. Soc. Ind. Appl. Math.*, **8**:181 (1960); Part II, **9**:514 (1961); *IBM Share Program* 1399.

Wolfe, P.: Methods of Nonlinear Programming, pp. 99–131 in J. Abadie (ed.), "Nonlinear Programming," North Holland Pub. Co., Amsterdam, 1967.

Zoutendijk, G.: "Methods of Feasible Directions," American Elsevier, New York, 1960.

Convergence of Algorithms

Topkis, D. M., and A. E. Veinott: On the Convergence of Some Feasible Direction Algorithms for Nonlinear Programming, *J. SIAM Control*, **5**:268 (1967).

Zangwill, W. I.: Convergence Conditions for Nonlinear Programming Algorithms, *Management Sci.*, **16**:1 (1969).

Additional Methods of Constrained Nonlinear Programming Using Linearization Techniques

Cheney, E. W., and A. A. Goldstein: Newton's Method for Convex Programming and Tchebycheff Approximation, *Numerical Math.*, **4**:253 (1959).

De Remus, L. V.: Nonlinear Partition Programming, paper presented at the SIGMAP Workshop on Nonlinear Programming held at IBM Corporation, Yorktown Heights, N.Y., 1968.

DiBella, C. W., and W. F. Stevens: Process Optimization by Nonlinear Programming, *Ind. Eng. Chem. Process Design Develop.*, **4**:16 (1965).

Glass, H., and L. Cooper: Sequential Search: A Method for Solving Constrained Optimization Problems, *J. ACM*, **12**:71 (1965).

Graves, G. W., and A. B. Whinston: The Application of a Nonlinear Programming Algorithm to a Second Order Representation of the Problem, University of California at Los Angeles, *Western Management Sci. Instit. Paper* 108, September, 1966 (AD 641196).

Hartley, H. O., and R. R. Hocking: Convex Programming by Tangential Approximation, *Management Sci.*, **9**:600 (1963).

———, et al.: Convex: A Computer Program for Solving Convex Programs, *Techn. Rep.* No. 23, Texas A&M University, College Station, Texas, July, 1970.

Hilleary, R. R.: The Tangent Search Method of Constrained Minimization, *U.S. Naval Postgraduate School Tech. Rept./Res. Paper* 59, March, 1966 (AD 632121).

Kelley, J. E.: The Cutting-plane Method for Solving Convex Programs, *J. Soc. Ind. Appl. Math.*, **8**:703 (1960); Method of Gradients, Chap. 6 in G. Leitmann (ed.), "Optimization Techniques with Applications," Academic, New York, 1962.

Künzi, H. P.: The Duoplex Method in Nonlinear Programming, *J. SIAM Control*, **4**:130 (1966).

McGuire, S. W., R. R. Hocking, and H. O. Hartley: "Spherical Programming: A Convex Programming Algorithm," *Techn. Rep.* No. 5, Institute of Statistics, Texas A&M University, College Station, Texas, October, 1968.

Miele, A., H. Y. Huang, and J. C. Heideman: Sequential Gradient-restoration Algorithm for Minimization of Constrained Functions—Ordinary and Conjugate Gradient Methods, *J. Optimization Theory Appl.*, **4**:213 (1969).

Mills, D. H.: Extending Newton's Method to Systems of Inequalities, *Proc. 6th Intl. Symp. on Math. Programming*, Princeton, N.J., August, 1967.

Mugele, R. A.: A Program for Optimal Control of Nonlinear Processes, *IBM Systems J.*, **1**:2 (1962).

Pinsker, I. S.: The Alternance Method (for Solution of Problems in Nonlinear Programming), transl., *Automatic Remote Control*, **25**:280 (1964).

Shanno, D. F.: An Accelerated Gradient Projection Method for Linearly Constrained Nonlinear Estimation, *SIAM J. Appl. Math.*, **18**:322 (1970).

Wolfe, P.: Accelerating the Cutting Plane Method for Nonlinear Programming, *J. Soc. Ind. Math.*, **9**:481 (1961).

———: Some Simplex-like Nonlinear Programming Procedures, *Operations Res.*, **10**:438 (1962).

PROBLEMS[1]

6.1 Linearize the objective function and constraints in Probs.

6.17	6.28
6.22	6.29

about a selected **x** vector. For the one- and two-dimensional problems plot the functions and their linearized approximates.

6.2 Can you linearize the objective function in Prob. 6.20?

6.3 Given the function for convergence to the solution of problem (6.0–1) (see p. 222), state whether or not Probs.

6.17	6.23
6.18	6.28
6.20	6.29

satisfy these conditions.

6.4 Carry out two stages of the Griffith and Stewart algorithm following the procedure described in Example 6.1–1 for the problem given in Example 6.2–1. Use a linear programming routine, or carry out the calculations by hand, to obtain a feasible **x** vector.

6.5 Repeat Prob. 6.4 for Prob. 6.25.

6.6 Obtain a computer code to execute the algorithm POP II. Solve the problem given in Example 6.2–1. Answer the following questions:

(*a*) What parameters must be adjusted in value from the recommended values to obtain a solution?

(*b*) How do the numerically computed values of the derivatives compare with the corresponding analytical values?

(*c*) Compare the difficulties experienced with those described in Sec. 6.1–3.

(*d*) What improvements can be recommended in the algorithm?

6.7 Prepare the incremental linear programming matrix shown in Fig. 6.1–3 for the POP algorithm for the problem in Example 6.1–1. Omit the $(n + 1)$ column and beyond and the $(n + m + 2)$ row and below. Use $\delta_j = 0.001$. Also compute the "linearity errors."

6.8 Find the projection of the gradient of the objective function

$$f(\mathbf{x}) = 5x_1 - 3x_2 + 6x_3$$

[1] Additional problems suitable for this chapter can be found in the problem set at the end of Chap. 7 and in Appendix A.

onto the $(x_1 - x_2)$ plane; this plane is the constraint $x_3 = 0$. Draw a sketch showing both the gradient and its projection.

6.9 Repeat Prob. 6.8, except show the projection of the gradient of

$$f(\mathbf{x}) = 2x_1^2 + x_2^2 + 2x_3^3$$

evaluated at the point $(1, -1, 1)$ onto the $(x_1 - x_2)$ plane.

6.10 Devise a minimization procedure based on the gradient projection concept that will find the minimum of the function

$$f(\mathbf{x}) = x_1^2 + x_2^2 + x_3^2 - 2x_1x_2$$

subject to

$$h_1(\mathbf{x}) = 2x_1 + x_2 - 4 = 0$$

and

$$h_2(\mathbf{x}) = 5x_1 - x_3 - 8 = 0$$

Carry out three stages of your method. List the gradient, projection matrix, the vector of independent variables, and the value of the objective function for each stage.

6.11 Find the projected gradient in the following problem.

Minimize: $f(\mathbf{x}) = 5x_1^2 - 3x_2^2$
Subject to: $x_1 \geq 0$
$x_2 \geq 0$

at the point $\mathbf{x} = [1 \quad 1]^T$.

6.12 Determine the projections of the gradient of the objective function

$$f(\mathbf{x}) = x_1^2 + x_2^2 + x_3^2 - 2x_1x_2 - 2x_1x_3 - 2x_2x_3$$

on the constraints

$$h_1(\mathbf{x}) = 2x_1 + x_2 - 6 = 0$$
$$g_1(\mathbf{x}) = x_1 - x_3 - 8 > 0$$

from the point $\mathbf{x} = [1 \quad 1 \quad 1]^T$.

6.13 Is the projection matrix supposed to be positive definite?

6.14 Show that Eq. (6.3–11) is the correct relationship for the generalized projection matrix.

6.15 Show that Eq. (6.3–14) is the correct relationship to remove one inequality constraint from the group of active constraints.

6.16 Prepare a computer program to execute the algorithm suggested by Davies (see Sec. 6.3–3). First prepare a code to be applied to problems with linear constraints, and then extend the code to accommodate nonlinear constraints. How can you include equality constraints effectively?

6.17 A mathematical model of a dryer can be represented as follows:

Minimize: $f(\mathbf{x}) = \underbrace{0.0064x_1 [\exp(-0.184x_1^{0.3}x_2 - 1)]}_{\text{revenue function}}$

Subject to (power constraint):

$$g_1(\mathbf{x}) = 1.2(10^{13}) - (3000 + x_1)x_1^2x_2 > 0$$
$$g_2(\mathbf{x}) = 4.1 - \exp(0.184x_1^{0.3}x_2) > 0$$

where x_1 = gas velocity and x_2 = bed depth. Starting from $\mathbf{x} = [31{,}000 \quad 0.345]^T$, locate the local optimal solution at $\mathbf{x}^* = [31{,}800 \quad 0.342]^T$. How well are the constraints satisfied at $\mathbf{x}^*$? Is the local minimum a true minimum? Is the local minimum a global minimum? (Refer to Chap. 2.) Can you obtain the same $\mathbf{x}^*$ from $\mathbf{x}^{(0)} = [0 \quad 0]^T$? from $\mathbf{x}^{(0)} = [1 \quad 1]^T$?

6.18 The cost of constructing a distillation column can be written

$$C = C_pAN + C_sHAN + C_f + C_d + C_b + C_\ell + C_x \tag{a}$$

where C = total cost, \$
C_p = cost per square foot of plate area, \$/ft^2
A = column cross-sectional area, ft^2
N = number of plates; N_{min} = minimum number of plates
C_s = cost of shell, \$/ft^3
H = distance between plates, ft
C_f = cost of feed pump, \$
C_d = cost of distillate pump, \$
C_b = cost of bottoms pump, \$
C_ℓ = cost of reflux pump, \$
C_x = other fixed costs, \$

The problem is to minimize the total cost, once produce specifications and the throughput are fixed and the produce and feed pumping costs are fixed; that is, C_f, C_d, C_ℓ, and C_b are fixed. After selection of the material of construction, the costs are determined; that is, C_p, C_s, C_x are also fixed.

The process variables can be related through two empirical equations:

$$\frac{L}{D} = \left[\frac{1}{1 - (N_{min}/N)}\right]^\alpha \left(\frac{L}{D}\right)_{min} \tag{b}$$

$$A = K(L + D)^\beta \tag{c}$$

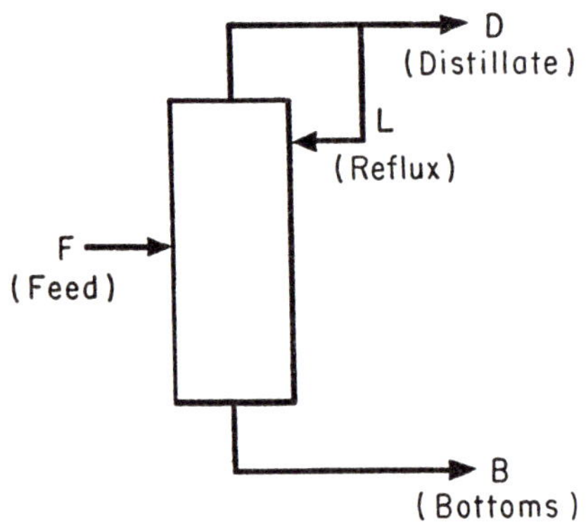

For simplicity choose $\alpha = \beta = 1$; then

$$\frac{L}{D} = \left[\frac{1}{1 - (N_{\min}/N)}\right]\left(\frac{L}{D}\right)_{\min} \tag{b'}$$

$$A = K(L + D) \tag{c'}$$

For a certain separation and distillation column the following parameters are known to apply:

$$\begin{aligned} C_p &= 30 & C_x &= 8000 \\ C_s &= 10 & F &= 1500 \\ H &= 2 & D &= 1000 \\ C_f &= 4000 & N_{\min} &= 5 \\ C_d &= 3000 & \frac{L}{D} &= 1 \\ C_b &= 2000 & K &= \frac{1}{100}\,\frac{(\text{hr})(\text{ft}^2)}{\text{lb}} \end{aligned}$$

The pump cost for the reflux stream can be expressed as

$$C_L = 5000 + 0.7L \tag{d}$$

(*a*) Determine the process decision or independent variables. Which variables are dependent?

(*b*) Find the minimum total cost and corresponding values of the variables.

6.19 Mylander[1] reported that a problem described by Box[2]

$$\text{Minimize:} \quad f(\mathbf{x}) = b_0 + a_{01}x_1 + \left(\sum_{j=2}^{5} a_{0j}x_j\right)x_1$$

$$\text{Subject to:} \quad 0 \le a_{i1}x_1 + \left(\sum_{j=2}^{5} a_{ij}x_j\right)x_1 \le b_1 \qquad i = 1,2,3$$

$$x_1 \ge 0,\ 1.2 \le x_2 \le 2.4,\ 20.0 \le x_3 \le 60,\ 9.0 \le x_4 \le 9.3,$$
$$6.5 \le x_5 \le 7.0$$

can be converted to a linear programming problem by letting $y_i = x_1x_i$, $i = 2,3,4,5$, and $y_1 = x_1$. The following linear programming problem is obtained:

$$\text{Minimize:} \quad g(\mathbf{y}) = b_0 + \sum_{j=1}^{5} a_{0j}y_j$$

$$0 \le \sum_{j=1}^{5} a_{ij}y_j \le b_i \qquad i = 1,2,3$$

$$\begin{aligned} y_i &\ge 0 & i &= 1,5 \\ y_2 - 1.2y_1 &\ge 0 & 2.4y_1 - y_2 &\ge 0 \\ y_3 - 20.0y_1 &\ge 0 & 60.0y_1 - y_3 &\ge 0 \\ y_4 - 9.0y_1 &\ge 0 & 9.3y_1 - y_4 &\ge 0 \\ y_5 - 6.5y_1 &\ge 0 & 7.0y_1 - y_5 &\ge 0 \end{aligned}$$

[1] W. C. Mylander, *Computer J.*, **8**:391 (1965).
[2] M. J. Box, *Computer J.*, **8**:42 (1965).

Use a nonlinear programming method to verify the solution obtained by linear programming

$$g = 5{,}280{,}344.9$$
$$y_1 = 4.53743 \quad y_2 = 10.88983 \quad y_3 = 272.24584$$
$$y_4 = 42.19811 \quad y_5 = 31.76202$$

which in terms of the original variables gives $f = -5{,}280{,}344.9$.

$$x_1 = 4.53743 \quad x_2 = 2.40000 \quad x_3 = 60.00000$$
$$x_4 = 9.30000 \quad x_5 = 7.00000$$

It is interesting to note that the original nonlinear problem is a nonconvex problem; the feasible region is not a convex region, nor is the objective function convex. Yet the transformation results in a convex, in this case linear, programming problem.

The values of the constants are:

a_{01}	$= -8{,}720{,}288.795$	a_{23}	$= 12.9492$
a_{02}	$= -150{,}512.524$	a_{24}	$= 10{,}236.8839$
a_{03}	$= -156.695$	a_{25}	$= 13{,}176.7859$
a_{04}	$= -476{,}470.319$	a_{31}	$= -326{,}669.5059$
a_{05}	$= -729{,}482.825$	a_{32}	$= 7{,}390.6840$
a_{11}	$= -145{,}421.4004$	a_{33}	$= -27.8987$
a_{12}	$= 2{,}931.1506$	a_{34}	$= 16{,}643.0759$
a_{13}	$= -40.4279$	a_{35}	$= 30{,}988.1459$
a_{14}	$= 5{,}106.1920$	b_0	$= -24{,}345.0$
a_{15}	$= 15{,}711.3600$	b_1	$= 294{,}000.0$
a_{21}	$= -155{,}011.1055$	b_2	$= 294{,}000.0$
a_{22}	$= 4{,}360.5334$	b_3	$= 277{,}200.0$

6.20 Find the minimum of the integral

$$f(\mathbf{x}) = \int_0^1 y\,dx$$

subject to: $$\int_0^1 \left[1 + \left(\frac{dy}{dx}\right)^2\right]^{1/2} dx = 4$$

6.21 Find the maximum and minimum distances to the origin from the curve $5x_1^2 + 6x_1x_2 + 5x_2^2 = 8$.

6.22 Find the maximum of the function

$$f(\mathbf{x}) = 20.21 - 46.38x_1 + 59.42x_2 + 16.30x_1x_2 + 8.34x_1^2 + 4.26x_2^2$$

on the bounding circle of radius equal to 3. What is the $\mathbf{x}$ vector?

6.23 A chemical manufacturing company sells three products and has found that its revenue function is $f = 10x + 4.4y^2 + 2z$, where x, y, and z are the monthly production rates of each chemical. It is found from breakeven charts that it is necessary to impose the following limits on the production rates:

$$x > 2$$
$$\tfrac{1}{2}z^2 + y^2 > 3$$

In addition, only a limited amount of raw material is available; hence the following restrictions must be imposed upon the production schedule:

$$x + 4y + 5z < 32$$
$$x + 3y + 2z < 29$$

Determine the best production schedule for this company and find the best value of the revenue function.

6.24 Minimize one-half the square of the distance from the point $\mathbf{x} = [2 \quad 3 \quad -1]^T$ to the tetrahedron given by

$$w = -x_1 - x_2 - x_3 + 3 \geq 0$$
$$x_1, x_2, x_3 \geq 0$$

{*Hint:* The objective function is $f(\mathbf{x}) = \dfrac{1}{2}[(x - 2)^2 + (y - 3)^2 + (z + 1)^2]$.}

6.25 A problem in chemical equilibrium is to minimize

$$f(\mathbf{x}) = \sum_{i=\ell}^{n} x_i \left(w_i + \ell nP + \ell n \frac{x_i}{\sum_{i=\ell}^{n} x_i} \right)$$

subject to the material balances

$$x_1 + 2x_2 + 2x_3 + x_6 + x_{10} = 2$$
$$x_4 + 2x_5 + x_6 + x_7 = 1$$
$$x_3 + x_7 + x_8 + 2x_9 + x_{10} = 1$$

Given $P = 750$ and w_i,

i	w_i	i	w_i
1	−10.021	6	−18.918
2	−21.096	7	−28.032
3	−37.986	8	−14.640
4	−9.846	9	−30.594
5	−28.653	10	−26.111

what is $\mathbf{x}^*$ and $f(\mathbf{x}^*)$?

6.26 A system of three heat exchangers in series (see diagram) is a typical stagewise process without recycle. The notation for the temperatures is indicated in the diagram; all are in degrees Fahrenheit. Cold fluid is being heated in each exchanger by hot fluid in cross flow. Assume that each exchanger can be modeled by a steady-state macroscopic (lumped) model

$$WC_p(T_n - T_{n-1}) = U_n A_n (t_{n1} - T_n)$$

and that the fluids all essentially have the same flow rates W and heat capacity C_p. The problem is to find each of the exchanger areas A, so that the total area of the three exchangers is minimized. The following are given input values or constant coefficients:

$$\begin{aligned} T_0 &= 100°\text{F} & U_1 &= 120 \text{ Btu/hr (ft}^2\text{) (°F)} \\ T_3 &= 500°\text{F} & U_2 &= 80 \text{ Btu/hr (ft}^2\text{) (°F)} \\ t_{11} &= 300°\text{F} & U_3 &= 40 \text{ Btu/hr (ft}^2\text{) (°F)} \\ t_{21} &= 400°\text{F} \\ t_{31} &= 600°\text{F} \\ WC_p &= 10^5 \text{ Btu/°F} \end{aligned}$$

(*Note:* This problem is often solved by dynamic programming.)

6.27 Minimize:

$$f(\mathbf{x}) = \frac{2}{x_1 + 0.5} + \frac{1}{x_2 + 0.2} + \frac{3}{x_3 + 0.5}$$

$$\begin{aligned} \text{Subject to:} \quad & 4x_1 + 7x_2 + 3x_3 \le 10 \\ & 3x_1 + 4x_2 + 5x_3 \le 8 \\ & x_1, x_2, x_3 \ge 0 \end{aligned}$$

6.28 Find the global minimum and maximum of

$$f(\mathbf{x}) = x_2 \sin x_2 - 4x_1$$

$$\begin{aligned} \text{subject to:} \quad g_1(\mathbf{x}) &= x_2 \sin x_2 - x_1^3 - x = 0 \\ g_2(\mathbf{x}) &= x_1 > 0 \\ g_3(\mathbf{x}) &= x_2 > 0 \\ g_4(\mathbf{x}) &= x_1 < 4 \\ g_5(\mathbf{x}) &= x_2 < 4 \end{aligned}$$

(*Note:* The objective function has multiple minima and maxima.)

6.29 Find the minimum of

$$f(\mathbf{x}) = x_1^2 + x_2^2 - 3x_1 + 15x_2$$

subject to: $(x_1 + x_2)^2 - 4(x_1 - x_2) = 0$

(*Note:* The objective function has two local minima.)

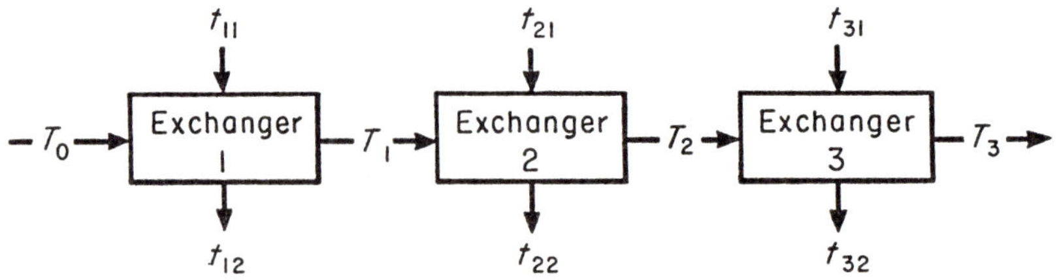

7

Constrained minimization procedures: penalty function methods

Several varieties of *penalty function* methods have been proposed, but the essence of all the methods is to transform a constrained nonlinear programming problem into an unconstrained problem or a sequence of unconstrained problems. For example, suppose we want to find the minimum of

$$f(\mathbf{x}) = (x_1 - 3)^2 + (x_2 - 2)^2$$

subject to $\qquad h(\mathbf{x}) = x_1 + x_2 - 4 = 0$

We can form a new unconstrained objective function

$$P(\mathbf{x}) = (x_1 - 3)^2 + (x_2 - 2)^2 + (x_1 + x_2 - 4)^2$$

by adding the square of the constraint to $f(\mathbf{x})$ as a "penalty." During the minimization of $P(\mathbf{x})$ the $\mathbf{x}$ vector is forced by the penalty to satisfy the constraint to some degree. Clearly, as long as $h(\mathbf{x})$ is satisfied (to within a specified tolerance) as $\mathbf{x} \to \mathbf{x}^*$, the value of the penalty becomes negligible and $P(\mathbf{x}^*) \to f(\mathbf{x}^*)$. The advantage of minimizing the unconstrained problem rather than the constrained problem is that much simpler algorithms can be employed for the minimization. Penalty function methods make the most of a constant trade-off between the satisfaction of the constraints and the minimization of $f(\mathbf{x})$ by assigning appropriate weights to $f(\mathbf{x})$ and the constraints. Figure 7.0–1 illustrates the character of the modified objective function formed by adding a penalty function to $f(\mathbf{x})$ (with a weight of unity).

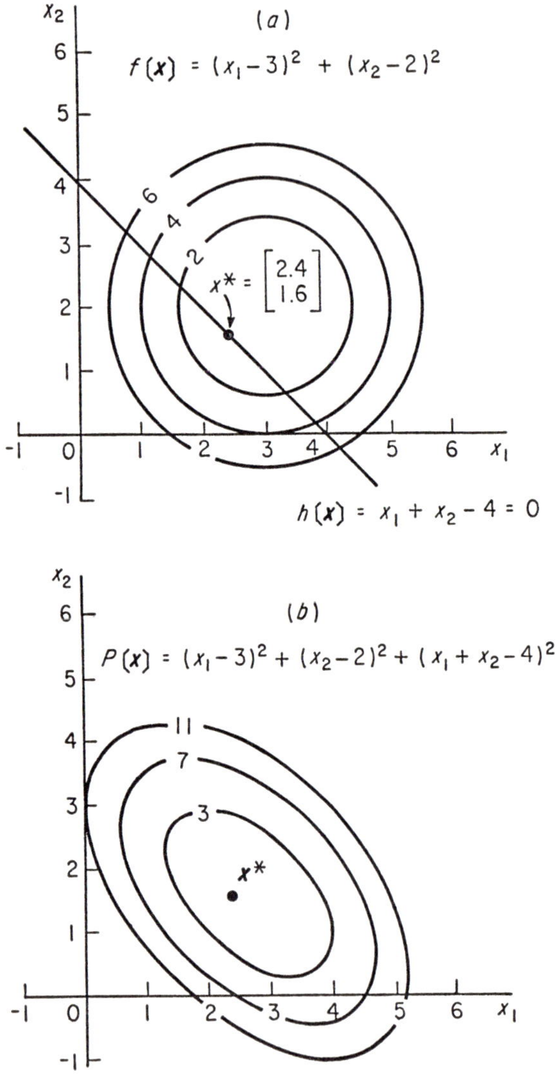

Fig. 7.0–1 (*a*) Representation of original problem; (*b*) penalty function contours.

Penalty function methods can be conveniently divided into two classes: (1) parametric methods and (2) nonparametric methods. Parametric methods are characterized by one or more adjustable parameters that weight the penalty function formed from the constraints. Typical parametric methods are the sequential unconstrained minimization technique (SUMT) of Fiacco and McCormick[1] and the algorithm of Zangwill.[2] On the other hand, nonparametric methods, such as Huard's "method of centers"[3] and SUMT without parameters by Fiacco and McCormick,[4] treat the objective function as an additional artificial constraint which is successively tightened from information developed in solving the problem.

The parametric techniques can themselves be subdivided into three categories: (1) interior point methods, (2) exterior point methods, and (3) mixed methods. In interior point methods the objective is to keep away from boundary of the feasible region (retain $\mathbf{x}^{(k)}$ in the interior region) by adding the penalty function. In contrast, the exterior point methods such as those of Zangwill, Pietrzykowski,[5] and another Fiacco and McCormick algorithm[6] generate a nonfeasible sequence of points that in the limit may yield a feasible solution. The penalty prevents the $\mathbf{x}$ vector from getting too far away from the feasible region. In mixed methods (required especially in the case of equality constraints), some constraints are satisfied in the minimization and others are not, but all the constraints are satisfied to within a given tolerance when the solution is reached. SUMT is a mixed method. To complete the classification, Fiacco[7] has mentioned nonparametric exterior point methods. An excellent historical survey of most of the penalty function methods can be found in the book by Fiacco and McCormick (1968).

To sum up, the essential idea of the penalty function approach to nonlinear programming is to transform the general nonlinear problem (2.2–1) to (2.2–3) into a sequence of unconstrained problems by adding one or more functions of the constraints to the objective function and deleting the constraints as such. Formally, the transformation of the problem represented

[1]A. V. Fiacco and G. P. McCormick, "Nonlinear Programming," John Wiley & Sons, Inc., New York, 1968.

[2]W. I. Zangwill, *Management Sci.*, **13**:344 (1967).

[3]P. Huard, Résolution de programmes mathématiques à contraintes nonlinéaires par la méthode des centres, *Note Electricité de France*, HR 5690/3/317, 1964; also see The Method of Centers in "Nonlinear Programming: A Course," North Holland Publishing Company, Amsterdam, 1965.

[4]A. V. Fiacco and G. P. McCormick, *Operations Res.*, **16**:820 (1968).

[5]T. Pietrzykowski, "Application of the Steepest Descent Method to Concave Programming," *Proc. IFIPS Congr.*, Munich, North Holland Publishing Company, Amsterdam, 1962.

[6]A. V. Fiacco and G. P. McCormick, *J. Soc. Ind. Appl. Math.*, **15**:505 (1967).

[7]A. V. Fiacco, Ph.D. dissertation, Northwestern University, Evanston, Ill., 1967.

by Eqs. (2.2–1) to (2.2–3) into an unconstrained minimization problem is

$$\text{Minimize:} \quad P(\mathbf{x}^{(k)},\rho^{(k)}) = f(\mathbf{x}^{(k)}) + \sum_{i=1}^{m} \rho_i^{(k)} H(h_i(\mathbf{x}^{(k)})) + \sum_{i=m+1}^{p} \rho_i^{(k)} G(g_i(\mathbf{x}^{(k)})) \tag{7.0–1}$$

We will call the function $P(\mathbf{x}^{(k)},\rho^{(k)})$ a generalized augmented function, or often just the "penalty function," $\rho_i^{(k)} \geq 0$ the weighting factors, $H(h_i(\mathbf{x}^{(k)}))$ and $G(g_i(x^{(k)}))$ functionals of $h_i(\mathbf{x}^{(k)})$ and $g_i(\mathbf{x}^{(k)})$, respectively (chosen in some well-defined manner to be described below), and $k = 0, 1, \ldots$ the number of completed stages in the numerical search.

Typical choices for the functions of the inequality constraints, $G(g_i(\mathbf{x}^{(k)}))$, are:

1. $G_1(g_i(\mathbf{x})) \to +\infty$ as $g_i(\mathbf{x}) \to 0^+$, which requires that the vector $\mathbf{x}$ always be an interior point, that is, $\{\mathbf{x} | g_i(\mathbf{x}) > 0, i = m + 1, \ldots, p\}$.
2. $G_2(g_i(\mathbf{x})) \to 0$ as $g_i(\mathbf{x}) \to 0^-$. Only exterior points, that is, $\{\mathbf{x} | g_i(\mathbf{x}) < 0\}$, are accepted in this choice.
3. $G_3(g_i(\mathbf{x})) > 0$ for $g_i(\mathbf{x}) < 0$ and $G_4(g_i(\mathbf{x})) = 0$ for $g_i(\mathbf{x}) \geq 0$. This choice is not concerned with constraint satisfaction except at the solution.

For equality constraints a typical choice of functionals is: $H(h_i(\mathbf{x})) \to 0$ as $h_i(\mathbf{x}) \to 0$. A common choice for the equality constraints is $H(h_i(\mathbf{x})) = h_i^2(\mathbf{x})$.

For all the choices above it is required that

$$\begin{aligned} &\lim_{k\to\infty} \sum_{i=m+1}^{p} \rho_i^{(k)} G(g_i(\mathbf{x}^{(k)}) = 0 \\ &\lim_{k\to\infty} \sum_{i=1}^{m} \rho_i^{(k)} H(h_i(\mathbf{x}^{(k)})) = 0 \\ &\lim_{k\to\infty} |P(\mathbf{x}^{(k)},\rho^{(k)}) - f(\mathbf{x}^{(k)})| = 0 \end{aligned} \tag{7.0–2}$$

In other words, the effect of the constraints in the augmented function, $P(\mathbf{x}^{(k)}, \rho^{(k)})$, on the value of the function is gradually diminished as the search continues, and completely removed in the limit, so that the value of the augmented function converges to the same value as $f(\mathbf{x})$ and the extremum of $P(\mathbf{x})$ is the same as that of $f(\mathbf{x})$.

In this chapter we will first briefly discuss some special cases of penalty function methods, and then go on to describe in somewhat more detail the SUMT method.

7.1 SPECIAL CASES OF PENALTY FUNCTION METHODS

7.1-1 Use of Lagrange Multipliers

Methods based on Lagrange multipliers are related to the parametric penalty function methods inasmuch as the former handles the constraints by incorporating them in a modified objective function together with a variable parameter. To generalize the technique of Lagrange multipliers, the inequality constraints must be treated as equalities by introduction of appropriate slack variables, one for each inequality constraint. The general nonlinear programming problem given by Eqs. (2.2–1) to (2.2–3) is converted into

$$\begin{aligned}
&\text{Minimize:} \quad f(\mathbf{x}) \qquad \mathbf{x} \in E^n \\
&\text{Subject to:} \qquad h_i(\mathbf{x}) = 0 \qquad i = 1, \dots, m \\
&\qquad\qquad g_i(\mathbf{x}) - v_i^2 = 0 \qquad i = m+1, \dots, p
\end{aligned} \tag{7.1–1}$$

By subtracting the square of the slack variable, v_i^2, from $g_i(\mathbf{x})$, $i = m + 1, \dots, p$, we can guarantee that the inequality constraints are satisfied. Then we can define in the usual fashion the Lagrange function.

$$P(\mathbf{x},\omega) = f(\mathbf{x}) + \sum_{i=1}^{m} \omega_i h_i(\mathbf{x}) + \sum_{i=m+1}^{p} \omega_i[g_i(\mathbf{x}) - v_i^2] \tag{7.1–2}$$

where the ω_i, $i = 1, \dots, p$, are nonnegative weighting factors independent of $\mathbf{x}$ identifiable as Lagrange multipliers. It has been demonstrated[1] that a necessary and sufficient condition for $\mathbf{x}^*$ to be a solution of the general nonlinear programming problem (2.2–1) to (2.2–3) is that $f(\mathbf{x}^*)$ be convex, that the constraint set be convex in the vicinity of $\mathbf{x}^*$, and that the following set of equations [yielding a stationary solution of (7.1–2)] be satisfied at $\mathbf{x}^*$.

$$\begin{aligned}
\frac{\partial P(\mathbf{x}^*)}{\partial x_j} &= 0 && \text{for } j = 1, \dots, n \\
\frac{\partial P(\mathbf{x}^*)}{\partial \omega_i} &= 0 && \text{for } i = 1, \dots, p \\
\frac{\partial P(\mathbf{x}^*)}{\partial v_i} &= 2\omega_i v_i = 0 && \text{for } i = m+1, \dots, p \\
\omega_i &\geq 0 && i = 1, \dots, p
\end{aligned} \tag{7.1–3}$$

[1] J. B. Dennis, "Mathematical Programs and Electrical Networks," John Wiley & Sons, Inc., New York, 1959.

In brief, the constrained minimum of $f(\mathbf{x})$ occurs at a stationary point of $P(\mathbf{x},\boldsymbol{\omega},\mathbf{v})$, and in particular, at a saddle point in the $(\mathbf{x},\boldsymbol{\omega},\mathbf{v})$ space, so that the constrained problem has been converted into an unconstrained saddle point problem.

Example 7.1-1 Use of Lagrange multipliers

As an example, consider the problem

$$\begin{aligned}&\text{Minimize:} \quad y = x_1 x_2 \qquad \mathbf{x} \in E^n\\&\text{Subject to:} \quad g_1(\mathbf{x}):\; 25 - x_1^2 - x_2^2 \geq 0\end{aligned} \tag{a}$$

The augmented function is

$$\text{Minimize:} \quad P(\mathbf{x},\boldsymbol{\omega}) = x_1 x_2 - \omega_1(25 - x_1^2 - x_2^2 - v_1^2) \tag{b}$$

The necessary conditions are

$$\begin{aligned}\frac{\partial P}{\partial x_1} &= x_2 + 2\omega_1 x_1 = 0\\\frac{\partial P}{\partial x_2} &= x_1 + 2\omega_1 x_2 = 0\\\frac{\partial P}{\partial \omega_1} &= 25 - x_1^2 - x_2^2 - v_1^2 = 0\\\frac{\partial P}{\partial v_1} &= 2\omega_1 v_1 = 0\end{aligned} \tag{c}$$

The simultaneous solutions of equations (c) for $\omega_1 = 0$ and for $\omega_1 \neq 0$ are listed in Table E7.1-1.

Table E7.1-1 Solution of problem (a) by the lagrange multiplier method

ω	x_1	x_2	*Point*	v_1	$f(\mathbf{x})$	*Remarks*
0	0	0	E	5	0	Saddle
0.5	+3.54	−3.54	D	0	−12.5	Minimum
	−3.54	+3.54	A	0	−12.5	Minimum
−0.5	+3.54	+3.54	B	0	+12.5	Maximum
	−3.54	−3.54	C	0	+12.5	Maximum

The vectors $\mathbf{x}^*$ are the stationary solutions of problem (a). Note that the solutions for $\omega_1 > 0$ are minima, those for $\omega_1 < 0$ are maxima, and $\omega_1 = 0$ is a saddle point of problem (a). Figure E7.1-1 illustrates the functions in problem (a). The contours of the objective function (hyperbolas) are represented by broken lines, and the feasible region is the shaded area enclosed by the circle $[g_1(\mathbf{x}) = 0]$. Points A and D correspond to the two minima, B and C to the two maxima, and E to the saddle point of $f(\mathbf{x})$.

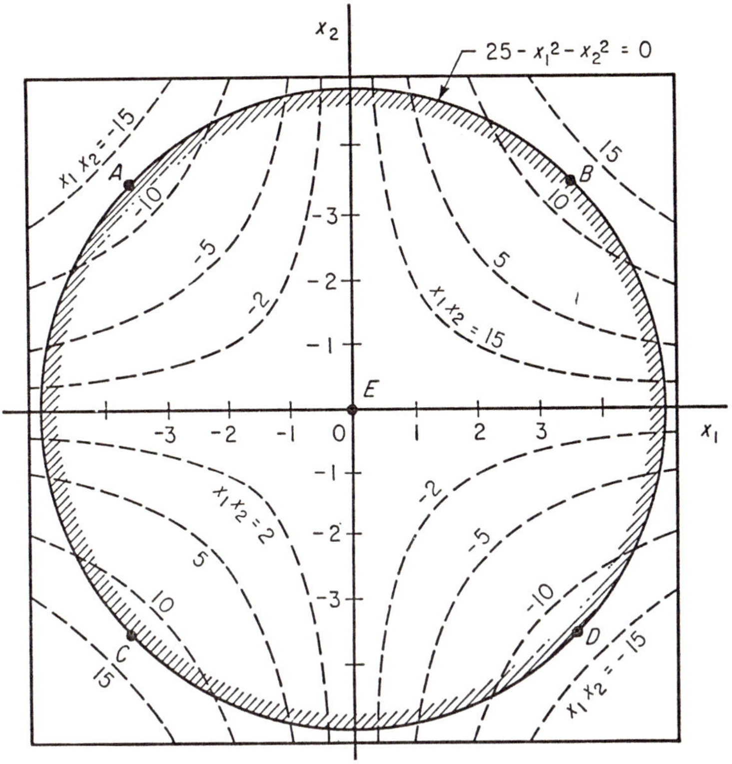

Fig. E7.1-1

The method of Lagrange multipliers has been studied extensively by many investigators, references for which can be found at the end of this chapter. The method may easily fail for nonconvex problems for which other penalty functions methods are successful. It is not a practical method for large nonlinear programming problems because the simultaneous solution of the system of equations analogous to equations (*c*) in Example E7.1-1 has to be accomplished using numerical procedures that are equally as difficult to carry out as the optimization techniques in themselves. Furthermore, multiple solutions of the equations must be isolated. Several computer programs incorporating the procedure have been written, but none of them seems to have been effective in the solution of general nonlinear programming problems.

7.1-2 Rosenbrock's Method for Constrained Optimization

The programming problem

$$\begin{aligned} &\text{Minimize:} \quad f(\mathbf{x}) && \mathbf{x} \in E^n \\ &\text{Subject to:} \quad g_i(\mathbf{x}) \geq 0 && i = 1, \ldots, p \end{aligned} \tag{7.1-4}$$

was transformed by Rosenbrock so that the method described earlier, in Sec. 4.3, could be applied. Minimization of an unconstrained augmented function of the following form is equivalent to solving problem (7.1–4).

$$\text{Minimize:} \quad P(\mathbf{x}^{(k)}, \mathscr{U}) = f(\mathbf{x}^{(k)}) \prod_{i=1}^{p} \mathscr{U}_i(\mathbf{x}^{(k)}) g_i(\mathbf{x}^{(k)}) \tag{7.1-5}$$

where $\mathscr{U}_i = 0$ for $g_i(\mathbf{x}^{(k)}) < 0$ and $\mathscr{U}_i = 1$ for $g_i(\mathbf{x}^{(k)}) > 0, i = 1, \ldots, p$. Thus the augmented function defined by Eq. (7.1–5) vanishes outside the feasible region. The objective function is assumed to be negative over the entire feasible region, that is, $\{f(\mathbf{x}) < 0 | \mathbf{x} \in R\}$. If $f(\mathbf{x})$ is positive for some or all $\mathbf{x} \in R$, a large constant K may be subtracted from $f(\mathbf{x})$ so that $\tilde{f}(\mathbf{x}) = [f(\mathbf{x}) - K] < 0$ without changing the character of $f(\mathbf{x})$. The numerical search must be initiated at not only an interior point $\mathbf{x}^{(0)}$, but also at a point that lies slightly within the bounding surface. Rosenbrock's unconstrained minimization procedure as described in Sec. 4.3 is used to minimize the augmented function $P(\mathbf{x})$. The sequence of points $\mathbf{x}^{(0)}, \mathbf{x}^{(1)}, \ldots, \mathbf{x}^{(k)}$ generated by the procedure is feasible.

To see the connection between Eq. (7.1–5) and the augmented function of the type defined by Eq. (7.0–1), we need only to take the logarithm of both sides of the negative of the equation in problem (7.1–5) and maximize the result.

Maximize:

$$\ln[-P(\mathbf{x}^{(k)})] = \ln[-f(\mathbf{x}^{(k)})] + \sum_{i=1}^{p} (\ln \mathscr{U}_i) + \sum_{i=1}^{p} \ln g_i(\mathbf{x}^{(k)}) \tag{7.1-6}$$

[The negative sign is necessary because $P(\mathbf{x}^{(k)})$ and $f(\mathbf{x}^{(k)})$ in Eq. (7.1–5) have negative values.] It is obvious that minimizing $f(\mathbf{x}) < 0$ is the same as maximizing $\ln[-f(\mathbf{x})] > 0$. Because $\sum_{i=1}^{p} \ln \mathscr{U}_i$ represents a constant at any stage of the calculation (although perhaps not well defined), we can identify $\rho_i = 1$, and $\ln g_i(\mathbf{x}^{(k)}) = G(g_i(\mathbf{x}^{(k)}))$, $i = 1, \ldots, p$, to establish the correspondence between Eqs. (7.1–5) and (7.0–1).

Computational experience with computer routines embodying the method of Rosenbrock indicates that the method cannot handle equality constraints and will not be generally satisfactory as applied to nonlinear inequality constraints (refer to Chap. 9).

7.1-3 CRST with Davidon (An Interior Point Method)

Box, Davies, and Swann[1] combined the Davidon method with the created response surface technique (CRST) of Carroll[2] to form an interior parametric method for nonlinear programming. Carroll's method was to set up a penalty function of the form

$$P(\mathbf{x},r) = f(\mathbf{x}) + r \sum_{i=1}^{p} \frac{\omega_i}{g_i(\mathbf{x})} \qquad (7.1\text{-}7)$$

where r is a parameter successively reduced from cycle to cycle, and the ω_i, $i = 1, \ldots, p$, are positive weights. As a boundary is approached from an interior point, i.e., as $g_i(\mathbf{x}) \to 0$, the penalty becomes large. Equation (7.1-7) transforms the constrained nonlinear programming problem without equality constraints into an unconstrained problem of a much more complex nature but with rather formidable barriers along the boundaries of the feasible region.

After the penalty function is formed and an interior point determined, the essence of the procedure is to minimize $P(\mathbf{x},r)$ for an initial $r^{(0)}$. Then the terminal $\mathbf{x}$ vector for this first stage becomes the starting point for minimization of the P function, employing a reduced value of r, and so on. The final minimization is carried out with r very small, so that the final $\mathbf{x}$ vector can, if required, be essentially on one or more boundaries to within a preselected tolerance. To carry out each stage of the unconstrained minimization, Box, Davies, and Swann used the Davidon-Fletcher-Powell method. Proof of the validity of this approach is given in Sec. 7.2-2.

The choice of the initial r, $r^{(0)}$, the method of reducing r, and the choice of the weights, all have considerable influence on the effectiveness of the CRST method. If too small a value of $r^{(0)}$ is used in $P(\mathbf{x},r)$, the initial minimization will drive $\mathbf{x}$ to the minimum of $f(\mathbf{x})$ itself, a point unlikely to be near a constrained minimum $\mathbf{x}^*$. Consequently, a considerable amount of time will be spent in following a path to reach $\mathbf{x}^*$. On the other hand, if $r^{(0)}$ is too large, the minima on the first few stages will each time be forced well away from the boundaries, and the search will also take a long time to retreat back to the binding constraints. Box, Davies, and Swann[3] suggest that an acute angle should exist between $\nabla f(\mathbf{x}^{(0)})$ and $\nabla P(\mathbf{x}^{(0)},r^{(0)})$ on the initial stage, and that the choice for the first r should be raised (or lowered) by multiplying (or dividing) a selected r by a factor until the angle changes from acute

[1] M. J. Box, D. Davies, and W. H. Swann, Nonlinear Optimization Techniques, ICI Monograph of Mathematics and Statistics, no. 5, Oliver and Boyd Ltd., London, 1969.

[2] C. W. Carroll, *Operations Res.*, **9**:169 (1961).

[3] *Op. cit.*

to obtuse. Also, $r^{(0)} \geq 10^{-4}$. (In practice, they often simply chose $r^{(0)} = 50$.) They recommended that r be successively multiplied by 0.1 (or some constant between 0.02 and 0.1) to reduce it from stage to stage. Fiacco and McCormick (1963) made some different recommendations concerning the choice of r that are detailed in Sec. 7.2–1.

As to the ω_i, Box, Davies, and Swann recommended that the ω_i be chosen so that each of the terms in the sum in Eq. (7.1–7) is scaled so as to be the same order of magnitude, insofar as possible, and they developed an empirical method of adjusting the ω_i based on the concept that an ω_i for a frequently violated constraint is too small and should be increased.

Davies[1] suggested that weights ($\omega_i > 0$) for inequality constraints for P functions such as

$$P_1 = f(\mathbf{x}) + k \sum_{i=1}^{m} \frac{\omega_i}{g_i(\mathbf{x})} \tag{7.1–8a}$$

$$P_2 = f(\mathbf{x}) + k \sum_{i=1}^{m} \frac{\omega_i}{g_i^2(\mathbf{x})} \tag{7.1–8b}$$

$$P_3 = f(\mathbf{x}) + k \sum_{i=1}^{m} \omega_i \log\left[-g_i(\mathbf{x})\right] \tag{7.1–8c}$$

(where $k > 0$) be set equal to zero until a constraint is violated. For active constraints, ω_i is placed equal to unity. He recommended using for the value of k the estimated lagrangian multiplier for the *first* violated constraint. For example, for P_1 above for the active constraint $g_i(\mathbf{x})$,

$$k = \frac{g_i^2(\mathbf{x})\left[\nabla^T f(\mathbf{x}) \nabla g(\mathbf{x})\right]}{\nabla^T g_i(\mathbf{x}) \nabla g_i(\mathbf{x})} \tag{7.1–9}$$

where the gradients of $f(\mathbf{x})$ and $g(\mathbf{x})$ are evaluated at the last feasible point. Rather than compute a k_i for each additional constraint and recompute k_i on each stage of the calculation, Davies recommended simply that k computed by Eq. (7.1–9) be reduced by a factor of from 10^{-2} to 10^{-4} from stage to stage. If equality constraints exist in the problem, Davies suggested that a term be added to P_1, P_2, or P_3 as in Eq. (7.0–1).

Fiacco and McCormick placed all the ω_i equal to unity in the SUMT algorithm but discussed the use of adjustable weights for each inequality constraint in their book (see references at the end of the chapter). Some test-problem results of CRST with Davidon are given in Table 9.3–4.

[1]D. Davies, Some Practical Methods for Optimization, Notes for the NATO Summer School on Integer and Nonlinear Programming, June 8–20, 1969.

7.1-4 MINIMAL

Weisman's MINIMAL[1] combined three techniques: the direct search of Hooke and Jeeves, random search, and the penalty function concept, into one computer code. The penalty function is formed as follows:

$$P(\mathbf{x},r) = f(\mathbf{x}) + \sum_{i=1}^{p} \delta_i r_i g_i^2(\mathbf{x}) \tag{7.1-10}$$

where $\delta_i = (1 - \mathscr{U}_i)$ is zero if the constraint is satisfied, and unity otherwise. Equality constraints are accommodated by writing each one as an inequality constraint.

$$g_i(\mathbf{x}) = |h_i(\mathbf{x})| - \varepsilon_i \leq 0$$

where ε_i is the acceptable tolerance for satisfaction of the equality constraint.

Minimization of the P function is carried out by the Hooke and Jeeves technique for a successive series of increasing values of r_i from stage to stage. The search terminates when all the constraints are satisfied or when the absolute difference between the value of a constraint at the beginning of the search and at the end is less than some prespecified tolerance, such as 10^{-4}. Weisman selected the initial values of r_i such that

$$r_i^{(0)} = \frac{0.02}{p^* g_i(\mathbf{x}^{(0)}) f(\mathbf{x}^{(0)})}$$

where p^* is the number of constraints. At the end of each stage the $r_i^{(k)}$ for the unsatisfied constraints for the kth stage are increased by a factor of 8 for use on the $(k + 1)$st stage.

Also, at the end of each stage of the Hooke and Jeeves search a random search is executed. The space E^n is divided into 10 hyperspheres centered at the best $\mathbf{x}$ vector found during the Hooke and Jeeves search. At a preselected number of randomly chosen points within each hypersphere the objective function is evaluated, and if a point is found whose value is within 10 percent of the previous minimum $\mathbf{x}$, another Hooke and Jeeves search is executed from the former. For the next stage, the $(k + 1)$st, the starting $\mathbf{x}$ is one that yields the lowest value of $f(\mathbf{x})$ during the previous k^{th} stage during either type of search.

7.1-5 Other Penalty Function Methods

1. SLUMT—an exterior point method. The treatment of inequalities in a manner akin to equalities through use of a positive slack constant [somewhat

[1]J. Weisman, Ph.D., dissertation, University of Pittsburgh, Pittsburgh, Pa., 1968.

along the lines of Eq. (7.1–1)] has been described by Fiacco and McCormick[1] in the SLUMT algorithm, which uses the P function.

$$P(\mathbf{x},r^{(k)},\mathbf{c}) = f(\mathbf{x}) + (r^{(k)})^{-1} \sum_{i=m+1}^{p} [g_i(\mathbf{x}^{(k)}) - c_i]^2 \qquad (7.1\text{–}11)$$

where $c_i \geq 0$. Such a function approaches the extremum from the infeasible region and has the advantage that the initial search for a feasible point can be omitted. Insufficient computational experience has been reported on such a P function to render an evaluation of its effectiveness.

2. An interior point method. Fiacco and McCormick (1968, Chap. 7) suggested another form of interior point penalty function.

$$P(\mathbf{x}^{(k)},\mathbf{x}^{(k-1)}) = [f(\mathbf{x}^{(k-1)}) - f(\mathbf{x}^{(k)})]^{-1} + \sum_i [g_i(\mathbf{x}^{(k)})]^{-1} \qquad (7.1\text{–}12)$$

Equality constraints can be added as in Eq. (7.0–1). Function (7.1–12) has not been extensively tested.

3. Method of centers (an interior point method). Huard[2] described the use of the modified objective function

$$P(\mathbf{x}^{(k)},\mathbf{x}^{(k-1)}) = [f(\mathbf{x}^{(k-1)}) - f(\mathbf{x}^{(k)})] \prod_i g_i(\mathbf{x}^{(k)}) \qquad (7.1\text{–}13)$$

Although the function (7.1–13) is not convex, Huard showed that a local optimum for stage k is also the global optimum. However, the method of centers has not performed too well in practice, and consequently the reader is referred to the original article for computational logic and programming details.

7.2 SUMT—A MIXED PENALTY FUNCTION METHOD

The nonlinear programming algorithm SUMT (sequential unconstrained minimization technique), developed at the Research Analysis Corp., McLean, Va., is an extension of the "created response surface technique" proposed by Carroll.[3] Fiacco and McCormick[4] subsequently developed and validated the method and extended it to accommodate equality con-

[1] A. V. Fiacco and G. P. McCormick, *SIAM J. Appl. Math.*, **15**:505 (1967).

[2] P. Huard, p. 209 in J. Abadie (ed.), "Nonlinear Programming," North Holland Publishing Company, Amsterdam, 1967.

[3] C. W. Carroll, *Operations Res.*, **9**:169 (1961); Ph.D. dissertation, Institute of Paper Chemistry, Appleton, Wis., 1959.

[4] A. V. Fiacco and G. P. McCormick, *Management Sci.*, **10**:360, 601 (1964); **12**:816 (1966).

straints. Computer codes are available from the Research Analysis Corp. and the Ballistics Research Laboratories, Aberdeen Proving Ground, Md.[1] The SUMT algorithm has been developed to solve the nonlinear programming problem stated by Eqs. (2.2–1) through (2.2–3), in which the objective function $f(\mathbf{x})$ and inequality constraints $g_i(\mathbf{x})$ can be nonlinear functions of the independent variables but the equality constraints $h_i(\mathbf{x})$ must be linear functions of the independent variables if convergence to the solution of the nonlinear programming problem is to be guaranteed.

The basic idea underlying SUMT is to solve repetitively a sequence of unconstrained problems whose solutions in the limit approach the minimum of the nonlinear programming problem. In the 1967 coded version of SUMT the nonlinear programming problem is converted into a sequence of unconstrained problems by defining the P function as follows:

$$P(\mathbf{x}^{(k)},r^{(k)}) = f(\mathbf{x}^{(k)}) + (r^{(k)})^{-1/2} \sum_{i=1}^{m} h_i^2(\mathbf{x}^{(k)}) + r^{(k)} \sum_{i=m+1}^{p} \frac{1}{g_i(\mathbf{x}^{(k)})} \tag{7.2–1}$$

where the weighting factors r are positive and form a monotonically decreasing sequence of values $\{r \mid r^0 > r^1 > \cdots > 0\}$. Figure 7.2–1 illustrates the P function.

$$P(\mathbf{x}) = (4x_1 - x_2^2 - 12) + r\left(\frac{1}{10x_1 - x_1^2 + 10x_2 - x_2^2 - 34} + \frac{1}{x_1} + \frac{1}{x_2}\right)$$

for three different values of r, a nonlinear programming problem in which the objective function and constraints can easily be identified by a term-by-term comparison with function (7.2–1). The dashed line in the figure represents the trajectory for minimization of $P(\mathbf{x},r)$.

Note that Fiacco and McCormick originally chose to make the functional of the inequality constraints in the form of an added "barrier" (subtracted for maximization):

$$G(\mathbf{g}(\mathbf{x}^{(k)})) = \sum_{i=1}^{p} \frac{1}{g_i(\mathbf{x}^{(k)})}$$

for as one or more $g_i(\mathbf{x}^{(k)}) \to 0$ from the feasible region, $G(\mathbf{g}(\mathbf{x}^{(k)})) \to \infty$; hence the concept of a "barrier." As $r^{(k)}$ is reduced, the effect of the barrier is reduced, and $\mathbf{x}$ may move closer to an inequality constraint boundary. As mentioned before, other possible choices exist for $G(\mathbf{g}(\mathbf{x}^{(k)}))$, such as

$$G(\mathbf{g}(\mathbf{x}^{(k)})) = \sum_{i=1}^{p} \min\,\{0, g_i(\mathbf{x}^{(k)})\}^2$$

[1] J. D. Wortman, BRL 1958 (NLPROG), January, 1969.

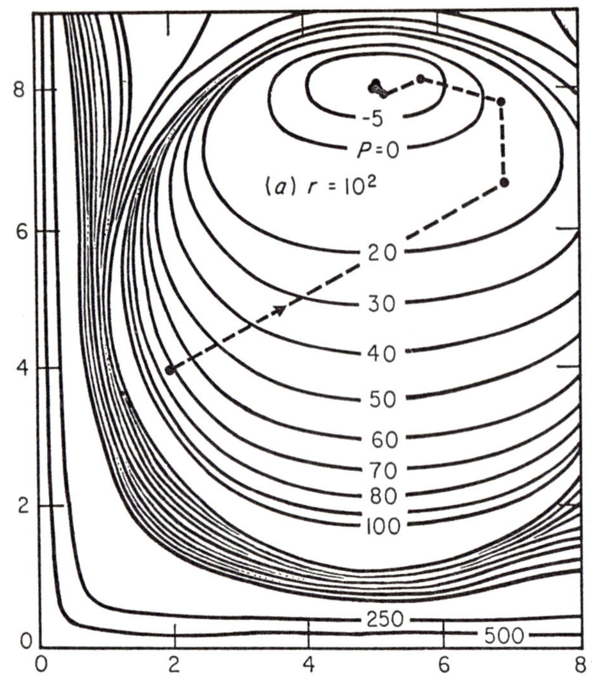
-5
P=0
(a) r = 10²
20
30
40
50
60
70
80
100
250
500
0
2
4
6
8

(a)

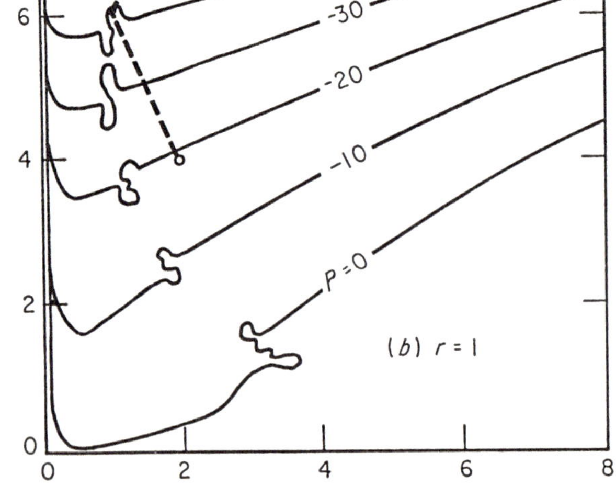
-70
-60
-50
-40
-30
-20
-10
P=0
(b) r = 1
0
2
4
6
8

(b)

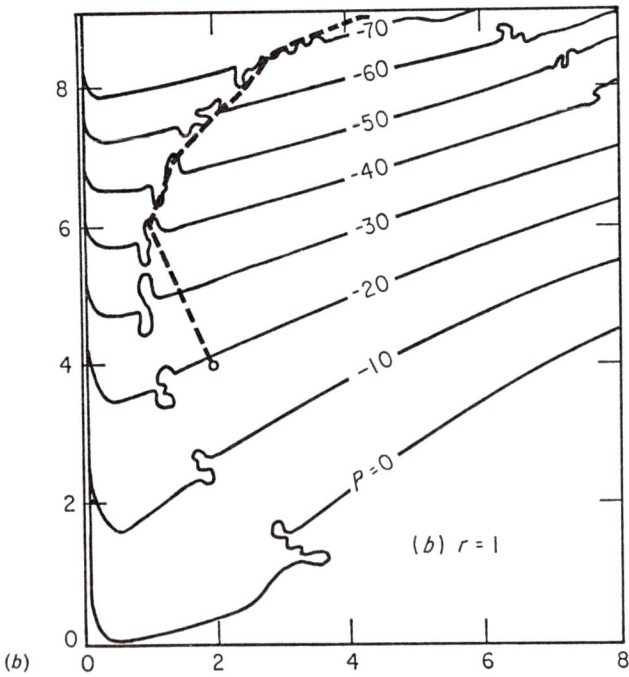

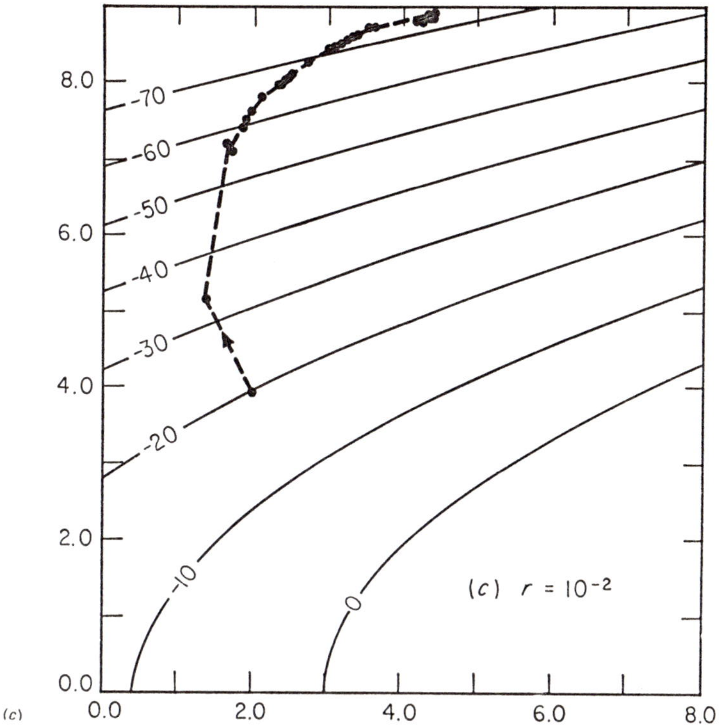

Fig. 7.2–1 Contours of the P function. (*a*) r = 10^2; (*b*) r = 1; (*c*) r = 10^{-2}.

or

$$G(\mathbf{g}(\mathbf{x}^{(k)})) = -\sum_{i=1}^{p} \ln (g_i(\mathbf{x}^{(k)})) = \sum_{i=1}^{p} \ln \frac{1}{g_i(\mathbf{x}^{(k)})}$$

and in the 1970 coded version of SUMT the penalty function used was

$$P(\mathbf{x}^{(k)}, r^{(k)}) = f(\mathbf{x}) + \frac{1}{r^{(k)}} \sum_{i=1}^{m} h_i^2(\mathbf{x}^{(k)}) - r^{(k)} \sum_{i=m+1}^{p} \ln g_i(\mathbf{x}^{(k)}) \quad (7.2\text{–}1a)$$

In both versions of the code the form of $H(\mathbf{h}(\mathbf{x}^{(k)}))$ chosen was simply the sum of the squares of the respective equality constraints, so that as $r^{(k)} \to 0$, the equality constraints are more and more closely satisfied. Although in principle the equality constraints each might be split up into two inequalities and treated as such, in practice this type of approach is quite unsatisfactory—it slows the search excessively and tends to cause premature termination.

The minimization of function (7.2–1) or (7.2–1*a*) is initiated at an interior point (or boundary point), that is, a point $\mathbf{x}^{(0)}$ at which all the inequality constraints are satisfied. After $r^{(0)}$ is computed, $\mathbf{x}^{(1)}$ is determined by minimizing

$P(\mathbf{x}, r^{(0)})$. Then $r^{(1)}$ is computed and $\mathbf{x}^{(2)}$ determined by minimizing $P(\mathbf{x}, r^{(1)})$, and so forth.

The procedure described suffers from several handicaps. First, the hessian matrix of the P function becomes progressively more ill-conditioned as the extremum is approached; hence the search directions may become misleading. Second, the rate of convergence depends on the initial choice of $r^{(0)}$ and the method of reducing $r^{(k)}$. Finally, most of the information about the topology of $f(\mathbf{x})$ and $P(\mathbf{x}, r)$ is discarded from one stage to the next, even if some type of extrapolation is incorporated in the algorithm.

7.2-1 Determination of *r*

Early versions of SUMT used a factor of $(r^{(k)})^{-1/2}$ as the weighting factor for $\sum_{i=1}^{m} h_i^2(\mathbf{x}^{(k)})$ because, by comparing the P function and $f(\mathbf{x})$ near the extremum for very small values of r, Fiacco (1966) demonstrated that the $\mathbf{x}$ vector at the respective minima of $P(\mathbf{x}, r)$ could be expressed as a polynomial in $r^{1/2}$; see Fig. 7.2-2. Later versions of SUMT used a weighting factor of $(r^{(k)})^{-1}$ for the sum of the equality constraints. The weighting factor for the sum over the inequality constraints was $r^{(k)}$ in both versions.

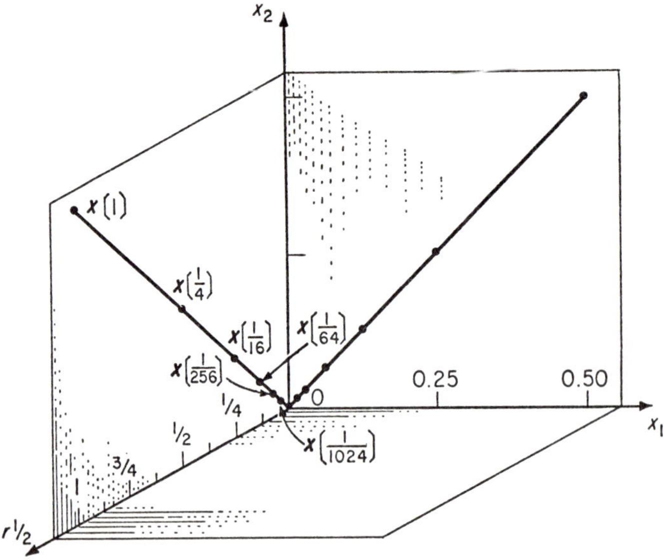

Fig. 7.2-2 Trajectory of the minimum of

$$P(\mathbf{x}, r^{(k)}) = (4x_1 + x_2) + r^{(k)}\left(\frac{1}{x_1} + \frac{1}{x_2}\right)$$

Fiacco and McCormick recommended three methods for selecting the initial value of $r^{(0)}$:

(a) $r^{(0)} = 1$ (7.2–2)

(b) The value of $r^{(0)}$ is chosen that minimizes the norm of the gradient of the P function, $P(\mathbf{x}^{(0)},r^{(0)})$, with respect to r, leading to

$$r^{(0)} = \frac{-\nabla^T f(\mathbf{x}^{(0)})\nabla R(\mathbf{x}^{(0)})}{\|\nabla R(\mathbf{x}^{(0)})\|^2} \tag{7.2–3}$$

where $\mathbf{x}^{(0)}$ is an interior feasible point, $R(\mathbf{x}^{(0)}) = \sum_{i=m+1}^{p} 1/g_i(\mathbf{x}^{(0)})$ and $\nabla R(\mathbf{x}^{(0)})$ is a column vector of the first-order partial derivatives of $R(\mathbf{x})$ with respect to $\mathbf{x}$ evaluated at $\mathbf{x}^{(0)}$. Only the inequality constraints are considered in forming $R(\mathbf{x}^{(0)})$.

(c) The value of $r^{(0)}$ is chosen that minimizes the estimate of the amount by which $P(\mathbf{x},r^{(0)})$ exceeds its minimum value (this estimate is called the metricized magnitude of the gradient of the P function), and for this choice $r^{(0)}$ is given (exactly if the P function is quadratic) by the relationship

$$r^{(0)} = \left\{\frac{\nabla^T f(\mathbf{x}^{(0)})[\nabla^2 R(\mathbf{x}^{(0)})]^{-1}\nabla f(\mathbf{x}^{(0)})}{\nabla^T R(\mathbf{x}^{(0)})[\nabla^2 R(\mathbf{x}^{(0)})]^{-1}\nabla R(\mathbf{x}^{(0)})}\right\}^{1/2} \tag{7.2–4}$$

where $\nabla^2 R(\mathbf{x}^{(0)})$ is the hessian matrix of $R(\mathbf{x}) = \sum_{i=1}^{p} 1/g_i(\mathbf{x})$ with components evaluated at $\mathbf{x}^{(0)}$. Expression (7.2–4) can be used only if $\nabla R(\mathbf{x}^{(0)}) \neq \mathbf{0}$, so that $r^{(0)} \neq 0$. Too large an $r^{(0)}$ pushes the initial minimization of P too far into the interior of the feasible region, while too small an $r^{(0)}$ may force the initial solution too close to a boundary. In either case excess time may be required to settle into the appropriate part of the feasible region.

Of these three methods, (7.2–2) seems to be the most practical for choosing $r^{(0)}$ (most computer programs written for SUMT choose $r^{(0)} = 1$) and has been used in the studies in Chap. 9. However, to obtain the best accuracy in the solution of the problem, the method given by (7.4–4) is preferred, but computation time in SUMT becomes larger due to the possibility of very large initial values for $r^{(0)}$. The method given by (7.2–3) is used when second partial derivatives of $R(\mathbf{x}^{(0)})$ with respect to $\mathbf{x}$ are not supplied. If $r^{(0)}$ as computed by (7.2–3) or (7.2–4) is less than or equal to zero, the search is initiated at $\mathbf{x}^{(0)}$, using one of the gradient or the second-derivative methods described in Chap. 3. The value of $r^{(0)}$ is computed at every new point $\mathbf{x}^{(k)}$ obtained by the gradient or second-derivative method, until either (1) a positive $r^{(0)}$ is obtained, in which case the search proceeds with SUMT thereafter or (2) the unconstrained minimum of the problem given by Eqs. (2.2–1) through (2.2–3) is achieved, in which case $\mathbf{x}^*$ is an interior point and the search is terminated. It has been demonstrated experimentally by Fiacco and McCormick (1964, p. 601) that after having computed $r^{(0)}$ by one of the three procedures outlined above, the effectiveness of the algorithm was not affected significantly if $r^{(1)}, r^{(2)}, \ldots, r^{(k)}$ was determined by the simple relation $r^{(k)} = r^{(k-1)}/c$, where $c > 1$ is a constant (usually, $c = 4$). This particular relationship makes the extrapolation step (Sec. 7.2–3) much simpler.

7.2–2 Conditions for Convergence of SUMT

Under certain conditions, it can be proved that the sequence of unconstrained minima of $P(\mathbf{x}, r^{(k)})$ will approach a solution of the nonlinear programming problem (2.2–1) through (2.2–3) as $r^{(k)}$ goes to zero (Fiacco and McCormick, 1966). The essential requirement is the convexity of the P function. The conditions are (compare them with those on page 223):

Condition 1: The union of the set containing all the points $\mathbf{x}$ that satisfy the equality constraints $h_i(\mathbf{x}) = 0$, $i = 1, \ldots, m$, and the set S^* containing all the points $\mathbf{x}$ that satisfy the inequality constraints $g_i(\mathbf{x}) \geq 0$, $i = m + 1, \ldots, p$, must be nonempty. In other words, the problem must have a feasible region.

Condition 2: The functions $f(\mathbf{x}), h_1(\mathbf{x}), \ldots, h_m(\mathbf{x}), g_{m+1}(\mathbf{x}), \ldots, g_p(\mathbf{x})$, must be twice continuously differentiable if a second-derivative method of optimization is to be used (see Sec. 7.2–3, step 3).

Condition 3: For every finite q and every $r^{(k)} > 0$, the set of points $\mathbf{x}$ that satisfy the inequality

$$f(\mathbf{x}) + (r^{(k)})^{-1/2} \sum_{i=1}^{m} h_i^2(\mathbf{x}) \leq q$$

and is contained in the set S^* must be a bounded set.

Condition 4: The objective function $f(\mathbf{x})$ must be convex, and the functions $h_i(\mathbf{x})$, $i = 1, \ldots, m$, must be linear (more precisely, $\sum h_i^2(\mathbf{x})$ must be convex).

Condition 5: The functions $g_i(\mathbf{x})$, $i = m + 1, \ldots, p$, must be concave.

Condition 6: The hessian matrix of the P function with respect to $\mathbf{x}$, that is, the matrix of the second partial derivatives of the P function with respect to the independent variables, must not vanish for any $\mathbf{x}$ vector contained in the set S^*.

While conditions 1 through 6 must be satisfied if convergence to the solution of the nonlinear programming problem is to be guaranteed, it should be noted that convergence may occur even if the conditions are not satisfied.

On the basis of conditions 1 through 6, Fiacco and McCormick (1966) derived the following convergence theorem:

Theorem 1 Primal convergence

If conditions 1 through 6 are satisfied by the nonlinear programming problem, then

(*a*) Each function $P(\mathbf{x},r^{(k)})$ is minimized at a point $\mathbf{x}(r^{(k)})$ in the set S^*, and

(*b*) $\lim_{r^{(k)}\to 0} P(\mathbf{x}(r^{(k)}),r^{(k)}) = \min f(\mathbf{x}) = f(\mathbf{x}^*)$

i.e., the sequence of unconstrained minima $P(\mathbf{x}(r^{(k)}),r^{(k)})$ will approach the solution of the nonlinear programming problem $f(\mathbf{x}^*)$ as k goes to infinity.

Also, under conditions 1 through 6, the P function is a convex function in S^*.

Associated with the nonlinear programming problem (2.2–1) through (2.2–3) are two duals, one for the case in which the functions $h_i(\mathbf{x})$, $i = 1, \ldots, m$, are nonlinear, and the other for the case in which they are linear. If the functions $h_i(\mathbf{x})$ are nonlinear, it is necessary to rewrite the nonlinear problem (2.2–1) through (2.2–3) in the following equivalent form, making use of the fact that an equality can be written as two inequalities.

Problem A:

$$\begin{array}{lll} \text{Minimize:} & f(\mathbf{x}) & \mathbf{x} \in E^n \\ \text{Subject to:} & h_i^2(\mathbf{x}) \geq 0 & i = 1, \ldots, m \\ & g_i(\mathbf{x}) \geq 0 & i = m+1, \ldots, p \end{array} \qquad (7.2\text{–}5)$$

The dual programming Problem A' can be written as:

Problem A':

$$\text{Maximize:} \quad E(\mathbf{x},\mathbf{u},\mathbf{w}) = f(\mathbf{x}) - \sum_{i=m+1}^{m} u_i g_i(\mathbf{x}) + \sum_{i=1}^{m} w_i h_i^2(\mathbf{x})$$

$$\text{Subject to:} \quad \nabla_{\mathbf{x}} E(\mathbf{x},\mathbf{u},\mathbf{w}) = 0 \tag{7.2–6}$$
$$u_i \geq 0 \qquad i = m+1, \ldots, p$$
$$w_i \geq 0 \qquad i = 1, \ldots, m$$

where $\nabla_{\mathbf{x}} E(\mathbf{x},\mathbf{u},\mathbf{w})$ is the vector comprising the first partial derivatives of $E(\mathbf{x},\mathbf{u},\mathbf{w})$ with respect to the independent variables. Keep in mind that when the functions $h_i(\mathbf{x})$ are nonlinear, it is not guaranteed that the solution to problem A' will coincide with $f(\mathbf{x}^*)$, the solution to problem A. (Based on computational experience, it is quite unlikely.)

If the functions $h_i(\mathbf{x})$ are linear, the programming problem A can be written in the equivalent form B.

Problem B:

$$\text{Minimize:} \quad f(\mathbf{x}) \qquad \mathbf{x} \in E^n$$
$$\text{Subject to:} \quad h_i(\mathbf{x}) \geq 0 \qquad i = 1, \ldots, m$$
$$-h_i(\mathbf{x}) \geq 0 \qquad i = 1, \ldots, m \tag{7.2–7}$$
$$g_i(\mathbf{x}) \geq 0 \qquad i = m+1, \ldots, p$$

The dual to Problem B is:

Problem B′:

$$\text{Maximize:} \quad E(\mathbf{x},\mathbf{u},\mathbf{w},\acute{\mathbf{w}}) = f(\mathbf{x}) - \sum_{i=m+1}^{p} u_i g_i(\mathbf{x}) + \sum_{i=1}^{m} w_i h_i(\mathbf{x}) - \sum_{i=1}^{m} \acute{w}_i h_i(\mathbf{x})$$

$$\text{Subject to:} \quad \nabla_{\mathbf{x}} E(\mathbf{x},\mathbf{u},\mathbf{w},\acute{\mathbf{w}}) = 0 \tag{7.2–8}$$
$$u_i \geq 0 \qquad i = m+1, \ldots, p$$
$$w_i \geq 0 \qquad i = 1, \ldots, m$$
$$\acute{w}_i \geq 0 \qquad i = 1, \ldots, m$$

The dual problem B' has a solution at some $(\mathbf{x}^*,\mathbf{u}^*,\mathbf{w}^*,\acute{\mathbf{w}}^*)$, where $E(\mathbf{x}^*,\mathbf{u}^*,\mathbf{w}^*,\acute{\mathbf{w}}^*) = f(\mathbf{x}^*)$, the solution to Problem B. Fiacco and McCormick have proved Theorem 2 for dual convergence.

Theorem 2 Convergence of the dual

Under conditions 1 through 6, SUMT yields the points $\{\mathbf{x}(r^{(k)}),\mathbf{u}(r^{(k)}),\mathbf{w}(r^{(k)}), \acute{\mathbf{w}}(r^{(k)})\}$ that are feasible and have the property that $\lim_{k\to\infty} E(x(\mathbf{r}^{(k)}),\mathbf{u}(r^{(k)}),\mathbf{w}(r^{(k)}),\acute{\mathbf{w}}(r^{(k)})) = f(\mathbf{x}^*)$.

Thus, besides solving Problem A (or B), the primal problem, the SUMT algorithm also generates a sequence of points that solve Problem A' (or B'), the dual of A (or B). Since $f(\mathbf{x}^*)$ is the maximum value of $E(\mathbf{x},\mathbf{u},\mathbf{w},\acute{\mathbf{w}})$, when conditions 1 through 6 are satisfied, the following inequalities exist:

$$E(\mathbf{x}(r^{(k)}),\mathbf{u}(r^{(k)}),\mathbf{w}(r^{(k)}),\acute{\mathbf{w}}(r^{(k)})) \leq f(\mathbf{x}^*) \leq P(\mathbf{x}(r^{(k)})) \qquad (7.2\text{–}9)$$

Inequality (7.2–9) can be used (for problems meeting conditions 1 through 6) to determine when convergence to the solution of the nonlinear programming problem has been achieved during the computer solution of the problem.

7.2–3 Summary of the Computational Procedure

The general steps in the computational algorithm are as follows. Figure 7.2–3 compares the trajectory of the sequence of minima of $P(\mathbf{x},r)$ by the SUMT method with the trajectory obtained by a projection method.

Step 1: The user selects an initial point, $\mathbf{x}^{(0)}$, which is contained in the set S^* (an $\mathbf{x}$ vector $\mathbf{x}^{(0)}$ such that the $g_i(\mathbf{x}^{(0)}) > 0$, $i = m + 1, \ldots, p$). In other words, the initial point must be an interior point as defined in Chap. 2. Because the P function may have more than one minimum, a nonfeasible

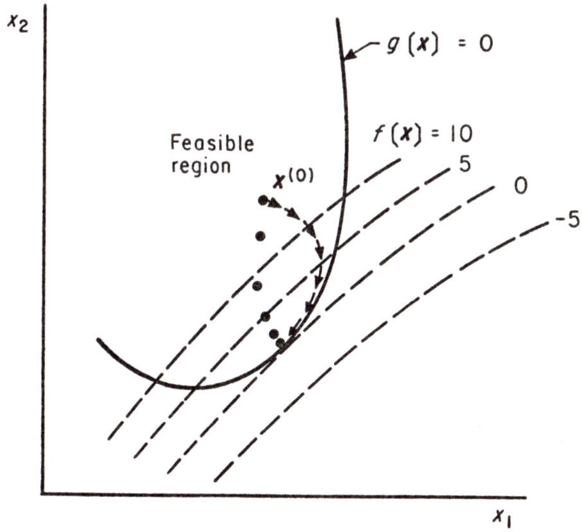

Fig. 7.2–3 Comparison of penalty function trajectory with a projection method of minimization; $g(\mathbf{x}) \geq 0$ is a nonlinear inequality constraint. →→→ represents a projection method, and · · · · represents the penalty function method.

minimum can be obtained if one does not start with or find an interior point before commencing to minimize P. If such an initial interior point is not known, repeated application of the SUMT method itself is used to obtain an $\mathbf{x}$ vector that is an interior point. In the 1967 version of SUMT the first unsatisfied inequality constraint was labeled for use as a temporary objective function and the SUMT routine minimized the negative value of the inequality constraint subject to the set of satisfied inequality constraints. As each constraint became satisfied, it was placed in the category of a constraint for the next temporary objective function, and the next unsatisfied constraint became the new temporary objective function. In the 1970 version of SUMT the negative of the sum of all the violated inequality constraints was minimized to obtain an interior point. By either version of the algorithm the equality constraints are satisfied only at the final solution of the problem.

It should be noted that if a number of highly nonlinear constraints are violated, a considerable amount of time may be consumed in determining a feasible starting vector. For this reason, a feasible starting point should be used whenever possible.

Step 2: The algorithm next locates the minimum of the P function [defined by Eq. (7.2–1) or (7.2–1a)] for the current value of $r^{(k)}$. Probably the bulk of the computational time required by SUMT is devoted to computing the sequence of interior points that minimize the P function for each value of $r^{(k)}$. The direction of search is obtained as described in Sec. 3.3 on Newton's method by premultiplying the gradient of $P(\mathbf{x},r^{(k)})$ by the inverse of the matrix of the second partial derivatives of $P(\mathbf{x},r^{(k)})$ with respect to the independent variables, or as an alternative option, by using Broyden's method (Sec. 3.4–1) to approximate $[\nabla^2 P(\mathbf{x},r^{(k)})]^{-1}$:

$$\mathbf{s}^{(k)} = -[\nabla^2 P(\mathbf{x}^{(k)},r^{(k)})]^{-1}\nabla P(\mathbf{x}^{(k)},r^{(k)}) \tag{7.2–10}$$

or

$$\mathbf{s}^{(k)} = -\boldsymbol{\eta}_p \nabla P(\mathbf{x}^{(k)},r^{(k)}) \tag{7.2–10a}$$

The step length, as usual, is determined by minimizing the modified P function. Once the search direction is established, SUMT employs a Fibonacci search to locate the minimum of $P(\mathbf{x},r^{(k)})$ at a distance $\Delta\mathbf{x}^{(k)}$ from $\mathbf{x}^{(k)}$ in the direction of search, while NLPROG makes use of both a mixture of search and extrapolation (fitting) methods to carry out the linear search once the search direction is evaluated.

There is some danger in using Newton's method because the inverse of the hessian matrix of the P function can become ill-conditioned. Murray[1] has shown that, even for a well-scaled problem, the hessian matrix of

[1] W. Murray, *Proc. 6th Intl. Symp. on Mathematical Programming*, Princeton, N.J., 1967.

$P(\mathbf{x},r^{(k)})$ is ill-conditioned. New information gathered at one stage may not be sufficient to compensate for the increase in the error of information gained at some previous stage.

Fletcher and McCann[1] examined the ratio of the largest to the smallest eigenvalues of the hessian matrix of P as a condition number, and pointed out that the use of Newton's method leads to ill-conditioning, whereas the Davidon-Fletcher-Powell method of minimization leads to a well-conditioned, although approximate, inverse of the hessian matrix of P. They proposed some strategies for accelerating the minimization of $f(\mathbf{x})$ by employing the eigenvalues of $P(\mathbf{x},r)$, together with the values of r, to predict more satisfactory direction matrices on each stage as r was reduced. Based on five test problems, including Problems 10, 11, and 18 in Appendix A, the extrapolation saved from 15 to as much as 50 percent in terms of total function evaluations (search directions + linear searches) as compared with Newton's method.

Because of the problem of the conditioning of the hessian matrix of the P function, in the SUMT method, if the hessian matrix of the P function is not positive definite, the search direction selected is that of the negative gradient; i.e., the inverse of the hessian matrix of the P function is placed equal to the identity matrix.

Although Fiacco and McCormick reported that their experiences with

Table 7.2-1 Comparison of search techniques to minimize the *P* function for Problem 18 of Appendix A

	*SUMT**	*Newton*	*Davidon-Fletcher-Powell*	*Powell search*	*Hooke and Jeeves*
$f(\mathbf{x}^*)$	32.3519	32.3488	32.3488	32.3488	32.3526
No. of stages				455	1363
Univariate linear searches	92	88	272	7164	
Objective function evaluations		292	1086	27,987	37,485
P-function evaluations		487	1331	27,458	34,054
Time, min		1.14	0.73	4.71	4.72

*Fiacco and McCormick.

[1] R. Fletcher and A. P. McCann, Chap 13 in R. Fletcher (ed.), "Optimization," Academic Press Inc., London, 1969.

first-derivative methods and Davidon's method in minimizing the P function were not as satisfactory as the use of Newton's method, Wortman[1] found that the Davidon-Fletcher-Powell minimization took the least time. Table 7.2–1 lists several of Wortman's results for Problem 18 of Appendix A, obtained using different minimization subroutines. Newton's method was the same as in Chap. 3, except that when $\nabla^2 P$ was not positive definite, $\nabla^2 P$ was replaced by the identity matrix $\mathbf{I}$; that is, a negative gradient search direction was chosen. A few minor differences existed in the termination conditions between SUMT and NLPROG, but the methods were basically the same.

For Hooke and Jeeves, a stage is an exploratory search plus perhaps a pattern search; for Powell, a stage consists in finding a linear minimum in each of the n independent directions plus, possibly, a stage in the composite direction (refer to Chap. 4). Except for Hooke and Jeeves, the components of the $\mathbf{x}$ vector were all within 10^{-5} to 10^{-4} of the correct values (see Appendix A for these). The inequality constraints were all satisfied. Both the Davidon-Fletcher-Powell method and Newton's method located the minimum accurately and quickly.

Table 7.2–2 Minimization of the *P* function by several methods

Method	*Comp. time, sec*	*Method*	*Comp. time, sec*
Newton	1.40	Broyden	6.63
Reduced gradient projection	2.10	Fletcher-Reeves	7.66
Projected Newton-Pearson	2.93	Pearson No. 2	32.24
Pearson No. 3	6.13	Steepest descent	57.53

In a different study Tabak[2] reported the times to minimize the P function on an IBM 360/91 as listed in Table 7.2–2 for the following problem.

Minimize: $f(\mathbf{x}) = cx_1 + x_3 + x_5$

Subject to: $(2x_3^2 - 1)x_4^2 + (2x_5^2 - 1)x_6^2 \geq 0$

$$x_1[4x_4^2x_6^2(4x_3^2x_5^2 - 2x_3^2 - 2x_5^2 + 1) + x_4^4 + x_6^4] + 1 - 2x_2(x_3x_4 + x_5x_6) \geq 0$$

$$2x_1x_4^2x_6^2[(2x_3^2 - 1)x_6^2 + (2x_5^2 - 1)x_4^2] + 2x_2x_4x_6(x_3x_6 + x_4x_5) - x_4^2 - x_6^2 - 4x_3x_4x_5x_6 \geq 0$$

[1] *Op. cit.*
[2] D. Tabak, IEEE Trans. Automatic Control, **AC14**:572 (1969).

$$x_{3,\,\min} \le x_3 \le x_{3,\,\max}$$
$$x_{5,\,\min} \le x_5 \le x_{5,\,\max}$$
$$x_4 \le x_{4,\,\max}$$
$$x_6 \le x_{6,\,\max}$$

Tests of Problems 1, 2, 4, 5, and 11 of Appendix A, the results of which are listed in Table 7.2–3, indicate that the methods of minimization in the 1970 SUMT code are roughly equivalent if analytical derivatives are employed, but that the search technique (derivative-free) is ineffective.

Table 7.2–3 Times* required to solve several problems by 1970 SUMT

Problem number	*1*		*2*		*4*		*5*		*11*
Termination criterion†	*1*	2	*1*	2	*1*	2	*1*	2	*1*
Minimization method									
Newton with analytical derivatives	0.53	0.67	0.76	0.68	2.05	2.27	0.99	1.33	0.98
Broyden	0.56	1.01	0.85	0.88	4.39	4.80	1.01	1.30	1.65
Function evaluation only, Fiacco and McCormick	0.94	1.23	‡	‡	‡	‡	‡	‡	3.40

*Central processing time in seconds on a CDC 6600.
†See Sec. 7.2–3, step 5.
‡Correct solution not obtained or failed.

Termination of the search for the minimum of the P function in SUMT on each stage is based on three convergence criteria, the choice of which is left to the user. The code will terminate the search if:

(*a*) $$\left|\nabla^T P(\mathbf{x}^{(k)},r^{(k)})[\nabla^2 P(\mathbf{x}^{(k)},r^{(k)})]^{-1}\nabla P(\mathbf{x}^{(k)},r^{(k)})\right| < \varepsilon$$

In other words [refer to Eq. (7.2–10)], terminate if

$$\frac{\partial P(\mathbf{x},r^{(k)})}{\partial x_i}(\Delta x_i) < \varepsilon, \qquad i = 1, \ldots, n$$

Or (*b*):

$$|\nabla^T P(\mathbf{x}^{(k)},r^{(k)})[\nabla^2 P(\mathbf{x}^{(k)},r^{(k)})]^{-1}\nabla P(\mathbf{x}^{(k)},r^{(k)})| < \frac{P(\mathbf{x}^{(k-1)}) - P(\mathbf{x}^{(k)})}{5}$$

This criterion will stop the minimization of P if

$$\frac{\partial P(\mathbf{x}^{(k)},r^{(k)})}{\partial x_i}(\Delta x_i) < \frac{P(\mathbf{x}^{(k-1)},r^{(k-1)}) - P(\mathbf{x}^{(k)},r^{(k)})}{5} \qquad i = 1, \ldots, n$$

or (*c*):

$$\left|\frac{\partial P(\mathbf{x}^{(k)},r^{(k)})}{\partial x_i}\right| < \varepsilon \qquad i = 1, \ldots, n$$

where the | | refer to absolute value. Criterion (*a*) has been used exclusively in the studies reported in Chap. 9, with a value of 10^{-7} for ε. Table 7.2–4 lists data for Problem 1 of Appendix A, comparing the effectiveness of the three termination criteria.

Table 7.2–4 Performance of 1970 SUMT for various termination criteria for Problem 1 of Appendix A showing the central processing time, in seconds; ( ) = no. of stages

*Termination of P function**	*Termination of overall minimization†*		
	Criterion 1	*Criterion 2*	*Criterion 3*
Newton's method:			
Criterion *a*	0.529 (32)	0.670 (38)	0.606 (38)
Criterion *b*	0.703 (106)	0.832 (129)	0.815 (129)
Criterion *c*	0.604 (93)	0.884 (127)	0.785 (127)
Broyden's method:	*Criterion 1*	*Criterion 2*	*Criterion 3*
Criterion *a*	0.563 (49)	1.013 (64)	0.967 (64)
Criterion *b*	0.729 (49)	1.190 (61)	0.955 (61)
Criterion *c*	0.597 (49)	0.974 (64)	1.112 (64)
Function evaluation only:	*Criterion 1*	*Criterion 2*	*Criterion 3*
Criterion *a*	0.944 (112)	1.234 (146)	1.231 (164)
Criterion *b*	1.316 (187)	1.679 (223)	1.462 (214)
Criterion *c*	0.703 (58)	1.002 (91)	1.051 (91)

*See Sec. 7.2–3, step 2.
†See Sec. 7.2–3, step 5.

Step 3: In SUMT the vector $\mathbf{x}^{(k+1)}$ is given by

$$\mathbf{x}^{(k+1)} = \mathbf{x}^{(k)} + \lambda^{(k)}\mathbf{s}^{(k)}$$

where $\mathbf{s}^{(k)}$ is determined by Eq. (7.2–10) or (7.2–10*a*). It is necessary that some method of detecting a violation of an inequality constraint be

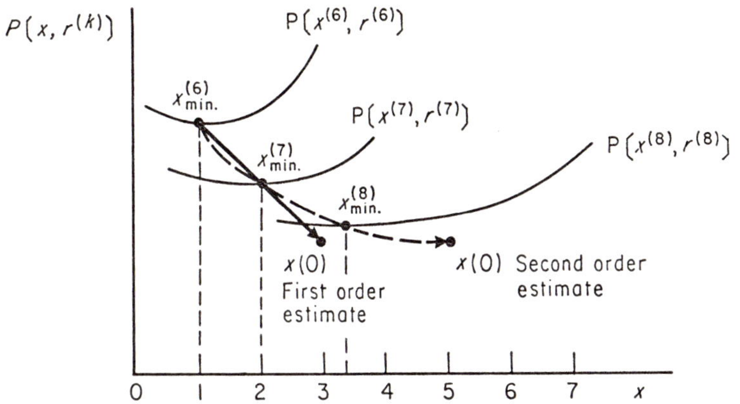

Fig. 7.2–4 Extrapolation techniques to accelerate the search in SUMT.

included in the unidimensional search if exterior **x** vectors are to be avoided.

Step 4: We here consider acceleration of the solution by extrapolation. Without an acceleration step, SUMT converges to a constrained extremum far too slowly; i.e., near a boundary, progress is slow. It is to meet this difficulty that several successively decreasing values of the weighting factor r are used to obtain successive minima of $P(\mathbf{x},r^{(k)})$ and corresponding successive values of $\mathbf{x}^{(k)}$. One can then extrapolate from $\mathbf{x}^{(k-1)}$ through $\mathbf{x}^{(k)}$ and $\mathbf{x}^{(k+1)}$ to an approximate extremum. This procedure works well for many problems, but can prove unsatisfactory if the **x**'s bunch up.

SUMT extrapolates the **x**-vector values at the known minima of $P(\mathbf{x}^{(k)},r^{(k)})$ by a polynomial in powers of $r^{1/2}$ after more than one minimum value of $P(\mathbf{x}^{(k)},r^{(k)})$ has been determined. (If $P(\mathbf{x}^{(k)},r^{(k)})$ is strictly convex, there is only one minimum of $P(\mathbf{x}^{(k)},r^{(k)})$ for each $r^{(k)}$.) The extrapolations using two and three successive values of **x** at the minima of the P function are called the first- and second-order-solution estimates, respectively, as illustrated in Fig. 7.2–4.

To be more specific, Fiacco and McCormick found that the trajectory of $\mathbf{x}(r^{(k)})$, the solution to the unconstrained minimization of $P(\mathbf{x},r^{(k)})$, was approximately linear in $(r^{(k)})^{1/2}$ as $r^{(k)}$ approached zero; i.e., for small $r^{(k)}$,

$$\mathbf{x}(r^{(k)}) \approx \mathbf{x}(0) + a(r^{(k)})^{1/2} \tag{7.2–11}$$

and

$$\mathbf{x}\left(\frac{r^{(k)}}{c}\right) \approx \mathbf{x}(0) + a\left(\frac{r^{(k)}}{c}\right)^{1/2} \tag{7.2–12}$$

for some constant a, where $\mathbf{x}(0)$ is the value of $\mathbf{x}(r^{(k)})$ as $r^{(k)}$ tends to zero. The first-order estimate of the solution to the nonlinear programming problem is given by solving Eqs. (7.2–11) and (7.2–12) for $\mathbf{x}(0)$, thus:

$$\mathbf{x}(0) \approx \frac{c^{1/2}\mathbf{x}(r^{(k)}/c) - \mathbf{x}(r^{(k)})}{c^{1/2} - 1} \tag{7.2-13}$$

To obtain the second-order extrapolation one assumes

$$\begin{aligned}
\mathbf{x}(r^{(k)}) &= \mathbf{x}(0) + a_1(r^{(k)})^{1/2} + a_2(r^{(k)}) \\
\mathbf{x}\left(\frac{r^{(k)}}{c}\right) &= \mathbf{x}(0) + a_1\left(\frac{r^{(k)}}{c}\right)^{1/2} + a_2\left(\frac{r^{(k)}}{c}\right) \\
\mathbf{x}\left(\frac{r^{(k)}}{c^2}\right) &= \mathbf{x}(0) + a_1\left(\frac{r^{(k)}}{c^2}\right)^{1/2} + a_2\left(\frac{r^{(k)}}{c^2}\right)
\end{aligned} \tag{7.2-14}$$

Solution of Eqs. (7.2–14) for $\mathbf{x}(0)$ yields

$$\mathbf{x}(0) \approx \frac{\mathbf{x}(r^{(k)}) - (c + c^{1/2})\mathbf{x}(r^{(k)}/c) + c^{3/2}\mathbf{x}(r^{(k)}/c^2)}{(c - 1)(c^{1/2} - 1)} \tag{7.2-15}$$

SUMT uses Eqs. (7.2–13) and (7.2–15) to accelerate the search and reduce the computation time.

Step 5: Tests for convergence are carried out. The algorithm includes three criteria for termination of the optimization, the choice of which is left to the user. The code will terminate the iterations if one of the three following criteria is met:

(1) $$\frac{f(\mathbf{x}(r^{(k)}))}{E(\mathbf{x}(r^{(k)}),\mathbf{u}(r^{(k)}),\mathbf{w}(r^{(k)}),\acute{\mathbf{w}}(r^{(k)}))} - 1 \le \theta_0$$

where the function E has been defined in Sec. 7.2–2.

(2) $$r^{(k)} \sum_{i=m+1}^{p} \frac{1}{g_i(\mathbf{x}(r^{(k)}))} \le \theta_0$$

[It should be noted that criterion (2) does *not* include a term which tests for satisfaction of the equality constraints $h_i(\mathbf{x}(r^{(k)}))$, $i = 1, \ldots, m$.]

(3) $$\frac{\text{First-order estimate of } f(\mathbf{x}^*)}{E(\mathbf{x}(r^{(k)}),\mathbf{u}(r^{(k)}),\mathbf{w}(r^{(k)}),\acute{\mathbf{w}}(r^{(k)}))} - 1 \le \theta_0$$

where θ_0 is a user-supplied constant. Criteria (1) and (3) are logical developments of Eq. (7.2–9). The values of the objective functions of the primal and dual solutions approach each other as $r^{(k)}$ is reduced, at least for problems with linear equality constraints, and the E and P functions approach $f(\mathbf{x}^*)$. The computations are terminated if the criterion selected is satisfied. If not, the algorithm continues to step 6. Table 7.2–4 lists some results for Problem 1 in Appendix A using these criteria; criterion (1) has been used in the evaluations in Chap. 9.

Step 6: The code reduces $r^{(k)}$ as described previously.

Step 7: The code estimates the minimum of the P function for the reduced value of $r^{(k)}$ using extrapolation formulas in step 4.

Step 8: Starting with the result of step 7, the code goes to step 3 and continues the iteration.

In the 1967 version of SUMT, the user had to supply, in addition to the equations relating the objective function and constraints to the independent variables, the equations relating the analytical first and second partial derivatives of the objective function and constraints with respect to the independent variables to the independent variables themselves. In the 1970 version of SUMT, an option exists permitting the user to compute approximate second derivatives by difference relations involving analytical first derivatives, but this feature has not been extensively tested. Other options are to use Broyden's algorithm with analytical first derivatives or to use a search method that employs no derivatives whatsoever. The user must also supply an initial **x** vector, which need not be feasible, together with several program parameters and constants.

Example 7.2-1 SUMT

The same problem solved in earlier examples will be solved here by the SUMT algorithm.

Minimize: $f(\mathbf{x}) = 4x_1 - x_2^2 - 12$

Subject to: $h_1(\mathbf{x}) = 25 - x_1^2 - x_2^2 = 0$

$g_2(\mathbf{x}) = 10x_1 - x_1^2 + 10x_2 - x_2^2 - 34 \geq 0$

$g_3(\mathbf{x}) = x_1 \geq 0$

$g_4(\mathbf{x}) = x_2 \geq 0$

Figure 6.0-1 illustrates the functions.

We start from $\mathbf{x}^{(0)} = [1 \quad 1]^T$, where $f(\mathbf{x}^{(0)}) = -9$, but because $\mathbf{x}^{(0)}$ is an exterior point, SUMT first locates an interior **x** vector (nonfeasible with respect to $h_1(\mathbf{x})$) by minimizing the negative of $g_2(\mathbf{x})$ subject to $g_3(\mathbf{x})$ and $g_4(\mathbf{x})$, which are satisfied. A preliminary P function is formed.

$$P' = -g_2(\mathbf{x}) + r \sum_{i=3}^{4} \frac{1}{g_i(\mathbf{x})}$$

$$= -(10x_1 - x_1^2 + 10x_2 - x_2^2 - 34) + (1)\left(\frac{1}{x_1} + \frac{1}{x_2}\right) \qquad (a)$$

At $\mathbf{x}^{(0)} = [1 \quad 1]^T$, $-g_2(\mathbf{x}) = 16$, and $[(1/x_1) + (1/x_2)] = 2$, so that $P'(\mathbf{x}^{(0)}) = 18$.

The value of the augmented objective function of the dual problem (to be maximized) is

$$E = -g_2(\mathbf{x}) - r\sum_{i=3}^{4}\frac{1}{g_i(\mathbf{x})} = 14 \qquad (b)$$

The minimization of this preliminary P' function is carried out by Newton's method, as described in Sec. 3.3. The partial derivatives of P' are

$$\frac{\partial P'}{\partial x_1} = -10 + 2x_1 - \frac{1}{x_1^2}$$

$$\frac{\partial P'}{\partial x_2} = -10 + 2x_2 - \frac{1}{x_2^2}$$

$$\frac{\partial^2 P'}{\partial x_1^2} = 2 + \frac{2}{x_1^3}$$

$$\frac{\partial^2 P'}{\partial x_2^2} = 2 + \frac{2}{x_2^3}$$

$$\frac{\partial^2 P'}{\partial x_1\, \partial x_2} = 0$$

Consequently, the direction and step length to minimize P' are given by

$$\mathbf{s} = -[\nabla^2 \quad P']^{-1}\nabla P'$$

$$= -\begin{bmatrix} 4 & 0 \\ 0 & 4 \end{bmatrix}^{-1}\begin{bmatrix} -9 \\ -9 \end{bmatrix} = \begin{bmatrix} 2.25 \\ 2.25 \end{bmatrix} \qquad (c)$$

A step length of 2.25 is taken in each coordinate direction to give an interior $\mathbf{x}$ of

$$\mathbf{x}^{(0)\prime} = \mathbf{x}^{(0)} + \mathbf{s} = \begin{bmatrix} 3.25 \\ 3.25 \end{bmatrix} \qquad (d)$$

where all the inequality constraints are satisfied and $f(\mathbf{x}) = -20.25$.

Now the regular P function is formed,

$$P = f(\mathbf{x}) + \frac{h_1^2(\mathbf{x})}{\sqrt{r}} + r\left(\frac{1}{x_1} + \frac{1}{x_2} + \frac{1}{10x_1 - x_1^2 + 10x_2 - x_2^2 - 34}\right) \qquad (e)$$

that has a value of 529.716 at $\mathbf{x} = [3.25 \quad 3.25]^T$ for $r = 1$. The objective function to be maximized of the dual problem is

$$E = f(\mathbf{x}) - r\left(\frac{1}{x_1} + \frac{1}{x_2} + \frac{1}{10x_1 - x_1^2 + 10x_2 - x_2^2 - 34}\right) + 2rh_1^2(\mathbf{x})$$

and has the value of 1047.72 at $\mathbf{x} = [3.25 \quad 3.25]^T$.

First, the derivatives of P are evaluated at $\mathbf{x} = [3.25 \quad 3.25]^T$.

$$\frac{\partial P}{\partial x_1} = -46.505 \qquad \frac{\partial^2 P}{\partial x_1^2} = 69.084 \qquad \frac{\partial^2 P}{\partial x_1\, \partial x_2} = 84.525$$

$$\frac{\partial P}{\partial x_2} = -57.006 \qquad \frac{\partial^2 P}{\partial x_2^2} = 69.084 \qquad \frac{\partial^2 P}{\partial x_2\, \partial x_1} = 84.525$$

Because the hessian matrix of the P function is not positive definite inasmuch as the leading element is positive but

$$\det \begin{bmatrix} 69.084 & 84.525 \\ 84.525 & 69.084 \end{bmatrix} < 0$$

the search component directions are along the components of negative gradient of the P function. The vector $\mathbf{x}^{(0)\prime}$ is changed as follows:

$$\mathbf{x} = \mathbf{x}^{(0)\prime} + \Delta\mathbf{x}^{(0)}$$

as the initial step, or

$$\begin{bmatrix} 49.755 \\ 60.256 \end{bmatrix} = \begin{bmatrix} 3.25 \\ 3.25 \end{bmatrix} + \begin{bmatrix} 46.505 \\ 57.006 \end{bmatrix}$$

Subsequently, a Fibonacci search is executed to minimize the P function until the vector $\mathbf{x} = [3.516 \quad 3.577]^T$ is reached (the precision of the search is actually five decimals).

Again the partial derivatives are computed:

$$\frac{\partial P}{\partial x_1} = 6.119 \qquad \frac{\partial^2 P}{\partial x_1^2} = 99.613 \qquad \frac{\partial^2 P}{\partial x_1\,\partial x_2} = 100.628$$

$$\frac{\partial P}{\partial x_2} = 2.160 \qquad \frac{\partial^2 P}{\partial x_2^2} = 101.024 \qquad \frac{\partial^2 P}{\partial x_2\,\partial x_1} = 100.628$$

and again the hessian matrix of the P function is not positive definite because

$$\det \begin{bmatrix} 99.613 & 100.628 \\ 100.628 & 101.024 \end{bmatrix} < 0$$

Hence the negative gradient direction is used again to initiate a Fibonacci search until the $\mathbf{x}$ vector $\mathbf{x} = [2.137 \quad 4.702]^T$ is reached. The minimization of the P function continues in this fashion. At $\mathbf{x}$ vectors in which the hessian matrix is positive definite, Eq. (7.2–10) is used.

After 23 successive search directions, the value of $r = 1$ is reduced to $r = 0.25$. Values of the variables and the $f(\mathbf{x})$, $P(\mathbf{x},r)$, and $E(\mathbf{x},r)$ functions at each reduction in r are:

Stage no.	r	$E(\mathbf{x},r)$	$f(\mathbf{x})$	$P(\mathbf{x},r)$	x_1	x_2	$h_1(\mathbf{x})$
13	1	−32.990	−31.583	−29.400	1.150	4.918	-1.01×10^{-1}
23	1/4	−32.270	−31.807	−30.959	1.073	4.909	-2.53×10^{-1}
33	1/16	−32.065	−31.902	−31.547	1.037	4.904	-1.26×10^{-1}
42	1/64	−32.011	−31.948	−31.788	1.019	4.902	-6.34×10^{-2}
51	1/256	−31.997	−31.970	−31.895	1.010	4.900	-3.17×10^{-2}
55	1/1024	−31.993	−31.944	−31.944	1.006	4.899	-1.58×10^{-2}
62	1/4096	−31.993	−31.987	−31.969	1.004	4.899	-7.94×10^{-3}
68	1/16,384	−31.992	−31.990	−31.981	1.002	4.899	-3.95×10^{-3}

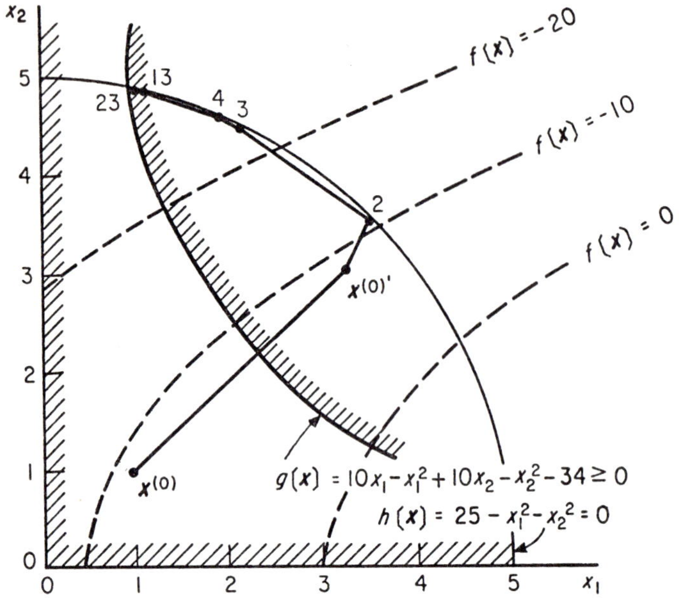

Fig. E7.2–1 Search trajectory for SUMT (numbers indicate sequence of stages in search).

Note the characteristic convergence of the values of the P and E functions to that of $f(\mathbf{x})$. Also note the upper bound provided by the P function and the lower bound provided by the E function. Within each stage there are various numbers of function and derivative evaluations ranging from 11 on the first stage to 4 on the last stage, the exact number depending on the preselected precision in the unidimensional search. Figure E7.2–1 illustrates the trajectory of the search.

SUPPLEMENTARY REFERENCES

Lagrange Multiplier Methods

Arrow, K. J., and L. Hurwicz: Gradient Methods for Constrained Optimization, *J. Operations Res. Soc.*, **5**:258 (1957).

Bard, Y., and J. L. Greenstadt: A Modified Newton Method for Optimization with Equality Constraints, in R. Fletcher (ed.), "Optimization," Academic, London, 1969.

Dorn, W. S.: On Lagrange Multipliers and Inequalities, *J. Operations Res. Soc.*, **9**:95 (1961).

Everett, H.: Generalized Lagrange Multiplier Methods for Solving Problems of Optimal Allocation of Resources, *Operations Res.*, **11**:399 (1969).

Falk, J. E.: Lagrange Multipliers and Nonconvex Programs, *Res. Analysis Corp. Tech. Paper* RAC-TP-335, November, 1968; Lagrange Multipliers and Nonlinear Programming, *J. Math. Analysis Appl.*, **19**:141 (1967).

Klein, B.: Direct Use of Extremal Principles in Solving Certain Optimizing Problems Involving Inequalities, *J. Operations Res. Soc.*, **3**:169 (1955).

Kuhn, H. W., and A. W. Tucker: Nonlinear Programming, *Proc. 2d Berkeley Symp. on Math. Statist. Prob.*, University California Press, Berkeley, Calif., 1951, pp. 481.

Takahashi, I.: Variable Separation Principle in Mathematical Programming, *J. Operations Res. Japan*, vol. 6, 1964.

Zwart. *J. Opt. Theory and Appl.*, **6**:150 (1970).

SUMT

Bracken, J., and G. P. McCormick, "Selected Applications of Nonlinear Programming," Wiley, New York, 1968.

Fiacco, A. V., and G. P. McCormick: "Nonlinear Programming: Sequential Unconstrained Minimization Techniques," Wiley, New York, 1968.

Lootsma, F. A.: Logarithmic Programming: A Method of Solving Nonlinear Programming Problems, *Phillips Res. Rept.*, **22**:329 (1967); Constrained Optimization via Penalty Functions, *ibid.*, **23**:408 (1968).

Pomentale, T.: A New Method for Solving Conditioned Maxima Problems, *J. Math. Analysis Appl.*, **10**:216 (1965).

Schmit, L. A.: An Integrated Approach to Structural Analysis and Synthesis, *AIAA J.*, **3**:1104 (1964).

Other Methods

Allran, R. R., and S. E. J. Johnsen: *Computer J.*, **13**:171 (1970).

Bellmore, M., H. J. Greenberg, and J. J. Jarvis: *Oper. Res.*, **17**:229 (1969).

Fletcher, R., and A. P. McCann: Acceleration Techniques for Nonlinear Programming, in R. Fletcher (ed.), "Optimization," Academic, London, 1969.

Haarhoff, P. C., and J. D. Buys: *Computer J.*, **13**:178 (1970).

Huard, P.: Resolution of Mathematical Programming with Nonlinear Constraints by the Method of Centers, in J. Abadie (ed.), "Nonlinear Programming," North Holland Pub. Co., Amsterdam, 1967.

Kelley, H. J., W. G. Denham, I. L. Johnson, and P. O. Wheatley, An Accelerated Gradient Method for Parameter Optimization with Nonlinear Constraints, *J. Astronautical Sci.*, **13**:166 (1966).

Kowalik, J., M. R. Osborne, and D. M. Ryan: A New Method for Constrained Optimization Problems, *Operations Res.*, **17**:973 (1969).

Lasdon, L. S.: An Efficient Algorithm for Minimizing Barrier and Penalty Functions, *Techn. Memorandum* No. 210, Operations Research Department, Case Western Reserve University, December, 1970.

Lootsma, F. A.: Boundary Properties of Penalty Functions for Constrained Minimization, National Technical Information Service, *Document* N70-33412, 1970.

Morrison, D. D., Optimization by Least Squares, *SIAM J., Numerical Analysis*, **5**:83 (1968).

Murray, W.: Constrained Optimization, *National Phys. Lab. Rept.* Ma 79, August, 1969.

———: Behavior of Hessian Matrices of Barrier and Penalty Functions Arising in Optimization, *National Phys. Lab. Rept.* No. NA 77, April, 1969.

Powell, M. J. D.: A Method for Nonlinear Constraints in Minimization Problems, in R. Fletcher (ed.), "Optimization," Academic, London, 1969.

Schwartz, L. E.: Large Step Gradient Methods, Chap. 8, in R. Fletcher (ed.), "Optimization," Academic, London, 1969.

Siddall, J. N., and J. F. McDonald: "OPTIPAC: The Designers Optimization Problem Solver," 2 vols., McMaster University, Mechanical Engineering Department, Hamilton, Ont., Canada, October, 1969.

PROBLEMS[1]

7.1 The problem is to

$$\text{Minimize:} \quad f(\mathbf{x}) = x_1^2 + 6x_1 + x_2^2 + 9$$

$$\text{Subject to:} \quad g_i(\mathbf{x}): \quad x_i \geq 0 \qquad \text{for } i = 1, 2$$

from the starting vector $\mathbf{x}^{(0)} = [1 \quad 0.5]^T$ by the SUMT method.

(*a*) Compute $r^{(0)}$ by Eqs. (7.2–2) through (7.2–4); which $r^{(0)}$ should be used?

(*b*) Formulate the function $P(\mathbf{x}, r^{(0)})$.

(*c*) Apply any unconstrained optimization procedure to obtain $\mathbf{x}^{(1)}$ and $f(\mathbf{x}^{(1)})$. How can you avoid jumping out of the feasible region?

(*d*) Repeat several sequences of the optimization.

(*e*) How many of the six conditions in Sec. 7.2–2 are satisfied? Which ones?

(*f*) Test for convergence on each cycle by the termination criteria in Sec. 7.2.

Hint: If the P function is convex, are the criteria satisfied?

7.2 Can the dual of Prob. 7.1 be formed? If so, solve the dual for several cycles. Examine the trend of the primal and dual solutions, and test the inequalities (7.2–9).

7.3 Repeat the steps of Prob. 7.1 for the following problems:

(*a*)
$$\text{Minimize:} \quad f(\mathbf{x}) = x_1^2 + x_2^2$$
$$\text{Subject to:} \quad h(\mathbf{x}) = x_1^2 + x_2^2 - 9x_2 + 4.25 = 0$$

(*b*)
$$\text{Minimize:} \quad f(\mathbf{x}) = e^{x_1} + e^{x_2}$$
$$\text{Subject to:} \quad h(\mathbf{x}) = x_1^2 + x_2^2 - 9 = 0$$
$$g_1(\mathbf{x}) = x_1 + x_2 - 1 \geq 0$$
$$g_2(\mathbf{x}) = x_1 \geq 0$$
$$g_3(\mathbf{x}) = x_2 \geq 0$$

[1] Additional problems suitable for this chapter can be found in the problem set at the end of Chap. 6 and in Appendix A.

7.4 Comment on the following proposed P functions suggested for use with the problem

Minimize: $f(\mathbf{x})$

Subject to: $g_i(\mathbf{x}) \geq 0, \qquad i = 1, 2, \ldots, m$

starting from a feasible point. The P functions are

(a) $P(\mathbf{x}, \mathbf{x}^{(k)}) = \dfrac{1}{f(\mathbf{x}^k) - f(\mathbf{x})} + \sum_{i=1}^{m} \dfrac{1}{g_i(\mathbf{x})}$

(b) $P(\mathbf{x}^{(k)}) = f(\mathbf{x}^{(k)}) - r^{(k)} \sum_{i=1}^{m} \ln g_i(\mathbf{x}^{(k)})$

What advantages might they have in comparison with Eq. (7.2–1)? What disadvantages?

7.5 Plot the contours of the Fiacco-McCormick penalty function for the following problem in two-dimensional space:

Minimize: $f(\mathbf{x}) = (x_1 - 3)^2 + (x_2 - 2)^2$

Subject to: $h(\mathbf{x}) = x_1 + x_2 - 4 = 0$

Use different values of r.

7.6 The problem of locating a piece of equipment relative to $n - 1$ other already fixed pieces of equipment in three-dimensional space can be expressed as

$$\text{Minimize:} \quad S = \sum_{i=1}^{n} c_j[(x_{1j} - x_1)^2 + (x_{2j} - x_2)^2 + (x_{3j} - x_3^2)]^{1/2}$$

where S = total cost

x_1, x_2, x_3 = coordinates of new facility relative to the origin

x_{1j}, x_{2j}, x_{3j} = coordinates of old facilities

The constraints are $3x_1 + 3x_3 \leq 30$ and $x_1, x_2, x_3 \geq 0$. For the listed c_j's and x_{ij}'s,

j	c_j	x_{1j}	x_{2j}	x_{3j}
1	1	0	0	0
2	1	10	0	0
3	1	10	10	0
4	1	0	10	0
5	1	0	0	10
6	1	10	0	10
7	1	10	10	10
8	1	0	10	10

do the following:

(a) Show that S is a convex function. {*Hint:* The linear sum of convex functions is a convex function; so show that $[(x_1 - a_1)^2 + (x_2 - a_2)^2 +$

$(x_3 - a_3)^2]^{1/2}$ is convex. Use Eq. (2.4–1) plus the Cauchy-Schwartz inequality

$$\left[\left(\sum_{i=1}^{3} x_i^2\right)\left(\sum_{i=1}^{3} y_i^2\right)\right]^{1/2} \geq \sum_{i=1}^{3} x_i y_i$$

and add $\theta^2 \sum_{i=1}^{3} x_i^2 + (1 - \theta)^2 \sum_{i=1}^{3} y_i^2$ to each side of (2.4–1). Or use the properties (*a*) or (*b*) associated with Eq. (2.4–2).}

(*b*) Show that the constraint is concave.
(*c*) Demonstrate that the conditions 1 through 6 of Sec. 7.2–2 are satisfied.
(*d*) Form the P function.
(*e*) Show that for $r^{(0)} = 100$, starting from the point $\mathbf{x}^{(0)} = [0 \quad 2 \quad 0]^T$, where $S = 86.540$, the first search along the gradient of $P(\mathbf{x})$ will yield $\mathbf{x}^{(1)} = [1.03 \quad 1.03 \quad 1.03]^T$, $P(\mathbf{x}) = 97.237$, and $S(\mathbf{x}) = 82.782$.
(*f*) What should the next value of r be?
(*g*) How many stages are needed to drop the values of the components of $\nabla P(\mathbf{x})$ below 10^{-2}? 10^{-4}?
(*h*) Show that the solution to the problem is

$$\mathbf{x}^* = [1/3 \quad 1/3 \quad 1/3]^T, \qquad P(\mathbf{x}) = 71.817, \qquad S(\mathbf{x}) = 71.816$$

7.7 Determine whether or not any of problems

6.17	6.25
6.18	6.27
6.20	

satisfy the conditions for convergence of SUMT.

7.8 Consider the following problem:

Minimize: $f(\mathbf{x}) = (x_1 - 2)^2 + (x_2 - 1)^2$

Subject to: $g_1(\mathbf{x}) = -\dfrac{x_1^2}{4} - x_2^2 + 1 \geq 0$

$h_2(\mathbf{x}) = x_1 - 2x_2 + 1 = 0$

(*a*) Form the Fiacco and McCormick P function for $r = 0.04$. Plot the P function if a contour-plotting routine is available.
(*b*) From an initial interior point $\mathbf{x}^{(0)} = [0.7489 \quad 0.5485]^T$ determine the search direction.
(*c*) Find the $\mathbf{x}^{(1)}$ vector.
(*d*) Can the $\mathbf{x}^{(k)}$ vector ever become an exterior point? Explain.

7.9 Convert the problems listed in Prob. 7.7 into penalty functions.

7.10 Compare the progress of the minimization for a few stages of the problem of Sec. 7.2–1 with the corresponding progress if the following generalized augmented functions are used instead:

(*a*) $P(\mathbf{x}^{(k)}, r^{(k)}) = f(\mathbf{x}) + \dfrac{1}{r^{(k)}} \sum_i [g_i(\mathbf{x}^{(k)}) - c]^2 + \dfrac{1}{r^k} \sum_i [h_i(\mathbf{x}^{(k)}) - c]^2$

(*b*) Equation (7.2–1*a*)
Choose *c* as some constant.

7.11 Compare the *P* function of Fig. 7.2–1 with that obtained from the three cases listed in Prob. 7.10. Plot the contours over the same range of x_1 and x_2 and answer the following questions for each method:
(*a*) Is there still a discontinuity at the boundary of the interior region?
(*b*) How will the starting point influence the trajectory of the search? Is an interior **x** vector still needed for each as the starting point?

7.12 The problem is

$$\text{Minimize:} \quad f(\mathbf{x}) = 4x_1 - x_2^2 - 12$$

$$\text{Subject to:} \quad g_1(\mathbf{x}) = 10x_1 - x_1^2 + 10x_2 - x_2^2 - 34 \geq 0$$

$$g_2(\mathbf{x}) = x_1 \geq 0$$

$$g_3(\mathbf{x}) = x_2 \geq 0$$

starting at $\mathbf{x}^{(0)} = [2 \quad 4]^T$.

Using a contour plotter, make a plot *A* of the contours of $f(\mathbf{x})$ in the region

$$0 < x_1 < 6$$

$$0 < x_2 < 6$$

Superimpose on this plot $g_1(\mathbf{x}) = 0$. Plot the contours of Eq. (7.1–7) with $\omega_i = 1$ and the following values of r: $r = 100, 1, 10^{-2}, 10^{-4}$ (four plots required: *B*1, *B*2, *B*3, and *B*4). For each r, minimize $P(\mathbf{x},r)$ from $\mathbf{x}^{(0)}$ using the Davidon-Fletcher-Powell code. Plot the trajectory of each search respectively on the *B* figures, and plot all four trajectories on figure *A*.

What can you conclude about the choice of $r^{(0)}$?

7.13 The power consumption of a heated stirred vessel is given by the relation

$$P = 2.63 \times 10^{-3} FsL^5 \left(\frac{n}{60}\right)^3$$

For Reynolds numbers (a dimension group incorporating the speed of rotation *N* and the diameter of the blade *L*) greater than 150, $F = (\mu/3750snL^2)^{0.05}$, and for Reynolds numbers smaller than 150, $F = 33.3/(3750snL^2/\mu)^{0.75}$.

Find the lowest power consumption to mix a vessel containing 6000 gal of a fluid for which $s = 0.8$ and $\mu = 200$.

Data: Assume for simplicity an 8-in. clearance between the impeller and the tank wall. The Reynolds number is defined as

$$\text{Re} = \frac{3750snL^2}{\mu}$$

The cost of the tank is \$100 per pound of metal, and the wall thickness must be at least $\frac{1}{4}$ in. up to a 6-ft height and $\frac{3}{8}$ in. for greater height. Assume capital charges per year of 0.25 of the cost of the tank and a power cost of \$0.01 per kilowatthour. The operating hours are 6000 per year.

Notation

F = empirical relation
L = impeller diameter, ft
n = impeller speed, rpm
s = specific gravity, dimensionless
μ = viscosity, lb/(ft)(hr)

7.14 A mathematical model of a chemical plant has been formulated as follows:

$$\text{Maximize:} \quad f(\mathbf{x}) = \frac{8400z - 2.2s - 1041.6(0.3x_5 + 0.0068d)}{6} - 10$$

where
$$z = 0.3x_5 - 0.02x_1 - 0.03x_2 - 0.01y_5 + 0.0068d$$
$$s = y_1 + y_2 + y_3 + y_4 + y_5 + y_6$$
$$x_5 = y_6 - 0.1y_4$$
$$d = (s - x_5 - y_5)x_3$$

$$\text{Subject to:} \quad x_1 - x_3y_1 - \frac{c_1y_1y_2}{s^2} = 0$$

$$x_2 - x_3y_2 - \frac{c_1y_1y_2}{s^2} - \frac{c_2y_2y_3}{s^2} = 0$$

$$-x_3y_3 + 2\frac{c_1y_1y_2}{s^2} - 2\frac{c_2y_2y_3}{s^2} - \frac{c_3y_3y_6}{s^2} = 0$$

$$-x_3y_4 + 2\frac{c_2y_2y_3}{s^2} = 0$$

$$-y_5 + 1.5\frac{c_3y_3y_6}{s^2} = 0$$

$$0.1y_4(1 - x_3) - y_6 + \frac{c_2y_2y_3}{s^2} - 0.5\frac{c_3y_3y_6}{s^2} = 0$$

where
$$c_1 = 5.9755(10^9)e^{-(12)(10^3)/(x_4+460)}$$
$$c_2 = 2.5962(10^{12})e^{-(15)(10^3)/(x_4+460)}$$
$$c_3 = 9.6283(10^{15})e^{-(20)(10^3)/(x_4+460)}$$

7.15 Galler and Gotas[1] proposed the following nonlinear programming problem for the cost of operating a trickling filter (the derivation of the problem can be found in the reference).

$$\text{Minimize:} \quad f(\mathbf{x}) = \left(\frac{2c_1\pi Wx_1x_2}{27} + \frac{2c_1\pi WFx_1}{27} + \frac{c_1\pi W^2x_2}{27} + c_2\pi x_1^2 + \frac{c_3\pi x_1^2x_2}{27} + 2c_4x_1 + \frac{x_3}{c_6 + c_7x_3}\right) + \frac{c_5S(8.34)(365)x_3(x_1 + 1)}{2.65p}$$

[1] W. S. Galler and H. B. Gotas, *J. Sanit. Eng. Div., Am. Soc. Civil Engr.*, SA1:163 (1966).

Subject to: $x_1 = \left[\dfrac{43{,}560(S + x_3)}{\pi Q}\right]^{1/2}$

$$K_1 \frac{(SL_i + x_3L_e)^{1.19}}{(S + x_3)^{0.78}(x_2 + 1)^{0.67}(x_1)^{0.25}} - L_e = 0$$

$$0 \leq x_3 \leq 4S$$

$$3 \leq x_2 \leq 10$$

$$\max\left\{10, \left(\frac{43{,}560(S + x_3)}{\pi Q}\right)^{1/2}\right\} \leq x_1 \leq 100$$

Find the minimum of $f(\mathbf{x})$ and find $\mathbf{x}^*$ based on the following data:

$c_1 = 80$	$K_1 = 0.219$
$c_2 = 4$	$W = 1$
$c_3 = 10$	$F = 1$
$c_4 = 53$	$S = 1$
$c_5 = 3.2 \times 10^{-4}$	$p = 0.7$
$c_6 = 5.55$	$\pi = 3.14159$
$c_7 = 0.01$	$L_i = 200$
	$L_e = 30$

7.16 Klein and Klimpel[1] described a nonlinear programming problem involving the optimal selection of plant sites and plant sizes over a period of time. The functions representing fixed and working capital were of the form

Fixed capital: Cost $= a_0 + a_1 S^{a_2}$

Working capital: Cost $= b_0 + b_1 P + b_2 S^{a_2}$

where S = plant size
P = annual production
a's, b's = known constants obtained empirically

Variable annual costs were expressed in the form of

$$\text{Cost} = P(c_1 + c_2 S + c_3 S^{c_4})$$

Transportation costs were assumed proportional to the size of the shipments for a given source and destination.

The objective function is the net present value, NPV (sum of the discounted cash flows), using a discount rate of 10 percent. All flows except capital were assumed to be uniformly distributed over the year; working capital was added or subtracted instantaneously at the beginning of each year, and fixed capital was added only the zero year.

[1] M. Klein and R. R. Klimpel, *J. Indus. Eng.*, **18**:90 (1967).

The continuous discounting factors were:

1. For instantaneous funds,

$$F_i = e^{-ry} \qquad (r = \text{interest rate, } y = \text{years hence})$$

2. For uniformly flowing funds,

$$F_u = \frac{e^r - 1}{r} e^{-ry}$$

The variable y may be positive (after year zero) or negative (before year zero) or zero (for year ending with point zero in time).

As prices and revenue were not considered, maximization of net present value was equivalent to minimization of net cost.

Let P_{ijk} be the amount of product shipped from location i ($i = 1,2,3,4$) to market j($j = 1,2,3$) in year k($k = 0,1,2,3$). Let S_i and $\bar{S}_1$ be, respectively, the size of plant in location i, and a variable restricted to 0 or 1, depending upon whether or not S_i is 0. Furthermore, let M_{ojk} be the market demand at center j in year k. Finally, for the sake of convenience, let P_{iok} denote the total production in plant i during year k.

The nonlinear programming problem is: Find S_i and P_{ijk} that will

$$\text{Maximize: } \sum_i \text{NPV (including shipping)}$$

$$\text{Subject to: } \sum_i P_{ijk} = M_{ojk}$$

$$S_i \geq 0_1, P_{ijk} \geq 0$$

Table A indicates how the net present value was determined for location 1; NPV relations for the other locations were similarly formed. Table B lists the overall objective function, and Table C lists (1) the 22 constraints, (2) one equation constraining the total plant capacity to be 10 million pounds per year, (3) nine equations requiring satisfaction of the three markets every year, and (4) 12 inequalities calling for plant production not to exceed plant capacity. In addition, there are the nonnegativity constraints applicable to all 40 variables. Thus the problem has 10 linear equality constraints and 52 inequality constraints.

Table A Net percent value

1. Contribution of Fixed Capital (Plant 1)

Year	*Fixed capital*	*Discount factor*	*Discounted cash flow*
0(1967)	$.7\bar{S}_1 + 1.5S_1^{.6}$	1.0517	$-.7362\bar{S}_1 - 1.5775S_1^{.6}$

2. Contribution of Working Capital (Plant 1)

Year end	*Working capital*	*Discount factor*	*Discounted cash flow at 10% discount rate*
0	$.4\bar{S}_1 + .2P_{101} + .05S_1^{.6}$	1.000	$-.4\bar{S}_1 - .2P_{101} - .05S_1^{.6}$
1	$.2(P_{102} - P_{101})$	.9048	$-.1810P_{102} + .1810P_{101}$
2	$.2(P_{103} - P_{102})$	.8187	$-.1637P_{103} + .1637P_{102}$
3	$-.4\bar{S}_1 - .2P_{103} - .05S_1^{.6}$	.7408	$+.2963\bar{S}_1 + .1482P_{103} + .0370S_1^{.6}$

3. Contribution of Operational Costs (Plant 1)

a. Cost tabulation (excluding shipping)

Year	*Amount*	*Depreciation**	*Other costs*
1	P_{101}	$.4667\bar{S}_1 + 1.0S_1^{.6}$	$.03\bar{S}_1 - .01S_1 + .05S_1^{.45} + .07S_1^{.6} + .1P_{101}$ $- .005P_{101}S_1 + .4P_{101}S_1^{-.55}$
2	P_{102}	$.1167\bar{S}_1 + .25S_1^{.6}$	$.03S_1 - .01S_1 + .05S_1^{.45} + .07S_1^{.6} + .095P_{102}$ $- .0048P_{102}S_1 + .38P_{102}S_1^{-.55}$
3	P_{103}	$.1166\bar{S}_1 + .25S_1^{.6}$	$.03S_1 - .01S_1 + .05S_1^{.45} + .07S_1^{.6} + .0903P_{103}$ $-.0045P_{103}S_1 + .361P_{103}S_1$

b. Discounted cash flow of costs (plant 1)*

Year	*Discount factor*	*Discounted cost flow at 10% discount rate*
1	.9516	$.1983S_1 + .0049\bar{S}_1 - .0247S_1^{.45} + .4221S_1^{.6} - .0495P_{101}$ $+ .0025P_{101}S_1 - .1979P_{101}S_1^{-.55}$
2	.8611	$.0348S_1 + .0045\bar{S}_1 - .0224S_1^{.45} + .0720S_1^{.6} - .0425P_{102}$ $+ .0020P_{102}S_1 - .1702P_{102}S_1^{-.55}$
3	.7791	$.0315S_1 + .0041\bar{S}_1 - .0203S_1^{.45} + .0651S_1^{.6} - .0366P_{103}$ $+ .0017P_{103}S_1 - .1463P_{103}S_1^{.55}$

4. Contribution of Shipping Costs (from Plant 1)

Year	*Discount factor*	*Shipping cost*	*Discounted cash flow at 10% discount rate*
1	.9516	$.8P_{121} + .5P_{121}$	$-.396P_{121} - .247P_{131}$
2	.8611	$.7P_{122} + .45P_{132}$	$-.313P_{122} - .201P_{132}$
3	.7791	$.6P_{123} + .4P_{133}$	$-.243P_{123} - .162P_{133}$

*Method of double rate-declining balance and straight-line crossover was used.

Table B The objective function

$$
\begin{aligned}
Z_{\max} = {} & -.5753\bar{S}_1 - 1.0313S_1^{.6} - .0685P_{101} - .0597P_{102} - .0522P_{103} + .0135S_1 \\
& - .0674S_1^{.45} + .0025P_{101}S_1 + .0020P_{102}S_1 + .0017P_{103}S_1 \\
& - .1979P_{101}S_1^{-.55} - .1702P_{102}S_1^{-.55} - .1463P_{103}S_1^{-.55} - .396P_{121} \\
& - .247P_{131} - .313P_{122} - .202P_{132} - .243P_{123} - .162P_{133} - .3428\bar{S}_2 \\
& - .8920S_2^{.6} - .0685P_{201} - .0597P_{202} - .0522P_{203} + .0135S_2 - .0809S_2^{.45} \\
& + .0025P_{201}S_2 + .0020P_{202}S_2 + .0017P_{203}S_2 - .2227P_{201}S_2^{-.55} \\
& - .1914P_{202}S_2^{-.55} - .1645P_{203}S_2^{-.55} - .396P_{211} - .495P_{231} - .313P_{212} \\
& - .448P_{232} - .243P_{213} - .405P_{233} - .3164\bar{S}_3 - 1.2987S_3^{.6} - .0942P_{301} \\
& - .0819P_{302} - .0712P_{303} - .0539S_3^{.45} + .0030P_{301}S_3 + .0026P_{302}S_3 \\
& + .0022P_{303}S_3 - .2227P_{301}S_3^{-.55} - .1914P_{302}S_3^{-.55} - .1645P_{303}S_3^{-.55} \\
& - .247P_{311} - .495P_{321} - .202P_{312} - .448P_{322} - .162P_{313} - .405P_{323} \\
& - .2441\bar{S}_4 - 1.3707S_4^{.6} - .0577P_{401} - .0504P_{402} - .0440P_{403} \\
& + .0020P_{401}S_4 + .0017P_{402}S_4 + .0015P_{403}S_4 - .1484P_{401}S_4^{-.55} \\
& - .1276P_{402}S_4^{-.55} - .1097P_{403}S_4^{-.55} - .495P_{411} - .099P_{421} - .040P_{431} \\
& - .448P_{412} - .090P_{422} - .040P_{432} - .405P_{413} - .088P_{423} - .041P_{433}
\end{aligned}
$$

Table C The constraints

(1) $S_1 + S_2 + S_3 + S_4 = 10$ (2) $P_{111} + P_{211} + P_{311} + P_{411} = 1$

(3) $P_{112} + P_{212} + P_{312} + P_{412} = 4$ (4) $P_{113} + P_{213} + P_{313} + P_{413} = 5$

(5) $P_{121} + P_{221} + P_{321} + P_{421} = 2$ (6) $P_{122} + P_{222} + P_{322} + P_{422} = 3$

(7) $P_{123} + P_{223} + P_{323} + P_{423} = 2$ (8) $P_{131} + P_{231} + P_{331} + P_{431} = 4$

(9) $P_{132} + P_{232} + P_{332} + P_{432} = 3$ (10) $P_{133} + P_{233} + P_{323} + P_{433} = 2$

(11) $P_{101} - S_2 \le 0$ (12) $P_{102} - S_1 \le 0$ (13) $P_{103} - S_1 \le 0$

(14) $P_{201} - S_2 \le 0$ (15) $P_{202} - S_2 \le 0$ (16) $P_{203} - S_2 \le 0$

(17) $P_{301} - S_3 \le 0$ (18) $P_{302} - S_3 \le 0$ (19) $P_{303} - S_2 \le 0$

(20) $P_{401} - S_4 \le 0$ (21) $P_{402} - S_4 \le 0$ (22) $P_{403} - S_4 \le 0$

8

Constrained minimization procedures: the flexible tolerance method

The general nonlinear programming problem is repeated here for convenience.

$$\begin{aligned} &\text{Minimize:} && f(\mathbf{x}) && \mathbf{x} \in E^n \\ &\text{Subject to:} && h_i(\mathbf{x}) = 0 && i = 1, \ldots, m \\ & && g_i(\mathbf{x}) \geq 0 && i = m + 1, \ldots, p \end{aligned} \tag{8.0–1}$$

where $f(\mathbf{x})$, $h_i(\mathbf{x})$, and $g_i(\mathbf{x})$ may be linear and/or nonlinear functions. In many nonlinear programming methods a considerable portion of the computation time is spent on satisfying rather rigorous feasibility requirements. The flexible tolerance algorithm,[1] on the other hand, improves the value of the objective function by using information provided by feasible points, as well as certain nonfeasible points termed *near-feasible points*. The near-feasibility limits are gradually made more restrictive as the search proceeds

[1] D. Paviani and D. M. Himmelblau, *Operations Res.*, vol. 17, 1969.

toward the solution of the programming problem, until in the limit only feasible $\mathbf{x}$ vectors in (8.0–1) are accepted. As a result of this basic strategy problem, (8.0–1) can be replaced by a simpler problem, having the same solution:

$$\begin{aligned} &\text{Minimize:} \quad f(\mathbf{x}) \qquad \mathbf{x} \in E^n \\ &\text{Subject to:} \quad \Phi^{(k)} - T(\mathbf{x}) \geq 0 \end{aligned} \tag{8.0–2}$$

where $\Phi^{(k)}$ is the value of the flexible tolerance criterion for feasibility on the kth stage of the search as defined by Eq. (8.1–1) below, and $T(\mathbf{x})$ is a positive functional of all the equality and/or inequality constraints of Problem (8.0–1) used as a measure of the extent of constraint violation and defined by Eq. (8.1–7) (in Sec. 8.1). Section 8.2 describes the strategy of the algorithm. Section 8.3 describes the procedure for obtaining either feasible or near-feasible points, and Sec. 8.4 describes the procedure for initiating the search. Although the flexible polyhedron search of Nelder and Mead (refer to Sec. 4.2) is used to implement the unconstrained searches in the flexible tolerance method because the method of Nelder and Mead is very effective, the particular unconstrained minimization technique used is independent of the flexible tolerance strategy. Thus any other effective unconstrained minimization algorithm could replace the method of Nelder and Mead, and the sequence of $\mathbf{x}$ vectors in the search would simply represent points in E^n, and not the vertices of a particular polyhedron.

8.1 DEFINITION OF Φ, $T(\mathbf{x})$, AND THE CONCEPT OF NEAR-FEASIBILITY

8.1–1 The Tolerance Criterion Φ

The tolerance criterion Φ is selected to be a positive decreasing function of the vertices of the flexible polyhedron in E^n; $\Phi^{(k)} = \Phi^{(k)}(\mathbf{x}_1^{(k)}, \mathbf{x}_2^{(k)}, \ldots, \mathbf{x}_{r+1}^{(k)}, \mathbf{x}_{r+2}^{(k)})$. The function Φ acts as a tolerance criterion for constraint violation throughout the entire search, and also serves as a criterion for termination of the search. Many alternative definitions of Φ are possible, but the one incorporated into the algorithm to be described is

$$\Phi^{(k)} = \min\left\{\Phi^{(k-1)}, \frac{m+1}{r+1}\sum_{i=1}^{r+1} \left\|\mathbf{x}_i^{(k)} - \mathbf{x}_{r+2}^{(k)}\right\|\right\} \qquad \Phi^{(0)} = 2(m+1)t \tag{8.1–1}$$

where
t = size of initial polyhedron
m = number of equality constraints
$\mathbf{x}_i^{(k)}$ = ith vertex of polyhedron in E^n

$r = (n - m)$ = number of degrees of freedom of $f(\mathbf{x})$ in Problem (8.0–1)

$\mathbf{x}_{r+2}^{(k)}$ = vertex corresponding to centroid as defined by Eq. (4.2–1), with $n = r$

$k = 0, 1, \ldots$ is an index referring to number of completed stages of search

$\Phi^{(k-1)}$ = value of tolerance criterion on $(k - 1)$st stage of search

Let the second term in the braces of expression (8.1–1) be denoted by $\theta^{(k)}$.

$$\theta^{(k)} = \frac{m+1}{r+1} \sum_{i=1}^{r+1} \left\| \mathbf{x}_i^{(k)} - \mathbf{x}_{r+2}^{(k)} \right\| = \frac{m+1}{r+1} \left\{ \sum_{i=1}^{r+1} \sum_{j=1}^{n} (x_{ij}^{(k)} - x_{r+2,j}^{(k)})^2 \right\}^{\frac{1}{2}} \tag{8.1–2}$$

where $x_{ij}^{(k)}$, $j = 1, \ldots, n$, are the coordinates of the ith vertex of the flexible polyhedron in E^n. Observe that $\theta^{(k)}$ represents the average distance from each $\mathbf{x}_i^{(k)}$, $i = 1, \ldots, r + 1$, to the centroid $\mathbf{x}_{r+2}^{(k)}$ of the polyhedron in E^n. To understand the behavior of $\Phi^{(k)}$ it is necessary first to understand the behavior of θ. It is obvious that the value of θ will depend on the size of the polyhedron in E^n, which may remain unchanged, expand, or contract, depending on which one of the four operations described in Sec. 4.2 is used to carry out the transition from $\mathbf{x}_i^{(k)}$ to $\mathbf{x}_i^{(k+1)}$. Thus $\Phi^{(k)}$ behaves as a positive decreasing function of $\mathbf{x}$, although $\theta^{(k)}$ may increase or decrease during the progress of the search, and as the solution of the problem is approached, both $\theta^{(k)}$ and $\Phi^{(k)}$ approach zero

$$\Phi^{(0)} \geq \Phi^{(1)} \geq \cdots \geq \Phi^{(k)} \geq 0 \tag{8.1–3}$$

In the method of Nelder and Mead, when it is not possible to find better values of $f(\mathbf{x})$ by Eq. (4.2–2), the vertices of the flexible polyhedron are drawn nearer and nearer to that vertex corresponding to the best value of the objective function. In the limit complete collapse of all the vertices of the flexible polyhedron takes place onto the stationary solution of $f(\mathbf{x})$. Thus, as the search approaches the stationary solution of $f(\mathbf{x})$, the value of $\theta^{(k)}$ given by Eq. (8.1–2) becomes progressively smaller because the average distance between the vertices and the centroid of the polyhedron shrinks to zero. Since on each kth stage of the search $\Phi^{(k)}$ is set equal to the smaller value of either $\Phi^{(k-1)}$ or $\theta^{(k)}$, the tolerance criterion $\Phi^{(k)}$ also collapses and in the limit,

$$\lim_{\mathbf{x} \to \mathbf{x}^*} \Phi^{(k)} = 0 \tag{8.1–4}$$

8.1-2 The Criterion for Constraint Violation $T(\mathbf{x})$

Consider now a functional of the equality and inequality constraints of Problem (8.0–1).

$$T(\mathbf{x}) = +\left[\sum_{i=1}^{m} h_i^2(\mathbf{x}) + \sum_{i=m+1}^{p} \mathcal{U}_i g_i^2(\mathbf{x})\right]^{\frac{1}{2}} \tag{8.1–5}$$

where $\mathcal{U}_i$ is the Heaviside operator such that $\mathcal{U}_i = 0$ for $g_i(\mathbf{x}) \geq 0$ and $\mathcal{U}_i = 1$ for $g_i(\mathbf{x}) < 0$. Therefore $T(\mathbf{x})$ is defined as the positive square root of the sum of the squared values of all the violated equality and/or inequality constraints of Problem (8.0–1). Note that $T(\mathbf{x}) \geq 0$ for all $\mathbf{x} \in E^n$ In particular, if $\sum_{i=1}^{m} h_i^2(\mathbf{x})$ is convex and the $g_i(\mathbf{x})$, $i = m + 1, \ldots, p$, are concave functions, then $T(\mathbf{x})$ is a convex function with a global minimum $T(\mathbf{x}) = 0$ for all feasible $\mathbf{x}$ vectors; i.e., for any $\{\mathbf{x} | h_i(\mathbf{x}) = 0, g_i(\mathbf{x}) \geq 0 \text{ for } i = 1, \ldots, p\}$. Also, $T(\mathbf{x}) > 0$ for all $\mathbf{x}$ vectors that are nonfeasible. For a given $\mathbf{x}^{(k)} \in E^n$, the value of $T(\mathbf{x})$ evaluated at $\mathbf{x}^{(k)}$ using Eq. (8.1–5) can be used to distinguish between feasible and nonfeasible points. If $T(\mathbf{x}^{(k)}) = 0$, $\mathbf{x}^{(k)}$ is feasible; if $T(\mathbf{x}^{(k)}) > 0$, $\mathbf{x}^{(k)}$ is nonfeasible. On the other hand, a small value of $T(\mathbf{x}^{(k)})$ implies that $\mathbf{x}^{(k)}$ is relatively near to the feasible region, and a large value for $T(\mathbf{x}^{(k)})$ implies that $\mathbf{x}^{(k)}$ is relatively far from the feasible region.

8.1-3 The Concept of Near-Feasibility

Near-feasible $\mathbf{x}$ vectors are those points in E^n that are not feasible, but nevertheless almost feasible, in the sense given below. To establish a clear-cut distinction between feasible, near-feasible, and nonfeasible points, let $\Phi^{(k)}$ be the value of Φ on the kth stage of the optimization search and let $\mathbf{x}^{(k)}$ be any vector in E^n. The $\mathbf{x}^{(k)}$ vector is said to be

1. Feasible, if $T(\mathbf{x}^{(k)}) = 0$
2. Near-feasible, if $0 \leq T(\mathbf{x}^{(k)}) \leq \Phi^{(k)}$
3. Nonfeasible, if $T(\mathbf{x}^{(k)}) > \Phi^{(k)}$

Thus the region of near-feasibility is defined as

$$\Phi^{(k)} - T(\mathbf{x}) \geq 0 \tag{8.1–6}$$

On any transition from $\mathbf{x}^{(k)}$ to $\mathbf{x}^{(k+1)}$, the move is said to be feasible if $T(\mathbf{x}^{(k+1)}) = 0$, near-feasible if $0 \leq T(\mathbf{x}^{(k+1)}) \leq \Phi^{(k)}$, and nonfeasible if

$T(\mathbf{x}^{(k+1)}) > \Phi^{(k)}$. Note that the value of Φ on the $(k + 1)$th stage of the search is determined only after $\mathbf{x}^{(k+1)}$ has been located as either a feasible or near-feasible point.

8.2 THE STRATEGY OF THE FLEXIBLE TOLERANCE ALGORITHM

In this section we demonstrate that the general nonlinear programming Problem (8.0–1) can be replaced by the easier problem of minimizing $f(\mathbf{x})$ subject to one gross inequality constraint as follows:

$$\begin{aligned} &\text{Minimize:} \quad f(\mathbf{x}) \qquad \mathbf{x} \in E^n \\ &\text{Subject to:} \quad \Phi^{(k)} - T(\mathbf{x}) \geq 0 \end{aligned} \tag{8.2–1}$$

The flexible polyhedron search of Nelder and Mead is a convenient and effective but not essential method of minimizing $f(\mathbf{x})$ as an unconstrained function when the constraint in (8.2–1) is not active, and is also used to minimize $T(\mathbf{x})$, as described in Sec. 8.3, to satisfy the single constraint in (8.2–1) when the constraint is active. The general strategy is to reduce $\Phi^{(k)}$ as the search progresses, thus tightening the region of near-feasibility, and to segregate the minimization of $f(\mathbf{x})$ from the steps taken to satisfy the constraint in (8.2–1). For a given value of $\Phi^{(k)}$, the value for $T(\mathbf{x})$ at $\mathbf{x}^{(k+1)}$ will be either (1) $T(\mathbf{x}^{(k+1)}) \leq \Phi^{(k)}$, in which case $\mathbf{x}^{(k+1)}$ is either a feasible or a near-feasible point and will be accepted as a permitted move, or (2) $T(\mathbf{x}^{(k+1)}) > \Phi^{(k)}$, in which case $\mathbf{x}^{(k+1)}$ is classed as nonfeasible, and an $\mathbf{x}$ vector closer to or in the feasible region must be found in lieu of $\mathbf{x}^{(k+1)}$. One way of getting an $\mathbf{x}^{(k+1)}$ closer to the feasible region is to minimize the value of $T(\mathbf{x}^{(k+1)})$ as defined by Eq. (8.1–5) until $T(\mathbf{x}^{(k+1)}) \leq \Phi^{(k)}$.

To demonstrate that the solution of problem (8.2–1) is equivalent to the solution of Problem (8.0–1), it is sufficient to consider the behavior of $\Phi^{(k)}$. Because $\Phi^{(k)}$ is a positive nonincreasing function such that $\Phi^{(k)} = 0$ only when it is no longer possible to improve the value of $f(\mathbf{x})$ in problem (8.2–1), the region of near-feasibility given by Eq. (8.1–6) is gradually restricted as the search proceeds toward the solution of problem (8.2–1). In the limit, that is, when all the vertices, $\mathbf{x}_i^{(k)}$, $i = 1, \ldots, r + 1$, of the flexible polyhedron in E^n have collapsed into one single point at $\mathbf{x}^*$, then $\Phi^* = 0$ and only $\mathbf{x}$ vectors that are feasible, that is, $\{\mathbf{x} | h_i(\mathbf{x}) = 0, g_i(\mathbf{x}) \geq 0 \text{ for all } i\}$, can satisfy the requirements of the inequality in Eq. (8.1–6). In other words, if $\Phi^{(k)} = 0$, since $T(\mathbf{x})$ cannot be negative, the only possible value for $T(\mathbf{x})$ is $T(\mathbf{x}) = 0$, which requires that all the constraints of Problem (8.0–1) be satisfied.

Because the tolerance criterion Φ is a positive nonincreasing function of the sequence of points $\mathbf{x}^{(0)}, \mathbf{x}^{(1)}, \ldots, \mathbf{x}^{(k)}, \ldots, \mathbf{x}^*$ generated during the progression of the search, because Φ does not depend on the value of the objective function nor on the values of the constraints, and because in the limit $\Phi^* = 0$, convergence of the algorithm is assured for the following reasons:

1. The manner in which Φ is computed by Eq. (8.1–1) prevents the tolerance criterion from increasing. If Φ were allowed to increase without bound, the possibility would arise of being able to improve the value of $f(\mathbf{x})$ at the expense of getting further and further away from the feasible region.
2. When the optimal solution of Problem (8.0–1) is an interior point (no equality constraints), convergence of the algorithm is assured because of the property of the flexible polyhedron of collapsing only when approaching the optimum of $f(\mathbf{x})$ in Problem (8.0–1). In these circumstances $T(\mathbf{x})$ has no effect on the convergence of the algorithm because, in the final stages of the search, $\mathbf{x}_i^k$, $i = 1, \ldots, r + 1$, are interior points yielding a $T(\mathbf{x}_i^{(k)}) = 0$, which implies that inequality (8.1–6) is satisfied for all $\mathbf{x}_i^{(k)}$ and that Problem (8.0–1) has not active constraints.
3. When the optimum of Problem (8.0–1) is not an interior point [either because $\mathbf{x}^*$ is a boundary point or because Problem (8.0–1) includes only equality constraints], convergence is assured because of the condition imposed by inequality (8.1–6), that is, $\Phi^{(k)} - T(\mathbf{x}) \geq 0$. The flexible polyhedron will not collapse as long as it is possible to find a better $f(\mathbf{x}_i^{(k)})$ such that $\Phi^{(k)} - T(\mathbf{x}_i^{(k)}) \geq 0$.

Let $\mathbf{x}_\ell^{(k)}$ be the vertex of the flexible polyhedron such that $\Phi^{(k)} - T(\mathbf{x}_\ell^{(k)}) \geq 0$; $f(\mathbf{x}_\ell^{(k)})$ is the best value of $f(\mathbf{x})$ obtained on the kth stage of the search. Let $\mathbf{x}_i^{(k+1)}$ be the vertices obtained during any reflection of $\mathbf{x}_h^{(k)}$ through the centroid of the polyhedron such that $\Phi^{(k)} - T(\mathbf{x}_i^{(k+1)}) \geq 0$. If $f(\mathbf{x}_i^{(k+1)}) > f(\mathbf{x}_\ell^{(k)})$ for every reflection of $\mathbf{x}_h^{(k)}$ through the centroid, the values of $\Phi^{(k)}$ will decrease because of contractions in the flexible polyhedron. In such a case, the values of $\Phi^{(k)}$ are reduced, and $\mathbf{x}_\ell^{(k)}$ must satisfy the constraints of Problem (8.0–1) more and more closely until the search is terminated because $\Phi^{(k)} \leq \varepsilon$.

On the other hand, if $f(\mathbf{x}_i^{(k+1)}) \leq f(\mathbf{x}_\ell^{(k)})$, the value of $\Phi^{(k)}$ will not decrease because no contraction of the polyhedron takes place and $\mathbf{x}_\ell^{(k)}$ is replaced by a better vertex. As long as it is possible to determine either a feasible or near-feasible point such that $f(\mathbf{x}_i^{(k+1)}) \leq f(\mathbf{x}_\ell^{(k)})$, there will be reflections and expansions of the flexible polyhedron. Thus premature termination of the search at a nonlocal optimum is avoided because the polyhedron will not collapse if there exists an $\mathbf{x}_i^{(k+1)}$ such that $\Phi^{(k)} - T(\mathbf{x}_\ell^{(k+1)}) \geq 0$ and $f(\mathbf{x}_i^{(k+1)}) \leq f(\mathbf{x}^* \pm \varepsilon)$.

One advantage of the flexible tolerance strategy typified by Problem (8.2–1) is that the extent of the violation of the constraints included in Problem (8.0–1) is progressively decreased as the search moves toward the solution of Problem (8.0–1). Because the equality and/or the inequality constraints are loosely satisfied in the early stages of the search, and more tightly satisfied only as the search approaches the solution of Problem (8.2–1), the overall computation effort required in the optimization is considerably reduced.

Another advantage of the flexible tolerance strategy is that $\Phi^{(k)}$ can be conveniently used as a criterion for termination of the search. For all practical purposes it is sufficient to continue the search until $\Phi^{(k)}$ becomes smaller than some arbitrarily selected positive number ε. In the final stages of the search, $\Phi^{(k)}$ is also a measure of the average distance from each vertex $\mathbf{x}_i^{(k)}$, $i = 1, \ldots, r + 1$, to the centroid $\mathbf{x}_{r+2}^{(k)}$ of the polyhedron in E^n. If $\Phi^{(k)} \leq \varepsilon$, a substantial number of the vertices $\mathbf{x}_i^{(k)}$ are contained in a hypersphere of radius ε. (If the last polyhedron of the search were regular, all the vertices $\mathbf{x}_i^{(k)}$ would be contained by the hypersphere of radius ε, but because the polyhedron is distorted, some vertices may be outside the sphere.) Therefore, if $\Phi^{(k)} \leq \varepsilon$, the chances are that the value of $f(\mathbf{x})$ cannot be improved without having to further reduce the size of the polyhedron. This implies that a change of 2ε in the $\mathbf{x}_i^{(k)}$ corresponding to the best value of $f(\mathbf{x})$, that is, $\mathbf{x}_\ell^{(k)}$, will not improve the value of the objective function. Hence, upon termination of the search, the following condition is satisfied:

$$f(\mathbf{x}_\ell^{(k)}) \leq f(\mathbf{x}^* \pm \varepsilon) \tag{8.2–2}$$

Since Eq. (8.1–6) is satisfied for every move, if $\Phi^{(k)} \leq \varepsilon$, it is obvious that the condition $\varepsilon - T(\mathbf{x}_\ell^{(k)}) \geq 0$ is also satisfied, or

$$T(\mathbf{x}_\ell^{(k)}) = \left[\sum_{i=1}^{m} h_i^2(\mathbf{x}) + \sum_{i=m+1}^{p} \mathscr{U}_i(\mathbf{x}) g_i^2(\mathbf{x}) \right]^{\frac{1}{2}} \leq \varepsilon \tag{8.2–3}$$

Equation (8.2–3) implies that, upon termination of the search, the combined value of all the violated constraints does not exceed ε. Certainly, no individual constraint can be violated by more than ε either.

Example 8.2-1 Flexible tolerance strategy

Consider the problem

$$\begin{aligned} &\text{Minimize:} \quad f(\mathbf{x}) = x_1^2 + x_2^2 \qquad \mathbf{x} \in E^n \\ &\text{Subject to:} \quad h_1(\mathbf{x}) = x_1^2 + x_2^2 - 9x_2 + 4.25 = 0 \end{aligned} \tag{a}$$

The contours of $f(\mathbf{x})$ and the locus of the points for which $h_1(\mathbf{x}) = 0$ are shown in Fig. E8.2-1. The solution of problem (*a*) is $\mathbf{x}^* = [0 \quad 0.5]^T$, at which $f(\mathbf{x}^*) = 0.25$ and $h_1(\mathbf{x}^*) = 0$. According to the flexible tolerance method, problem (*a*) is converted into

$$\begin{aligned} &\text{Minimize:} \quad f(\mathbf{x}) = x_1^2 + x_2^2 \qquad \mathbf{x} \in E^n \\ &\text{Subject to:} \quad \Phi^{(k)} - T(\mathbf{x}) \geq 0 \end{aligned} \tag{b}$$

where $T(\mathbf{x}) = [(x_1^2 + x_2^2 - 9x_2 + 4.25)^2]^{\frac{1}{2}}$. Note that $r = n - m = 1$ in this example, so that $r + 1 = 2$ vertices can be used in the search for the minimum of $f(\mathbf{x})$, but because the interpolation technique described in Sec. 8.3-2 requires three points, the number of vertices must always be ≥ 3; hence three vertices are used in the example. With ten variables and five constraints, only five vertices need be used.

We will present a detailed description of the operations involved in the first two stages for solving problem (*b*) to illustrate the strategy of the flexible tolerance algorithm. The

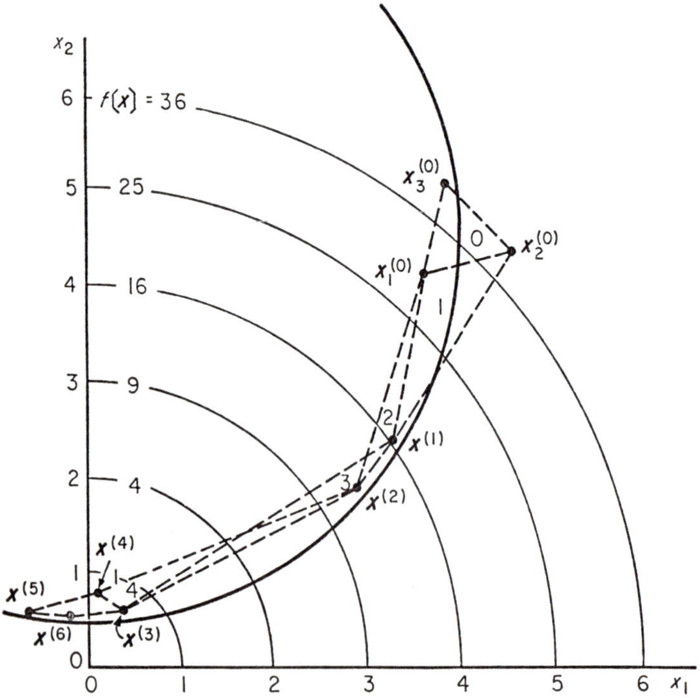

Fig. E8.2-1 Constrained minimization by the flexible tolerance algorithm.

starting vector is $\mathbf{x}^{(0)} = [4 \quad 4.5]^T$, and the size of the initial polyhedron is $t = 1$, which will yield a polyhedron with unit edges about $\mathbf{x}^{(0)}$ as the centroid. From Eq. (8.1-1), with $t = 1$ and $m = 1$, $\Phi^{(0)} = 4$. The vertices of the initial polyhedron are $\mathbf{x}_1^{(0)} = [3.592 \quad 4.092]^T$, $\mathbf{x}_2^{(0)} = [4.558 \quad 4.351]^T$, and $\mathbf{x}_3^{(0)} = [3.85 \quad 5.06]^T$. The corresponding values of $f(\mathbf{x})$ are $f(\mathbf{x}_1^{(0)}) = 29.64$, $f(\mathbf{x}_2^{(0)}) = 40.4$, and $f(\mathbf{x}_3^{(0)}) = 40.4$.

THE ($k = 0$) STAGE OF THE SEARCH

The vertex with the best value of $f(\mathbf{x})$ is $\mathbf{x}_\ell^{(0)} = \mathbf{x}_1^{(0)}$, at which $f(\mathbf{x}_\ell^{(0)}) = 29.64$, and the vertex with the largest value of $f(\mathbf{x})$ is $\mathbf{x}_h^{(0)} = \mathbf{x}_3^{(0)}$, at which $f(\mathbf{x}_h^{(0)}) = 40.4$. The value of $T(\mathbf{x}) = [(x_1^2 + x_2^2 - 9x_2 + 4.25)^2]^{\frac{1}{2}}$ at $\mathbf{x}_\ell^{(0)}$ is $T(\mathbf{x}_\ell^{(0)}) = 2.65$, and since $\Phi^{(0)} - T(\mathbf{x}_\ell^{(0)}) > 0$, inequality (8.1-6) is satisfied and $\mathbf{x}_\ell^{(0)}$ is accepted as a near-feasible point. It is not necessary to satisfy (8.1-6) for the other two vertices because, in the progress of the optimization, they are replaced by other vertices with better values of $f(\mathbf{x})$. From Eq. (4.2-1), the centroid of the residual vertices is $\mathbf{x}_4^{(0)} = [4.07 \quad 4.22]^T$. From Eq. (4.2-2) with $\alpha = 1$, the reflection of $\mathbf{x}_h^{(0)}$ through $\mathbf{x}_4^{(0)}$ yields $\mathbf{x}_5^{(0)} = [4.28 \quad 3.37]^T$.

Next, we compute $T(\mathbf{x})$ at $\mathbf{x}_5^{(0)}$: $T(\mathbf{x}_5^{(0)}) = 3.75$. Since $\Phi^{(0)} - T(\mathbf{x}_5^{(0)}) > 0$, $\mathbf{x}_5^{(0)}$ is near-feasible, and $f(\mathbf{x})$ is evaluated at $\mathbf{x}_5^{(0)}$, where $f(\mathbf{x}_5^{(0)}) = 29.6$. Because $f(\mathbf{x}_5^{(0)}) < f(\mathbf{x}_\ell^{(0)})$, from Eq. (4.2-3), with $\gamma = 2$, the next step is an expansion, which gives $\mathbf{x}_6^{(0)} = [4.49 \quad 2.52]^T$, at which $T(\mathbf{x}_6^{(0)}) = 8$. Since $\Phi^{(0)} - T(\mathbf{x}_6^{(0)}) < 0$, $\mathbf{x}_6^{(0)}$ is nonfeasible and is not acceptable; hence $T(\mathbf{x})$ is minimized starting with $\mathbf{x}_6^{(0)}$ until inequality (8.1-6) is satisfied.

The replacement vertex for $\mathbf{x}_6^{(0)}$ obtained by minimizing $T(\mathbf{x})$ is $\mathbf{x}_6^{(0)} = [3.32 \quad 2.40]^T$, at which $T(\mathbf{x}_6^{(0)}) = 0.59$, and therefore the replacement $\mathbf{x}_6^{(0)}$ is a near-feasible point. Next, $f(\mathbf{x})$ is evaluated at the near-feasible $\mathbf{x}_6^{(0)}$ to obtain $f(\mathbf{x}_6^{(0)}) = 16.8$. Since $f(\mathbf{x}_6^{(0)}) < f(\mathbf{x}_\ell^{(0)})$, $\mathbf{x}_h^{(0)} = \mathbf{x}_3^{(0)}$ is replaced by $\mathbf{x}_6^{(0)}$ and the $k = 0$ stage of the search is completed. The vertex $\mathbf{x}_6^{(0)}$ as shown in Fig. E8.2-1 becomes $\mathbf{x}^{(1)}$.

THE ($k = 1$) STAGE OF THE SEARCH

The vertices of the flexible polyhedron at the beginning of the ($k = 1$) stage of the search are $\mathbf{x}_1^{(0)} = [3.592 \quad 4.092]^T$, $\mathbf{x}_2^{(0)} = [4.558 \quad 4.351]^T$, and $\mathbf{x}^{(1)} = [3.32 \quad 2.40]^T$. Notice that only one vertex of the polyhedron is replaced per stage. The tolerance criterion $\Phi^{(1)} = 0.745$ is computed from Eq. (8.1-1). The vertices with the largest and smallest value of $f(\mathbf{x})$ are $\mathbf{x}_h^{(1)} = \mathbf{x}_2^{(0)}$ and $\mathbf{x}_\ell^{(1)} = \mathbf{x}^{(1)}$, and $f(\mathbf{x}_\ell^{(1)}) = 16.8$ and $T(\mathbf{x}_\ell^{(1)}) = 0.59$. Because $\Phi^{(1)} - T(\mathbf{x}_\ell^{(1)}) > 0$, inequality (8.1-6) is satisfied, and the search is continued. The centroid is $\mathbf{x}_4^{(1)} = [3.45 \quad 3.29]^T$. The reflection of $\mathbf{x}_h^{(1)} = \mathbf{x}_2^{(0)}$ through $\mathbf{x}_4^{(1)}$ yields $\mathbf{x}_5^{(1)} = [2.34 \quad 2.23]^T$, at which $T(\mathbf{x}_5^{(1)}) = 5.50$. Since $\Phi^{(1)} - T(\mathbf{x}_5^{(1)}) < 0$, $\mathbf{x}_5^{(1)}$ is nonfeasible and $T(\mathbf{x})$ is minimized, with $\mathbf{x}_5^{(1)}$ as the initial point.

The replacement $\mathbf{x}_5^{(1)}$ vertex is obtained at $\mathbf{x}_5^{(1)} = [3.1 \quad 2.1]^T$, at which $T(\mathbf{x}_5^{(1)}) = 0.64$. Since $\Phi - T(\mathbf{x}_5^{(1)}) > 0$, $f(\mathbf{x})$ is evaluated next to give $f(\mathbf{x}_5^{(1)}) = 14.01$. Because $f(\mathbf{x}_5^{(1)}) < f(\mathbf{x}_\ell^{(1)})$, according to Eq. (4.2-3), $\mathbf{x}_5^{(1)}$ is expanded to give $\mathbf{x}_6^{(1)} = [2.75 \quad 0.9]^T$, at which $T(\mathbf{x}_6^{(1)}) = 4.5$. Since $\mathbf{x}_6^{(1)}$ is nonfeasible, $T(\mathbf{x})$ is minimized starting at $\mathbf{x}_6^{(1)}$, and the replacement vertex $\mathbf{x}_6^{(1)} = [2.92 \quad 1.90]^T$ is obtained, at which $T(\mathbf{x}_6^{(1)}) = 0.71$, so that the replacement $\mathbf{x}_6^{(1)}$ is near-feasible. Because $f(\mathbf{x}_6^{(1)}) < f(\mathbf{x}_\ell^{(1)})$, $\mathbf{x}_h^{(1)} = \mathbf{x}_2^{(0)}$ is replaced by $\mathbf{x}_6^{(1)}$, and the ($k = 1$) stage is completed. The vector $\mathbf{x}_6^{(1)}$ becomes the $\mathbf{x}^{(2)}$ illustrated in Fig. E8.2-1.

The procedure described for the first and second stages of the search is continued for $k = 2, 3, \ldots$, replacing on each stage the vertex corresponding to the largest value of $f(\mathbf{x})$, with a new vertex obtained by carrying out the appropriate operations of the method of Nelder and Mead, until $\Phi^{(k)}$ computed from Eq. (8.1–1) becomes smaller or equal to a preselected number ε, in which case the search is terminated.

A detailed listing of each one of the steps involved in the flexible tolerance, together with a flow-diagram algorithm, is given in Sec. 8.4.

8.3 A PROCEDURE FOR FINDING FEASIBLE OR NEAR-FEASIBLE POINTS

It was pointed out in the preceding section that only feasible or near-feasible points are accepted in the search to improve the values of $f(\mathbf{x})$. If $\mathbf{x}^{(k)}$ proves to be a nonfeasible point with respect to the tolerance criterion Φ, a different $\mathbf{x}$ vector must be obtained, one that is close enough to the feasible region so that it qualifies as either a feasible or a near-feasible point. Either feasible or near-feasible points may be obtained by minimizing the function $T(\mathbf{x}^{(k)})$ with respect to the $\mathbf{x}$ vector until the inequality in (8.1–6) is satisfied.

To minimize $T(\mathbf{x})$ by the method of Nelder and Mead, it is necessary to build a new polyhedron at a nonfeasible $\mathbf{x}^{(k)}$. To avoid any confusion between the vertices of the polyhedrons in the procedure used to improve the value of $f(\mathbf{x})$ and the vertices of the different polyhedrons used to minimize $T(\mathbf{x})$, we will let the vectors $\mathbf{x}_i^{(k)}$, $i = 1, \ldots, r + 1$, stand for vertices of the polyhedron used to improve the value of $f(\mathbf{x})$ and the vectors $\hat{\mathbf{x}}_i^{(s)}$, $i = 1, \ldots, n + 1$, stand for vertices of the polyhedron used to obtain feasible or near-feasible points by minimizing $T(\mathbf{x})$. The sequence of $\mathbf{x}$ vectors generated in the minimization of $T(\mathbf{x})$ for each nonfeasible $\mathbf{x}_i^{(k)}$ will thus be represented by $\hat{\mathbf{x}}_i^{(0)}$, $\hat{\mathbf{x}}_i^{(1)}, \ldots, \hat{\mathbf{x}}_i^{(s)}, \ldots, i = 1, \ldots, n + 1$, where s is the index used to denote the number of completed stages during the minimization of $T(\mathbf{x})$. The starting point in any minimization of $T(\mathbf{x})$ is always $\hat{\mathbf{x}}^{(0)} = \mathbf{x}_i^{(k)}$, where $\mathbf{x}_i^{(k)}$ is the nonfeasible point on the kth stage of the search for the minimum of $f(\mathbf{x})$. The last vertex of the sequence $\hat{\mathbf{x}}_i^{(0)}, \hat{\mathbf{x}}_i^{(1)}, \ldots, \hat{\mathbf{x}}_i^{(s)}, \ldots$, is obtained when, for some $\hat{\mathbf{x}}_i^{(s)}$, $T(\hat{\mathbf{x}}_i^{(s)}) \leq \Phi^{(k)}$. When this happens, the nonfeasible vertex $\hat{\mathbf{x}}_i^{(k)}$ is replaced by the feasible or near-feasible vertex $\hat{\mathbf{x}}_i^{(s)}$, so that $\Phi^{(k)} - T(\mathbf{x}_i^{(k)}) \geq 0$, where $\mathbf{x}_i^{(k)} = \hat{\mathbf{x}}_i^{(s)}$.

The procedure for finding feasible or near-feasible points will be described in Sec. 8.3–3, after first discussing two essential techniques:

1. A technique to obtain the $(n + 1)$ vertices of an initial polyhedron in E^n (described in Sec. 8.3–1)
2. A technique to interpolate between interior and exterior nonfeasible points (described in Sec. 8.3–2)

8.3-1 A Technique to Obtain the $(n + 1)$ Vertices of an Initial Polyhedron in E^n

Let $\hat{\mathbf{x}}^{(0)} = \mathbf{x}_i^{(k)}$ be a nonfeasible point in E^n. To initiate the search to reduce the value of $T(\mathbf{x})$ using the unconstrained method of Nelder and Mead, $(n + 1)$ initial vertices, $\hat{\mathbf{x}}_i^{(0)}$, $i = 1, \ldots, n + 1$, that may or may not form a regular polyhedron in E^n, are required. The $(n + 1)$ vertices should be chosen in such a way that any subset of n vectors is linearly independent. For all practical purposes it is most convenient to build a regular polyhedron using $\hat{\mathbf{x}}^{(0)}$ as the base point. The $(n + 1)$ vertices of the initial polyhedron in E^n are found from

$$\hat{\mathbf{x}}_i^{(0)} = \hat{\mathbf{x}}^{(0)} + \mathbf{D}_i \qquad i = 1, \ldots, n + 1 \tag{8.3-1}$$

where $\mathbf{D}_i$ is a column vector in which the components are the elements of the ith column of the $n \times (n + 1)$ matrix $\mathbf{D}$, defined previously, in Sec. 4.2.

The search path followed, using the procedure of Nelder and Mead in the minimization of $T(\mathbf{x})$, depends upon the size and orientation of the initial polyhedron. When the size of the initial polyhedron is small compared with the size of the feasible region, the search path is nearly independent of the orientation of the initial polyhedron. For small values of t, the search path follows the direction of steepest descent with respect to the function $T(\mathbf{x})$ fairly closely, at least during the early stages of the search.

To illustrate the effect of the size of the polyhedron on the initial stages of the search, consider the constraint set (8.3-2) as illustrated in Fig. 8.3-1.

$$\begin{aligned} g_1(\mathbf{x})&: \; 9 - x_1^2 - x_2^2 \geq 0 \\ g_2(\mathbf{x}), g_3(\mathbf{x})&: \; x_1, x_2 \geq 0 \end{aligned} \tag{8.3-2}$$

The area within the shaded boundaries represents the feasible region. At any point in the feasible region, the value of $T(\mathbf{x}) = 0$, while $T(\mathbf{x}) > 0$ for any point outside the feasible region. The contours of $T(\mathbf{x}) = 12$, $T(\mathbf{x}) = 9.5$, and $T(\mathbf{x}) = 4$ in the nonfeasible region of interest are shown in Fig. 8.3-1 by dashed lines. Two equilateral triangles of different sizes are also shown in Fig. 8.3-1, having a common vertex at the nonfeasible point $\mathbf{x}^{(k)} = [1.2 \quad 3.4]^T$, at which $T(\mathbf{x}^{(k)}) = 4$. Using the method of Nelder and Mead, it takes only one stage to locate the feasible point $\hat{\mathbf{x}}^{(1)}$ starting with the larger triangle (two). It takes three stages to find the feasible point $\hat{\mathbf{x}}^{(3)}$ starting with the smaller triangle. The direction of steepest descent of $T(\mathbf{x})$ at $\mathbf{x}^{(k)}$ is $\mathbf{s} = [-0.4 \quad -0.9]^T$ and is also shown in Fig. 8.3-1. The smaller the size of the initial polyhedron, the more closely will the path of the search approach the direction of steepest descent. To prevent wandering in and out of the feasible region it is preferable that the search path followed in the minimization of $T(\mathbf{x})$ does not deviate too far from the direction of steepest descent of $T(\mathbf{x})$.

In the flexible tolerance algorithm the size of the initial polyhedron for the minimization of $T(\mathbf{x})$ at each stage k is calculated from the empirical relation

$$t = 0.05\Phi^{(k)} \tag{8.3-3}$$

where $\Phi^{(k)}$ is the value of the tolerance criterion on the kth stage as computed from Eq. (8.1-1). Keep in mind that the size of the polyhedron used to minimize $f(\mathbf{x})$ is fixed at an initial size at the start of the search for the minimum of $f(\mathbf{x})$, and is reduced only as the $\mathbf{x}$ vectors fail to improve $f(\mathbf{x})$.

In the early part of the search, the near-feasible points $\mathbf{x}^{(k)}$ are further from the boundaries of the feasible region than in the stages when the search is nearing completion. In Fig. 8.3-1 the set of $\mathbf{x}$ vectors for which $T(\mathbf{x}) = 0$ defines the feasible region and the set of $\mathbf{x}$ vectors for which $0 < T(\mathbf{x}) \leq \Phi^{(k)}$ defines the near-feasible region. The near-feasible region for $\Phi^{(k)} = 1$ is illustrated in Fig. 8.3-1 by the narrow annular area surrounding the feasible region. Note that the near-feasible region is wider for the linear constraints than it is for the nonlinear constraints.

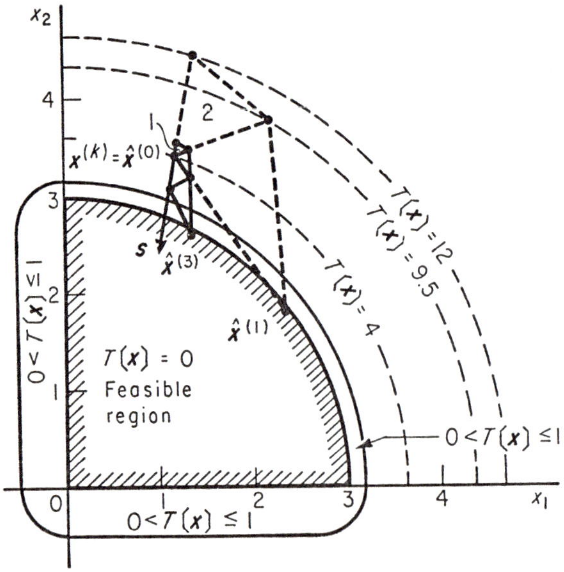

Fig. 8.3-1 Effect of the size of the initial polyhedron in the minimization of $T(\mathbf{x})$.

8.3-2 A Technique to Interpolate between Interior and Exterior Points

When Problem (8.0–1) contains *only* inequality constraints, the minimization of $T(\mathbf{x})$ by the method of Nelder and Mead can be inefficient, as illustrated by the following problem:

$$\begin{aligned} \text{Minimize:}\quad & f(\mathbf{x}) = -x_1 - x_2 \\ \text{Subject to:}\quad & g_1(\mathbf{x}):\ 9 - x_1^2 - x_2^2 \geq 0 \qquad (8.3\text{–}4) \\ & g_2(\mathbf{x}), g_3(\mathbf{x}):\ x_1, x_2 \geq 0 \end{aligned}$$

Figure 8.3–2 outlines the feasible region of (8.3–4) by the shaded area bounded by $g_i(\mathbf{x}) = 0$, $i = 1, \ldots, 3$, while the contours of $f(\mathbf{x})$ are represented by slanted broken lines. Assume that on the kth stage of the search, the vertices of the polyhedron used for the minimization of $f(\mathbf{x})$ are $\mathbf{x}_1^{(k)} = [0.7 \quad 0.7]^T$, $\mathbf{x}_2^{(k)} = [1 \quad 2.7]^T$, and $\mathbf{x}_3^{(k)} = [2.5 \quad 1.8]^T$, also shown in the figure. The values of $f(\mathbf{x})$ at these vertices are $f(\mathbf{x}_1^{(k)}) = -1.4$, $f(\mathbf{x}_2^{(k)}) = -3.7$, and $f(\mathbf{x}_3^{(k)}) = -4.3$. The reflection of $\mathbf{x}_1^{(k)}$ through the centroid of $\mathbf{x}_2^{(k)}$ and $\mathbf{x}_3^{(k)}$ by the procedure discussed in Sec. 4.2 gives the nonfeasible point $\mathbf{x}_5^{(k)} = [2.8 \quad 3.8]^T$.

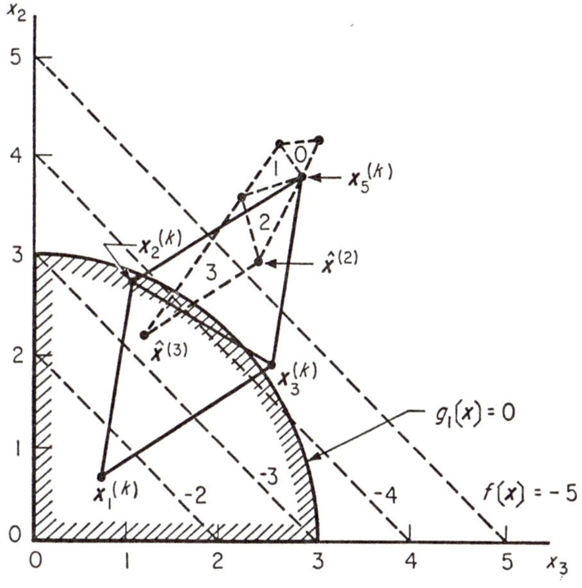

Fig. 8.3-2 Overshooting of the violated constraints by the method of Nelder and Mead.

After minimizing $T(\mathbf{x})$ by the unconstrained method of Nelder and Mead, the feasible point $\hat{\mathbf{x}}^{(3)} = [1.15 \quad 2.15]^T$ is obtained; refer to Fig. 8.3–2. The search path followed to determine $\hat{\mathbf{x}}^{(3)}$ is traced by the broken-line triangles numbered 0, 1, 2, 3. Since $\mathbf{x}_5^{(k)}$ was relatively far from the feasible region, the point $\hat{\mathbf{x}}^{(3)}$ proved to be deep inside the feasible region of Problem (8.3–4).

After replacing $\mathbf{x}_5^{(k)}$ by $\hat{\mathbf{x}}^{(3)}$, the latter now being designated $\boldsymbol{x}_5^{(k)}$ for clarity, $f(\boldsymbol{x}_5^{(k)}) = -3.3$ is obtained. Notice, however, that $\boldsymbol{x}_5^{(k)}$ is now the vertex with the largest value of $f(\mathbf{x})$; that is, $f(\boldsymbol{x}_5^{(k)}) = -3.3$, as compared with $f(\mathbf{x}_2^{(k)}) = -3.7$ and $f(\mathbf{x}_3^{(k)}) = -4.3$ for the other two vertices. As a consequence, $\boldsymbol{x}_5^{(k)}$ will be reflected through the centroid of $\mathbf{x}_2^{(k)}$ and $\mathbf{x}_3^{(k)}$ and a new nonfeasible point will be obtained. The alternating sequence of feasible and nonfeasible points may be repeated several times without substantially improving the value of $f(\mathbf{x})$. To alleviate this inefficiency, which is commonly experienced with inequality constraints, a quadratic interpolation can be carried out between interior and exterior points to find an $\mathbf{x}$ vector that is close to the boundary formed by the unsatisfied constraints. In Fig. 8.3–2 the violated constraint is $g_1(\mathbf{x})$.

Let $\hat{\mathbf{x}}^{(s)}$ be the interior point and $\hat{\mathbf{x}}^{(s-1)}$ the nearest exterior point obtained in the minimization of $T(\mathbf{x})$. With reference to Fig. 8.3–2, $\hat{\mathbf{x}}^{(s)} = \hat{\mathbf{x}}^{(3)} = [1.15 \quad 2.15]^T$ and $\hat{\mathbf{x}}^{(s-1)} = \hat{\mathbf{x}}^{(2)} = [2.35 \quad 2.9]^T$. Any point on the line segment from $\hat{\mathbf{x}}^{(s)}$ to $\hat{\mathbf{x}}^{(s-1)}$ is given by

$$\hat{\mathbf{x}} = \hat{\mathbf{x}}^{(s)} + \lambda^{(s)}\hat{\mathbf{s}} \qquad \text{for } 0 \leq \lambda^{(s)} \leq \lambda^* \tag{8.3–5}$$

where $\lambda^* = \left[\sum_{j=1}^{n} (\hat{x}_j^{(s-1)} - \hat{x}_j^{(k)})^2\right]^{\frac{1}{2}}$ represents the distance from $\hat{\mathbf{x}}^{(s)}$ to $\hat{\mathbf{x}}^{(s-1)}$, and $\hat{\mathbf{s}} = (\mathbf{x}^{(s-1)} - \hat{\mathbf{x}}^{(s)})/\lambda^*$ is the unit vector in the direction of $(\hat{\mathbf{x}}^{(s-1)} - \hat{\mathbf{x}}^{(s)})$.

Let $Z(\mathbf{x}) = \sum_{i=1}^{\hat{p}} g_i^2(\mathbf{x})$, where $\hat{p}$ is the total number of inequality constraints that are violated at $\hat{\mathbf{x}}^{(s-1)}$. Compute $Z(\mathbf{x})$ at $\hat{\mathbf{x}}^{(s)}$, at $\hat{\mathbf{x}}^{(s)} + 0.5\lambda^*\hat{\mathbf{s}}$, and at $\hat{\mathbf{x}}^{(s-1)} = \hat{\mathbf{x}}^{(s)} + \lambda^*\hat{\mathbf{s}}$, and let $z_1 = Z(\hat{\mathbf{x}}^{(s)})$, $z_2 = Z(\hat{\mathbf{x}}^{(s)} + 0.5\lambda^*\hat{\mathbf{s}})$, and $z_3 = Z(\hat{\mathbf{x}}^{(s-1)})$. Therefore z_1, z_2, and z_3 are the values of $Z(\mathbf{x})$ at three equally spaced points along the vector from $\hat{\mathbf{x}}^{(s)}$ to $\hat{\mathbf{x}}^{(s-1)}$. It is desired to find $\hat{\mathbf{x}}^*$ so that $Z(\hat{\mathbf{x}}^*)$ is nearly zero. The vector $\hat{\mathbf{x}}^*$ at which $Z(\hat{\mathbf{x}}^*)$ is nearly zero is given by

$$\hat{\mathbf{x}}^* = \hat{\mathbf{x}}^{(s)} + \left(\frac{\beta + \sqrt{\beta^2 - 8\alpha z_1}}{4\alpha}\right)\lambda^*\hat{\mathbf{s}} \tag{8.3–6}$$

where $\alpha = z_1 - 2z_2 + z_3$ and $\beta = 3z_1 - 4z_2 + z_3$. Equation (8.3–6) is obtained from writing a second-order approximation to $Z(\mathbf{x})$ in the interval defined by λ^*. Only the positive real roots of $(\beta^2 - 8\alpha z_1)^{\frac{1}{2}}$ are considered.

In the example illustrated in Fig. 8.3–2, $Z(\mathbf{x}) = (9 - x_1^2 - x_2^2)^2$, $\hat{\mathbf{x}}^{(s)} = [1.15 \quad 2.15]^T$, and $\hat{\mathbf{x}}^{(s-1)} = [2.3 \quad 2.59]^T$. Therefore $\lambda^* = 1.37$, $\hat{\mathbf{s}} = [0.837 \quad 0.548]^T$, and $\hat{\mathbf{x}}^{(s)} + 0.5\lambda^*\hat{\mathbf{s}} = [1.72 \quad 2.53]^T$. The three equally spaced values of z are $z_1 = Z(\hat{\mathbf{x}}^{(s)}) = 9.3$, $z_2 = Z(\hat{\mathbf{x}}^{(s)} + 0.5\lambda^*\hat{\mathbf{s}}) = 0.36$, $z_3 = Z(\hat{\mathbf{x}}^{(s-1)}) = 22$. Therefore $\alpha = 30.6$ and $\beta = 48.4$. From Eq. (8.3–6)

$$\hat{\mathbf{x}}^* = \begin{bmatrix} 1.15 \\ 2.15 \end{bmatrix} + 0.47 \times 1.37 \begin{bmatrix} 0.835 \\ 0.548 \end{bmatrix} = \begin{bmatrix} 1.68 \\ 2.50 \end{bmatrix}$$

The value of $Z(\mathbf{x})$ at $\hat{\mathbf{x}}^*$ is $Z(\hat{\mathbf{x}}^*) = 0.005$, and therefore $\hat{\mathbf{x}}^*$ may essentially be considered a boundary point. It is not necessary to determine the position of $\hat{\mathbf{x}}^*$ very accurately. If $T(\hat{\mathbf{x}}^*)$ as computed from Eq. (8.1–5) does not satisfy the feasibility requirements defined by (8.1–6), a new vector $\hat{\mathbf{x}}^*$ may be determined by stepping toward $\hat{\mathbf{x}}^s$ in the direction of $\hat{\mathbf{s}}$ until $T(\hat{\mathbf{x}}^*) \le \Phi^{(k)}$.

8.3–3 The Procedure for Finding Feasible or Near-feasible Points

The procedure for obtaining either a feasible or a near-feasible point can be summarized as follows:

1. Let $\hat{\mathbf{x}}^{(0)} = \mathbf{x}_i^{(k)}$ be a nonfeasible point in E^n and $\Phi^{(k)}$ be the value of the tolerance criterion determined by Eq. (8.1–1) on the kth stage of the search procedure. Let $t = 0.05\Phi^{(k)}$ be the size of the initial polyhedron for the minimization of $T(\mathbf{x})$ starting from $\hat{\mathbf{x}}^{(0)}$. Use the procedure described in Sec. 8.3–1 to determine the $(n + 1)$ vertices $\hat{\mathbf{x}}_i^{(0)}$, $i = 1, \ldots, n + 1$, that are required to initiate the minimization of $T(\mathbf{x})$. From Eq. (8.1–5), compute $T(\mathbf{x})$ at each one of the $(n + 1)$ vertices, that is, $T(\hat{\mathbf{x}}_i^{(0)})$, $i = 1, \ldots, n + 1$.
2. With $\alpha = 1$, $\beta = 0.5$, and $\gamma = 2$, use the procedure of Nelder and Mead to minimize $T(\mathbf{x})$. At the end of each stage s, compare the smallest value of $T(\hat{\mathbf{x}}_i^{(s)})$ for $i = 1, \ldots, n + 1$, that is, $T(\hat{\mathbf{x}}_\ell^{(s)})$, with the value of $\Phi^{(k)}$.
3. If $T(\hat{\mathbf{x}}_\ell^{(s)}) \ge \Phi^{(k)}$, either a feasible or near-feasible point has been determined. If $T(\hat{\mathbf{x}}_\ell^{(s)}) > 0$, replace the nonfeasible point $\mathbf{x}_i^{(k)}$ by $\hat{\mathbf{x}}_\ell^{(s)}$ so that $\mathbf{x}_i^{(k)} = \hat{\mathbf{x}}_\ell^{(s)}$ is either feasible or near-feasible and terminate the minimization of $T(\mathbf{x})$. If $T(\hat{\mathbf{x}}_\ell^{(s)}) = 0$ and $m = 0$, go to step 7 below.
4. If $T(\hat{\mathbf{x}}_\ell^{(s)}) \ge \Phi^{(k)}$, compute

$$\mathscr{A}^{(s)} = \frac{1}{n+1}\left[\sum_{i=1}^{n+1} \{T(\hat{\mathbf{x}}_i^{(s)}) - T(\hat{\mathbf{x}}_{n+2}^{(s)})\}^2\right]^{\frac{1}{2}} \qquad (8.3\text{–}7)$$

where $T(\hat{\mathbf{x}}_{n+2}^{(s)})$ is the value of $T(\mathbf{x})$ at the centroid of the polyhedron on the sth stage of the minimization of $T(\mathbf{x})$.

5. If $\mathscr{A}^{(s)} > 10^{-7}$, return to step 2 and proceed with the minimization of $T(\mathbf{x})$ on to the $(s + 1)$st stage.
6. If $\mathscr{A}^{(s)} \leq 10^{-7}$, the flexible polyhedron is about to collapse into a point without a feasible or a near-feasible point having been found. The procedure of Nelder and Mead may encounter difficulties when $\mathscr{A}^{(s)} \leq 10^{-7}$ if a large number of nonlinear equality and inequality constraints are involved in the definition of $T(\mathbf{x})$ at the vertices $\hat{\mathbf{x}}_i^{(s)}$ because $\mathscr{A}^{(s)} \leq 10^{-7}$. Under such conditions $T(\mathbf{x})$ turns out to be quite a complex function in the nonfeasible region. Let $\hat{\mathbf{x}}_\ell^{(s)}$ be the vertex corresponding to the lowest value of $T(\mathbf{x})$ obtained by the procedure of Nelder and Mead. Instead of terminating the search at $\hat{\mathbf{x}}_\ell^{(s)}$ without being able to find a feasible or near-feasible point, the algorithm then searches along each one of the directions parallel to the coordinate axis of $\mathbf{x}$ to determine the minimum of $T(\mathbf{x})$ as follows. Let $\hat{\mathbf{x}}_j^*$, $j = 1, \ldots, n$, be the minima of $T(\mathbf{x})$ along each respective direction parallel to the coordinate axis of x_j. From $\hat{\mathbf{x}}_\ell^{(s)}$, determine $\hat{\mathbf{x}}_1^*$ so that $T(\mathbf{x})$ is a minimum in the direction parallel to the coordinate of x_1, from $\hat{\mathbf{x}}_1^*$ determine $\hat{\mathbf{x}}_2^*$, and so on, until all $\hat{\mathbf{x}}_j^*$ for $j = 1, \ldots, n$, are determined. The technique used consists in determining the interval ℓ_0 that contains the minimum of $T(\mathbf{x})$ in the direction under consideration. Then a unidimensional search is carried out by golden section[1] until the size of the interval that contains $\hat{\mathbf{x}}_j^*$ is reduced to less than 1 percent of the value of $\Phi^{(k)}$. The purpose of carrying out the unidimensional searches is to locate a new point away from $\hat{\mathbf{x}}_\ell^{(s)}$ and then repeat the search, starting from step 1, with a larger initial polyhedron.

At the end of each unidimensional search in the directions parallel to the coordinate axis, a test is executed to determine if the new value of $T(\hat{\mathbf{x}}_j^*) \leq \Phi^{(k)}$, in which case $\mathbf{x}_i^{(k)}$ is replaced by $\hat{\mathbf{x}}_j^*$ and the minimization of $T(\mathbf{x})$ is terminated. If after searching in all coordinate directions a feasible or a near-feasible point still has not been found, the algorithm returns to step 1 and repeats the search, using the method of Nelder and Mead, once again starting with $\hat{\mathbf{x}}_n^*$, that is, the point at which $T(\mathbf{x})$ is a minimum in the direction parallel to the nth coordinate axis. If the procedure—steps 1 through 6—fails to find a feasible

[1] D. J. Wilde, "Optimum Seeking Methods," Prentice-Hall, Inc., Englewood Cliffs, N.J., 1962, p. 32.

or a near-feasible point three times in a row, the minimization is terminated as a failure.

7. If $T(\hat{\mathbf{x}}_\ell^{(s)}) = T(\mathbf{x}_i^{(k)}) = 0$, before returning to the minimization of $f(\mathbf{x})$, the interpolation described in Sec. 5.4–2 is carried out to make certain that $\mathbf{x}_i^{(k)} = \hat{\mathbf{x}}_\ell^{(s)}$ is not far from the boundaries of the constraints that were violated just prior to obtaining $\hat{\mathbf{x}}_\ell^{(s)}$.

8.4 HOW THE SEARCH IS INITIATED AND TERMINATED

This section describes the procedure whereby the search for the minimization of $f(\mathbf{x})$ is initiated. Recall that $(n + 1)$ vertices, where n is the total number of variables (dependent and independent) in Problem (8.0–1), are used in the minimization of $T(\mathbf{x})$, whereas $(r + 1)$ vertices, where $r = n - m$ is the number of degrees of freedom in Problem (8.0–1), are used in the minimization of $f(\mathbf{x})$. If $m = 0$, that is, when Problem (8.0–1) has no equality constraints, then $r = n$ and the minimization of $f(\mathbf{x})$ involves the same number of degrees of freedom as does the minimization of $T(\mathbf{x})$.

To initiate the search for the minimization of $f(\mathbf{x})$ using the flexible tolerance algorithm, one needs to know an initial $\mathbf{x}^{(0)}$, the size of the initial polyhedron t, the value of $\Phi^{(0)}$, and r. In order to start the minimization of $f(\mathbf{x})$ with the appropriate polyhedron size, t should be selected as a function of the expected range of variation of the variables $\mathbf{x}$. Usually upper and lower bounds on $\mathbf{x}$ are known, in which case the following equation can be used as a reasonable estimate of t.

$$t = \min\left\{\left[\frac{0.2}{n}\sum_{n=1}^{n}(U_i - L_i)\right], (U_1 - L_1), \ldots, (U_n - L_n)\right\} \tag{8.4-1}$$

where $(U_i - L_i)$ is the difference between the upper and lower bounds on the variable x_i. If upper and lower bounds of $\mathbf{x}$ are not known, a reasonable guess for t will have to suffice.

With the algorithm proposed in this study, nonglobal solutions are easier to avoid if the initial polyhedron is spread out widely over the topology of $f(\mathbf{x})$. The strategy of the algorithm does not depend on any local property of $f(\mathbf{x})$ nor on any combination of the properties of $f(\mathbf{x})$ and the constraints, such as in the gradient projection methods, for instance. In each stage of the search using the flexible tolerance algorithm, information for the next move is provided by the $(r + 1)$ vertices of the polyhedron in E^n. Therefore an important advantage of the proposed algorithm is that, in the beginning of the search, a large number of vertices are widely used to obtain information

START

Choose $\mathbf{x}^{(o)}$, t, α, β, γ, ϵ, and $\Phi^{(o)} = 2(m+1)t$.
Obtain $\mathbf{x}_i^{(o)}$, $i = 1, \ldots, r+1$, according to the procedure described in Section 5.5

$k = k + 1$

Is $T(\mathbf{x}_i^{(k)}) \leqslant \Phi^{(k)}$?

Minimize $T(\mathbf{x}_i^{(k)})$ so that $T(\mathbf{x}_i^{(s)}) \leqslant \Phi^{(k)}$. Let $\mathbf{x}_i^{(k)} = \mathbf{x}_i^{(s)}$. Compute $f(\mathbf{x}_i^{(k)})$.

Yes

No

Determine $\mathbf{x}_{r+2}^{(k)} = \frac{1}{r}\left[\left(\sum_{i=1}^{r+1} \mathbf{x}_i^{(k)}\right) - \mathbf{x}_h^{(k)}\right]$

Is $\Phi^{(k)} \leqslant \epsilon$?

Yes → STOP

No

Determine $\mathbf{x}_{r+3}^{(k)} = \mathbf{x}_{r+2}^{(k)} + \alpha(\mathbf{x}_{r+2}^{(k)} - \mathbf{x}_h^{(k)})$

Minimize $T(\mathbf{x}_{r+3}^{(k)})$ so that $T(\mathbf{x}_i^{(s)}) \leqslant \Phi^{(k)}$. Let $\mathbf{x}_{r+3}^{(k)} = \mathbf{x}_i^{(s)}$. Compute $f(\mathbf{x}_{r+3}^{(k)}.)$

No ← Is $T(\mathbf{x}_{r+3}^{(k)}) \leqslant \Phi^{(k)}$?

Yes

Determine $\mathbf{x}_{r+4}^{(k)} = \mathbf{x}_{r+3}^{(k)} + \gamma(\mathbf{x}_{r+3}^{(k)} - \mathbf{x}_{r+2}^{(k)})$

Is $T(\mathbf{x}_{r+4}^{(k)}) \leqslant \Phi^{(k)}$?

Yes

No

Minimize $T(\mathbf{x}_{r+4}^{(k)})$ so that $T(\mathbf{x}_i^{(s)}) \leqslant \Phi^{(k)}$. Let $\mathbf{x}_{r+4}^{(k)} = \mathbf{x}_i^{(s)}$. Compute $f(\mathbf{x}_{r+4}^{(k)})$.

Is $f(\mathbf{x}_{r+3}^{(k)}) < f(\mathbf{x}_h^{(k)})$?

Is $f(\mathbf{x}_{r+4}^{(k)}) \leqslant f(\mathbf{x}_l^{(k)})$

Yes

No

Is $f(\mathbf{x}_{r+3}^{(k)}) < f(\mathbf{x}_h^{(k)})$?

No ← Is $f(\mathbf{x}_{r+3}^{(k)}) < f(\mathbf{x}_s^{(k)})$?

Yes

No

Determine $\mathbf{x}_h^{(k)} = \mathbf{x}_{r+3}^{(k)}$

Determine $\mathbf{x}_h^{(k)} = \mathbf{x}_{r+3}^{(k)}$
$f(\mathbf{x}_h^{(k)}) = f(\mathbf{x}_{r+3}^{(k)})$

Yes

Determine $\mathbf{x}_h^{(k)} = \mathbf{x}_{r+3}^{(k)}$
$f(\mathbf{x}_h^{(k)}) = f(\mathbf{x}_{r+3}^{(k)})$

Determine $\mathbf{x}_{r+5}^{(k)} = \mathbf{x}_{r+2}^{(k)} + \beta(\mathbf{x}_h^{(k)} - \mathbf{x}_{r+2}^{(k)})$

Determine $\mathbf{x}_h^{(k)} = \mathbf{x}_{r+4}^{(k)}$
$f(\mathbf{x}_h^{(k)}) = f(\mathbf{x}_{r+4}^{(k)})$

Is $T(\mathbf{x}_{r+5}^{(k)}) \leqslant \Phi^{(k)}$?

No

Minimize $T(\mathbf{x}_{r+5}^{(k)})$ so that $T(\mathbf{x}_i^{(s)}) \leqslant \Phi^{(k)}$. Let $\mathbf{x}_{r+5}^{(k)} = \mathbf{x}_i^{(s)}$ Compute $f(\mathbf{x}_{r+5}^{(k)})$

Yes

Determine $\mathbf{x}_h^{(k)} = \mathbf{x}_{r+5}^{(k)}$
$f(\mathbf{x}_h^{(k)}) = f(\mathbf{x}_{r+5}^{(k)})$

Determine new values for $f(\mathbf{x}_i^{(k)})$, $i = 1, \ldots, r+1$

Is $f(\mathbf{x}_{r+5}^{(k)}) < f(\mathbf{x}_h^{(k)})$?

Yes

No

Determine $\mathbf{x}_i^{(k)} = \mathbf{x}^{(k)} + 0.5(\mathbf{x}_i^{(k)} - \mathbf{x}^{(k)})$, $i = 1, \ldots, r+1$

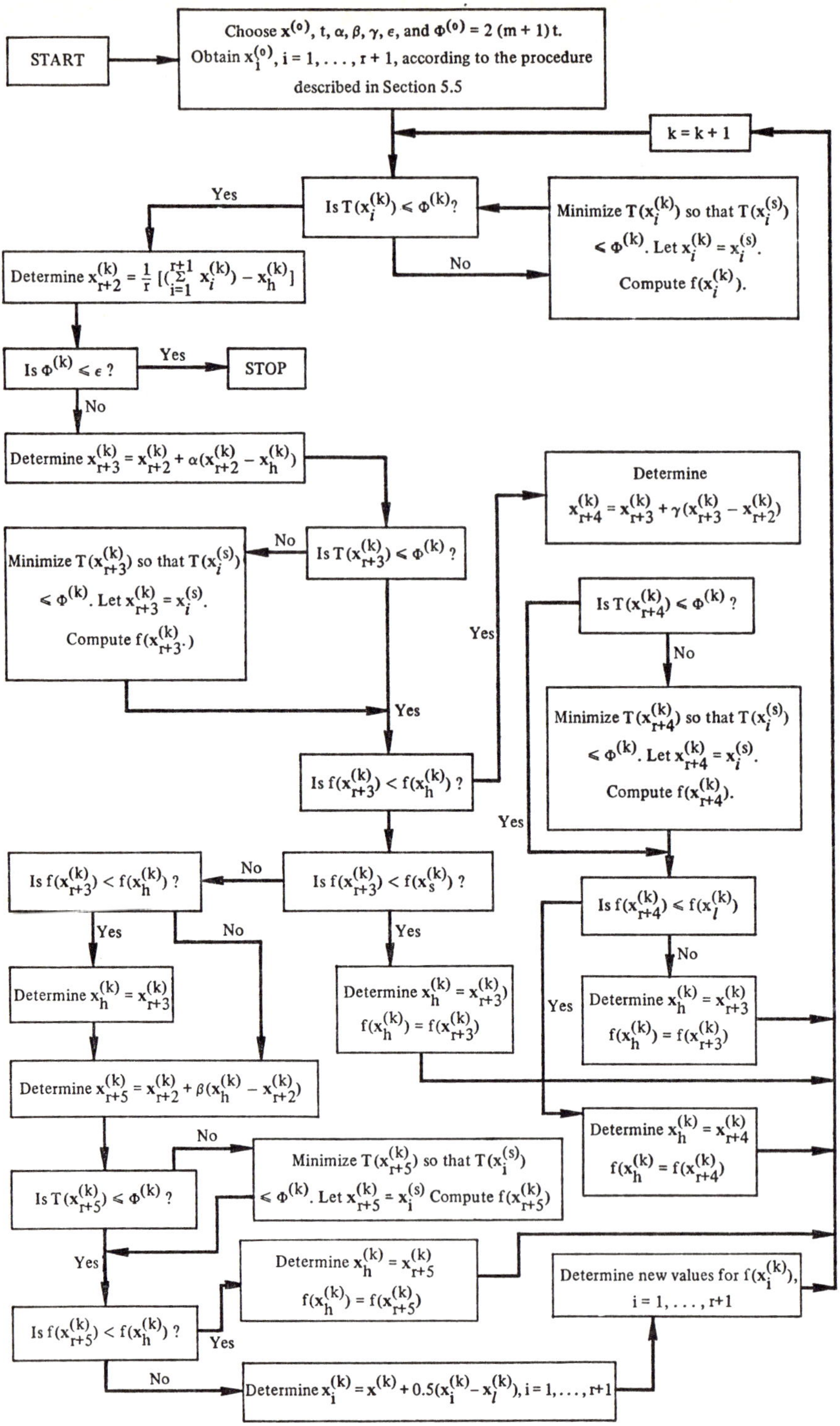

Fig. 8.4–1   Flow diagram of the flexible tolerance algorithm.

about $f(\mathbf{x})$, enhancing the chance that some $x_i^{(k)}$ will be found that leads to a local optimum that is better than any other local optimum. Computational experience with problems having many local optima demonstrates the effectiveness of the proposed algorithm in avoiding undesirable local optima. Of course, no general nonlinear programming procedure can *guarantee* that the local optimum obtained is the global optimum if the programming problem has several local solutions.

It is also advantageous to build the initial polyhedron with an $\mathbf{x}^{(0)}$ that is feasible or near-feasible. If the initial polyhedron is built far away from the feasible region, $(r + 1)$ vertices will have to be replaced by vertices closer to the feasible region.

The procedure for obtaining the vertices $\mathbf{x}_i^{(0)}$, $i = 1, \ldots, r + 1$, required to start the search is as follows. From (8.1–1) compute $\Phi^{(0)} = 2(m + 1)t$ and compute the value of $T(\mathbf{x})$ at the initial vector $\mathbf{x}^{(0)}$. If $T(\mathbf{x}^{(0)}) \leq \Phi^{(0)}$, then $\mathbf{x}^{(0)}$ is a feasible or near-feasible point and the initial vertices, $\mathbf{x}_i^{(0)}$, $i = 1, \ldots, r + 1$, are obtained from the procedure described in Sec. 8.3–1. If $T(\mathbf{x}^{(0)}) > \Phi^{(0)}$, $T(\mathbf{x})$ is minimized until a feasible or near-feasible $\mathbf{x}$ vector is obtained, and this $\mathbf{x}$ vector becomes the base point for building the initial polyhedron.

The algorithm terminates under two circumstances:

1. When $\Phi^{(k)} \leq \varepsilon$, in which case the search is considered completed and successful (this is by far the most common case).
2. When a feasible or a near-feasible point cannot be obtained by the procedure described in Sec. 8.3, in which case the search is terminated and the user is instructed to choose a different starting point $\mathbf{x}^{(0)}$ and/or a different set of parameters α, β, γ, t, and ε. Under normal conditions the values of $\alpha = 1$, $\beta = 0.5$, $\gamma = 2$, and $\varepsilon = 10^{-5}$ are recommended.

Figure 8.4–1 is an information flow diagram outlining the logic of the flexible tolerance algorithm. Appendix B contains a listing of a Fortran computer code.

Example 8.4–1 Flexible tolerance method

As an example problem we consider

$$\text{Minimize:} \quad f(\mathbf{x}) = 4x_1 - x_2^2 - 12$$

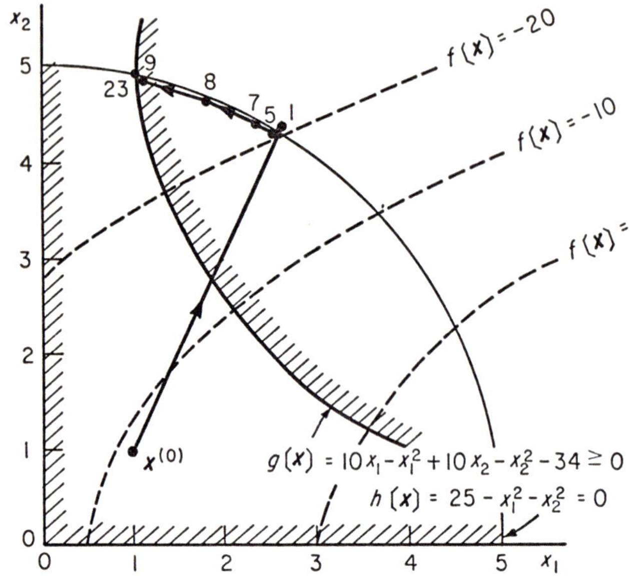

Fig. E8.4–1 Search trajectory for flexible tolerance algorithm (numbers indicate sequence of stages in search).

$$\text{Subject to:}\quad h_1(\mathbf{x}) = 25 - x_1^2 - x_2^2 = 0$$

$$g_2(\mathbf{x}) = 10x_1 - x_1^2 + 10x_2 - x_2^2 - 34 \geq 0$$

$$g_3(\mathbf{x}) = x_1 \geq 0$$

$$g_4(\mathbf{x}) = x_2 \geq 0$$

Figures 6.0–1 and E8.4–1 illustrate the objective function and constraints. For the starting vector we choose the nonfeasible point $\mathbf{x}_0^{(0)} = [1 \quad 1]^T$, and as the initial size of the polyhedron, $t = 0.30$. Consequently, the value of the initial-tolerance criterion $\Phi^{(0)}$ by Eq. (8.1–1) is

$$\Phi^{(0)} = 2(m + 1)t = 2(1 + 1)(0.30) = 1.20$$

At $\mathbf{x}_0^{(0)} = [1 \quad 1]^T$, the values of the unsatisfied constraints are

$$h_1(\mathbf{x}^{(0)}) = 23 \qquad g_2(\mathbf{x}^{(0)}) = -16$$

so that the value of $T(\mathbf{x}_0^{(0)})$ computed by Eq. (8.1–5),

$$T(\mathbf{x}_0^{(0)}) = [(23)^2 + (-16)2]^{1/2} = 28.02$$

is greater than the tolerance $\Phi^{(0)}$. Thus the first cycle of the algorithm is a search for a near-feasible $\mathbf{x}$ vector.

A polyhedron (an equilateral triangle with a side of length 0.06) of three vertices is constructed to initiate the minimization of $T(\hat{\mathbf{x}})$.

Vertex	$\hat{x}_1$	$\hat{x}_2$
1	1.000	1.000
2	1.057	1.015
3	1.015	1.057

Then $T(\hat{\mathbf{x}}) = [h_1^2(\hat{\mathbf{x}}) + \mathscr{U}_2 g_2^2(\hat{\mathbf{x}}) + \mathscr{U}_3 g_3^2(\hat{\mathbf{x}}) + \mathscr{U}_4 g_4^2(\hat{\mathbf{x}})]^{1/2}$ is minimized by the flexible polyhedron method discussed in Sec. 4.2, to yield the following sequence of vertices ($\mathscr{U}_i$ is the Heaviside operator):

New vertex	$\hat{x}_1$	$\hat{x}_2$	*Inequality constraints satisfied(?)*		
			$g_2(\hat{\mathbf{x}})$	$g_3(\hat{\mathbf{x}})$	$g_4(\hat{\mathbf{x}})$
4	1.110	1.110	No	Yes	Yes
5	1.072	1.221	No	Yes	Yes
6	1.243	1.381	No	Yes	Yes
7	1.253	1.683	No	Yes	Yes
8	1.600	2.154	No	Yes	Yes
7	1.794	2.993	Yes	Yes	Yes
8	1.426	1.918	No	Yes	Yes
9	2.584	4.356	Yes	Yes	Yes

(Recall that $\mathscr{U}_i = 0$ if the respective constraint is satisfied.) At $\hat{\mathbf{x}}_9^{(0)}$ the inequality constraints are all satisfied, so that the only constraint unsatisfied is $h(\hat{\mathbf{x}}_9^{(0)}) = 0.648$. Hence $T(\hat{\mathbf{x}}_9^{(0)}) = 0.648 < \Phi^{(0)}$, and $\mathbf{x}_0^1 = \hat{\mathbf{x}}_9^{(0)}$.

The algorithm now shifts to the minimization of the objective function $f(\mathbf{x})$. At $\mathbf{x}_0^{(1)} = [2.584 \quad 4.356]^T$, $f(\mathbf{x}_0^1) = 2.063$. A new simplex is constructed, and the series of vertices are:

New vertex	x_1	x_2
0	2.584	4.356
1	2.559	4.331
2	2.617	4.347
3	2.574	4.389

at which stage the tolerance criterion $\Phi^{(1)}$ given by Eq. (8.1-1), $\Phi^{(1)} = \min\{1.20, 0.0447\} = 0.0447$, is violated by the value of $T(\mathbf{x}_3^{(1)})$. Consequently, the search for a near-feasible point commences again from $\hat{\mathbf{x}}_0^{(2)} = \mathbf{x}_3^{(1)} = [2.574 \quad 4.389]^T$.

Subsequent searches are merely repetitions of the above two phases, details of which will be omitted. Table E8.4-1 summarizes the main steps in the progress of the algorithm (the numbers are truncated). In the last ten stages it appears as if little progress is being made in $\mathbf{x}$ or $f(\mathbf{x})$, but actually, what is happening is that the equality constraint becomes successively more closely satisfied. Figure E8.4-1 illustrates the trajectory of the search. Note how the search hugs the equality constraint.

Table E8.4-1

Stage	x_1	x_2	$f(\mathbf{x})$	ϕ	$h_1(\mathbf{x})$
1	2.574	4.389	−20.966	4.47×10^{-2}	-8.94×10^{-1}
2	2.600	4.274	−19.867	7.13×10^{-3}	-3.01×10^{-2}
3	2.599	4.270	−19.836	6.33×10^{-3}	6.68×10^{-3}
4	2.578	4.284	−20.041	1.22×10^{-3}	-6.74×10^{-4}
5	2.549	4.301	−20.029	6.33×10^{-3}	6.33×10^{-4}
6	2.457	4.355	−21.137	6.33×10^{-3}	-2.06×10^{-4}
7	2.278	4.451	−22.703	6.33×10^{-3}	-5.42×10^{-3}
8	1.814	4.659	−26.457	6.22×10^{-3}	-6.05×10^{-3}
9	1.059	4.886	−31.636	6.33×10^{-3}	4.79×10^{-3}
10	1.015	4.896	−31.916	6.33×10^{-3}	-3.64×10^{-3}
11	1.015	4.896	−31.916	6.33×10^{-3}	-3.64×10^{-3}
12	1.003	4.898	−31.983	6.33×10^{-3}	-1.77×10^{-3}
13	1.003	4.898	−31.983	6.33×10^{-3}	-1.77×10^{-3}
14	1.003	4.898	−31.983	6.33×10^{-3}	-1.77×10^{-3}
15	1.002	4.899	−31.989	2.24×10^{-3}	-2.03×10^{-4}
16	1.001	4.899	−31.993	1.11×10^{-3}	-1.43×10^{-3}
17	1.001	4.899	−31.992	2.43×10^{-4}	-7.01×10^{-4}
18	1.001	4.899	−31.991	2.43×10^{-4}	6.59×10^{-5}
19	1.001	4.898	−31.991	3.95×10^{-5}	7.69×10^{-5}
20	1.001	4.898	−31.992	3.95×10^{-5}	-3.34×10^{-5}
21	1.001	4.898	−31.992	3.95×10^{-5}	-3.50×10^{-5}
22	1.001	4.898	−31.992	1.00×10^{-5}	-3.50×10^{-5}
23	1.001	4.989	−31.992	8.82×10^{-6}	5.53×10^{-6}

8.5 TECHNIQUES TO HANDLE PROGRAMMING PROBLEMS THAT ARE NOT DEFINED FOR CERTAIN x VECTORS IN E^n

There are instances in which the objective function or perhaps some of the constraints are not defined over some portion of E^n. To avoid premature termination of the search in such cases, it is necessary to reformulate the problem so as to prohibit the selection of any $\mathbf{x}$ vector for which functions are not defined in the programming problem. As an illustration consider the problem

$$\text{Minimize:} \quad f(\mathbf{x}) = (x_1^2 + x_2^2 - 4x_2 - 45)^{0.5} + [\ln x_1(x_2 - 2)]^2 \qquad \mathbf{x} \in E^n \qquad (8.5\text{–}1)$$

$$\text{Subject to:} \quad g_1(\mathbf{x}): \ 64 - x_1^2 - x_2^2 \geq 0$$

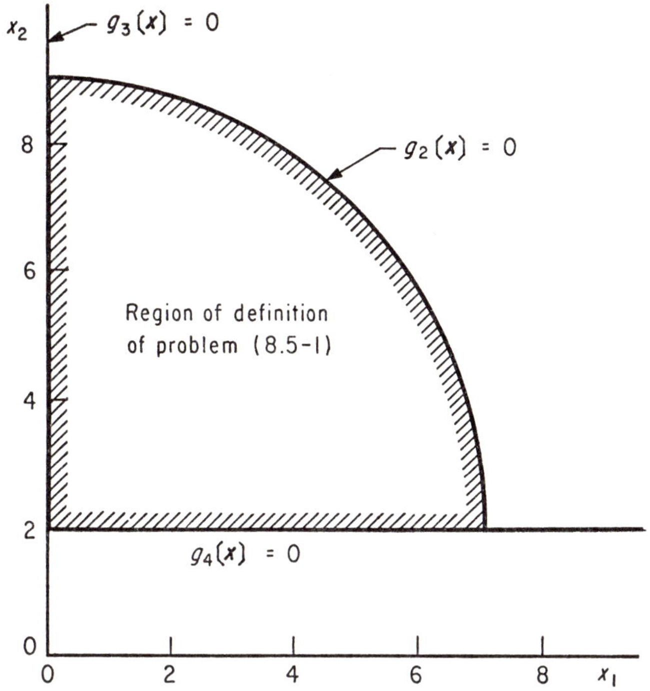

Fig. 8.5–1 Geometric interpretation of the region of definition of Problem (8.5–1).

Since it is not possible to raise a negative base to a noninteger power nor to obtain the logarithm of negative numbers, the objective function of Problem (8.5–1) is not defined for any **x** vector at which either $(x_1^2 + x_2^2 - 4x - 45) < 0$, $x_1 < 0$, or $(x_2 - 2) < 0$. The shaded area of Fig. 8.5–1, bounded by the circle $g_2(\mathbf{x})$: $(x_1^2 + x_2^2 - 4x_2 - 45) = 0$ and by the straight lines $g_3(\mathbf{x})$: $x_1 = 0$ and $g_4(\mathbf{x})$: $x_2 - 2 = 0$, shows the region in which all the functions of Problem (8.5–1) are defined. Note that a considerable portion of the feasible region defined by $g_1(\mathbf{x}) \geq 0$ is eliminated because of the restrictions in the objective function of Problem (8.5–1). Test Problems 4, 9, and 17 in Appendix A provide other examples in which certain functions can become undefined.

If the proposed algorithm is to be used to solve programming problems in general, it is necessary to transform the problem so as to avoid selecting any **x** vector at which the problem functions are not defined. One recommended procedure is to transform the variables in the problem in such a way as to eliminate the undefined region. For example, if the variables x_1 and x_2 in

Problem (8.5–1) are transformed as follows:

$$x_1 = 7 + e^{z_1}$$

$$x_2 = 2 + e^{z_2}$$

where **z** is a new vector of variables, the introduction of these new variables into Problem (8.5–1) gives

$$\text{Minimize:}\quad f(\mathbf{z}) = (e^{2z_1} + 14e^{z_1} + e^{2z_2})^{0.5} + [\ln(8 + e^{z_1})e^{z_2}]^2 \qquad \mathbf{z} \in E^n \qquad (8.5\text{–}2)$$

$$\text{Subject to:}\quad g_1(\mathbf{z}):\quad 11 - 14e^{z_1} - e^{2z_1} - 4e^{z_2} - e^{2z_2} \geq 0$$

where $f(\mathbf{z})$ is now defined for any **z**. The transformed Problems (8.5–2) is now in suitable form and can be solved using the flexible tolerance algorithm. After the optimal solution $\mathbf{z}^*$ of Problem (8.5–2) is obtained, the value of **x** is computed from the transformation equations.

In large problems it may be rather difficult to find the appropriate transformation as illustrated above. In such cases, the following procedure is recommended.

When *only* the objective function is not defined over some portions of the **x** domain, each of the terms in $f(\mathbf{x})$ whose arguments make $f(\mathbf{x})$ undefined requires an additional inequality constraint added to the problem, written in the following manner:

$$g_{p+i}(\mathbf{x}):\quad F_{p+i}(\mathbf{x}) - \Phi^{(k)} \geq 0 \qquad i = p + 1, \ldots, p + q \qquad (8.5\text{–}3)$$

where $F_{p+i}(\mathbf{x})$ is the ith argument, and q is the total number of such arguments in $f(\mathbf{x})$. The additional constraints defined by (8.5–3) are added to the p constraints of the programming problem under consideration, and the amended problem is solved in the usual manner. The effect of subtracting $\Phi^{(k)}$ from each one of the functions $F_{p+i}(\mathbf{x})$ is to eliminate the **x** vectors for which $F_{p+i}(\mathbf{x}) < 0$ when inequality (8.1–6) is satisfied. In this manner inequality (8.1–6) can be satisfied only if $F_{p+i}(\mathbf{x}) \geq 0$ for $i = p + 1, \ldots, p + q$.

By way of further explanation, assume first that one of the arguments of $f(\mathbf{x})$ evaluated at **x** is such that $-F_{p+i}(\mathbf{x}) > 0$; that is, $F_{p+i}(\mathbf{x}) < 0$. Since $\Phi^{(k)} \geq 0$ by definition, the $g_{p+i}(\mathbf{x})$ constraint in (8.5–3) is negative, that is, $g_{p+i}(\mathbf{x}) = F_{p+i}(\mathbf{x}) - \Phi^{(k)} < 0$. Assume further all the other constraints, $h_i(\mathbf{x}) = 0$, $i = 1, \ldots, m$, $g_i(\mathbf{x}) \geq 0$, $i = m + 1, \ldots, p + i - 1, p + i + 1, \ldots, p + q$. Therefore $T(\mathbf{x}) = +[(-F_{p+i}(\mathbf{x}) - \Phi^{(k)})^2]^{1/2} = F_{p+i}(\mathbf{x}) + \Phi^{(k)}$. Since $T(\mathbf{x}) > \Phi^{(k)}$, inequality (8.1–6) is not satisfied, and it is necessary to minimize $T(\mathbf{x})$ until $F_{p+i}(\mathbf{x}) \geq 0$.

It is apparent from the definition of $T(\mathbf{x})$ that any $0 \leq F_{p+i}(\mathbf{x}) < \Phi^{(k)}$ satisfies inequality (8.1–6), even though $g_{p+i}(\mathbf{x}) < 0$. For $F_{p+i}(\mathbf{x}) \geq \Phi^{(k)}$, $g_{p+i}(\mathbf{x}) > 0$, and will have no effect in $T(\mathbf{x})$. The same reasoning is true when several constraints $h_i(\mathbf{x})$, $i = 1, \ldots, m$, and/or $g_i(\mathbf{x})$, $i = m + 1, \ldots, p + q$, are not satisfied at $\mathbf{x}$, because all the violated constraints are included in the definition of $T(\mathbf{x})$. Addition of the constraints given by (8.5–3) to the constraints in the general programming Problem (8.0–1) leads to a definition of $T(\mathbf{x})$ as follows:

$$T(\mathbf{x}) = +\left[\sum_{i=1}^{m} h_i^2(\mathbf{x}) + \sum_{i=m+1}^{p+q} \mathscr{U}_i g_i^2(\mathbf{x})\right]^{\frac{1}{2}} \qquad (8.5\text{–}4)$$

Equation (8.1–5) is used to define $T(\mathbf{x})$ when all the functions in Problem (8.0–1) are defined for all values of $\mathbf{x}$ in E^n; Eq. (8.5–4) is used when some functions of (8.0–1) are not defined for all $\mathbf{x} \in E^n$.

To illustrate the procedure described above, Problem (8.5–1) is transformed into the problem

$$\begin{aligned} \text{Minimize:} \quad & f(\mathbf{x}) = (x_1^2 + x_2^2 - 4x_2 - 45)^{0.5} + [\ln x_1(x_2 - 2)]^2 \\ \text{Subject to:} \quad & g_1(\mathbf{x}): \quad 64 - x_1^2 - x_2^2 \geq 0 \\ & g_2(\mathbf{x}): \quad x_1^2 + x_2^2 - 4x_2 - 45 - \Phi^{(k)} \geq 0 \\ & g_3(\mathbf{x}): \quad x_1 - \Phi^{(k)} \geq 0 \\ & g_4(\mathbf{x}): \quad x_2 - 2 - \Phi^{(k)} \geq 0 \end{aligned} \qquad (8.5\text{–}5)$$

The constraints of Problem (8.5–5) are defined for any $\mathbf{x}$ vector in E^n, but since inequality (8.1–6) must be satisfied before evaluating $f(\mathbf{x})$, negative values for the arguments in (8.5–1) are not permitted. Test Problems 4, 9, and 17 were solved successfully by this type of scheme.

The procedure described above is not applicable when both the objective function *and* the constraints in Problem (8.0–1) have arguments that are not defined for some $\mathbf{x}$ vectors in E^n.

9

Evaluation of constrained nonlinear programming techniques

Justification for the use of any algorithm rests on its efficacy to solve problems by means of a computer implementation. As might be expected, no single one of the nonlinear programming algorithms described in Chaps. 6 through 8 has proved to be superior for all nonlinear programming problems under all circumstances. To evaluate the respective algorithms, we will examine first the question of what criteria to use in the evaluation, and then describe the results of several comparative studies of the various algorithms. Finally, some general conclusions are given to serve as a guide to the reader who wishes to apply the algorithms.

9.1 CRITERIA FOR EVALUATION

The question as to what is "best" in evaluating a nonlinear programming algorithm can only be given a complex answer. Much of the answer depends on the type of problem to be solved, the degree of preparation undertaken by the user, and the available information about the region of feasibility of the $\mathbf{x}$ vectors. Specifically, the question as to what is the best in an algorithm encompasses the following criteria:

1. Time required in a series of tests (execution time and/or number of functional evaluations)
2. Size (dimensionality, number of inequality constraints, number of equality constraints) of the problem
3. Accuracy of the solution with respect to the optimal vector $\mathbf{x}^*$ and/or with respect to $f(\mathbf{x}^*)$, $\mathbf{h}(\mathbf{x}^*)$, $\mathbf{g}(\mathbf{x}^*)$, and $\nabla f(\mathbf{x}^*)$
4. Simplicity of use (time required to introduce data and functions into the computer program)
5. Simplicity of computer program to execute the algorithm

A final attribute of an algorithm is that

6. It solves real-world problems most of the time (we cannot expect that the algorithm will be successful in all applications nor require that it solve pathological problems, i.e., those specially designed to trip up a proposed code).

Note that these criteria are global criteria rather than local criteria in the sense that they relate to the overall performance of the optimization from start to end rather than to the performance at a single stage.

The most common criteria used to evaluate the relative effectiveness of programming codes have been (1) the number of functional evaluations required to obtain the optimal solution of a given test problem to a given degree of precision and/or (2) the computation time required to reach the solution of the given test problem. The number of functional evaluations refers to the number of times that it is necessary to evaluate the objective function and/or each one of the constraints, as well as the derivatives of the functions, before achieving the solution of the programming problem. The number of functional evaluations is a less meaningful criterion for large constrained problems of several variables because the time required by the algorithm to determine the point at which to evaluate the functions can often be several times greater than that required for the evaluation of the functions.

Thus, by default, computation time is the most commonly used criterion for comparing the effectiveness of different programming algorithms. Three studies of computation times for certain programming codes are available in the literature, one by Stocker,[1] one by Holzman,[2] and another by Colville.[3]

[1] D. C. Stocker, A Comparative Study of Nonlinear Programming Codes, M.S. thesis, The University of Texas, Austin, Tex., 1969.

[2] A. G. Holzman, Comparative Analysis of Nonlinear Programming Codes with the Weisman Algorithm, *SRCC Rept.* 113, University of Pittsburgh, Pittsburgh, Pa., November, 1969.

[3] A. R. Colville, *IBM N.Y. Sci. Center Rept.* 320-2949, June, 1968.

To offset the fact that computers have different characteristics and speeds, standard timing programs have been provided to adjust the times from one computer to another and put them all on the same basis (referred to as *standardized times*). A typical Fortran standard timing program developed by Colville (listed in Appendix D) simply inverts a 40 × 40 matrix ten times. Table 9.1–1 lists the times to execute the standard timing program reported by some of the various participants in Colville's study and by Stocker and Holzman.

Table 9.1–1 Time required to execute standard timing program

Participant	*Machine*	*Code*	*Time, sec*
Abadie	IBM 7094	GRG	63.0
	CDC 6400	GRG (revised)	20.5
Boas		Optim	119.7
Colville	IBM 360/50	POP II	168.0
Davies	English Electric KDF 9	Several	362.0
Kephart	IBM 7094	GGS	128.2
McCormick		SUMT	599.0
Holzman	IBM 360/50		140.0
Stocker	CDC 6600		22.0

It is necessary to point out, however, that the comparison of standardized times is not a very precise measure of the relative effectiveness of different computer codes. There seems to be quite a discrepancy between the standardized times obtained for the same programming codes when solving the same test problem on two different computers. As an illustration, Table 9.1–2 compares the standardized times for SUMT to solve Test Problems 10, 11, 15, and 19 in Appendix A, as reported by Colville, with the corresponding standardized times reported by Stocker for the identical code.

Table 9.1–2 Comparison of standardized times

	Problem no.			
Method	*10*	*11*	*15*	*19*
Colville	0.0162	0.0282	0.1511	0.238
Stocker	0.127	0.048	0.253	0.719

From the data it appears that the comparison of the effectiveness of programming codes based on standardized times is somewhat misleading. The only meaningful standard timing program would be one that somehow takes into account the polymorphic factors of the arithmetic logic, access to memory, storage capacity, allocation of central processing vs. peripheral processing times, quantity of information printed out, and so forth, of the various computers and the computer codes.

The net[1] computation time required to solve a given test problem is significantly influenced by the required accuracy of the optimal solution and how precisely the algorithm must satisfy the constraints in the problem before termination of the search. To have a meaningful criterion to compare the effectiveness of programming algorithms, it is necessary to reach the same degree of accuracy in the solution of the test problem. Thus it is possible for a code that solved a problem rapidly, but inaccurately, to appear more favorable than a code that solved the same problem in a longer time but to a greater accuracy in the $\mathbf{x}$ vector, in $f(\mathbf{x})$, and/or in $h_i(\mathbf{x})$ and $g_i(\mathbf{x})$. Unfortunately, the termination criteria used by different codes are different, and thus the accuracy to which a given problem is solved also differs from code to code. In the comparison in Sec. 9.3, rather than attempt to insert uniform termination criteria into the codes, a step that can drastically change their performance, the codes were tested as programmed by the author.

Another significant criterion for the comparison among codes is the ease of preparation by the user. Although a somewhat qualitative basis for comparison, this criterion incorporates two factors of considerable importance and relevance to the utilization of a programming code. The first is the factor of human error. Codes which require lengthy and difficult preparation are more susceptible to human error than codes more easily prepared. In particular, the taking of analytical derivatives is a major source of human error. The second factor is an economic factor. The cost of solving a mathematical programming problem must be divided into the cost of preparation and the cost of computer time incurred in solving the problem. Thus a problem solved by a less efficient but easily prepared code may in fact cost less to solve than if the same problem were solved by a highly efficient code which required many hours to make operational. Such economic considerations are difficult to include in a comparison because the component costs vary over a wide range from situation to situation, but nevertheless they are quite significant.

Some computer codes have a large number of adjustable parameters,

[1] Net time excludes the time to execute, read, and print statements, delays in time sharing, peripheral processing time, and the like.

suitable choices of which make the execution of the corresponding algorithm more efficient. Each author of a code has recommended suitable average values for the parameters and constants that his code requires, but these recommended values may not cause the code to operate at its maximum efficiency for a given problem. In some codes so many parameters can be varied that the net effect is to vary the programming algorithm as a function of the selected parameters. If the code is not successful with one choice of parameters, another selection may improve the results. POP II especially suffers from an excessive number of adjustable parameters.

All the factors described above tend to cloud the interpretation of the results of evaluating algorithms by solving test problems. In particular, the computation times taken by the computer codes to solve the test problems and, to a lesser extent, the number of test problems solved by each code are much more qualitative forms of evidence than they might seem to be at first glance.

With these qualifications in mind, the following criteria were used to compare the effectiveness of the various algorithms. First and most important was the success or failure of a given code to solve a given problem. This criterion was chosen because the ability of an algorithm to solve a wide variety of problems is the most valuable feature to the user of a programming code. The second criterion was the computation time. Another criterion also considered was the ease of problem preparation for computation by the user. This criterion becomes rather important when comparing preparation times for direct search methods with those for methods that require analytical derivatives.

9.2 COMPARISON OF SEVERAL CONSTRAINED ALGORITHMS FOR MINIMIZING PROBLEMS IN TWO DIMENSIONS

To illustrate the trajectory of the search for an extremum of a constrained nonlinear programming problem in two-dimensional space, the special objective function as listed in Table 9.2–1 was developed by multiple regression. It had one peak and a saddle point within the specified range of the two variables. The specific problems to be portrayed are each to maximize the objective function subject to a subset of the inequality constraints listed in Table 9.2–2. Five such problems are listed in Table 9.2–3, and the objective function, constraints, and the corresponding trajectories from the nonfeasible initial vector $\mathbf{x}^{(0)} = [95 \quad 10]^T$ are illustrated in Figs. 9.2–1 through

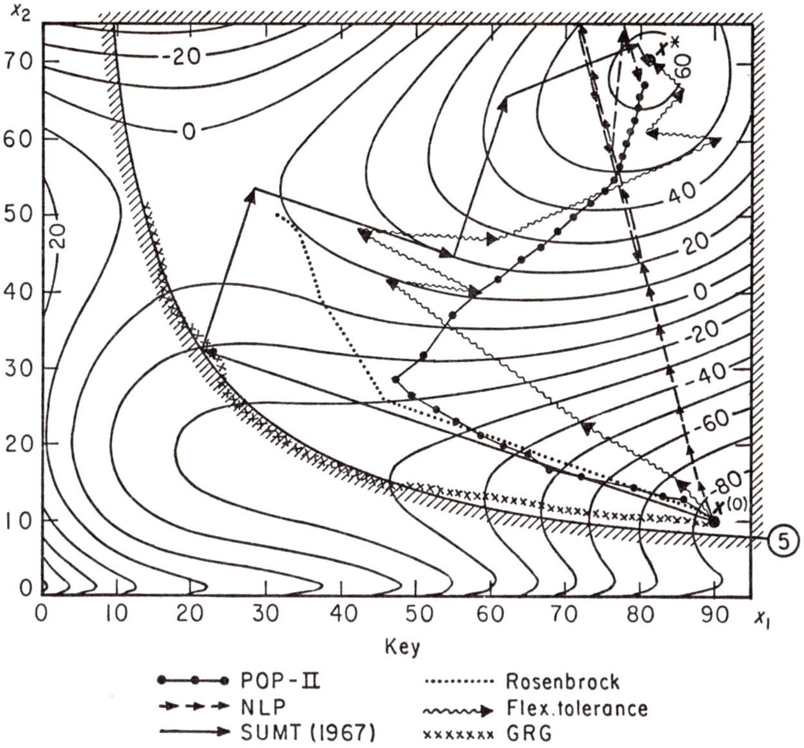

Fig. 9.2–1 Problem 1.

9.2–5. The peak of the objective function was at the point $x_1 = 81.154841$ and $x_2 = 69.135588$, where the objective function had a value of 61.9059345; the constrained maximum was at the point $x_1 = 75.000000$ and $x_2 = 65.000000$, where the objective function had a value of 58.9034360.

Problem 3 (Fig. 9.2–3) depicts several of the typical characteristics of each of the codes, which will now be discussed.

1. Flexible tolerance. Each of the vectors in Fig. 9.2–3 joins successive "best" points in the search. It will be recalled that the flexible tolerance method uses a simplex with $(n + 1)$ vertices, where n is the number of independent variables; hence the "best" point referred to above is the vertex with the largest value of the objective function in each successive simplex.

Since the starting point was nonfeasible, the code first executed a search for a new point which satisfied the initial tolerance criterion. This search is represented by the first vector drawn from $x_1 = 90.0$ and $x_2 = 10.0$ to the point at $x_1 = 68.787$ and $x_2 = 31.213$. It should be noted that the search for

Table 9.2-1 Objective function

$$
\begin{aligned}
f(\mathbf{x}) = {} & B_1 + B_2(x_1) + B_3(x_1)^2 + B_4(x_1)^3 + B_5(x_1)^4 + B_6(x_2) \\
& + B_7(x_1)(x_2) + B_8(x_1)^2(x_2) + B_9(x_1)^3(x_2) \\
& + B_{10}(x_1)^4(x_2) + B_{11}(x_2)^2 + B_{12}(x_2)^3 + B_{13}(x_2)^4 \\
& + B_{14}\left[\frac{1.0}{x_2 + 1.0}\right] + B_{15}(x_1)^2(x_2)^2 + B_{16}(x_1)^3(x_2)^2 \\
& + B_{17}(x_1)^3(x_2)^3 + B_{18}(x_1)(x_2)^2 + B_{19}(x_1)(x_2)^3 \\
& + B_{20}\{\exp[0.0005(x_1)(x_2)]\}
\end{aligned}
$$

$B_1 =$	75.1963666677	$B_{11} =$	0.2564581253
$B_2 =$	−3.8112755343	$B_{12} =$	−0.0034604030
$B_3 =$	0.1269366345	$B_{13} =$	0.0000135139
$B_4 =$	−0.0020567665	$B_{14} =$	−28.1064434908
$B_5 =$	0.0000103450	$B_{15} =$	−0.0000052375
$B_6 =$	−6.8306567613	$B_{16} =$	−0.0000000063
$B_7 =$	0.0302344793	$B_{17} =$	0.0000000007
$B_8 =$	−0.0012813448	$B_{18} =$	0.0003405462
$B_9 =$	0.0000352559	$B_{19} =$	−0.0000016638
$B_{10} =$	−0.0000002266	$B_{20} =$	−2.8673112392

Table 9.2-2 Inequality constraints for two-dimensional models

$g_1(\mathbf{x})$: $x_1 \geq 0$

$g_2(\mathbf{x})$: $x_2 \geq 0$

$g_3(\mathbf{x})$: $95.0 - x_1 \geq 0$

$g_4(\mathbf{x})$: $75.0 - x_2 \geq 0$

$g_5(\mathbf{x})$: $x_1 x_2 - 700.0 \geq 0$

$g_6(\mathbf{x})$: $75.0 - x_1 \geq 0$

$g_7(\mathbf{x})$: $65.0 - x_2 \geq 0$

$g_8(\mathbf{x})$: $x_2 - 5.0\left\{\dfrac{x_1}{25.0}\right\}^2 \geq 0$

$g_9(\mathbf{x})$: $(x_2 - 50.0)^2 - 5.0(x_1 - 55.0) \geq 0$

$g_{10}(\mathbf{x})$: $x_1 - 54.0 \geq 0$

$g_{11}(\mathbf{x})$: $\dfrac{30.0}{20.0}(x_2 - 45.0) - (x_1 - 45.0) \geq 0$

$g_{12}(\mathbf{x})$: $x_1 - 35.0 - \dfrac{40.0}{25.0}(x_2 - 40.0) \geq 0$

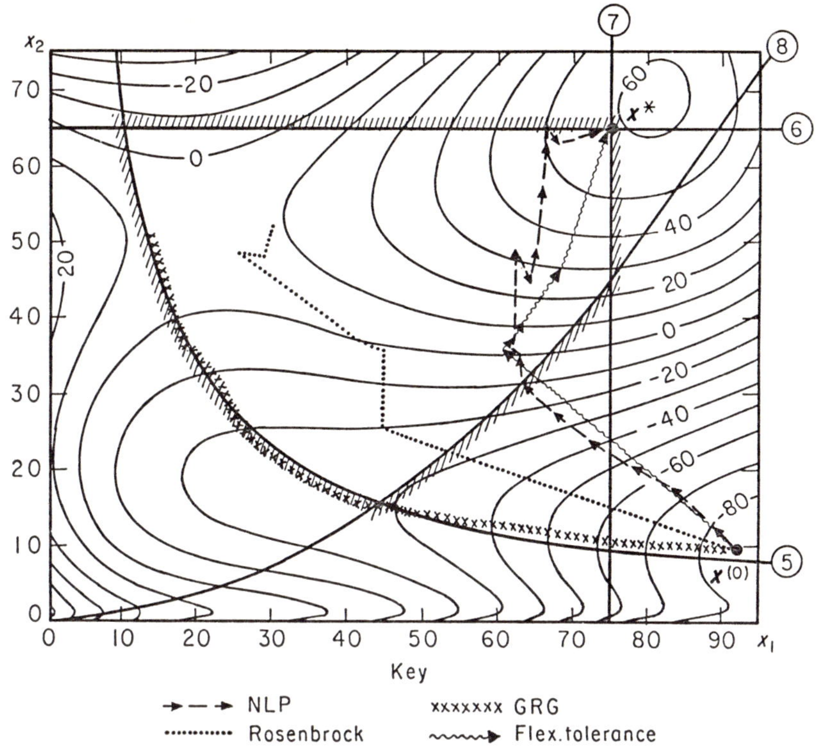

Fig. 9.2–2 Problem 2.

Table 9.2–3 Constrained two-dimensional problems

Problem no.	*Figure no.*	*Constraint numbers*
1	9.2–1	1,2,3,4,5
2	9.2–3	5,6,7,8
3	9.2–3	5,6,7,8,9
4	9.2–4	5,6,7,8,9,10
5	9.2–5	5,6,7,8,9,11,12

a point which satisfied the tolerance criterion followed the *shortest* path to the proximity of the feasible region. The fact that this path was also perpendicular to the contours of the objective function was a coincidence.

The subsequent four steps in the search were large relative to the size of the feasible region, because an edge of five units in length was specified for the initial simplex. If the initial simplex size had been smaller, the search would have followed constraint 9 even more closely, thereby taking

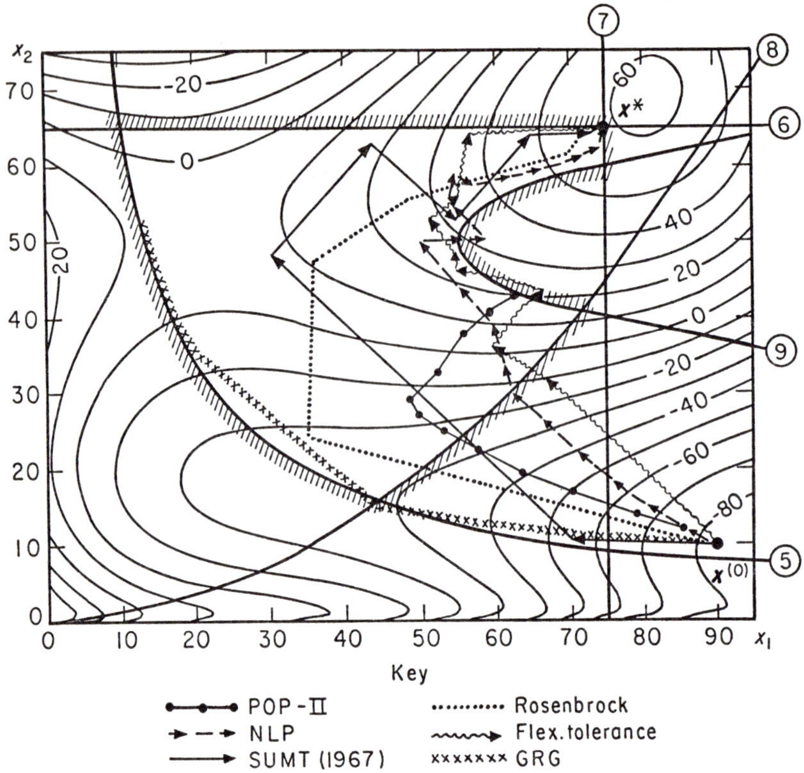

Fig. 9.2-3 Problem 3.

considerably more computation time.

The first five steps took the search into close proximity of the optimum, but final convergence to the exact optimum required a further 39 stages because of the gradual reduction in the size of the simplex. (All the 39 steps are not included in Fig. 9.2-3, for the sake of clarity.) The **x** vector oscillated around a point some five units distant from the optimum until the simplex was reduced to a sufficiently small size for further progress to be made to the optimum.

2. NLP. Each of the vectors constituting the trajectory connects successive points in the search. The first five steps from the starting point were steepest descent moves since the points were far outside the feasible region. The sixth step, from a point outside the feasible region, took the search into the feasible region, and was a linear programming step. All subsequent steps were linear programming steps. Linear programming moves follow the constraints—note particularly the last steps along constraints 9 and 7.

3. SUMT (1967 version). SUMT first executed a search for an interior point

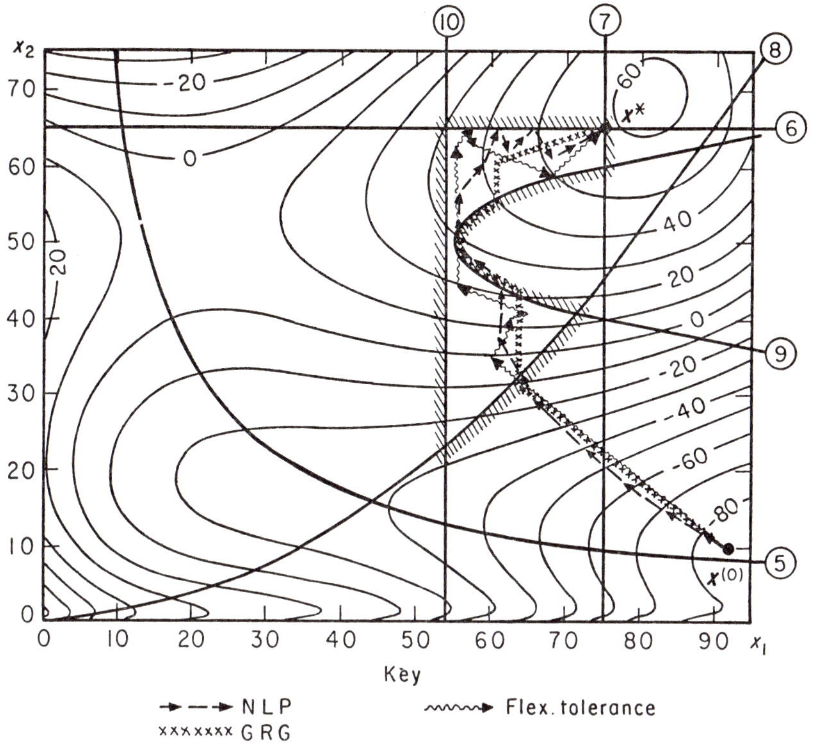

Fig. 9.2–4 Problem 4.

as follows. The given starting point for the problem violated constraints 7 and 8; so SUMT first minimized the negative of constraint 7 subject to the satisfied constraints 5, 6, and 9, and then minimized the negative of constraint 8 subject to constraints 5, 6, 7, and 9 being satisfied, yielding an interior point in the vicinity of $x_1 = 31$ and $x_2 = 48$. Thus the first two vectors connecting the original nonfeasible starting point to the interior (feasible) point include a large number of stages not illustrated.

The remaining portion of the search involved the solution of nine subproblems, after which SUMT had converged to the constrained optimum. For the sake of clarity, the final steps have been condensed somewhat in Fig. 9.2–3. A different ordering of the constraints in the 1967 version of SUMT would yield a different search trajectory, but this would not be true for the 1970 version, in which the sum of all the violated constraints is minimized at once. As a matter of interest, the 1970 version of SUMT terminated near the saddle point in Problem 1, and was not successful in solving the other problems.

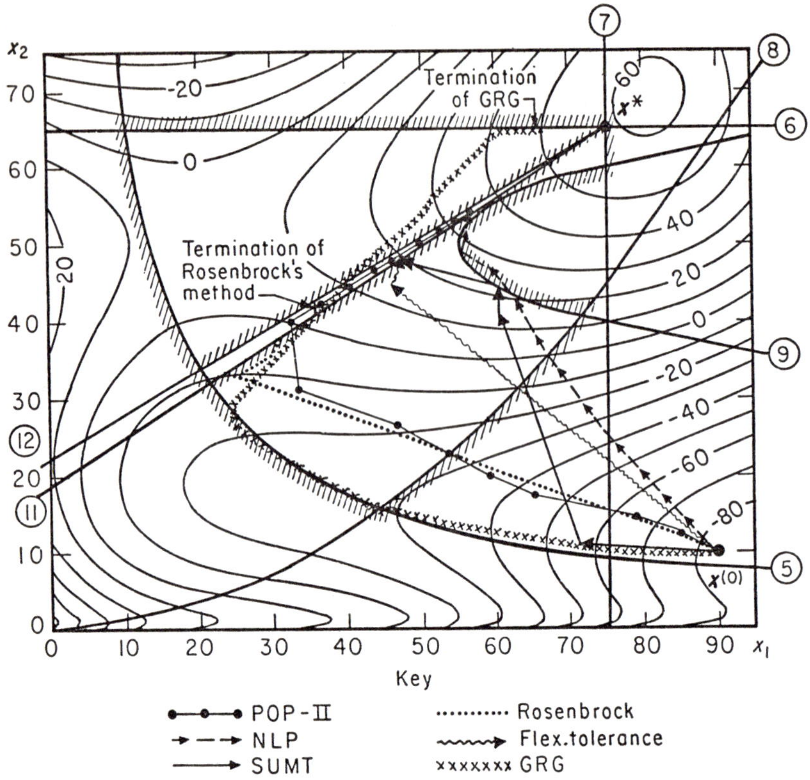

Fig. 9.2–5 Problem 5.

4. Rosenbrock. With the exception of the first vector in the trajectory that connects the original starting point to the interior (feasible) point located by Rosenbrock, each of the vectors represents the progress made by the code in executing each successive stage of Rosenbrock's algorithm. The code finds a feasible starting point by maximizing the sum of the values of the violated constraints until the sum is zero, i.e., all the constraints are satisfied. For clarity, only the vector connecting the original starting point to the first feasible point has been shown in Fig. 9.2–3. Because the direction taken in the search for a feasible point in Rosenbrock's method selects the initial step lengths as 0.1 or one-tenth of the initial value of each independent variable, whichever is greater, the first steps were nine units in the x_1 direction and one unit in the x_2 direction. Since the value of the violated constraints was improved, the search continued in much the same direction, steps in the x_1 direction being much larger than in the x_2 direction.

The subsequent search for the optimum from the first feasible starting point required a further 136 stages before termination. The first six stages took the search very close to the constrained optimum, to $x_1 = 74.72669$ and $x_2 = 64.99136$. Details of the last 130 stages have not been shown in Fig. 9.2–3. (As a matter of interest, Rosenbrock's method led to the saddle point in Problems 1, 2, and 5, and in Problem 4 was not successful in finding a feasible point.)

5. POP II. Probably the most noteworthy feature of the search executed by the code POP II was the small steps taken. The linear programming mode of POP II caused the search trajectory to follow constraints 9 and 7 very closely. (After hitting constraint 9 the dots have been suppressed in Fig. 9.2–3 because they fall too close together.)

6. Union Carbide GGS. This code was not able to solve Problem 3. In Problem 1 a vector $\mathbf{x} = [13.8 \quad 50.6]^T$ near the saddle point was reached. In Problems 2 through 5, at one phase in the search after projection, the partial derivatives became identical with zero.

7. GRG. The GRG method is one that follows an inequality constraint boundary quite closely, and as a result, in Problem 3, terminates at a local optimum in the vicinity of $x_1 = 12$ and $x_2 = 53$ rather than at the global optimum. Starting at another initial point could lead to a different result. [In Problem 4 the global optimum is reached from the given starting point because the local (nonglobal) optimum and the saddle point are excluded from the feasible region by constraint 10.]

9.3 COMPARISON OF SEVERAL CONSTRAINED ALGORITHMS FOR MORE COMPLEX PROBLEMS

To evaluate the computational efficiency and make other comparisons among certain of the constrained nonlinear programming algorithms, Stocker[1] applied a number of the algorithms to test problems on a CDC 6600 digital computer. Another source of information is the study by Colville,[2] which incorporates many more algorithms but gives less detail concerning their merits and imperfections. To complement those studies, some additional unpublished information has been included in this section. Most of the test problems listed in Appendix A have been taken from the literature; the rest have been specially prepared. Some of them are intended to be typical of the programming problems evolving from real-world problems. The test problems as a whole represent a rather varied group with respect to types

[1] *Op. cit.*

[2] *Op. cit.*, and Supplement, 1969.

Table 9.3-1

Inequality constraints	*Equality constraints*		
	Nonlinear	*Linear*	*None*
Nonlinear	*A*1	*B*1	*C*1
Linear	*A*2	*B*2	*D*
None	*A*3	*C*2	*E*

of functions, structure, complexity, and number of independent variables.

Practically all the problems incorporated nonlinear objective functions. The constraint sets varied from linear inequality constraints alone to a combination of nonlinear equality and nonlinear inequality constraints. Table 9.3-1 shows the classification of the problems into five main categories according to the type of constraints in the problem. The sequence *A*, *B*, *C*, *D*, and *E* (and subclasses 1, 2, and 3) roughly represents the order of decreasing difficulty, although problems with only one nonlinear equality constraint in category *A* may be less complex than a problem with many linear equality constraints and nonlinear inequality constraints in category *B*.

Colville collected information on the effectiveness of over thirty different nonlinear programming codes and their behavior in solving a set of eight standard test problems, Problems 7, 8, 10, 11, 14, 15, 18, and 19 in Appendix A. The study was a "cooperative venture" in which each participant was asked to solve a set of test problems using his own method, computer program, and computer. Colville grouped the codes into the four general classes listed in Table 9.3-2. The effectiveness of each class from one viewpoint can be evaluated from the average standardized times required to solve each test problem as listed in Table 9.3-3. Because many of the codes were not particularly effective, because there was no control over the number of occasions the problem was solved before reporting a time, because the printout and termination conditions all differ, and because of the many other obstacles to evaluation mentioned in Secs. 5.1 and 9.1, the averaged standardized times are only a very rough measure of the characteristics of each class of algorithms. In Colville's study, no average standardized times were given for Problem 14 because a large number of local optima existed, and no direct search method was reported to have solved Problems 18 and 19 satisfactorily. As might be expected, Table 9.3-3 indicates that search methods (DSM) are the slowest, and large-step gradient methods (LSGM)

Table 9.3-2 Classification of programming codes included in Colville's study

	Derivatives	*Ref. in Sec.*
Direct search methods (DSM):		
Optim (Mobile Oil)	None	4.5-2
Sequential search (Glass and Cooper)	None	6*
Complex	None	4.5-1
Rosenbrock	None	7.1-2
Multiple gradient summation technique (Klingman and Himmelblau)	Analytic	†
Simplex search (Shell Development Corp.)	None	
Probe	None	6*
Flexible tolerance‡	None	8.1
Small-step gradient methods (SSGM):		
POP/360 (IBM)	Numeric	6.1-2
Ricochet (Greenstadt)	Analytic	§
Carbide optimization package	Numeric	
Generalized gradient search	Analytic	6.3-2
Method of approximation programming	Numeric	6.1-1
Deflected ascent (Shell Development Corp.)	Numeric	
NLP‡	Analytic	6.2
Large-step gradient methods (LSGM):		
Generalized reduced gradient¶	Analytic	6.5
Method of feasible directions (IBM)	Analytic	6.4
Davidon with CRST	Analytic	7.1-3
Convex program (IBM France)	Analytic	
Conjugate gradient (Goldfarb)	Analytic	6.3-3
Variable metric projection (Murtagh)‡	Analytic	6.3-3
Gradient projection (Shell Development Corp.)	Analytic	6.3-1
Gradient projection corrige (B. Pascal Ins.)	Analytic	
Revised reduced gradient (B. Pascal Ins.)	Analytic	
Modified feasible directions (IBM Germany)	Analytic	6.4
Second-derivative methods (SDM):		
Gauss-Newton-Carroll	Analytic	5.3
SUMT	Analytic or numeric	7.2
Solver	Analytic	6.1-4

*Reference is at the end of the indicated chapter.
†*J. Assoc. Computer Mach.*, **11**:400 (1964).
‡Not included in Colville's 1968 report.
§*J. SIAM Appl. Math.*, **14**:3 (1966).
¶Revised version not included in Colville's 1968 report.

Table 9.3–3 Average standardized times for the classes of programming methods *A, B, C, D,* and *E**

Problem no. (App. A)	*Class*	*Category*†			
		DSM	*SSMG*	*LSGM*	*SDM*
15	*A*2	0.179	0.060	0.049	
19	*B*2		0.305	0.148	0.238
7	*C*1	0.089	0.054	0.033	
11	*C*1	0.295	0.017	0.023	0.019
14	*C*1				
18	*C*1	—	0.326	0.220	0.151
10	*D*	0.384	0.055	0.027	0.023
8	*E*	0.026	0.049	0.025	0.025

*From Colville's study, 1968.
†As listed in Table 9.3–2.

and second-derivative methods (SDM) the fastest. Surprisingly, the small-step gradient methods (SSGM) are equally fast.

Preparation times to solve a test problem are another valid criterion of the effectiveness of a computer program to execute a nonlinear programming algorithm. Table 9.3–4 lists various preparation times for several of the codes listed in Table 9.3–2. These times probably represent lower bounds on the preparation times that can be expected by the user experienced with the program for a single trial of the computer code, and do not include the time required to become familiar with the code nor the time for repeated trials engendered by lack of success on earlier trials. Preparation times for users unfamiliar with SUMT, POP II, and the NLP codes have proved to be two to five times the figures listed in Table 9.3–4. It seems unlikely that the times reported for a method using analytical second derivatives, such as SUMT, will be representative of other problems, because, for example, in a problem with one objective function, nine nonlinear constraints, and ten variables, 100 first partial derivatives must be computed and 550 second partial derivatives must be formed without error. Unless most of the derivatives are zero or constants, this will take some time. On the other hand, by using a supplementary symbolic manipulation program, the derivatives perhaps could be obtained in a reasonable time. Only the flexible tolerance code is quick to prepare for the novice; only the objective function, the constraints, and $\mathbf{x}^{(0)}$ need be punched.

Stocker evaluated some of the same codes that appeared in Colville's study and, in addition, tested the flexible search and NLP algorithms.

Table 9.3-4 Preparation times (in hours) required for test problem by some of the algorithms listed in Table 9.3-1

Algorithm	*Derivative*	*Problem no. (Appendix A)* 7	8	10	11	14	15	18	19
Flexible tolerance*	O	0.3	0.1	0.5	0.1	0.4	0.1	0.5	0.5
Optim (Mobile)†	O	1.5	0.1	1.0	1.0	2.0			
POP 360†	N	1.0	0.5	2.0	1.0	2.0	2.0	2.0	2.0
MAP†	N		1.0						
NLP*	A	1.5	1.0	1.0	0.8	1.5	1.3	1.2	0.8
GGS*	A		0.5	0.5	0.4	1.5	1.2	0.7	2.0
GGS†	N	6.0	3.0	5.0	4.0		6.0	4.0	6.0
GRG* (1970)	A	6.0	0.4	1.0	1.0	1.0	1.5	1.0	3.5
GRG†	A	5.0	1.5	2.0	2.0		4.0	2.0	4.0
Davidon-CRST†	A	6.0	1.0	2.0	3.0			4.0	4.0
Minimal†	O	0.8	0.5	1.5	1.0		1.0		1.0
SUMT (1967)	A‡	4.0*	1.5*	3.5†	4.0†			6.0†	3.0†
Rosenbrock*	O	0.3		0.8	0.8				
Variable metric projection†	A	6.0	2.0	2.0	3.0			3.0	4.0
Courant†	A	4.0	1.0	3.0	2.0		3.0	2.0	4.0

*From unpublished data.
†From Colville's study, 1968.
‡Requires second derivatives.
Notation: A = Analytic derivative; N = numerically evaluated derivative; O = no derivative used.

Table 9.3-5 summarizes the standardized times reported by Colville and Stocker, together with some additional unpublished information for the eight test problems of Table 9.3-3. Observe that somewhat different times and performances have been reported in the different studies. Usually, a blank entry in the table for Colville's study implies that the algorithm was not successful in solving the particular problem—at least no solution was reported, and presumably a solution to the problem was attempted. All the factors remarked on in Sec. 9.1 influence the variation in times reported, so that it is really not possible to draw any general conclusions as to the relative effectiveness of the respective algorithms from Table 9.3-5. It would appear, superficially at least, that for simply solving a reasonable variety of problems the flexible tolerance, POP, NLP, GRG, variable metric projection, Courant, and SUMT codes merit further consideration.

To this end Stocker carried out a study in depth on 5 algorithms and 15 test problems, the results of which are included in Table 9.3–6, together with some unpublished information on two other algorithms and 5 additional test problems. The relative performance of the seven codes for the 20 test problems as measured by execution time can be seen in Table 9.3–6. We will discuss first, in Sec. 9.3–1, the characteristics of the codes for certain problems of interest and then summarize, in Sec. 9.3–2, the capabilities of each individual code.

9.3–1 Performance of Algorithms for Certain Problems of Special Interest

Problem 11[1] With the exception of POP II, all the codes were able to solve Problem 11, which had a quadratic objective function, five independent variables, six quadratic inequality constraints, and upper and lower bounds on all five variables. Code Rosenbrock was unable to achieve the accuracy of the other successful codes because the search was terminated due to excessively slow progress along a constraint in the neighborhood of the optimum. POP II located a lower minimum value of the objective function than the other codes, but the extremum was well outside the feasible region. The flexible tolerance, NLP, SUMT, Rosenbrock, and GRG codes solved the problem from the nonfeasible starting point.

Problem 7 This problem is a typical process optimization problem in which the functions are described in terms of a self-contained simulation model written as a computer code. The reader interested in the manner in which such models, and in particular this model, are developed should refer to Sauer, Colville, and Burwick.[2]

Analytical functions are not explicitly given in the problem, so that expressions for the partial derivatives cannot be easily formed, and the task of deriving these expressions was both difficult and lengthy. The preparation of NLP for the solution of Problem 7 took 1.5 hr; the derivation of the analytical second partial derivatives took an additional 2.5 hr, making a total of 4 hr for the preparation of SUMT. However, repeated attempts to solve this problem using SUMT terminated after converging to the wrong solution, the failure undoubtedly being due to human errors made in taking the second partial derivatives of the objective function and constraints with respect to the independent variables. Considerable additional time was spent attempting to locate the source of the difficulty, without success. It should

[1]The problems are listed in Appendix A.

[2]R. N. Sauer, A. R. Colville, and C. W. Burwick, *Hydrocarbon Process. Petrol. Refiner,* **43**:85 (1964).

be noted that the direct search methods, flexible tolerance and Rosenbrock, and the linear approximate programming technique POP II, which do not require derivatives, each took approximately 15 min of preparation for the solution of the problem.

Problem 18 Problem 18, which is the dual of Problem 10, had a cubic objective function with 15 independent variables and 5 cubic constraints; the 15 variables also had lower bounds. Only codes GRG, NLP, and SUMT were able to solve Problem 18 satisfactorily; the codes located the maximum from both the feasible and nonfeasible starting vectors. Problem 18 showed SUMT and GRG off to considerable advantage. Note, though, that in this particular problem the form of the objective function and constraints made the task of taking the derivatives rather easy, the preparation time for SUMT being only 30 min. The flexible tolerance code appeared to be converging very slowly to the optimal solution, but only after excessive computation time, and although the optimal value of the objective function was almost achieved, the **x** vector corresponding to the best solution achieved bore no resemblance to the optimal **x** vector located by both NLP and SUMT. Code Rosenbrock, GGS, and POP II failed to converge to a solution.

Problem 12 Problem 12 is the model of a hypothetical wood-pulp plant with a highly nonlinear objective function that is a complex function of 5 independent variables subject to upper and lower bounds, 3 linear inequality constraints, and 35 nonlinear inequality constraints. Only the codes flexible tolerance and NLP were successful in locating the optimal solution. The solution vector found by the flexible tolerance code, however, did not satisfy the constraints within a reasonable tolerance, and the code seemed to be unable to proceed to a feasible optimum. The direct search executed by code Rosenbrock was terminated prematurely because of the exceedingly slow progress being made along one of the constraints, termination being due to an insufficient rate of increase in the value of the objective function. Code POP II failed for reasons not fully understood. Repeated attempts to solve Problem 12 using code SUMT almost certainly failed because of undiscovered errors in one or more of the 315 second partial derivatives. Problem 12 was similar to Problem 7 in the complexity of the objective function and the constraint functions, and we note once again that the formation of analytical first and second derivatives with respect to the independent variables is liable to human error. Although a comparison of the relative computation times of flexible tolerance and NLP indicated the superior computational efficiency of the algorithm executed by NLP, it must be noted that code NLP required several hours of preparation to solve

Table 9.3–5 Standardization times required by various algorithms to execute eight test problems

Algorithm	Section no.	Problem number (Appendix A)							
		7	8	10	11[a]	14[a]	15	18	19
Optim	4.5	0.142[b]	0.010[b]	0.100[b]	0.014[b]	0.250[b]	[e, c]	[e, b]	[e, c]
POP 360[b]	6.1	0.044	0.011	0.037	0.016	0.067	0.090	0.168	0.313
POP II[d]	6.1	0.078	0.135	[e]	[e]	[e]	[f]	[e]	[f]
MAP[b]	6.1	[e]	0.086						
NLP[d]	6.2	0.073	0.638	0.074	0.110	[g]	0.353	4.15	2.52
Gradient projection[b]	6.3–1	[f]	0.040	0.0127	[f]	[f]	[f]	[f]	0.0936
Generalized gradient search (GGS)[b]	6.3–2	0.094	0.062	0.023	0.016	0.031	0.049	0.686	0.328
GGS[c]	6.3–2		[e]	[e]	0.104	[f]	[e]	[e]	0.589
General reduced gradient [b] (GRG) (1970)	6.5	0.022	0.010	0.008	0.006		0.008	0.084	0.018
GRG (1970)[c]	6.5	0.176	0.072	0.069	[e]	[e]	0.415	0.242	0.132
Davidon-CRST[b]	7.1–3	0.022	0.006	0.039	0.015	[f]	[f]	0.384	0.272
Minimal[h]	7.1–4	0.118	0.087	0.412	0.103	[e]	0.184	[e]	0.875
Method of centers[b]	7.1–5				0.186				
SUMT (1968)									
[b]	7.2			0.016	0.028		[f]	0.151	0.238
[d]	7.2	[f]	0.082	0.127	0.048	[g]	[f]	2.53	0.719
(1970)[c]	7.2						[f]	0.159	
Rosenbrock									
[b]	4.3–6			0.424	0.358	[f]	[f]	[e]	[f]
[d]	7.1–2	0.045	0.032	[e]	0.078	[f]	[f]	[e]	[f]
Flexible tolerance[i]	8.3	0.193	0.023	0.344	0.121	1.31	0.214	22.8[j]	6.45
Variable metric projection[b]	6.3–3	0.025	0.016	0.006	0.006		[f]	0.574	0.062
Courant[b]		0.036	0.004	0.026	0.025		0.072	0.380	0.209

Table 9.3-5a Footnotes for Table 9.3-5

[a]For feasible initial vector.

[b]A. R. Colville, A Comparative Study on Nonlinear Programming Codes, *IBM N.Y. Sci. Center Rept.* 320–2949, June, 1968; Supplement, 1969.

[c]Unpublished.

[d]D. C. Stocker, M.S. thesis, The University of Texas, Austin, Tex., 1969.

[e]Unable to solve problem.

[f]Algorithm cannot be applied to problem.

[g]Error in derivatives prevented solution.

[h]A. G. Holzman, Comparative Analysis of Nonlinear Programming Codes with the Weismann Algorithm, *SRCC Rept.* 113, University of Pittsburgh, Pittsburgh, Pa., November, 1969.

[i]D. A. Paviani, Ph.D. dissertation, The University of Texas, Austin, Tex., 1969.

[j]Problem terminated with error in $f(\mathbf{x})$ of 1 percent because of excessive computation time.

Problem 12, while code flexible tolerance was prepared in less than thirty minutes.

Problem 1 Problem 1 is the simplest of the problems included in category B, having a quadratic objective function of two independent variables, only one linear equality constraint, and one nonlinear inequality constraint. Recall that the codes Rosenbrock and POP II cannot directly handle equality constraints, but the suggestion has been made that equality constraints be included in the constraint set by formulating an equality constraint

$$h_i(\mathbf{x}) = 0$$

as

$$\left.\begin{aligned} h_i(\mathbf{x}) &\geq -\xi_i \\ h_i(\mathbf{x}) &\leq \xi_i \end{aligned}\right\} \qquad i = 1, \ldots, m$$

Table 9.3–6 Computation times in seconds for several algorithms as related to the degree of difficulty of the nonlinear programming problem

	A				B				C									D	E		
Category (see Fig. 9.3–1)	*A1*		*A2*		*B1*	*B2*			*C1*												
Problem no. (App. A)	20	15	5	13[a]	1	4[b]	6	19	3	7	9	11[b]	12	14	16	18[b]	13[a]	10	17	2	8
No. of variables	24	3	3	12	2	10	45	16	2	3	4	5	5	6	9	15	5	5	10	2	4
No. of equality constraints:																					
Linear	2	2	1	4	1	3	12	8													
Nonlinear	12	4	1	3																	
No. of inequality constraints:																					
Linear													3					10			
Nonlinear	6				1				3	14	1	6	35	4	13	5	3				
Upper and lower bounds	24	12	3	16		10	45	32	4	6	5	10	10		1	15	10	5	20	0	8
Time, sec:																					
GRG (1969–1970)	4.98[l]	9.14	1.21		1.06	1.45	[h]	2.92	[g]	3.83	[e]	3.57 (6.51)		[e]	[e]	5.38	2.25	1.54	0.35[l]	0.99	1.59
Flexible tolerance	511	4.71	0.84	[c]	0.43	27.9	[c]	142	0.34	4.23	3.63	2.67 (13.9)	103.3	29.1	59.6	[c]	72.1	7.58	2.92[d]	0.86	0.50
NLP	[e]	7.76	0.33		0.07	5.37[f]		55.4	[g]	1.60		2.31 (0.64)	4.88		[e]	91.4 (84.1)		1.62	[h]	0.18	14.04
SUMT (1968)	[i]	[i]	[a]	[j]	0.51	2.44	29.4	15.6	0.82	[k]	[j]	1.05 (2.98)	[k]	[j]	[j]	5.58 (6.71)		2.79	1.32	0.11	1.80
(1970) best options					0.22					12.66			76.0					1.99			
POP II	[i]	[i]	[c]	[i]	[i]	[i]	[i]	[i]	0.63	1.72		[c]	[e]	[e]	[e]	[e]		[c]	0.65	[e]	3.93
Rosenbrock	[i]	[i]	[c]	[i]	4.52	[i]	[i]	[i]	1.31	0.52	[e]	1.71 (3.00)	[c]	[e]	[c]	[e]		[c]	[h]	0.21	0.70
GGS	[e]	[e]	[e]	[c]	5.18	1.15 6.63)	[e]	13.06	[e]		17.37	2.30 [e]		[e]	[e]	[e]		[e]	2.08	4.52	[e]

All computation times are for the CDC 6600 that has a standard time of 22.0 sec. Categories in order of decreasing difficulty are *A* to *E*. The objective functions are all nonlinear, except in Problem 20, in which $f(\mathbf{x})$ is linear. A blank entry indicates that the problem was not attempted.

[a]Nonfeasible solution obtained or constraint not satisfied.
[b]Time in parentheses is for nonfeasible starting point.
[c]No solution obtained because of slowness of search.
[d]Constraints not satisfied adequately.
[e]
[f]For Problem 4*a*.
[g]Reaches local but not global extremum.
[h]Negative argument of logarithmic objective function obtained.
[i]Algorithm cannot be applied to problem.
[j]Determination of second derivatives too difficult
[k]Unable to reach solution, probably because of errors in some second derivations.
[l]1970 code.

Codes Rosenbrock and POP II can accommodate constraints in such a form if the user specifies the upper and lower bounds on the functions $h_i(\mathbf{x})$, that is, $-\xi_i$ and ξ_i.

The suggested technique of accommodating equality constraints was tried out in applying codes Rosenbrock and POP II to solve Problem 1 using a value of 10^{-4} for ξ_i, since equality constraints with values in the range $-10^{-4} < h_i(\mathbf{x}) < 10^{-4}$ are well satisfied. The code Rosenbrock was reasonably successful in solving the problem, although the optimal solution did not correspond exactly to the slightly better solution found by codes flexible tolerance, NLP, GGS, GRG, and SUMT. Moreover, the computation time taken by Rosenbrock to achieve this solution compared very poorly with the times taken by some of the other successful codes. Code POP II did not converge to the correct optimal solution, and the value of the equality constraint was approximately 10^{-1} at the minimum found.

Problem 4 Problems 4 and 6 are both examples of the problem of determining the chemical composition of a complex mixture under conditions of chemical equilibrium. A mixture of chemical species held at a constant temperature and pressure reaches its chemical equilibrium state concurrently with the reduction of the objective function, the free energy of the mixture, to a minimum. The nonlinear objective function was a logarithmic function of ten independent variables subject to three linear equality constraints; the independent variables all had zero lower bounds.

Since both codes NLP and flexible tolerance permit a certain degree of infeasibility in any given $\mathbf{x}$ vector, the possibility of negative values for the independent variables arose in Problem 4. These negative x_j in turn cause the arguments of one or more of the natural logarithms in the objective function to become negative and thus undefined, aborting the search. At no time in the solution of Problem 11 did the flexible tolerance code give negative values for any of the 10 independent variables; consequently, the flexible tolerance code solved the problem as stated in Appendix A. However, the search executed by code NLP was aborted when the value of one of the independent variables became negative.

To overcome this difficulty, the independent variables were redefined. If we designate the redefined variable by x_j', the relationship between the redefined variables and the original variables was

$$x'_j = \ln x_j \qquad j = 1, \ldots, 10$$

The redefined programming problem is given in Appendix A as Test Problem 4*a*. It should be noted that the redefined problem had three nonlinear equality constraints rather than three linear equality constraints as in the original problem, and therefore might more properly belong to category *A* of the test problems.

After redefinition of the variables, the code NLP succeeded in solving Problem 4 and obtained, roughly, the same optimal value for the objective function as did codes SUMT and GRG. The optimal-solution **x** vector found by Bracken and McCormick,[1] who also used code SUMT, was reproduced exactly by the GRG code. However, the optimal-solution **x** vectors obtained by the flexible tolerance, NLP, and GGS codes were not exactly the same (refer to Appendix A), and it must be concluded that the objective function of Problem 4 has a somewhat flat minimum.

Problem 6 Problem 6 also was a chemical equilibrium problem but included 45 independent variables and 16 linear equality constraints; hence the dimensionality of Problem 6 was considerably greater than that of Problem 4. Of the four codes (flexible tolerance, NLP, GRG, and SUMT) applied to this problem, the first three encountered the obstacle of a negative argument of a logarithm mentioned in connection with Problem 4. An attempt was made to circumvent the difficulty by redefining the independent variables for NLP as in Problem 4, and the addition of constraints for the flexible tolerance algorithm as mentioned in Sec. 8.6. Only SUMT successfully solved the problem as stated, although the optimal **x** vector did not agree with that given by A. P. Jones (the originator of the problem), which is also included in Appendix A for comparison. Moreover, Jones' optimal **x** vector did not satisfy the equality constraints. Jones did not quote the minimum value of the objective function which he found, but substitution of his solution vector into the expression for the objective function yielded a value of -79.108. The minimum value of the objective function obtained using SUMT was -1910.446, a considerable improvement. The latter minimum value was reproduced from three starting vectors, that is, $x_{jk} = 10^{-1}$, $x_{jk} = 10^{-10}$, and Jones' optimal **x** vector.

Neither code Rosenbrock nor POP II was applied to Problem 6.

[1] J. Bracken and G. P. McCormick, "Selected Applications of Nonlinear Programming," John Wiley & Sons, Inc., New York, 1968.

Problem 5 Problem 5 included a quadratic objective function of three independent variables subject to one nonlinear equality constraint and one linear equality constraint. The three independent variables were also constrained to positive values. Thus Problem 5 is classified as a category *A* problem. Only the flexible tolerance, GGS, GRG, and NLP algorithms were developed to solve nonlinear programming problems subject to nonlinear equality constraints, and only four algorithms were able to solve Problem 5.

Code SUMT failed to solve Problem 5 in the sense that it converged to a solution which did not satisfy the equality constraints with sufficient precision; refer to Appendix A. Several attempts to force SUMT to satisfy the equality constraints more exactly also failed. The failure of SUMT to solve Problem 5 was unexpected, but convergence to the solution of a programming problem with nonlinear equality constraints is not guaranteed with SUMT (see Chap. 7).

The codes Rosenbrock and POP II were applied to Problem 5 using the technique described in connection with Problem 1 for accommodating equality constraints. Neither code was successful in converging to the optimal solution. Code Rosenbrock terminated the search when progress toward the minimum became extremely slow and effectively stationary. Code POP II converged to a lower value of the objective function than did codes flexible tolerance and NLP, but only by violating the equality constraints.

Problem 20 Problem 20 includes a linear objective function of 24 independent variables which are subject to 12 nonlinear equality constraints, 2 linear equality constraints, and 6 nonlinear inequality constraints. The independent variables are also constrained to positive values. It is probably the most difficult problem of all those in Appendix A. No attempts were made to solve Problem 20 using either code Rosenbrock or code POP II.

The codes flexible tolerance, NLP, GGS, and SUMT were all able to improve the value of the objective function from the starting $\mathbf{x}$ vector, but only flexible tolerance and GRG (1970 version) *converged* to a solution. Neither code NLP nor code SUMT converged to a solution, but continued to oscillate around the best solution they were able to locate until the computations were terminated at the time limit specified. Moreover, the best solutions found by NLP and SUMT were inferior to the best solution by flexible tolerance and GRG, and the solution by SUMT did not satisfy the equality constraints with sufficient accuracy.

9.3-2 Evaluation of the Performance of Algorithms Based on the Test Problems

In this section we characterize each nonlinear programming algorithm individually on the basis of its performance in solving the test problems listed in Table 9.3–5.

1. GRG (1969 version). From the viewpoint of robustness in obtaining a solution to a nonlinear programming problem, the GRG code gave quite favorable results, especially on the difficult category *A* problems (Problem 20 was solved with the 1970 nondegeneracy version of the code). In category *C*, Problems 9, 11, 14, and 16 were unsuccessful because of premature termination, but Abadie has reported solving Problems 11 and 14. For those problems solved, the execution times were very favorable in comparison with the other algorithms solving the same problem; hence the GRG code appears to be one of the best currently available.

2. Flexible tolerance. With only two exceptions, the flexible tolerance algorithm proved to be capable of solving problems in all five categories *A* through *E*. Problems 6 and 18 have been discussed in Sec. 9.3–1, and it must be concluded that the flexible tolerance code spent too long a time in satisfying the equality constraints to solve the problems in a reasonable time. Because it was a search technique, the algorithm did not require the formation of analytical derivatives; hence, generally speaking, the preparation times for all the test problems were quite short. Moreover, the ease of preparation resulted in very few human errors. On the other hand, the computer running times for large-dimensional problems (such as Problems 18 through 20) were longer than for the GRG, SUMT, and NLP codes.

3. NLP. Code NLP solved most of the test problems in categories *B* through *E*, except for Problems 6, 14, and 16, and a redefinition of the variables in Problem 6, which converted the 16 linear equality constraints into 16 nonlinear equality constraints, made it possible to solve Problem 6. Strictly speaking, therefore, the revised Problem 6 should be classed as a category *A* problem. The performance of NLP in attempting to solve category *A* problems was fair; NLP did not converge to a solution to Problem 20. Code NLP required analytical first derivatives of the objective function and constraints; consequently, preparation times for several problems were lengthy and human errors all too frequent. The execution times in general are less than those of the flexible tolerance method, with a few exceptions.

4. SUMT (1968 version). The results obtained using SUMT were in accordance with the mathematical basis of the sequential unconstrained minimization technique discussed in Chap. 7. SUMT solved every test problem in categories *B* through *E* with the exceptions of problems in which human error in deriving the second analytical derivatives may have been the cause of the failure. Code SUMT, however, failed to locate the optimal solution to any of the category *A* problems. Also, the discontinuous first derivatives in Problem 15 made an attempt to solve the problem using SUMT impossible. It will be recalled from Chap. 7 that the technique executed by SUMT does not guarantee convergence to the optimal solution of a category *A* problem. The necessity of providing first and second partial derivatives of the objective function and constraints led to a considerable number of errors of human origin and to long preparation times. Fortunately, several of the test problems had objective functions that were symmetrical in each of the independent variables, e.g., Test Problems 4, 6, 10, 18, 19, so that the task of deriving first and second partial derivatives was considerably simplified for these problems. For the problems in categories *B* through *E*, SUMT required less computer time in general than those grounded on search techniques.

5. Rosenbrock. Code Rosenbrock succeeded in solving only a few problems belonging to categories *C*, *D*, and *E*. The reason for the observed failures was primarily premature termination of the search when progress of the code along a constraint (or constraints) was exceedingly slow.

One success was recorded for code Rosenbrock in the category *B* problems, i.e., Problem 1, but the excessive computation time required for the solution of this problem, which had only two variables, suggested that further attempts to solve category *B* problems would be fruitless. The failure of code Rosenbrock to solve Problem 5, the simplest of the category *A* problems, suggested that Rosenbrock was not well suited to the solution of problems belonging to category *A*.

6. POP II. The overall performance of code POP II was marked by a lack of success, only four of the possible 12 problems having been solved. These results are quite different from those reported by Colville. Since POP II was not developed to solve problems belonging to categories *B* and *A*, its failure in these two categories was not unexpected. The high failure rate in categories *D* and *C*, however, was surprising.

7. GGS. In general, the GGS algorithm terminated prematurely for a number of different reasons that we do not have the space to describe. Often the

Table 9.3–7 Comparison of the nonlinear programming codes

	Problem category				
Algorithm	*A*	*B*	*C*	*D*	*E*
GRG (1970)	Yes	Yes	Yes	Yes	Yes
Flexible tolerance	Yes*	Yes	Yes	Yes	Yes
NLP	?	Yes	Yes	Yes	Yes
SUMT (1968)	No	Yes	Yes	Yes	Yes
Rosenbrock	No	No	No	No	Yes
POP II†	No	No	No	No	Yes
GGS	No	?	No	?	Yes

*Except for many equality constraints.
†Performance can be improved by adjusting parameters.

elements of the search direction or of the gradient became zero because of coincidence or numerical roundoff.

Table 9.3–7 summarizes the capabilities of the seven nonlinear programming codes, and is designed to assist the analyst faced with the task of solving a mathematical programming problem in selecting a code. A "Yes" element in the column of Table 9.3–7 means that the corresponding algorithm is recommended as being generally capable of solving nonlinear programming problems belonging to the corresponding problem category. A "No" element in the matrix indicates that the corresponding code is not recommended for the solution of nonlinear programming problems belonging to the corresponding problem category. A question mark indicates uncertainty as to effectiveness.

SUPPLEMENTARY REFERENCES

Rastrigin, L. A.: Criteria for Comparing Methods of Seeking an Extremum (English trans.), *Zavod. Lab.*, **32**:1248, 1529 (1966).

Rosen, J. B., and S. Suzuki: Construction of Nonlinear Programming Test Problems, *Commun. ACM*, **8**:113 (1965).

appendix a

Nonlinear programming problems and their solutions

Problem 1

Source: J. Bracken and G. P. McCormick, "Selected Applications of Nonlinear Programming," John Wiley & Sons, Inc., New York, 1968.

No. of variables: 2

No. of constraints: 1 linear equality constraint
1 nonlinear inequality constraint

Objective function:

Minimize: $f(\mathbf{x}) = (x_1 - 2)^2 + (x_2 - 1)^2$

Constraints:

$$h_1(\mathbf{x}) = x_1 - 2x_2 + 1 = 0$$

$$g_1(\mathbf{x}) = -\frac{x_1^2}{4} - x_2^2 + 1 \geq 0$$

Nonfeasible starting point:

$$\mathbf{x}^{(0)} = [2 \quad 2]^T$$

$$f(\mathbf{x}^{(0)}) = 1$$

Results:

$$f(\mathbf{x}^*) = 1.393$$
$$x_1^* = 0.823$$
$$x_2^* = 0.911$$

Problem 2

Source: H. H. Rosenbrock, An Automatic Method for Finding the Greatest and Least Value of a Function, *Computer J.*, **3**:175 (1960).
No. of variables: 2
No. of constraints: 0
Objective function:

$$\text{Minimize:} \quad f(\mathbf{x}) = 100(x_2 - x_1^2)^2 + (1 - x_1)^2$$

Starting point:

$$\mathbf{x}^{(0)} = [-1.2 \quad 1]^T$$
$$f(\mathbf{x}^{(0)}) = 24.20$$

Results:

$$\mathbf{x}^* = [1 \quad 1]^T$$
$$f(\mathbf{x}^*) = 0$$

Problem 3

Source: G. K. Barnes, M.S. thesis, The University of Texas, Austin, Tex., 1967.
No. of variables: 2
No. of constraints: 3 nonlinear inequality constraints
4 bounds on independent variables
Objective function:

$$\begin{aligned}\text{Maximize:} \quad f(\mathbf{x}) = {} & 75.196 - 3.8112x_1 + 0.12694x_1^2 - 2.0567 \\ & \times 10^{-3}x_1^3 + 1.0345 \times 10^{-5}x_1^4 - 6.8306x_2 \\ & + 0.030234x_1x_2 - 1.28134 \times 10^{-3}x_2x_1^2 + 3.5256 \\ & \times 10^{-5}x_2x_1^3 - 2.266 \times 10^{-7}x_2x_1^4 + 0.25645x_2^2 \\ & - 3.4604 \times 10^{-3}x_2^3 + 1.3514 \times 10^{-5}x_2^4 \\ & - \frac{28.106}{x_2 + 1} - 5.2375 \times 10^{-6}x_1^2x_2^2 - 6.3 \\ & \times 10^{-8}x_1^3x_2^2 + 7 \times 10^{-10}x_1^3x_2^3 + 3.4054 \\ & \times 10^{-4}x_1x_2^2 - 1.6638 \times 10^{-6}x_1x_2^3 \\ & - 2.8673 \exp(0.0005x_1x_2)\end{aligned}$$

Constraints:

$$0 \le x_1 \le 75$$
$$0 \le x_2 \le 65$$
$$x_1 x_2 - 700 \ge 0$$
$$x_2 - 5\left(\frac{x_1}{25}\right)^2 \ge 0$$
$$(x_2 - 50)^2 - 5(x_1 - 55) \ge 0$$

Nonfeasible starting point:

$$\mathbf{x}^{(0)} = [90 \quad 10]^T$$
$$f(\mathbf{x}^{(0)}) = -82.828$$

Results:

$$\mathbf{x}^* = [75 \quad 65]^T$$
$$f(\mathbf{x}^*) = 58.903$$

Problem 4

Source: J. Bracken and G. P. McCormick, "Selected Applications of Nonlinear Programming," John Wiley & Sons, Inc., New York, 1968.

No. of variables: 10

No. of constraints: 3 linear equality constraints
10 bounds on independent variables

Problem 4 is a problem in the chemical equilibrium at constant temperature and pressure.

Objective function:

$$\text{Minimize:} \quad f(\mathbf{x}) = \sum_{i=1}^{10} x_i \left(c_i + \ln \frac{x_i}{\sum_{j=1}^{10} x_j} \right)$$

where $c_1 = -6.089$ $\quad c_2 = -17.164$ $\quad c_3 = -34.054$ $\quad c_4 = -5.914$

$c_5 = -24.721$ $\quad c_6 = -14.986$ $\quad c_7 = -24.100$ $\quad c_8 = -10.708$

$c_9 = -26.662$ $\quad c_{10} = -22.179$

Constraints:

$$h_1(\mathbf{x}) = x_1 + 2x_2 + 2x_3 + x_6 + x_{10} - 2 = 0$$
$$h_2(\mathbf{x}) = x_4 + 2x_5 + x_6 + x_7 - 1 = 0$$
$$h_3(\mathbf{x}) = x_3 + x_7 + x_8 + 2x_9 + x_{10} - 1 = 0$$
$$x_i \ge 0 \qquad i = 1, \ldots, 10$$

Nonfeasible starting point:

$$\mathbf{x}_i^{(0)} = 0.1 \qquad i = 1, \ldots, 10$$
$$f(\mathbf{x}^{(0)}) = -20.961$$

Results: See Problem 4*a*.

Problem 4*a*

No. of independent variables: 10
No. of constraints: 3 nonlinear equality constraints
Objective function:

$$\text{Minimize:} \quad f(\mathbf{x}') = \sum_{i=1}^{10} \left\{ e^{x_i'} \left[c_i + x_i' - \ln\left(\sum_{i=1}^{10} e^{x_i'} \right) \right] \right\}$$

Constraints:

$$h_1(\mathbf{x}') = e^{x_1'} + 2e^{x_2'} + 2e^{x_3'} + e^{x_6'} + e^{x_{10}'} - 2 = 0$$
$$h_2(\mathbf{x}') = e^{x_4'} + 2e^{x_5'} + e^{x_6'} + e^{x_7'} - 1 = 0$$
$$h_3(\mathbf{x}') = e^{x_3'} + e^{x_7'} + e^{x_8'} + 2e^{x_9'} + e^{x_{10}'} - 1 = 0$$

Nonfeasible starting point:

$$x_i' = -2.3 \qquad i = 1, \ldots, 10$$

Results:

	NLP	*Flexible tolerance*	*GGS*	*GRG*	*SUMT*
$f(\mathbf{x})$	−47.751	−47.736	−47.656	−47.761	−47.761
x_1	0.0350	0.0128	0	0.0406	0.0407
x_2	0.1142	0.1433	0.1695	0.1477	0.1477
x_3	0.8306	0.8078	0.7536	0.7832	0.7832
x_4	0.0012	0.0062	0	0.0014	0.0014
x_5	0.4887	0.4790	0.5000	0.4853	0.4853
x_6	0.0005	0.0033	0	0.0007	0.0007
x_7	0.0209	0.0324	0	0.0274	0.0274
x_8	0.0157	0.0281	0	0.0180	0.0180
x_9	0.0289	0.0250	0.0464	0.0375	0.0373
x_{10}	0.0751	0.0817	0.1536	0.0969	0.0969
$h_1(\mathbf{x})$	3.E−12	3.E−05	0	1.E−06	−8.E−08
$h_2(\mathbf{x})$	3.E−12	2.E−05	0	1.E−06	−1.E−07
$h_3(\mathbf{x})$	2.E−11	9.E−05	0	1.E−06	−1.E−07

Problem 5

Source: D. A. Paviani, Ph.D. dissertation, The University of Texas, Austin, Tex., 1969.
No. of variables: 3
No. of constraints: 1 nonlinear equality constraint
1 linear equality constraint
3 bounds on independent variables

Objective function:

$$\text{Minimize:} \quad f(\mathbf{x}) = 1000 - x_1^2 - 2x_2^2 - x_3^2 - x_1x_2 - x_1x_3$$

Constraints:

$$h_1(\mathbf{x}) = x_1^2 + x_2^2 + x_3^2 - 25 = 0$$
$$h_2(\mathbf{x}) = 8x_1 + 14x_2 + 7x_3 - 56 = 0$$
$$x_i \geq 0 \qquad i = 1,2,3$$

Nonfeasible starting point:

$$x_i^{(0)} = 2; \text{also } x_i^0 = 10 \qquad i = 1,2,3$$
$$f(\mathbf{x}^{(0)}) = 976$$

Results:

$f(\mathbf{x}^*)$	961.715
x_1	3.512
x_2	0.217
x_3	3.552
$h_1(\mathbf{x}^*)$	0
$h_2(\mathbf{x}^*)$	0

Problem 6

Source: A. P. Jones, "The Chemical Equilibrium Problem: An Application of SUMT," Research Analysis Corporation, McLean, Va., RAC-TP-272, 1967.
No. of variables: 45
No. of constraints: 16 linear equality constraints

Objective function:

$$\text{Minimize:} \quad f(\mathbf{x}) = \sum_{k=1}^{7} \left[\sum_{j=1}^{n_k} x_{jk} \left(c_{jk} + \ln \frac{x_{jk}}{\sum_{j=1}^{n_k} x_{jk}} \right) \right]$$

Note: See accompanying tables for n_k and c_{jk}.
Constraints:

$$h_i(\mathbf{x}) = \sum_{k=1}^{7} \left(\sum_{j=1}^{n_k} E_{ijk} x_{jk} \right) - b_i = 0 \qquad i = 1, \ldots, 16$$

$$x_{jk} \geq 0 \qquad [(j = 1, \ldots, n_k), k = 1, \ldots, 7]$$

Nonfeasible starting point:

$$x_{jk} = 0.1 \qquad [(j = 1, \ldots, n_k), k = 1, \ldots, 7]$$

$$f(\mathbf{x}^{(0)}) = -30.958$$

Results:

	NLP	*SUMT*	*Jones* (*SUMT*)
$f(\mathbf{x}^*)$	−1909.740	−1910.361	−79.108
x_{11}^*	7.854E − 07	6.599E − 06	6.440E − 01
x_{21}^*	8.078E − 02	2.512E − 01	2.590E − 01
x_{31}^*	3.706E − 00	3.705E − 00	3.705E − 00
x_{41}^*	8.855E − 02	2.535E − 01	2.997E − 01
x_{12}^*	6.894E − 01	6.529E − 01	5.617E − 05
x_{22}^*	3.020E − 02	1.235E − 03	6.880E − 04
x_{32}^*	1.398E − 04	3.667E − 04	2.062E − 04
x_{42}^*	1.626E − 04	2.794E − 06	1.101E − 06
x_{52}^*	0	5.441E − 06	2.433E − 06
x_{62}^*	2.782E − 02	7.363E − 02	5.715E − 02
x_{72}^*	7.950E − 02	8.791E − 02	7.938E − 02
x_{82}^*	3.421E − 02	3.542E − 02	3.231E − 03
x_{92}^*	2.486E + 01	4.458E + 01	2.839E − 01
$x_{10,2}^*$	3.873E − 02	2.669E − 02	1.388E − 02
$x_{11,2}^*$	1.500E − 04	7.709E − 06	3.283E − 06
$x_{12,2}^*$	1.170E − 05	3.764E − 05	1.738E − 05
$x_{13,2}^*$	1.550E − 02	1.550E − 02	1.155E − 02
x_{13}^*	0	9.900E − 07	5.956E − 05

	NLP	*SUMT*	*Jones (SUMT)*
x^*_{23}	2.649E − 02	5.077E − 05	4.419E − 04
x^*_{33}	1.251E − 04	3.107E − 05	2.205E − 04
x^*_{43}	1.064E − 01	1.546E − 06	1.095E − 06
x^*_{53}	0	3.102E − 06	1.852E − 06
x^*_{63}	5.253E − 02	6.416E − 03	2.291E − 02
x^*_{73}	8.710E − 03	2.202E − 04	8.751E − 03
x^*_{83}	1.471E − 02	1.287E − 02	4.506E − 02
x^*_{93}	4.735E − 02	2.165E − 00	1.832E − 01
$x^*_{10,3}$	9.208E − 02	2.675E − 00	6.396E − 03
$x^*_{11,3}$	3.119E − 04	3.437E − 06	2.855E − 06
$x^*_{12,3}$	1.560E − 02	1.400E − 05	7.806E − 06
$x^*_{13,3}$	2.421E − 02	1.927E − 02	2.113E − 02
$x^*_{14,3}$	2.448E − 03	1.855E − 03	7.429E − 06
$x^*_{15,3}$	8.398E − 03	3.264E − 06	3.017E − 05
$x^*_{16,3}$	5.285E − 03	7.579E − 07	5.056E − 05
$x^*_{17,3}$	0	3.510E − 07	4.871E − 05
$x^*_{18,3}$	1.601E − 03	2.513E − 07	2.142E − 03
x^*_{14}	4.968E − 07	0	2.337E − 06
x^*_{24}	1.978E − 02	4.200E − 07	1.821E − 04
x^*_{34}	6.271E − 03	7.063E − 06	8.583E − 05
x^*_{15}	5.328E − 02	0	2.355E − 05
x^*_{25}	0	0	1.251E − 03
x^*_{35}	0	1.305E − 06	7.573E − 03
x^*_{16}	2.510E − 02	1.465E − 05	3.038E − 04
x^*_{26}	1.220E − 06	1.382E − 05	3.902E − 05
x^*_{17}	0	2.872E − 06	2.879E − 02
x^*_{27}	0	2.476E − 06	1.499E − 03
$h_1(\mathbf{x}^*)$	5.118E − 02	2.529E − 07	−4.800E − 07
$h_2(\mathbf{x}^*)$	2.407E − 03	2.263E − 07	1.592E − 06
$h_3(\mathbf{x}^*)$	2.559E − 05	1.917E − 07	2.631E − 06
$h_4(\mathbf{x}^*)$	4.493E − 02	1.112E − 06	−4.624E + 01
$h_5(\mathbf{x}^*)$	2.389E − 02	−4.518E − 07	−4.624E + 01
$h_6(\mathbf{x}^*)$	3.100E − 04	−3.946E − 07	1.340E − 06
$h_7(\mathbf{x}^*)$	6.692E − 06	6.771E − 07	1.362E − 06
$h_8(\mathbf{x}^*)$	6.376E − 04	5.101E − 07	1.362E − 06
$h_9(\mathbf{x}^*)$	0	−1.869E − 07	−3.948E − 03
$h_{10}(\mathbf{x}^*)$	2.082E − 02	−1.950E − 07	2.280E − 03
$h_{11}(\mathbf{x}^*)$	−2.273E − 03	−2.273E − 03	−2.273E − 03
$h_{12}(\mathbf{x}^*)$	−1.380E − 02	−5.583E − 07	−2.699E − 04
$h_{13}(\mathbf{x}^*)$	6.946E − 04	6.001E − 07	−8.575E − 03
$h_{14}(\mathbf{x}^*)$	5.331E − 02	1.169E − 06	8.847E − 03
$h_{15}(\mathbf{x}^*)$	7.789E − 06	2.180E − 07	−5.529E − 07
$h_{16}(\mathbf{x}^*)$	3.528E − 09	1.284E − 07	−3.330E − 07

b_i's and c_{jk}'s for Problem 6

i	b_i	j	k	c_{jk}	j	k	c_{jk}
1	0.6529581	1	1	0.0	6	3	0.0
2	0.281941	2	1	−7.69	7	3	2.2435
3	3.705233	3	1	−11.52	8	3	0.0
4	47.00022	4	1	−36.60	9	3	−39.39
5	47.02972	1	2	−10.94	10	3	−21.49
6	0.08005	2	2	0.0	11	3	−32.84
7	0.08813	3	2	0.0	12	3	6.12
8	0.04829	4	2	0.0	13	3	0.0
9	0.0155	5	2	0.0	14	3	0.0
10	0.0211275	6	2	0.0	15	3	−1.9028
11	0.0022725	7	2	0.0	16	3	−2.8889
12	0.0	8	2	2.5966	17	3	−3.3622
13	0.0	9	2	−39.39	18	3	−7.4854
14	0.0	10	2	−21.35	1	4	−15.639
15	0.0	11	2	−32.84	2	4	0.0
16	0.0	12	2	6.26	3	4	21.81
		13	2	0.0	1	5	−16.79
		1	3	10.45	2	5	0.0
		2	3	0.0	3	5	18.9779
		3	3	−0.50	1	6	0.0
		4	3	0.0	2	6	11.959
		5	3	0.0	1	7	0.0
					2	7	12.899

E_{ijk} Data for Problem 6

x_{jk} \ i	1	2	3	4	5	6	7	8	9	10	11	12	13	14	15	16
x_{11}	1															
x_{21}		1														
x_{31}			1													
x_{41}				1	1											
x_{12}	1															
x_{22}		1														
x_{32}			1													
x_{42}				1								1				
x_{52}					1							−1				
x_{62}						1						−1				
x_{72}							1					1				
x_{82}								1				1				
x_{92}				1	1											
$x_{10,2}$		1			1							−1				

x_{jk} \ i	1	2	3	4	5	6	7	8	9	10	11	12	13	14	15	16
$x_{11.2}$		1		1	1											
$x_{12.2}$		1		−1	1							−2				
$x_{13.3}$									1			−1				
x_{13}	1															
x_{23}		1														
x_{33}			1													
x_{43}				1												
x_{53}					1											
x_{63}						1										
x_{73}							1									
x_{83}								1								
x_{93}				1	1											
$x_{10.3}$		1			1											
$x_{11.3}$		1		1	1											
$x_{12.3}$		1		−1	1											
$x_{13.3}$										1						
$x_{14.3}$											1	−4				
$x_{15.3}$	1										1	−3	−1			
$x_{16.3}$	2										1	−2	−2			
$x_{17.3}$	3										1	−1	−3			
$x_{18.3}$	4										1		−4			
x_{14}				1									1			
x_{24}													1			
x_{34}				−1									1		−4	
x_{15}				1										1		
x_{25}														1		
x_{35}				−1										1		−4
x_{16}															1	
x_{26}		1		−1											1	
x_{17}																1
x_{27}		1		−1												1

Problem 7

Source: A. R. Colville, A Comparative Study on Nonlinear Programming Codes, *IBM N.Y. Sci. Center Rept.* 320–2949, June, 1968, p. 31.

No. of variables: 3

No. of constraints: 14 nonlinear inequality constraints
6 bounds on independent variables

Problem 7 was typical of problems in which functions are described by a self-contained computer subroutine.

Objective function:

$$\text{Maximize:} \quad f(\mathbf{x}) = 0.063y_2y_5 - 5.04x_1 - 3.36y_3 - 0.035x_2 - 10x_3$$

Constraints:

$$0 \le x_1 \le 2000$$
$$0 \le x_2 \le 16{,}000$$
$$0 \le x_3 \le 120$$
$$0 \le y_2 \le 5000$$
$$0 \le y_3 \le 2000$$
$$85 \le y_4 \le 93$$
$$90 \le y_5 < 95$$
$$3 \le y_6 \le 12$$
$$0.01 \le y_7 \le 4$$
$$145 \le y_8 \le 162$$

Fortran description of the calculation of y_2 to y_8.

```
     Y(2) = 1.6*X(1)
10   Y(3) = 1.22*Y(2) - X(1)
     Y(6) = (X(2) + Y(3))/X(1)
     Y2CALC = X(1)*(112. + 13.167*Y(6) - 0.6667*Y(6)**2)/100.
     IF(ABS(Y2CALC - Y(2)) - 0.001) 30,30,20
20   Y(2) = Y2CALC
     GO TO 10
30   CONTINUE
     Y(4) = 93.
100  Y(5) = 86.35 + 1.098*Y(6) - 0.038*Y(6)**2 + 0.325*(Y(4) - 89.)
     Y(8) = -133. + 3.*Y(5)
     Y(7) = 35.82 - 0.222*Y(8)
     Y4CALC = 98000.*X(3)/(Y(2)*Y(7) + X(3)*1000.)
     IF(ABS(Y4CALC - Y(4)) - 0.0001) 300,300,200
200  Y(4) = Y4CALC
     GO TO 100
300  CONTINUE
```

Feasible starting point:

$$\mathbf{x}^{(0)} = [1745 \quad 12000 \quad 110]^T$$
$$f(\mathbf{x}^{(0)}) = 868.6458$$

Results:

$$\mathbf{x}^* = [1728.37 \quad 16000 \quad 98.13]^T$$
$$f(\mathbf{x}^*) = 1162.036$$

Problem 8

Source: C. F. Wood, Westinghouse Research Laboratory (cited in Colville, *IBM N.Y. Sci. Center Rept.* 320–2949, June, 1968).

No. of variables: 4

No. of constraints: 8 bounds on the independent variables

Problem 8 was designed to have a nonoptimal stationary point at $f(\mathbf{x}) \approx 8$ that can cause premature convergence.

Objective function:

$$\text{Minimize:}\quad f(\mathbf{x}) = 100(x_2 - x_1^2)^2 + (1 - x_1)^2 + 90(x_4 - x_3^2)^2 + (1 - x_3)^2 + 10.1[(x_2 - 1)^2 + (x_4 - 1)^2] + 19.8(x_2 - 1)(x_4 - 1)$$

Constraints:

$$-10 \le x_i \le 10 \qquad i = 1,2,3,4$$

Feasible starting point:

$$\mathbf{x}^{(0)} = [-3 \quad -1 \quad -3 \quad -1]^T$$

$$f(\mathbf{x}^{(0)}) = 19{,}192$$

Results:

$$\mathbf{x}^* = [1 \quad 1 \quad 1 \quad 1]^T$$

$$f(\mathbf{x}^*) = 0$$

Problem 9

Source: D. M. Himmelblau and R. V. Yates, A New Method of Flow Routing, *Water Resources Res.*, **4**:1193 (1968).

No. of variables: 4

No. of constraints: 1 nonlinear inequality constraint

Objective function:

$$\text{Minimize:}\quad f(\mathbf{x}) = \sum_{i=1}^{19} (y_{i,\,\text{cal}} - y_{i,\,\text{obs}})^2$$

$$y_{i,\,\text{cal}} = \frac{x_3 \beta^{x_2} \left(\dfrac{x_2}{6.2832}\right)^{\frac{1}{2}} \left(\dfrac{c_i}{7.658}\right)^{(x_2 - 1)} \exp\left(x_2 - \beta \dfrac{c_i x_2}{7.658}\right)}{1 + \dfrac{1}{12 x_2}}$$

$$+\frac{(1-x_3)\left(\dfrac{\beta}{x_4}\right)^{x_1}\left(\dfrac{x_1}{6.2832}\right)^{\frac{1}{2}}\left(\dfrac{c_i}{7.658}\right)^{x_1-1}\exp\left(x_1-\beta\dfrac{c_i x_1}{7.658x_4}\right)}{1+\dfrac{1}{12x_1}}$$

where $\beta = x_3 + (1 - x_3)x_4$. (*Note:* The c_i and $y_{i,\text{obs}}$ are given in the accompanying table.)

Constraints:

$$x_3 + (1 - x_3)x_4 \geq 0$$
$$x_4 \geq 0 \qquad i = 1, \ldots, 4$$
$$x_3 \leq 1$$

Starting point:

$$\mathbf{x}^{(0)} = [2 \quad 4 \quad 0.04 \quad 2]^T$$
$$f(\mathbf{x}^{(0)}) = 4.8024$$

Results:

$$\mathbf{x}^* = [12.277 \quad 4.632 \quad 0.313 \quad 2.029]^T$$
$$f(\mathbf{x}^*) = 0.0075$$

c_i and $y_{i,\text{obs}}$ for Test Problem 9

i	c	$y_{i,\text{obs}}$	i	c	$y_{i,\text{obs}}$
1	0.1	0.00189	11	10	0.702
2	1	0.1038	12	11	0.528
3	2	0.268	13	12	0.385
4	3	0.506	14	13	0.257
5	4	0.577	15	14	0.159
6	5	0.604	16	15	0.0869
7	6	0.725	17	16	0.0453
8	7	0.898	18	17	0.01509
9	8	0.947	19	18	0.00189
10	9	0.845			

Problem 10

Source: Shell Development Co. (cited in Colville, *IBM N.Y. Sci. Center Rept.* 320–2949, June, 1968, p. 21).

No. of variables: 5

No. of constraints: 10 linear inequality constraints
5 bounds on independent variables

Objective function:

$$\text{Minimize: } f(\mathbf{x}) = \sum_{j=1}^{5} e_j x_j + \sum_{i=1}^{5}\sum_{j=1}^{5} c_{ij} x_i x_j + \sum_{j=1}^{5} d_j x_j^3$$

Constraints:

$$\sum_{j=1}^{5} a_{ij} x_j - b_i \geq 0 \qquad i = 1, \ldots, 10$$

$$x_j \geq 0 \qquad j = 1, \ldots, 5$$

(*Note:* The e_j, c_{ij}, d_j, a_{ij}, and b_j are given in the accompanying table.)
Feasible starting point:

$$\mathbf{x}^{(0)} = [0 \quad 0 \quad 0 \quad 0 \quad 1]^T$$

$$f(\mathbf{x}^{(0)}) = 20$$

Results:

$$\mathbf{x}^* = [0.3000 \quad 0.3335 \quad 0.4000 \quad 0.4285 \quad 0.224]^T$$

$$f(\mathbf{x}^*) = -32.349$$

Data for Test Problems 10 and 18

j	1	2	3	4	5
e_j	−15	−27	−36	−18	−12
c_{1j}	30	−20	−10	32	−10
c_{2j}	−20	39	−6	−31	32
c_{3j}	−10	−6	10	−6	−10
c_{4j}	32	−31	−6	39	−20
c_{5j}	−10	32	−10	−20	30
d_j	4	8	10	6	2
a_{1j}	−16	2	0	1	0
a_{2j}	0	−2	0	.4	2
a_{3j}	−3.5	0	2	0	0
a_{4j}	0	−2	0	−4	−1
a_{5j}	0	−9	−2	1	−2.8
a_{6j}	2	0	−4	0	0
a_{7j}	−1	−1	−1	−1	−1
a_{8j}	−1	−2	−3	−2	−1
a_{9j}	1	2	3	4	5
a_{10j}	1	1	1	1	1

b_1	b_2	b_3	b_4	b_5	b_6	b_7	b_8	b_9	b_{10}
−40	−2	−.25	−4	−4	−1	−40	−60	5	1

Problem 11

Source: Proctor and Gamble Co. (cited in Colville, *IBM N.Y. Sci.Center Rept.* 320–2949, June, 1968, p. 24).

No. of variables: 5

No. of constraints: 6 nonlinear inequality constraints
10 bounds on independent variables

Note that x_2 and x_4 are not included in the definition of $f(\mathbf{x})$.

Objective function:

$$\text{Minimize:}\quad f(\mathbf{x}) = 5.3578547x_3^2 + 0.8356891x_1x_5 + 37.293239x_1 - 40792.141$$

Constraints:

$$0 \le 85.334407 + 0.0056858x_2x_5 + 0.0006262x_1x_4 - 0.0022053x_3x_5 \le 92$$

$$90 \le 80.51249 + 0.0071317x_2x_5 + 0.0029955x_1x_2 + 0.0021813x_3^2 \le 110$$

$$20 \le 9.300961 + 0.0047026x_3x_5 + 0.0012547x_1x_3 + 0.0019085x_3x_4 \le 25$$

$$78 \le x_1 \le 102$$

$$33 \le x_2 \le 45$$

$$27 \le x_3 \le 45$$

$$27 \le x_4 \le 45$$

$$27 \le x_5 \le 45$$

Feasible starting point:

$$\mathbf{x}^{(0)} = [78.62 \quad 33.44 \quad 31.07 \quad 44.18 \quad 35.22]^T$$

$$f(\mathbf{x}^{(0)}) = -30367$$

Results:

$$x^* = [78.000 \quad 33.000 \quad 29.995 \quad 45.000 \quad 36.776]^T$$

$$f(\mathbf{x}^*) = -30665.5$$

Nonfeasible starting point:

$$\mathbf{x}^{(0)} = [78 \quad 33 \quad 27 \quad 27 \quad 27]^T$$

$$f(\mathbf{x}^{(0)}) = -32217$$

Results:

$f(\mathbf{x}^*) = -30665.5$ $\quad$ x_i's as for feasible starting point

Problem 12

Source: G. K. Barnes, M.S. thesis, The University of Texas, Austin, Tex., 1967. Adapted from C. W. Carroll, Ph.D. dissertation, The Institute of Paper Chemistry, Appleton, Wis., 1959.

No. of variables: 5

No. of constraints: 4 linear inequality constraints
34 nonlinear inequality constraints (as listed—some can be eliminated)
10 bounds on independent variables

The objective function in Problem 12 was the net profit of a hypothetical wood-pulp plant. The constraints (or model) included the usual material and energy balances as well as several empirical equations.

Objective function:

Maximize:
$$f(\mathbf{x}) = 0.0000005843y_{17} - 0.000117y_{14} - 0.1365 - 0.00002358y_{13} - 0.000001502y_{16} - 0.0321y_{12} - 0.004324y_5 - 0.0001\frac{c_{15}}{c_{16}} - 37.48\frac{y_2}{c_{12}}$$

Calculation of y_i's and c_i's:

$$y_1 = x_2 + x_3 + 41.6$$

$$c_1 = 0.024x_4 - 4.62$$

$$y_2 = \frac{12.5}{c_1} + 12.0$$

$$c_2 = 0.0003535x_1^2 + 0.5311x_1 + 0.08705y_2x_1$$

$$c_3 = 0.052x_1 + 78 + 0.002377y_2x_1$$

$$y_3 = \frac{c_2}{c_3}$$

$$y_4 = 19y_3$$

$$c_4 = 0.04782(x_1 - y_3) + \frac{0.1956(x_1 - y_3)^2}{x_2} + 0.6376y_4 + 1.594y_3$$

$$c_5 = 100x_2$$

$$c_6 = x_1 - y_3 - y_4$$

$$c_7 = 0.950 - \frac{c_4}{c_5}$$

$$y_5 = c_6 c_7$$

$$y_6 = x_1 - y_5 - y_4 - y_3$$

$$c_8 = (y_5 + y_4)0.995$$

$$y_7 = \frac{c_8}{y_1}$$

$$y_8 = \frac{c_8}{3798}$$

$$c_9 = y_7 - \frac{0.0663 y_7}{y_8} - 0.3153$$

$$y_9 = \frac{96.82}{c_9} + 0.321 y_1$$

$$y_{10} = 1.29 y_5 + 1.258 y_4 + 2.29 y_3 + 1.71 y_6$$

$$y_{11} = 1.71 x_1 - 0.452 y_4 + 0.580 y_3$$

$$c_{10} = \frac{12.3}{752.3}$$

$$c_{11} = (1.75 y_2)(0.995 x_1)$$

$$c_{12} = 0.995 y_{10} + 1998$$

$$y_{12} = c_{10} x_1 + \frac{c_{11}}{c_{12}}$$

$$y_{13} = c_{12} - 1.75 y_2$$

$$y_{14} = 3623 + 64.4 x_2 + 58.4 x_3 + \frac{146{,}312}{y_9 + x_5}$$

$$c_{13} = 0.995 y_{10} + 60.8 x_2 + 48 x_4 - 0.1121 y_{14} - 5095$$

$$y_{15} = \frac{y_{13}}{c_{13}}$$

$$y_{16} = 148{,}000 - 331{,}000 y_{15} + 40 y_{13} - 61 y_{15} y_{13}$$

$$c_{14} = 2324 y_{10} - 28{,}740{,}000 y_2$$

$$y_{17} = 14{,}130{,}000 - 1328 y_{10} - 531 y_{11} + \frac{c_{14}}{c_{12}}$$

$$c_{15} = \frac{y_{13}}{y_{15}} - \frac{y_{13}}{0.52}$$

$$c_{16} = 1.104 - 0.72 y_{15}$$

$$c_{17} = y_9 + x_5$$

Constraints

$$y_4 - \frac{0.28}{0.72} y_5 \geq 0$$

$$1.5x_2 - x_3 \geq 0$$

$$21.0 - 3496 \frac{y_2}{c_{12}} \geq 0$$

$$\frac{62{,}212}{c_{17}} - 110.6 - y_1 \geq 0$$

$$213.1 \leq y_1 \leq 405.23$$

$$17.505 \leq y_2 \leq 1053.6667$$

$$11.275 \leq y_3 \leq 35.03$$

$$214.228 \leq y_4 \leq 665.585$$

$$7.458 \leq y_5 \leq 584.463$$

$$0.961 \leq y_6 \leq 265.916$$

$$1.612 \leq y_7 \leq 7.046$$

$$0.146 \leq y_8 \leq 0.222$$

$$107.99 \leq y_9 \leq 273.366$$

$$922.693 \leq y_{10} \leq 1286.105$$

$$926.832 \leq y_{11} \leq 1444.046$$

$$18.766 \leq y_{12} \leq 537.141$$

$$1072.163 \leq y_{13} \leq 3247.039$$

$$8961.448 \leq y_{14} \leq 26844.086$$

$$0.063 \leq y_{15} \leq 0.386$$

$$71{,}084.33 \leq y_{16} \leq 140{,}000$$

$$2{,}802{,}713 \leq y_{17} \leq 12{,}146{,}108$$

$$704.4148 \leq x_1 \leq 906.3855$$

$$68.6 \leq x_2 \leq 288.88$$

$$0 \leq x_3 \leq 134.75$$

$$193 \leq x_4 \leq 287.0966$$

$$25 \leq x_5 \leq 84.1988$$

Feasible starting point:

$$\mathbf{x}^{(0)} = [900 \quad 80 \quad 115 \quad 267 \quad 27]^T$$
$$f(\mathbf{x}^{(0)}) = 0.939$$

Results:

$$\mathbf{x}^* = [705.060 \quad 68.600 \quad 102.900 \quad 282.341 \quad 35.627]^T$$
$$f(\mathbf{x}^*) = 1.905$$

Problem 13

Source: M. J. Box, A New Method of Constrained Optimization and a Comparison with Other Methods, *Computer J.*, **8**:42 (1965).

This problem can be regarded as having (*a*) 12 variables, 7 equality constraints, and 16 upper and lower bounds, or more simply, (*b*) 5 variables, 3 nonlinear inequality constraints, and 10 upper and lower bounds.

Problem 13 is an example of determining parameters in highly nonlinear differential equations from experimental data. The objective function was the sum of squared residuals between experimental data and numerically integrated solutions of the differential equations.

Objective function:

$$\text{Maximize:} \quad f(\mathbf{x}) = [50y_1 + 9.583y_2 + 20y_3 + 15y_4 - 852{,}960 - 38{,}100(x_2 + 0.01x_3) + k_{31} + k_{32}x_2 + k_{33}x_3 + k_{34}x_4 + k_{35}x_5]x_1 - 24{,}345 + 15x_6$$

Calculation of x_6, the y_i's, and x_7, x_8:

$$x_6 = (k_1 + k_2x_2 + k_3x_3 + k_4x_4 + k_5x_5)x_1$$
$$y_1 = k_6 + k_1x_2 + k_8x_3 + k_9x_4 + k_{10}x_5$$
$$y_2 = k_{11} + k_{12}x_2 + k_{13}x_3 + k_{14}x_4 + k_{15}x_5$$
$$y_3 = k_{16} + k_{17}x_2 + k_{18}x_3 + k_{19}x_4 + k_{20}x_5$$
$$y_4 = k_{21} + k_{22}x_2 + k_{23}x_3 + k_{24}x_4 + k_{25}x_5$$
$$x_7 = (y_1 + y_2 + y_3)x_1$$
$$x_8 = (k_{26} + k_{27}x_2 + k_{28}x_3 + k_{29}x_4 + k_{30}x_5)x_1 + x_6 + x_7$$

where:

$k_1 = -145{,}421.402$	$k_{19} = 329.574$
$k_2 = 2{,}931.1506$	$k_{20} = -2{,}882.082$
$k_3 = -40.427932$	$k_{21} = 74{,}095.3845$
$k_4 = 5{,}106.192$	$k_{22} = -306.262544$
$k_5 = 15{,}711.36$	$k_{23} = 16.243649$
$k_6 = -161{,}622.577$	$k_{24} = -3{,}094.252$
$k_7 = 4{,}176.15328$	$k_{25} = -5{,}566.2628$
$k_8 = 2.8260078$	$k_{26} = -26{,}237$
$k_9 = 9{,}200.476$	$k_{27} = 99$
$k_{10} = 13{,}160.295$	$k_{28} = -0.42$
$k_{11} = -21{,}686.9194$	$k_{29} = 1{,}300$
$k_{12} = 123.56928$	$k_{30} = 2{,}100$
$k_{13} = -21.1188894$	$k_{31} = 925{,}548.252$
$k_{14} = 706.834$	$k_{32} = -61{,}968.8432$
$k_{15} = 2{,}898.573$	$k_{33} = 23.3088196$
$k_{16} = 28{,}298.388$	$k_{34} = -27{,}097.648$
$k_{17} = 60.81096$	$k_{35} = -50{,}843.766$
$k_{18} = 31.242116$	

Constraints:

$$0 \le x_1 \le 5$$
$$1.2 \le x_2 \le 2.4$$
$$20 \le x_3 \le 60$$
$$9 \le x_4 \le 9.3$$
$$6.5 \le x_5 \le 7$$
$$0 \le x_6 \le 294{,}000$$
$$0 \le x_7 \le 294{,}000$$
$$0 \le x_8 \le 277{,}200$$

Starting point:

$$\mathbf{x}^{(0)} = [2.52 \quad 2 \quad 37.5 \quad 9.25 \quad 6.8]^T$$
$$f(\mathbf{x}^{(0)}) = 2{,}351{,}243.5$$

Results:

$$\mathbf{x}^* = [4.538 \quad 2.400 \quad 60.000 \quad 9.300 \quad 7.000]^T$$
$$f(\mathbf{x}^*) = 5{,}280{,}254$$
$$x_6^* = 75{,}570$$
$$x_7^* = 198{,}157$$
$$x_8^* = 277{,}200$$

Problem 14

Source: M. A. Efroymson, Esso Research and Engineering Co. (cited in Colville, *IBM N.Y. Sci. Center Rept.* 320–2949, June, 1968, p. 26).

No. of variables: 6

No. of constraints: 4 nonlinear inequality constraints

Problem 14 was obtained from an actual "refinery heat integration" problem, and it contained a myriad of local optima of many different values.

Objective function:

$$\text{Minimize:} \quad f(\mathbf{x}) = \sum_{i=1}^{4} c(x_i) + \sum_{i=5}^{6} 100c(x_i)$$

Constraints:

$$t_3 - 300 \geq 0$$
$$t_4 - 300 \geq 0$$
$$280 - T_5 \geq 0$$
$$250 - T_6 \geq 0$$

Calculation of $c(x_i)$, t_i's, and T_i's:

$$c(x_i) = 2.7x_i + 1300 \qquad \left(\text{smallest integer} \geq \frac{x_i}{2000}\right)$$

$$T_1 = \frac{0.0285x_1 + 300}{1 + 0.0001425x_1} \qquad T_4 = \frac{t_2 + (70 - t_2)e^{-\alpha_4}}{1 - 0.8e^{-\alpha_4}}$$

$$t_1 = 500 - T_1 \qquad t_4 = 350 + (t_2 - T_4)e^{\alpha}{}_4$$

$$\alpha_2 = -0.0001665x_2 \qquad T_{j2} = 0.8T_3 + 0.2T_4$$

$$\alpha_5 = 0.000375x_5$$

$$T_2 = \frac{200 - 350e^{-\alpha_2}}{1 - 1.5e^{-\alpha_2}}$$

$$t_2 = 300 + (200 - T_2)e^{\alpha_2}$$
$$\alpha_3 = (0.085)(9.36)10^{-5}x_3$$
$$T_3 = \frac{t_1 + (29.75 - t_1)e^{-\alpha_3}}{1 - 0.915e^{-\alpha_3}}$$
$$t_3 = 350 + (t_1 - T_3)e^{\alpha_3}$$
$$\alpha_4 = 0.00025x_4$$
$$T_5 = 80 + (T_{j2} - 80)e^{-\alpha_5}$$
$$T_{j1} = 0.7T_1 + 0.3T_2$$
$$\alpha_6 = 0.0003x_6$$
$$T_6 = 80 + (T_{j1} - 80)e^{-\alpha_6}$$

Starting point:

$$\mathbf{x}^{(0)} = [8000 \quad 3000 \quad 14000 \quad 2000 \quad 300 \quad 10]^T$$
$$f(\mathbf{x}^{(0)}) = 459{,}100$$

Results with flexible tolerance

$$\mathbf{x}^* = [11{,}884 \quad 3288 \quad 20{,}000 \quad 4000 \quad 114.18 \quad -155.03]^T$$
$$f(\mathbf{x}^*) = 250{,}799.9$$

Values of $f(\mathbf{x})$ at the optimum $\mathbf{x}$ vector reported by Colville:

Feasible starting point	*Code*	*Nonfeasible starting point**
255,303.5	Generalized gradient search	266,754.0
389,858.0	POP-360	
132,518.0	Optim (Mobile Oil)	125,578.0

*Nonfeasible starting vector:

$$\mathbf{x}^0 = [8000 \quad 3000 \quad 10{,}000 \quad 2000 \quad 200 \quad 10]^T$$

Problem 15

Source: P. Huard, *Electricité de France*, Directions des Études et Recherches (cited in Colville, *IBM N.Y. Sci. Center Rept.* 320–2949, June, 1968, p. 28).

No. of variables: 6 total variables; 2 independent

No. of constraints: 4 nonlinear equality constraints
2 constraints on derivatives (discontinuous)
6 lower and 6 upper bounds on the variables

This problem was the optimization of an electrical network.

Objective function:

Minimize: $f(\mathbf{x}) = f_1(x_1) + f_2(x_2)$

Constraints:

$$f_1(x_1) = \begin{cases} 30x_1 & 0 \le x_1 < 300 \\ 31x_1 & 300 \le x_1 < 400 \end{cases}$$

$$f_2(x_2) = \begin{cases} 28x_2 & 0 \le x_2 < 100 \\ 29x_2 & 100 \le x_2 < 200 \\ 30x_2 & 200 \le x_2 < 1000 \end{cases}$$

$$x_1 = 300 - \frac{x_3x_4}{131.078}\cos(1.48577 - x_6) + \frac{0.90798x_3^2}{131.078}\cos(1.47588)$$

$$x_2 = -\frac{x_3x_4}{131.078}\cos(1.48477 + x_6) + \frac{0.90798x_4^2}{131.078}\cos(1.47588)$$

$$x_5 = -\frac{x_3x_4}{131.078}\sin(1.48477 + x_6) + \frac{0.90798x_4^2}{131.078}\sin(1.47588)$$

$$200 - \frac{x_3x_4}{131.078}\sin(1.48477 - x_6) + \frac{0.90798}{131.078}x_3^2\sin(1.47588) = 0$$

$$0 \le x_1 \le 400$$

$$0 \le x_2 \le 1000$$

$$340 \le x_3 \le 420$$

$$340 \le x_4 \le 420$$

$$-1000 \le x_5 \le 1000$$

$$0 \le x_6 \le 0.5236$$

Starting point:

$$\mathbf{x}^{(0)} = [390 \quad 1000 \quad 419.5 \quad 340.5 \quad 198.175 \quad 0.5]^T$$

$$f(\mathbf{x}^{(0)}) = 9074.14$$

Results: Different results can be obtained, depending upon the precision of the **x** vector; the discontinuity in the two derivative constraints forces jump changes in $f(\mathbf{x})$ and $\mathbf{x}^*$.

	High precision	*Moderate precision*
x_1^*	107.81	201.78
x_2^*	196.32	100.00
x_3^*	373.83	383.07
x_4^*	420.00	420.00
x_5^*	21.31	−10.907
x_6^*	0.153	0.07314
$f(\mathbf{x}^*)$	8,927.5888	8,853.44 or 8,953,40

Problem 16

Source: J. D. Pearson, On Variable Metric Methods of Minimization, *Research Analysis Corp. Rept.* RAC-TP-302, McLean, Va., May, 1968.

No. of variables: 9

No. of constraints: 13 nonlinear inequality constraints
1 upper bound

The problem was to maximize the area of a hexagon in which the maximum diameter was unity.

Objective function:

$$\text{Maximize:}\quad f(\mathbf{x}) = 0.5(x_1x_4 - x_2x_3 + x_3x_9 - x_5x_9 + x_5x_8 - x_6x_7)$$

Constraints:

$$1 - x_3^2 - x_4^2 \geq 0$$

$$1 - x_9^2 \geq 0$$

$$1 - x_5^2 - x_6^2 \geq 0$$

$$1 - x_1^2 - (x_2 - x_9)^2 \geq 0$$

$$1 - (x_1 - x_5)^2 - (x_2 - x_6)^2 \geq 0$$

$$1 - (x_1 - x_7)^2 - (x_2 - x_8)^2 \geq 0$$

$$1 - (x_3 - x_5)^2 - (x_4 - x_6)^2 \geq 0$$

$$1 - (x_3 - x_7)^2 - (x_4 - x_8)^2 \geq 0$$

$$1 - x_7^2 - (x_8 - x_9)^2 \geq 0$$

$$x_1x_4 - x_2x_3 \geq 0$$

$$x_3x_9 \geq 0$$

$$-x_5x_9 \geq 0$$

$$x_5x_8 - x_6x_7 \geq 0$$

$$x_9 \geq 0$$

Starting point:

$$x_i^{(0)} = 1 \qquad i = 1, \ldots, 9$$

$$f(\mathbf{x}^{(0)}) = 0$$

Results:

$$\mathbf{x}^* = [0.9971 \quad -0.0758 \quad 0.5530 \quad 0.8331 \quad 0.9981 \quad -0.0623 \quad 0.5642 \quad 0.8256 \quad 0.0000024]^T$$

$$f(\mathbf{x}^*) = 0.8660$$

Problem 17

Source: D. A. Paviani, Ph.D. dissertation, The University of Texas, Austin, Tex., 1969.

No. of variables: 10

No. of constraints: 20 lower and upper bounds

The objective function was undefined outside the feasible region.

Objective function:

$$\text{Minimize:} \quad f(\mathbf{x}) = \sum_{i=1}^{10} \{[\ln (x_i - 2)]^2 + [\ln (10 - x_i)]^2\} - \left(\prod_{i=1}^{10} x_i\right)^{0.2}$$

Constraints:

$$2.001 < x_i < 9.999 \qquad i = 1, \ldots, 10$$

Starting point:

$$x_i^{(0)} = 9 \qquad i = 1, \ldots, 10$$

Results:

$$\mathbf{x}^* = [9.351 \quad 9.351 \quad 9.351 \quad 9.351 \quad 9.351 \quad 9.351 \quad 9.351 \quad 9.351 \quad 9.351 \quad 9.351]^T$$

$$f(\mathbf{x}^*) = -45.778$$

Problem 18

Source: Shell Development Co. (cited in Colville, *IBM N.Y. Sci. Center Rept.* 320–2949, June, 1968, p. 22).

No. of variables: 15

No. of constraints: 5 nonlinear inequality constraints
15 bounds on independent variables

This problem is the dual of Problem 10.

Objective function:

$$\text{Maximize:} \quad f(\mathbf{x}) = \sum_{i=1}^{10} b_i x_i - \sum_{j=1}^{5} \sum_{i=1}^{5} c_{ij} x_{10+i} x_{10+j} - 2 \sum_{j=1}^{5} d_j x_{10+j}^3$$

Constraints:

$$2 \sum_{i=1}^{5} c_{ij} x_{10+i} + 3 d_j x_{10+j}^2 + e_j - \sum_{i=1}^{10} a_{ij} x_i \geq 0 \qquad j = 1, \ldots, 5$$

$$x_i \geq 0 \qquad i = 1, \ldots, 15$$

Note: The e_j, c_{ij}, d_j, a_{ij}, and b_j were given in Problem 10.
Feasible starting point:

$$x_i^{(0)} = 0.0001 \qquad i = 1, \ldots, 15, i \neq 7$$
$$x_7^{(0)} = 60$$
$$f(\mathbf{x}^{(0)}) = -2400.01$$

Results:

$$\mathbf{x}^* = [0.0000 \quad 0.0000 \quad 5.1740 \quad 0.0000 \quad 3.0611 \quad 11.8395 \quad 0.0000 \quad 0.0000 \quad 0.1039 \quad 0.0000 \quad 0.3000 \quad 0.3335 \quad 0.4000 \quad 0.4283 \quad 0.2240]^T$$

$$f(\mathbf{x}^*) = -32.386$$

Nonfeasible starting point:

$$x_i^{(0)} = b_i^{(0)} \qquad i = 1, \ldots, 10$$
$$x_i^{(0)} = 0 \qquad i = 11, \ldots, 14$$
$$x_i^{(0)} = 1 \qquad i = 15$$
$$f(\mathbf{x}^{(0)}) = 6829.06$$

Results: Same $\mathbf{x}^*$ vector and value of $f(\mathbf{x}^*)$ as for feasible starting point.

Problem 19

Source: J. M. Gauthier, IBM France (cited in Colville, *IBM N.Y. Sci. Center Rept.* 320–2949, June, 1968, p. 29).
No. of variables: 16
No. of constraints: 8 linear equality constraints
32 upper and lower bounds on the variables
Objective function:

$$\text{Maximize:} \quad f(\mathbf{x}) = -\sum_{i=1}^{16}\sum_{j=1}^{16} a_{ij}(x_i^2 + x_i + 1)(x_j^2 + x_j + 1)$$

Constraints:

$$\sum_{j=1}^{16} b_{ij}x_j = c_i \qquad i = 1, \ldots, 8$$

$$0 \leq x_j \leq 5 \qquad j = 1, \ldots, 16$$

Data for Problem 19

j	1	2	3	4	5	6	7	8	9	10	11	12	13	14	15	16
a_{1j}	1			1			1	1								1
a_{2j}		1	1				1			1						
a_{3j}			1				1		1	1				1		
a_{4j}				1			1				1				1	
a_{5j}					1	1				1		1				1
a_{6j}						1		1							1	
a_{7j}							1				1		1			
a_{8j}								1		1					1	
a_{9j}									1			1				1
a_{10j}										1				1		
a_{11j}											1		1			
a_{12j}												1		1		
a_{13j}													1	1		
a_{14j}														1		
a_{15j}															1	
a_{16j}																1
b_{1j}	0.22	0.20	0.19	0.25	0.15	0.11	0.12	0.13	1.00							
b_{2j}	−1.46		−1.30	1.82	−1.15		0.80			1.00						
b_{3j}	1.29	−0.89			−1.16	−0.96		−0.49			1.00					
b_{4j}	−1.10	−1.06	0.95	−0.54		−1.78	−0.41					1.00				
b_{5j}				−1.43	1.51	0.59	−0.33	−0.43					1.00			
b_{6j}		−1.72	−0.33		1.62	1.24	0.21	−0.26						1.00		
b_{7j}	1.12			0.31			1.12		−0.36						1.00	
b_{8j}		0.45	0.26	−1.10	0.58		−1.03	0.10								1.00
c_i	2.5	1.1	−3.1	−3.5	1.3	2.1	2.3	−1.5								

Note: The a_{ij}, b_{ij}, and c_i are given in the accompanying table.
Nonfeasible starting point:

$$x_i^{(0)} = 10 \qquad i = 1, \ldots, 16$$
$$f(\mathbf{x}^{(0)}) = -209{,}457$$

Results:

$$\mathbf{x}^* = [0.040 \quad 0.792 \quad 0.203 \quad 0.844 \quad 1.270 \quad 0.935 \quad 1.682 \quad 0.155$$
$$1.568 \quad 0.000 \quad 0.000 \quad 0.000 \quad 0.660 \quad 0.000 \quad 0.674 \quad 0.000]^T$$
$$f(\mathbf{x}^*) = -244.900$$

Problem 20

Source: D. A. Paviani, Ph.D. dissertation, The University of Texas, Austin, Tex., 1969.
No. of variables: 24
No. of constraints: 12 nonlinear equality constraints
2 linear equality constraints
6 nonlinear inequality constraints
24 bounds on independent variables

This problem represents the minimization of the cost of blending multicomponent mixtures.
Objective function:

$$\text{Minimize:} \quad f(\mathbf{x}) = \sum_{i=1}^{24} a_i x_i$$

Note: See accompanying tables for the a_i's, b_i's, c_i's, d_i's, e_i's.
Constraints:

$$h_i(\mathbf{x}) = \frac{x_{(i+12)}}{b_{(i+12)} \sum_{j+13}^{24} \frac{x_j}{b_j}} - \frac{c_i x_i}{40 b_i \sum_{j=1}^{12} \frac{x_j}{b_j}} = 0 \qquad i = 1, \ldots, 12$$

$$h_{13}(\mathbf{x}) = \sum_{i=1}^{24} x_i - 1 = 0$$

$$h_{14}(\mathbf{x}) = \sum_{i=1}^{12} \frac{x_i}{d_i} + f \sum_{i=13}^{24} \frac{x_i}{b_i} - 1.671 = 0$$

where

$$f = (0.7302)(530)\left(\frac{14.7}{40}\right)$$

$$\frac{-[x_i + x_{(i+12)}]}{\sum_{j=1}^{24} x_j + e_i} \geq 0 \qquad i = 1,2,3$$

$$\frac{-[x_{(i+3)} + x_{(i+15)}]}{\sum_{j=1}^{24} x_j + e_i} \geq 0 \qquad i = 4,5,6$$

$$x_i \geq 0 \qquad i = 1, \ldots, 24$$

Nonfeasible starting point:

$$x_i^{(0)} = 0.04 \qquad i = 1, \ldots, 24$$

$$f(\mathbf{x}^{(0)}) = 0.14696$$

Results:

	Flexible tolerance	*NLP*	*SUMT*
$f(\mathbf{x})$	0.05700	0.09670	0.07494
x_1^*	7.804E − 03	9.537E − 07	9.109E − 03
x_2^*	1.121E − 01	0	3.739E − 02
x_3^*	1.136E − 01	4.215E − 03	8.961E − 02
x_4^*	0	1.039E − 04	1.137E − 02
x_5^*	0	0	4.155E − 03
x_6^*	0	0	4.184E − 03
x_7^*	6.609E − 02	2.072E − 01	5.980E − 02
x_8^*	0	5.979E − 01	1.554E − 02
x_9^*	0	1.298E − 01	1.399E − 02
x_{10}^*	0	3.350E − 02	8.780E − 03
x_{11}^*	1.914E − 02	1.711E − 02	1.231E − 02
x_{12}^*	6.009E − 03	8.427E − 03	1.153E − 02
x_{13}^*	5.008E − 02	4.657E − 10	7.570E − 02
x_{14}^*	1.844E − 01	0	7.997E − 02
x_{15}^*	2.693E − 01	0	2.797E − 01
x_{16}^*	0	0	1.168E − 02
x_{17}^*	0	0	2.347E − 02
x_{18}^*	0	0	6.368E − 03
x_{19}^*	1.704E − 01	2.868E − 04	2.028E − 01
x_{20}^*	0	1.193E − 03	7.451E − 03
x_{21}^*	0	8.332E − 05	4.547E − 03
x_{22}^*	0	1.239E − 04	1.010E − 02
x_{23}^*	8.453E − 04	2.070E − 05	1.220E − 03
x_{24}^*	1.980E − 04	1.829E − 05	1.810E − 03
$h_1(\mathbf{x}^*)$	0	4.908E − 07	−1.182E − 03
$h_2(\mathbf{x}^*)$	0	0	−4.329E − 04

	Flexible tolerance	*NLP*	*SUMT*
$h_3(\mathbf{x}^*)$	0	0	3.467E − 03
$h_4(\mathbf{x}^*)$	0	0	2.217E − 04
$h_5(\mathbf{x}^*)$	0	0	−2.550E − 04
$h_6(\mathbf{x}^*)$	0	0	−7.368E − 04
$h_7(\mathbf{x}^*)$	0	−2.209E − 08	1.982E − 03
$h_8(\mathbf{x}^*)$	0	−8.521E − 08	−2.334E − 05
$h_9(\mathbf{x}^*)$	0	−5.854E − 09	1.629E − 03
$h_{10}(\mathbf{x}^*)$	0	8.137E − 08	−4.397E − 04
$h_{11}(\mathbf{x}^*)$	0	−2.596E − 08	9.431E − 04
$h_{12}(\mathbf{x}^*)$	0	5.766E − 08	1.853E − 03
$h_{13}(\mathbf{x}^*)$	0	0	−1.741E − 02
$h_{14}(\mathbf{x}^*)$	N	0	8.743E − 03

Data for Test Problems 10 and 18

i	a_i	b_i	c_i	d_i	e_i
1	0.0693	44.094	123.7	31.244	0.1
2	0.0577	58.12	31.7	36.12	0.3
3	0.05	58.12	45.7	34.784	0.4
4	0.20	137.4	14.7	92.7	0.3
5	0.26	120.9	84.7	82.7	0.6
6	0.55	170.9	27.7	91.6	0.3
7	0.06	62.501	49.7	56.708	
8	0.10	84.94	7.1	82.7	
9	0.12	133.425	2.1	80.8	
10	0.18	82.507	17.7	64.517	
11	0.10	46.07	0.85	49.4	
12	0.09	60.097	0.64	49.1	
13	0.0693	44.094			
14	0.0577	58.12			
15	0.05	58.12			
16	0.20	137.4			
17	0.26	120.9			
18	0.55	170.9			
19	0.06	62.501			
20	0.10	84.94			
21	0.12	133.425			
22	0.18	82.507			
23	0.10	46.07			
24	0.09	60.097			

Problem 21

Source: A. G. Holzman, *SRCC Rept.* 113, University of Pittsburgh, Pittsburgh, Pa., 1969.
No. of independent variables: 3
No. of constraints: 6 bounds on independent variables
Objective function:

$$\text{Minimize:}\quad f(\mathbf{x}) = \sum_{i=1}^{99}\left[\exp - \frac{(u_i - x_2)^{x_3}}{x_1} - 0.01i\right]^2$$

$$u_i = 25 + \left(-50 \ln 0.01i\right)^{\frac{1}{1.5}}$$

Constraints:

$$0.1 \leq x_1 \leq 100.0$$
$$0.0 \leq x_2 \leq 25.6$$
$$0.0 \leq x_3 \leq 5.0$$

Feasible starting point:

$$\mathbf{x}^{(0)} = [100.0 \quad 12.5 \quad 3.0]^T$$

Results:

$$\mathbf{x}^* = [50.0 \quad 25.0 \quad 1.5]^T$$
$$f(\mathbf{x}^*) = 0.0$$

Problem 22

Source: U.S. Steel Co. (cited by Holzman, *SRCC Rept.* 113, 1969).
No. of independent variables: 6
No. of constraints: 4 nonlinear inequality constraints
12 bounds on independent variables
Objective function:

$$\text{Minimize:}\quad f(\mathbf{x}) = 4.3x_1 + 31.8x_2 + 63.3x_3 + 15.8x_4 + 68.5x_5 + 4.7x_6$$

Constraints:

$$17.1x_1 + 38.2x_2 + 204.2x_3 + 212.3x_4 + 623.4x_5 + 1495.5x_6$$
$$- 169x_1x_3 - 3580x_3x_5 - 3810x_4x_5 - 18{,}500x_4x_6 - 24{,}300x_5x_6 \geq b_1$$
$$17.9x_1 + 36.8x_2 + 113.9x_3 + 169.7x_4 + 337.8x_5 + 1385.2x_6$$
$$- 139x_1x_3 - 2450x_4x_5 - 16{,}600x_4x_6 - 17{,}200x_5x_6 \geq b_2$$
$$-273x_2 - 70x_4 - 819x_5 + 26{,}000x_4x_5 \geq b_3$$
$$159.9x_1 - 311x_2 + 587x_4 + 391x_5 + 2198x_6 - 14{,}000x_1x_6 \geq b_4$$
$$0 \leq x_1 \leq 0.31 \qquad 0 \leq x_4 \leq 0.042$$
$$0 \leq x_2 \leq 0.046 \qquad 0 \leq x_5 \leq 0.028$$
$$0 \leq x_3 \leq 0.068 \qquad 0 \leq x_6 \leq 0.0134$$

Starting point:

For:				*Results:*						
b_1	b_2	b_3	b_4	x_1	x_2	x_3	x_4	x_5	x_6	$f(\mathbf{x}^*)$
4.97	−1.88	−29.08	−78.02	0	0	0	0	0	0.00333	0.0156
4.97	−1.88	−69.08	−118.02	0	0	0	0	0	0.00332	0.0156
32.97	25.12	−29.08	−78.02	0	0	0.0633	0	0	0.0134	4.070
32.97	25.12	−124.08	−173.02	0	0	0.0633	0	0	0.0134	4.070

Problem 23

Source: J. Bracken and G. P. McCormick, "Selected Applications of Nonlinear Programming," John Wiley & Sons, Inc., New York, 1968, p. 26. (A weapon assignment problem.)

No. of independent variables: 100

No. of constraints: 12 linear constraints
100 lower bounds on the independent variables

Objective function:

$$\text{Minimize:} \quad f(\mathbf{x}) = \sum_{j=1}^{20} u_j \left(\prod_{i=1}^{5} a_{ij}^{x_{ij}} - 1 \right)$$

Constraints:

$$\left(\sum_{i=1}^{5} x_{ij} \right) - b_j \geq 0 \qquad j = 1,6,10,14,15,16,20$$

$$-\left(\sum_{j=1}^{20} x_{ij} \right) - c_i \geq 0 \qquad i = 1, \ldots, 5$$

Data for Problem 23

a_{ij}: probability that weapon i will not damage target j

j \ i	1	2	3	4	5	6	7	8	9	10	11	12	13	14	15	16	17	18	19	20	c_1: *no. of weapons i available*
1	1	.95	1	1	1	.85	.90	.85	.80	1	1	1	1	1	1	1	1	.95	1	1	200
2	.84	.83	.85	.84	.85	.81	.81	.82	.80	.86	1	.98	1	.88	.87	.88	.85	.84	.85	.85	100
3	.96	.95	.96	.96	.96	.90	.92	.91	.92	.95	.99	.98	.99	.98	.97	.98	.95	.92	.93	.92	300
4	1	1	1	1	1	1	1	1	1	.96	.91	.92	.91	.92	.98	.93	1	1	1	1	150
5	.92	.94	.92	.95	.95	.98	.98	1	1	.90	.95	.96	.91	.98	.99	.99	1	1	1	1	250

b_j: minimum no. of weapons to be assigned to target j

30					100				40				50	70	35				10

u_j: military value of target j

60	50	50	75	40	60	35	30	25	150	30	45	125	200	200	130	100	100	100	150

Feasible solutions obtained for weapons assignment problem x_{ij}

Weapon type i	Target j																				Total
	1	2	3	4	5	6	7	8	9	10	11	12	13	14	15	16	17	18	19	20	
1		24 (16)				32 (100)	37 (38)	28 (26)	22 (20)						5			52			200 (200)
2	1	8	2	18 (23)	11 (20)										29 (25)	9 (31)	21 (1)				99 (100)
3		9			29	62									35 (45)		17 (76)	25 (56)	62 (62)	60 (61)	299 (300)
4											9	39 (39)	(50)	58 (57)		44 (4)					150 (150)
5	47 (50)	5 (46)	36 (47)	12		6				50 (50)	42 (57)		51		1						250 (250)
Total	48 (50)	46 (62)	38 (47)	30 (23)	40 (20)	100 (100)	37 (38)	28 (26)	22 (20)	50 (50)	51 (57)	39 (39)	51 (50)	58 (57)	70 (70)	53 (35)	38 (77)	77 (56)	62 (62)	60 (61)	

Notes: No.( ) from Holzman; with ( ) from Bracken and McCormick.
$f(\mathbf{x}) = 1732$.

Problem 24

Source: J. Bracken and G. P. McCormick, "Selected Applications of Nonlinear Programming," John Wiley & Sons, Inc., New York, 1968, p. 19.

No. of independent variables: 2

No. of constraints: 1 nonlinear inequality constraint
1 linear inequality constraint

Objective function:

Minimize: $f(\mathbf{x}) = (x_1 - 2)^2 + (x_2 - 1)^2$

Constraints:

$$g_1(\mathbf{x}) = -x_1^2 + x_2 \geq 0$$
$$g_2(\mathbf{x}) = -x_1 - x_2 + 2 \geq 0$$

Nonfeasible starting point:

$$\mathbf{x}^{(0)} = [2 \quad 2]^T$$
$$f(\mathbf{x}^{(0)}) = 1$$

Results:

$$f(\mathbf{x}^*) = 1$$
$$\mathbf{x}^* = [1 \quad 1]^T$$

Problem 25

Source: Unpublished

No. of independent variables: 2

No. of constraints: None

Objective function:

Minimize: $f(\mathbf{x}) = 4(x_1 - 5)^2 + (x_2 - 6)^2$

Starting point:

$$\mathbf{x}^{(0)} = [8 \quad 9]^T$$

$$f(\mathbf{x}^{(0)}) = 45$$

Results:

$$\mathbf{x}^* = [5 \quad 6]^T$$

$$f(\mathbf{x}^*) = 0$$

Problem 26

Source: M. J. D. Powell, *Computer J.*, **5**:147 (1962).
No. of independent variables: 4
No. of constraints: None
Objective function:

$$\text{Minimize:}\quad f(\mathbf{x}) = (x_1 + 10x_2)^2 + 5(x_3 - x_4)^2 + (x_2 - 2x_3)^4 + 10(x_1 - x_4)^4$$

Starting point:

$$\mathbf{x}^{(0)} = [3 \quad -1 \quad 0 \quad 1]^T \qquad \text{and} \qquad [1 \quad 1 \quad 1 \quad 1]^T$$
$$f(\mathbf{x}^{(0)}) = 215 \qquad\qquad f(\mathbf{x}^{(0)}) = 125$$

Results:

$$\mathbf{x}^* = [0 \quad 0 \quad 0 \quad 0]^T$$
$$f(\mathbf{x}^*) = 0$$

Problem 27

Source: Unpublished
No. of independent variables: 2
No. of constraints: None
Objective function:

$$\text{Minimize:}\quad f(\mathbf{x}) = (x_1x_2)^2(1 - x_1)^2[1 - x_1 - x_2(1 - x_1)^5]^2$$

Starting point:

$$\mathbf{x}^{(0)} = [-1.2 \quad 1]^T$$
$$f(\mathbf{x}^{(0)}) = 26{,}656$$

Results:

$$\mathbf{x}^* = [1 \quad \text{unbounded}]^T \text{ or } [0 \quad \text{unbounded}]^T \text{ or } [\text{unbounded} \quad 0]^T$$
$$f(\mathbf{x}^*) = 0$$

Problem 28

Source: Unpublished; solution of a set of equations
No. of independent variables: 2
No. of constraints: None

Objective function:

Minimize: $f(\mathbf{x}) = (x_1^2 + x_2 - 11)^2 + (x_1 + x_2^2 - 7)^2$

Starting point:

$$\mathbf{x}^{(0)} = [1 \quad 1]^T$$
$$f(\mathbf{x}^{(0)}) = 106$$

Results:

$$\mathbf{x}^* = [3.58443 \quad -1.84813]^T \quad \text{and} \quad [3 \quad 2]^T$$
$$f(\mathbf{x}^*) = 0$$

Note: All the computer codes tested from $\mathbf{x}^0 = [1 \quad 1]^T$ yielded the second solution.

Problem 29

Source: Unpublished
No. of independent variables: 2
No. of constraints: None
Objective function:

Minimize: $f(\mathbf{x}) = (x_1^2 + 12x_2 - 1)^2 + (49x_1^2 + 49x_2^2 + 84x_1 + 2324x_2 - 681)^2$

Starting point:

$$\mathbf{x}^{(0)} = [1 \quad 1]^T$$
$$f(\mathbf{x}^{(0)}) = 3.3306 \times 10^6$$

Results:

$$\mathbf{x}^* = [0.28581 \quad 0.27936]^T$$
$$f(\mathbf{x}^*) = 5.9225$$

or

$$\mathbf{x}^* = [-21.026653 \quad -36.760090]^T$$
$$f(\mathbf{x}^*) = 0$$

Problem 30

Source: Unpublished
No. of independent variables: 3
No. of constraints: None

Objective function:

$$\text{Minimize:}\quad f(\mathbf{x}) = 100\left[x_3 - \left(\frac{x_1 + x_2}{2}\right)^2\right]^2 + (1 - x_1)^2 + (1 - x_2)^2$$

Starting point:

$$\mathbf{x}^{(0)} = [-1.2 \quad 2 \quad 0]^T$$
$$f(\mathbf{x}^{(0)}) = 8.40$$

Results:

$$\mathbf{x}^* = [1 \quad 1 \quad 1]^T$$
$$f(\mathbf{x}^*) = 0$$

Problem 31

Source: J. Bracken and G. P. McCormick, "Selected Applications of Nonlinear Programming," John Wiley & Sons, Inc., New York, 1968, p. 18.

No. of independent variables: 2

No. of constraints: None

Objective function:

$$\text{Minimize:}\quad f(\mathbf{x}) = (x_1 - 2)^2 + (x_2 - 1)^2 + \frac{0.04}{g_1(\mathbf{x})} + \frac{h_1^2(\mathbf{x})}{0.2}$$

$$g_1(\mathbf{x}) = -\frac{x_1^2}{4} - x_2^2 + 1 \qquad \text{and} \qquad h_1(\mathbf{x}) = x_1 - 2x_2 + 1$$

Starting point:

$$\mathbf{x}^{(0)} = [2 \quad 2]^T$$
$$f(\mathbf{x}^{(0)}) = 5.99$$

Results:

$$\mathbf{x}^* = [1.7954 \quad 1.3779]^T \qquad \text{(local minimum)}$$
$$f(\mathbf{x}^*) = 0.16904$$

Note: Other starting vectors yield other results; the solution vector reported in the source was not obtained, nor was the solution vector given in the source obtained from the source starting vector. Too large an initial step from $\mathbf{x}^{(0)}$ will bypass the local minimum and drive $f(\mathbf{x})$ to the global minimum at $g_1(\mathbf{x}) = -0$, where $f(\mathbf{x}) \to -\infty$.

Problem 32

Source: Unpublished (estimation of coefficients from experimental data by least squares)
No. of independent variables: 4
No. of constraints: None
Objective function:

$$\text{Minimize:} \quad f(\mathbf{x}) = 10^4 \sum_{i=1}^{7} \left(\frac{\dfrac{x_1^2 + x_2^2 a_i + x_3^2 a_i^2}{1 + x_4^2 a_i} - b_i}{b_i} \right)$$

Starting point:

$$\mathbf{x}^{(0)} = [2.7 \quad 90 \quad 1500 \quad 10]$$

$$f(\mathbf{x}^{(0)}) = 2.905 \times 10^4$$

Results:

$$\mathbf{x}^* = [2.714 \quad 140.4 \quad 1707 \quad 31.51]$$

$$f(\mathbf{x}^*) = 318.572$$

i	a_i	b_i
1	0.0	7.391
2	0.000428	11.18
3	0.00100	16.44
4	0.00161	16.20
5	0.00209	22.20
6	0.00348	24.02
7	0.00525	31.32

Problem 33

Source: Unpublished
No. of independent variables: 2
No. of constraints: None
Objective function:

$$\text{Maximize:} \quad f(\mathbf{x}) = e^{-x_1 - x_2}(2x_1^2 + 3x_2^2)$$

Starting point:

$$\mathbf{x}^{(0)} = [2.5 \quad 2.5]$$

$$f(\mathbf{x}^{(0)}) = 2.3299 \times 10^{-5}$$

Results:

$$\mathbf{x}^* = [0 \quad 1]^T \qquad \text{or} \qquad [0 \quad -1]^T$$
$$f(\mathbf{x}^*) = 1.1036$$

Problem 34

Source: R. Fletcher and M. J. D. Powell, *Computer J.*, **6**:33 (1963). (A helical valley in the x_3 direction.)
No. of independent variables: 3
No. of constraints: None
Objective function:

$$\text{Minimize:}\quad f(\mathbf{x}) = 100\{[x_3 - 10\theta(x_1,x_2)]^2 + [(x_1^2 + x_2^2)^{\frac{1}{2}} - 1]^2\} + x_3^2$$

$$\theta(x_1,x_2) = \begin{cases} \dfrac{1}{2\pi}\tan^{-1}\dfrac{x_2}{x_1} & x_1 > 0 \\ \dfrac{1}{2} + \dfrac{1}{2\pi}\tan^{-1}\dfrac{x_2}{x_1} & x_1 < 0 \end{cases}$$

Starting point:

$$\mathbf{x}^{(0)} = [-1 \quad 0 \quad 0]^T$$

Results:

$$\mathbf{x}^* = [1 \quad 0 \quad 0]^T$$
$$f(\mathbf{x}^*) = 0$$

Problem 35

Source: Unpublished
No. of independent variables: 2
No. of constraints: None
Objective function:

$$\text{Minimize:}\quad f(\mathbf{x}) = u_1^2 + u_2^2 + u_3^2$$

$$u_i = c_i - x_1(1 - x_2^i) \qquad c_1 = 1.5, c_2 = 2.25, c_3 = 2.625$$

Starting point:

$$\mathbf{x}^{(0)} = [2 \quad 0.2]^T$$
$$f(\mathbf{x}^{(0)}) = 0.52978$$

Results:

$$\mathbf{x}^* = [3.0000 \quad 0.5000]^T$$
$$f(\mathbf{x}^*) = 0$$

appendix b

Computer codes (in Fortran) that are not available commercially

The codes listed are:

Unconstrained NLP

1. Broyden
2. Davidon-Fletcher-Powell
3. Pearson 2
4. Pearson 3
5. Fletcher-Reeves
6. Newton
7. Projected Newton
8. Goldstein-Price
9. Powell
10. Nelder-Mead

Constrained NLP

1. Flexible tolerance

Grateful acknowledgment is made to Michael Andenberg for his preparation of the computer codes 1 to 8.

B.1 UNCONSTRAINED NLP ALGORITHMS EMPLOYING DERIVATIVES

These instructions describe how to use the computer code encompassing the following algorithms:

1. Davidon-Fletcher-Powell
2. Pearson
3. Pearson 3
4. Broyden
5. Projected Newton
6. Fletcher-Reeves
7. Newton
8. Goldstein-Price

using (*a*) Golden section search
(*b*) DSC-Powell (Coggin) search

1. *Structure of the Program*

1.1 *Calling Program* (EXEC). The calling program initializes INDIC and IPRINT and measures the time for execution (excluding initialization). Place IPRINT = 1 if a complete printout stage by stage is desired; place IPRINT = 2 if only the final values of the objective function and **x** vector at termination are desired. Program EXEC calls MINI. (For the INDIC to use, see subroutine SEARCH.)

1.2 *Subroutine MINI.* This subroutine controls the selection of the algorithm to be used. It calls DER, FUN, ETA, and CONVRG. There is a separate MINI for (*a*) Davidon-Fletcher-Powell, Broyden, Pearson 2, Pearson 3, Projected Newton, (*b*) Newton, (*c*) Goldstein-Price, and (*d*) Fletcher-Reeves. MINI also prints the information on each stage if called for by IPRINT.

1.3 *Subroutine ETA.* Contains the computation of the direction matrix for the first five algorithms above (there are five different ETA's).

1.4 *Subroutine CONVRG.* Contains the convergence criteria (tested at the end of each stage) based on the values of $f(\mathbf{x})$, $\mathbf{x}$, and the derivatives of $f(\mathbf{x})$.

1.5 *Subroutine SEARCH.* These are the unidimensional search routines and are interchangeable with each other.

1.6 *Subroutine FUN.* Contains the function to be minimized. Place $f(\mathbf{x})$ as

$$\text{FX} = \ldots.$$

1.7 *Subroutine DER.* Contains the analytical first partial derivatives of $f(\mathbf{x})$ in sequence

$$GX(1) = \text{partial derivative with respect to } x_1$$

$$GX(2) = \text{partial derivative with respect to } x_2$$

etc.

1.8 *BLOCK DATA.* The initial **x**-vector elements and the number of independent variables, N, are entered here, the latter as an integer.

2. *User-supplied Information*

No parameter data have to be introduced into the program. It is possible to add subroutines to accomplish this.

2.1 To select the linear search routine (DSC-Powell, called Coggin, or the golden section search), use the appropriate subroutine SEARCH (as identified by the comment cards below the title) with MINI.

2.2 To select the proper ETA for the desired algorithm for the group of algorithms 1 through 5, read the comment cards below the title. Be sure to remove the old ETA when inserting a new one.

2.3 In subroutine BLOCK DATA insert the initial guesses for the **x** vector $\mathbf{x}^{(0)}$ and the dimensions of the **x** vector, the number of variables. Replace the statement that now commences with the word DATA with your initial **x** and the dimension number N (an integer). See the sample in the program for the format.

```
      PROGRAM EXEC(INPUT,OUTPUT)
      COMMON /THREE/ N,NFUNCT,NDRV,ITER,INDIC,IPRINT
      NFUNCT=0
      N4RV=0
      INDIC=2
      IPRINT = 1
      CALL SECOND(TIME)
      PRINT 2000, TIME
      CALL MINI
      CALL SECOND(TIME)
      PRINT 2000, TIME
      CALL EXIT
 2000 FORMAT(*0TIME IS NOW*,F10.3,* SECONDS.*,/)
      END


      SUBROUTINE CONVRG(GY,IPASS)
      COMMON /ONE/ X(10),Y(10),S(10),FX,FY
      COMMON /THREE/ N,NFUNCT,NDRV,ITER,INDIC,IPRINT
      DIMENSION GY(10)
      XTOL=0.00001
```

```
      FTOL=0.00001
      GTOL=0.0001
C   CHECK FUNCTION VALUES
      IF(ABS(FX).LE.FTOL) GOTO10
      IF(ABS((FX-FY)/FX).GT.FTOL) GO TO 60
      GO TO 20
10    IF(ABS(FX-FY).GT.FTOL) GO TO 60
C   CHECK TEST POINT
20    DO 40 I=1,N
      IF(ABS(X(I)).LE.XTOL) GO TO 30
      IF(ABS((X(I)-Y(I))/X(I)).GT.XTOL) GO TO 60
      GO TO 40
30    IF(ABS(X(I)-Y(I)).GT.XTOL) GO TO 60
40    CONTINUE
C   CHECK GRADIENT
      DO 50 I=1,N
50    IF(ABS(GY(I)).GT.GTOL) GO TO 60
C   ALL CONVERGENCE CRITERIA SATISFIED
      IPASS=1
      RETURN
C   CONVERGENCE NOT ACHIEVED
60    IPASS=2
      RETURN
      END


      BLOCK DATA
      COMMON /ONE/ X(10),Y(10),S(10),FX,FY
      COMMON /THREE/ N,NFUNCT,NDRV,ITER,INDIC,IPRINT
      DATA (X(I),I=1,4),N/-3.,-1.,-3.,-1.,4/
      END


      SUBROUTINE DER(Z,GX)
      COMMON /THREE/ N,NFUNCT,NDRV,ITER,INDIC,IPRINT
      DIMENSION Z(10)
      DIMENSION TM(6)
      DIMENSION GX(10)
      TM(1)=Z(2)-Z(1)*Z(1)
      TM(2)=1-Z(1)
      TM(3)=Z(4)-Z(3)*Z(3)
      TM(4)=1-Z(3)
      TM(5)=Z(2)-1
      TM(6)=Z(4)-1
      GX(1)=-400.*Z(1)*TM(1)-2.*TM(2)
      GX(2)=200.*TM(1)+20.2*TM(5)+19.8*TM(6)
      GX(3)=-360*Z(3)*TM(3)-2.*TM(4)
      GX(4)=180.*TM(3)+20.2*TM(6)+19.8*TM(5)
      NDRV=NDRV+4
      RETURN
      END

      SUBROUTINE FUN(Z,FX)
      COMMON /THREE/ N,NFUNCT,NDRV,ITER,INDIC,IPRINT
      DIMENSION Z(10)
      DIMENSION TM(6)
      TM(1)=Z(2)-Z(1)*Z(1)
      TM(2)=1-Z(1)
      TM(3)=Z(4)-Z(3)*Z(3)
      TM(4)=1-Z(3)
      TM(5)=Z(2)-1
      TM(6)=Z(4)-1
      FX=100.*TM(1)*TM(1)+TM(2)*TM(2)+90.*TM(3)*TM(3)+TM(4)*TM(4)+
     A10.1*(TM(5)*TM(5)+TM(6)*TM(6))+19.8*TM(5)*TM(6)
      NFUNCT=NFUNCT+1
      RETURN
      END
```

```
      SUBROUTINE MINI
C  NEWTON METHOD
C  THE ETA SUBROUTINE MUST CALCULATE THE ACTUAL HESSIAN MATRIX AND
C  RETURN THE INVERSE IN THE H ARRAY.
      COMMON /ONE/ X(10),Y(10),S(10),FX,FY
      COMMON /TWO/ H(10,10),DELX(10),DELG(10),GX(10)
      COMMON /THREE/ N,NFUNCT,NDRV,ITER,INDIC,IPRINT
      ITER=0
C  EVALUATE INITIAL POINY
      CALL FUN(X,FX)
      KOUNTS=KOUNTS+1
      PRINT 2000, ITER,FX,(X(I),I=1,N)
      CALL DER(X,GX)
C  ITERATE FOR SOLUTION
10    ITER=ITER+1
      CALL ETA
      DO 30 I=1,N
      S(I)=0.
      DO 20 J=1,N
20    S(I)=S(I)-H(I,J)*GX(J)
30    Y(I)=X(I)+S(I)
      CALL FUN(Y,FY)
      KOUNTS=KOUNTS+1
C  TEST FOR CONVERGENCE
      CALL DER(Y,GX)
      CALL CONVRG(GX,IPASS)
      IF(IPASS.EQ.1) GO TO 50
C  CONVERGENCE CRITERIA NOT SATISFIED
      FX=FY
      DO 40 I=1,N
40    X(I)=Y(I)
      IF(IPRINT.EQ.1) PRINT2000, ITER,FX,(X(I),I=1,N)
      GO TO 10
C  CONVERGENCE CRITERIA SATISFIED
50    PRINT 2000, ITER,FY,(Y(I),I=1,N)
2000  FORMAT(1X,I6,E16.8,(5E16.8))
      RETURN
      END
```

```
      SUBROUTINE MINI
      COMMON /ONE/ X(10),Y(10),S(10),FX,FY
      COMMON /TWO/ H(10,10),DELX(10),DELG(10),GX(10)
      COMMON /THREE/ N,NFUNCT,NDRV,ITER,INDIC,IPRINT
      DIMENSION GY(10)
C  EXECUTIVE PROGRAM FOR METHODS WHICH APPROXIMATE THE INVERSE OF THE
C  HESSIAN MATRIX INCLUDING
C   1 DAVIDON-FLETCHER,POWELL
C   2 BROYDEN
C   3 PEARSON 2
C   4 PEARSON 3
      ITER=0
C  EVALUATE THE INITIAL POINT
      CALL FUN(X,FX)
      CALL DER(X,GX)
      PRINT 2000, ITER,NFUNCT,NDRV,FX,(X(I),I=1,N)
C  SET UP THE IDENTITY MATRIX
5     DO 20 I=1,N
      DO 10 J=1,N
10    H(I,J)=0.0
20    H(I,I)=1.0
C  TAKE GRADIENT STEP
      IF(IPRINT.EQ.1) PRINT 2100
2100  FORMAT(* GRADIENT STEP*)
      DO 30 I=1,N
30    S(I)=-GX(I)
C  FIND NEXT POINT
40    CALL SEARCH
```

```
C  CHECK WHETHER SEARCH WAS A SUCCESS.  IF NOT, RESET H AND TAKE GRADIENT STEP
      IF(FY.GE.FX) GO TO 5
      ITER=ITER+1
      CALL DER(Y,GY)
      CALL CONVRG(GY,IPASS)
      IF(IPASS.EQ.1) GO TO 70
C  CONVERGENCE CRITERIA NOT SATISFIED.  FIND A NEW DIRECTION MATRIX
      IF(IPRINT.EQ.1) PRINT 2000, ITER,NFUNCT,NDRV,FY,(Y(I),I=1,N)
      DO 50 I=1,N
      DELG(I)=GY(I)-GX(I)
      DELX(I)=Y(I)-X(I)
      GX(I)=GY(I)
50    X(I)=Y(I)
      FX=FY
      CALL ETA
C  SET UP NEW SEARCH DIRECTION
      DO 60 I=1,N
      S(I)=0.
      DO 60 J=1,N
60    S(I)=S(I)-H(I,J)*GY(J)
      GO TO 40
C  CONVERGENCE CRITERIA SATISFIED
70    PRINT 2000, ITER,NFUNCT,NDRV,FY,(Y(I),I=1,N)
2000  FORMAT(1X,3I7,E16.8,(5E16.8))
      RETURN
      END


      SUBROUTINE MINI
C  FLETCHER-REEVES CONJUGATE GRADIENT METHOD, SECTION 3.3-2
      COMMON /ONE/ X(10),Y(10),S(10),FX,FY
      COMMON /TWO/ H(10,10),DELX(10),DELG(10),GX(10)
      COMMON /THREE/ N,NFUNCT,NDRV,ITER,INDIC,IPRINT
      ITER=0
      IRESET=N+1
      INDEX=IRESET
C  EVALUATE STARTING POINT
      CALL FUN(X,FX)
      CALL DER(X,GX)
      PRINT 2000, ITER,NFUNCT,NDRV,FX,(X(I),I=1,N)
C  CALCULATE SQUARED NORM OF GRADIENT
10    SQNOR1=0.
      DO 20 I=1,N
20    SQNOR1=SQNOR1+GX(I)*GX(I)
      IF(INDEX.NE.IRESET) GO TO 50
C  SET SEARCH DIRECTION TO NEGATIVE GRADIENT
30    IF(IPRINT.EQ.1) PRINT 2100
2100  FORMAT(* GRADIENT STEP*)
      INDEX=0
      DO 40 I=1,N
40    S(I)=-GX(I)
      GO TO 70
C  SET SEARCH DIRECTION USING RATIO OF SQUARED NORMS
50    DO 60 I=1,N
60    S(I)=-GX(I)+S(I)*SQNOR1/SQNOR2
C  FIND NEXT POINT
70    CALL SEARCH
C  CHECK WHETHER SEARCH WAS A SUCCESS.  IF NOT TAKE A GRADIENT STEP.
      IF(FY.GE.FX) GO TO 30
      CALL DER(Y,GX)
      INDEX=INDEX+1
      ITER=ITER+1
      CALL CONVRG(GX,IPASS)
      IF(IPASS.EQ.1) GO TO 90
C  CONVERGENCE CRITERIA NOT SATISFIED.  CONTINUE SEARCH.
      IF(IPRINT.EQ.1) PRINT 2000, ITER,NFUNCT,NDRV,FY,(Y(I),I=1,N)
C  SAVE INFORMATION FOR NEXT STAGE
      DO 80 I=1,N
```

```
      DELX(I)=Y(I)-X(I)
80    X(I)=Y(I)
      FX=FY
      SQNOR2=SQNOR1
      GO TO 10
C  CONVERGENCE CRITERIA SATISFIED
90    PRINT 2000, ITER,NFUNCT,NDRV,FY,(Y(I),I=1,N)
2000  FORMAT(1X,3I7,E16.8,(5E16.8))
      RETURN
      END


      SUBROUTINE ETA
C  DAVIDON, FLETCHER-POWELL METHOD, SECTION 3.4-2
      COMMON /TWO/ H(10,10),DELX(10),DELG(10),GX(10)
      COMMON /THREE/ N,NFUNCT,NDRV,ITER,INDIC,IPRINT
      DIMENSION  HDG(10),DGH(10)
      DXDG=0.
      DGHDG=0.
      DO 20 I=1,N
      HDG(I)=DGH(I)=0.
      DO 10  J=1,N
      HDG(I)=HDG(I)-H(I,J)*DELG(J)
10    DGH(I)=DGH(I)+DELG(J)*H(J,I)
      DXDG=DXDG+DELX(I)*DELG(I)
20    DGHDG=DGHDG+DGH(I)*DELG(I)
      DO 30 I=1,N
      DO 30 J=1,N
30    H(I,J)=H(I,J)+DELX(I)*DELX(J)/DXDG+HDG(I)*DGH(J)/DGHDG
      RETURN
      END


      SUBROUTINE ETA
C  BROYDEN METHOD, SECTION 3.4-1
      COMMON /TWO/ H(10,10),DELX(10),DELG(10),GX(10)
      COMMON /THREE/ N,NFUNCT,NDRV,ITER,INDIC,IPRINT
      DIMENSION DXHDG(10)
      DGTERM=0.
      DO 20 I=1,N
      DXHDG(I)=DELX(I)
      DO 10 J=1,N
10    DXHDG(I)=DXHDG(I)-H(I,J)*DELG(J)
20    DGTERM=DGTERM+DXHDG(I)*DELG(I)
      DO 30 I=1,N
      DO 30 J=I,N
30    H(I,J)=H(J,I)=H(I,J)+DXHDG(I)*DXHDG(J)/DGTERM
      RETURN
      END


      SUBROUTINE ETA
C  PEARSON 2 METHOD, SECTION 3.4
      COMMON /TWO/ H(10,10),DELX(10),DELG(10),GX(10)
      COMMON /THREE/ N,NFUNCT,NDRV,ITER,INDIC,IPRINT
      DIMENSION DXHDG(10)
      DXDG=0.
      DO 20 I=1,N
      DXHDG(I)=DELX(I)
      DO 10 J=1,N
10    DXHDG(I)=DXHDG(I)-H(I,J)*DELG(J)
20    DXDG=DXDG+DELX(I)*DELG(I)
      DO 30 I=1,N
      DO 30 J=1,N
30    H(I,J)=H(I,J)+DXHDG(I)*DELX(J)/DXDG
      RETURN
      END
```

```
      SUBROUTINE ETA
C  PEARSON 3 METHOD, SECTION 3.4
      COMMON /TWO/ H(10,10),DELX(10),DELG(10),GX(10)
      COMMON /THREE/ N,NFUNCT,NDRV,ITER,INDIC,IPRINT
      DIMENSION DXHDG(10),DGH(10)
      DGHDG=0.
      DO 20 I=1,N
      DXHDG(I)=DELX(I)
      DGH(I)=0.
      DO 10 J=1,N
      DXHDG(I)=DXHDG(I)-H(I,J)*DELG(J)
10    DGH(I)=DGH(I)+DELG(J)*H(J,I)
20    DGHDG=DGHDG+DGH(I)*DELG(I)
      DO 30 I=1,N
      DO 30 J=1,N
30    H(I,J)=H(I,J)+DXHDG(I)*DGH(J)/DGHDG
      RETURN
      END


      SUBROUTINE ETA
C  PROJECTED NEWTON METHOD, SECTION 3.4   (SAME AS ZOUTENDIJK PROJECTION
C  METHOD, SECTION 3.3-4)
C  THE H MATRIX MUST RESET TO THE IDENTITY MATRIX EVERY N STEPS
      COMMON /TWO/ H(10,10),DELX(10),DELG(10),GX(10)
      COMMON /THREE/ N,NFUNCT,NDRV,ITER,INDIC,IPRINT
      DIMENSION HDG(10),DGH(10)
      DGHDG=0.
      DO 20 I=1,N
      HDG(I)=0.
      DGH(I)=0.
      DO 10 J=1,N
      HDG(I)=HDG(I)+H(I,J)*DELG(J)
10    DGH(I)=DGH(I)+DELG(J)*H(J,I)
20    DGHDG=DGHDG+DELG(I)*HDG(I)
      DO 30 I=1,N
      DO 30 J=1,N
30    H(I,J)=H(I,J)-DGH(I)*HDG(J)/DGHDG
      RETURN
      END


      SUBROUTINE MINI
C  GOLDSTEIN-PRICE METHOD, SECTION 3.4
C  VERSION 2.  THE SEARCH DIRECTION (PHI) IS SET TO THE GRADIENT ONLY ON
C  THE FIRST STEP AND WHEN Q IS SINGULAR
      COMMON /ONE/ X(10),Y(10),PHI(10),FX,FY
      COMMON /TWO/ Q(10,10),DELX(10),DELG(10),GX(10)
      COMMON /THREE/ N,NFUNCT,NDRV,ITER,INDIC,IPRINT
      DIMENSION GY(10)
      R=0.0001
      THETA=R
      ITER=0
C  EVALUATE STARTING POINT
      CALL FUN(X,FX)
      CALL DER(X,GX)
C  PRINT POINT
      PRINT 2000, ITER,NFUNCT,NDRV,FX,(X(I),I=1,N)
      GO TO 70
C  GENERATE THE Q MATRIX
10    DO 30 J=1,N
      XSAVE=X(J)
      X(J)=X(J)+THETA
      CALL DER(X,GY)
      DO 20 I=1,N
20    Q(I,J)=(GY(I)-GX(I))/THETA
30    X(J)=XSAVE
C  INVERT Q
```

```
      CALL SYMINV(Q,N,10,ISF)
      IF(ISF.NE.1) GO TO 40
      IF(IPRINT.EQ.1) PRINT 2200
2200  FORMAT(1X,*Q IS SINGULAR*)
      GO TO 70
C  FORM THE PHI VECTOR USING Q
40    DO 50 I=1,N
      PHI(I)=0.
      DO 50 J=1,N
50    PHI(I)=PHI(I)+Q(I,J)*GX(J)
      GO TO 110
70    IF (IPRINT.EQ.1) PRINT 2100
2100  FORMAT(1X,*GRADIENT STEP*)
C  SET PHI TO THE GRADIENT
      DO 80  I=1,N
80    PHI(I)=GX(I)
110   CONTINUE
      CALL SEARCH
      IF(FY.GE.FX) GO TO 70
C  CALCULATE THETA FOR NEXT ITERATION
      PHNORM=0.
      DO 120 I=1,N
120   PHNORM=PHNORM+PHI(I)*PHI(I)
      PHNORM=SQRT(PHNORM)
      THETA=R*PHNORM
C  TEST FOR CONVERGENCE
      ITER=ITER+1
      CALL DER(Y,GX)
      CALLCONVRG(GX,IPASS)
      IF(IPASS.EQ.1) GO TO 140
C CONVERGENCE CRITERIA NOT SATISFIED
      IF(IPRINT.EQ.1) PRINT 2000, ITER,NFUNCT,NDRV,FY,(Y(I),I=1,N)
      FX=FY
      DO 130 I=1,N
      DELX(I)=Y(I)-X(I)
130   X(I)=Y(I)
      GO TO 10
C  CONVERGENCE CRITERIA SATISFIED
140   PRINT 2000, ITER,NFUNCT,NDRV,FY,(Y(I),I=1,N)
2000  FORMAT(1X,3I7,E16.8,(5E16.8))
      RETURN
      END
      SUBROUTINE SYMINV(A,NC,ND,ISF)
      DIMENSION A(ND,ND),T(20),Q(20),R(20)
      ZERO=0.0 $ ONE=1.0 $ ISF=0 $ DO 21 M=1,NC
21    R(M)=ONE
      DO 38 M=1,NC $ BIG=ZERO
      DO 24 L=1,NC $ AB=ABS(A(L,L)) $ IF(AB-BIG)24,24,22
22    IF(R(L))23,24,23
23    BIG=AB $ K=L
24    CONTINUE $ IF(BIG)26,25,26
25    PRINT 13 $ ISF=1 $ RETURN
13    FORMAT(10X,23HMATRIX INVERSION FAILED)
26    R(K)=ZERO $ Q(K)=ONE/A(K,K) $ T(K)=ONE $ A(K,K)=ZERO $ KM1=K-1
      IF(KM1.EQ.0)31,27
27    DO 30 L=1,KM1 $ T(L)=A(L,K) $ IF(R(L))29,28,29
28    Q(L)=A(L,K)*Q(K) $ GO TO 30
29    Q(L)=-A(L,K)*Q(K)
30    A(L,K)=ZERO
31    CONTINUE $ KP1=K+1 $ IF(KP1.GT.NC)37,32
32    DO 36 L=KP1,NC $ IF(R(L))33,34,33
33    T(L)=A(K,L) $ GO TO 35
34    T(L)=-A(K,L)
35    Q(L)=-A(K,L)*Q(K)
36    A(K,L)=ZERO
37    CONTINUE
      DO 38 L=1,NC $ DO 38 K=L,NC
38    A(L,K)=A(L,K)+T(L)*Q(K) $ M=NC+1 $ L=NC
```

```
      DO 39 K=2,NC $ M=M-1 $ L=L-1 $ DO 39 J=1,L
39    A(M,J)=A(J,M)
      RETURN               $      END



      SUBROUTINE SEARCH
C   COGGIN METHOD OF UNIDIMENSIONAL SEARCH
      COMMON /ONE/ X(10),Y(10),S(10),FX,FY
      COMMON /TWO/ H(10,10),DELX(10),DELG(10),GX(10)
      COMMON /THREE/ N,NFUNCT,NDRV,ITER,INDIC,IPRINT
C *** THE INITIAL VARIABLE VALUES ARE IN X, AND THE CORRESPONDING
C *** FUNCTION VALUE IS FX.
C *** THE SEARCH DIRECTION VECTOR IS S, AND THE INITIAL STEP SIZE STEP.
      IEXIT=0
      NTOL=0
      FTOL=.001
      FTOL2=FTOL/100.
      FA=FB=FC=FX
      DA=DB=DC=0.
      K=-2
      M=0
      STEP=1.0
      D=STEP
C   USE THE PARAMETER INDIC TO INDICATE HOW THE SEARCH VECTOR LENGTH
C   SHOULD BE SCALED.
C     INDIC=2  DO NOT SCALE.  TAKE LENGTH GIVEN BY MINI CALCULATION
C     INDIC=1  SCALE ONLY IF THE LENGTH OF THE LAST STEP WAS SHORTER THAN
C              THE LENGTH OF THE SEARCH VECTOR.  SCALE TO LENGTH OF LAST STEP.
C     INDIC=ANYTHING BUT 1 OR 2 RESULTS IN SCALING TO LENGTH OF LAST STEP.
      IF(INDIC.EQ.2.OR.ITER.EQ.0) GO TO 1
C   FIND NORM OF S AND NORM OF DELX
      DXNORM=0.
      SNORM=0.
      DO 102 I=1,N
      DXNORM=DXNORM+DELX(I)*DELX(I)
102   SNORM=SNORM+S(I)*S(I)
      IF(INDIC.EQ.1.AND.DXNORM.GE.SNORM) GO TO 1
      RATIO=DXNORM/SNORM
      STEP=SQRT(RATIO)
      D=STEP
C *** START THE SEARCH THE BOUND THE MINIMUM
    1 DO 2  I=1,N
    2 Y(I)=X(I)+D*S(I)
      CALL FUN(Y,F)
      K=K+1
      IF(F-FA) 5,3,6
C *** NO CHANGE IN FUNCTION VALUE.  RETURN WITH VECTOR CORRESPONDING TO
C     FUNCTION VALUE OF FA, BECAUSE IF THE FUNCTION VALUE IS INDEPENDENT
C     OF THIS SEARCH DIRECTION, THEN CHANGES IN THE VARIABLE VALUES MAY
C     UPSET THE MAIN PROGRAM CONVERGENCE TESTING.
    3 DO 4  I=1,N
    4 Y(I)=X(I)+DA*S(I)
      FY=FA
      IF(IPRINT.EQ.1) PRINT 2100
2100  FORMAT(* SEARCH FAILED.  FUNCTION VALUE INDEPENDENT OF SEARCH DIRE
     ACTION*)
      GO TO 326
C *** THE FUNCTION IS STILL DECREASING.  INCREASE THE STEP SIZE BY
C     DOUBLE THE PREVIOUS INCREASE IN STEP SIZE.
    5 FC=FB  $  FB=FA  $  FA=F
      DC=DB  $  DB=DA  $  DA=D
      D=2.0*D+STEP
      GO TO 1
C *** MINIMUM IS BOUNDED IN AT LEAST ONE DIRECTION.
    6 IF(K) 7,8,9
C     MINIMUM IS BOUNDED IN ONE DIRECTION ONLY.  REVERSE THE SEARCH
C     DIRECTION AND RECYCLE.
```

```
    7 FB=F
      DB=D  $  D=-D  $  STEP=-STEP
      GO TO 1
C     MINIMUM IS BOUNDED IN BOTH DIRECTIONS AFTER ONLY TWO FUNCTION
C     EVALUATIONS 'ONE EITHER SIDE OF THE ORIGINZ.  PROCEED TO THE
C     PARABOLIC INTERPOLATION.
    8 FC=FB  $  FB=FA  $  FA=F
      DC=DB  $  DB=DA  $  DA=D
      GO TO 21
C     THE MINIMUM IS BOUNDED AFTER AT LEAST TWO FUNCTION EVALUATIONS IN
C     THE SAME DIRECTION.  EVALUATE THE FUNCTION AT STEP SIZE=(DA+DB)/2.
C     THIS WILL YEILD 4 EQUALLY SPACED POINTS BOUNDING THE MINIMUM.
    9 DC=DB  $  DB=DA  $  DA=D
      FC=FB  $  FB=FA  $  FA=F
   10 D=0.5*(DA+DB)
      DO 11  I=1,N
   11 Y(I)=X(I)+D*S(I)
      CALL FUN(Y,F)
C *** NOW HAVE THAT  FA*FBOFC  AND THAT  FA*FOFC  ASSUMING THAT THE
C     FUNCTION IS UNIMODAL.  REMOVE EITHER POINT A OR POINT B IN SUCH A
C     WAY THAT THE FUNCTION IS BOUNDED AND  FA*FBOFC  'THE CORRESPONDING
C     STEP SIZES ARE  DA*DB*DC  OR  DAODBODC  Z.
   12 IF((DC-D)*(D-DB)) 15,13,18
C *** LOCATION OF MINIMUM IS LIMITED BY ROUNDING ERRORS. RETURN WITH B.
   13 DO 14  I=1,N
   14 Y(I)=X(I)+DB*S(I)
      FY=FB
      IF(IEXIT.EQ.1) GO TO 32
      IF(IPRINT.EQ.1) PRINT 2200
2200  FORMAT(* SEARCH FAILED.  LOCATION OF MINIMUM LIMITED BY ROUNDING*)
      GO TO 325
C *** THE POINT D IS IN THE RANGE DA TO DB.
   15 IF(F-FB) 16,13,17
   16 FC=FB  $  FB=F
      DC=DB  $  DB=D
      GO TO 21
   17 FA=F
      DA=D
      GO TO 21
C *** THE POINT D IS IN THE RANGE DB TO DC
   18 IF(F-FB) 19,13,20
   19 FA=FB  $  FB=F
      DA=DB  $  DB=D
      GO TO 21
   20 FC=F
      DC=D
C *** NOW PERFORM THE PARABOLIC INTERPOLATION.
   21 A=FA*(DB-DC)+FB*(DC-DA)+FC*(DA-DB)
      IF(A) 22,30,22
   22 D=0.5*((DB*DB-DC*DC)*FA+(DC*DC-DA*DA)*FB+(DA*DA-DB*DB)*FC)/A
C     CHECK THAT THE POINT IS GOOD. IF SO, EVALUATE THE FUNCTION.
      IF((DA-D)*(D-DC)) 13,13,23
   23 DO 24  I=1,N
   24 Y(I)=X(I)+D*S(I)
      CALL FUN(Y,F)
C *** CHECK FOR CONVERGENCE.  IF NOT ACHEIVED, RECYCLE.
      IF(ABS(FB)-FTOL2) 25,25,26
   25 A=1.0  $  GO TO 27
   26 A=1.0/FB
   27 IF((ABS(FB-F)*A)-FTOL) 28,28,12
C *** CONVERGENCE ACHEIVED.  RETURN WITH THE SMALLER OF F AND FB.
   28 IEXIT=1
      IF(F-FB) 29,13,13
   29 FY=F
      GO TO 32
C *** THE PARABOLIC INTERPOLATION WAS PREVENTED BY THE DIVISOR BEING
C     ZERO.  IF THIS IS THE FIRST TIME THAT IT HAS HAPPENED, TRY AN
C     INTERMEDIATE STEP SIZE AND RECYCLE) OTHERWISE GIVE UP AS IT LOOKS
```

```
C     LIKE A LOST CAUSE.
   30 IF(M) 31,31,13
   31 M=M+1
      GO TO 10
   32 DO 99 I=1,N
      IF(Y(I).NE.X(I)) GO TO 325
   99 CONTINUE
      GO TO 33
  325 IF(NTOL.NE.0.AND.IPRINT.EQ.1) PRINT 3000, NTOL
3000  FORMAT(1X,*TOLERANCE REDUCED *,I1,* TIME(S)*)
  326 IF(FY.LT.FX) RETURN
      IF(S(1).NE.-GX(1)) .OR.(FY.LT.FX)) RETURN
      PRINT5000
5000  FORMAT(* SEARCH FAILED ON A GRADIENT STEP.  JOB TERMINATED.*)
      PRINT 5100, ITER,NFUNCT,NDRV,FY,(Y(I),I=1,N)
5100  FORMAT(1X,3I7,E16.8,(5E16.8))
      STOP
   33 IF(NTOL.EQ.5) GO TO 34
      IEXIT=0
      NTOL=NTOL+1
      FTOL=FTOL/10.
      GO TO 12
34    IF(IPRINT.EQ.1) PRINT 2000
2000  FORMAT(* A POINT BETTER THAN THE ENTERING POINT CANNOT BE FOUND.*)
      RETURN
      END


      SUBROUTINE SEARCH
C  UNIDIMENSIONAL SEARCH USING GOLDEN SECTION.  VERSION 2, MOD 4.
      COMMON /ONE/ X(10),Y(10),S(10),FX,FY
      COMMON /TWO/ H(10,10),DELX(10),DELG(10),GX(10)
      COMMON /THREE/ N,NFUNCT,NDRV,ITER,INDIC,IPRINT
      DIMENSION Z(10),W(10),P(10),R(10),DIFF(10),SS(10)
      DATA F1/0.618033989/
C  P=OLDEST OF LAST THREE POINTS
C  Z=MIDDLE POINT
C  W=CURRENT POINT
      NTRIES=0
      NTOL=0
C  TOL=SQUARED NORM OF VECTOR FROM W TO Z WHICH MUST BE ACHIEVED FOR
C     CONVERGENCE
      TOL=0.000001
      NTIMES=0
C  USE THE PARAMETER INDIC TO INDICATE HOW THE SEARCH VECTOR LENGTH
C  SHOULD BE SCALED.
C     INDIC=2  DO NOT SCALE.  TAKE LENGTH GIVEN BY MINI CALCULATION
C     INDIC=1  SCALE ONLY IF THE LENGTH OF THE LAST STEP WAS SHORTER THAN
C              THE LENGTH OF THE SEARCH VECTOR.  SCALE TO LENGTH OF LAST STEP.
C     INDIC=ANYTHING BUT 1 OR 2 RESULTS IN SCALING TO LENGTH OF LAST STEP.
      IF(INDIC.EQ.2.OR.ITER.EQ.0) GO TO 4
C  NORMALIZE THE SEARCH VECTOR TO THE LENGTH USED ON THE PREVIOUS STEP.
      DXNORM=0.
      SNORM=0.
      DO 2 I=1,N
      DXNORM=DXNORM+DELX(I)*DELX(I)
2     SNORM=SNORM+S(I)*S(I)
      IF(INDIC.EQ.1. AND.DXNORM.GE.SNORM) GO TO 4
      DXNORM=SQRT(DXNORM)
      SNORM=SQRT(SNORM)
      RATIO=DXNORM/SNORM
      DO 3 I=1,N
3     SS(I)=S(I)*RATIO
      GO TO 10
C  MAINTAIN THE INTEGRITY OF THE SEARCH VECTOR BY CONSTRUCTING AN IDENTICAL
C  VECTOR AND OPERATING ON IT.
4     DO 5 I=1,N
5     SS(I)=S(I)
```

```
C***BRACKET THE MINIMUM IN THE S DIRECTION
C   TAKE STEP FROM ORIGINAL POINT
10      DO 20 I=1,N
        Z(I)=X(I)
20      W(I)=X(I)+SS(I)
        FZ=FX
        NTIMES=NTIMES+1
        CALL FUN(W,FW)
        IF(FW-FZ) 30,70,50
C   CONTINUE SEARCH IN SAME DIRECTION
30      DO 40 I=1,N
        P(I)=Z(I)
        Z(I)=W(I)
        SS(I)=2.*SS(I)
40      W(I)=W(I)+SS(I)
        FP=FZ
        FZ=FW
        NTIMES=NTIMES+1
        CALL FUN(W,FW)
        IF(FW-FZ) 30,70,120
C   FW.GT.FZ, DECIDE WHETHER TO REVERSE SEARCH DIRECTION
50      IF(NTIMES.NE.1)  GO TO 120
C   REVERSE SEARCH DIRECTION
        DO 60 I=1,N
        SS(I)=-SS(I)
60      P(I)=W(I)
        FP=FW
        GO TO 10
C   FZ=FW, CHECK MIDPOINT
70      DO 80 I=1,N
80      R(I)=(Z(I)+W(I))/2.
        NTIMES=NTIMES+1
        CALL FUN(R,FR)
        MIN=1
        IF(FR-FZ) 140,300,90
90      IF(NTIMES.NE.2) GO TO 110
C   REVERSE SEARCH DIRECTION
        DO 100 I=1,N
        SS(I)=-SS(I)
100     P(I)=R(I)
        FP=FR
        GO TO 10
C   R AND P BRACKET Z AND THE MINIMUM
110     DO 115 I=1,N
        W(I)=R(I)
        R(I)=Z(I)
115     Z(I)=P(I)
        MIN=1
        FW=FR
        FR=FZ
        FZ=FP
        GO TO 140
C   P AND W BRACKET Z AND THE MINIMUM
120     DO 130 I=1,N
        R(I)=Z(I)
130     Z(I)=P(I)
        MIN=1
        FR=FZ
        FZ=FP
C***GOLDEN SEARCH)  Z AND W BRACKET THE MINIMUM
140     WZNORM=0.
        DO 145 I=1,N
        DIFF(I)=W(I)-Z(I)
145     WZNORM=WZNORM+DIFF(I)*DIFF(I)
        IF(WZNORM.LT.TOL) GO TO 290
146     DO 150 I=1,N
        SECT=F1*DIFF(I)
        P(I)=Z(I)+SECT
```

```
150   R(I)=W(I)-SECT
      CALL FUN(P,FP)
      CALL FUN(R,FR)
160   IF(FR-FP) 170,230,200
C  REPLACE W BY P AND P BY R
170   WZNORM=0.
      DO 180 I=1,N
      W(I)=P(I)
      P(I)=R(I)
      DIFF(I)=W(I)-Z(I)
      WZNORM=WZNORM+DIFF(I)*DIFF(I)
180   R(I)=W(I)-F1*DIFF(I)
      FW=FP
      FP=FR
      IF(WZNORM.LT.TOL) GO TO 320
      CALL FUN(R,FR)
      GO TO 160
C  REPLACE Z BY R AND R BY P
200   WZNORM=0.
      DO 210 I=1,N
      Z(I)=R(I)
      R(I)=P(I)
      DIFF(I)=W(I)-Z(I)
      WZNORM=WZNORM+DIFF(I)*DIFF(I)
210   P(I)=Z(I)+F1*DIFF(I)
      FZ=FR
      FR=FP
      IF(WZNORM.LT.TOL) GO TO 300
      CALL FUN(P,FP)
      GO TO 160
C  FP=FR, CHECK MIDPOINT
230   DO 240 I=1,N
240   Y(I)=(P(I)+R(I))/2.
      CALL FUN(Y,FY)
      IF(FY-FP) 250,340,270
C  P AND R BRACKET THE MINIMUM (YIS BRACKETED)
250   DO 260 I=1,N
      Z(I)=R(I)
      W(I)=P(I)
260   R(I)=Y(I)
      FZ=FR
      FW=FP
      FR=FY
      MIN=1
      GO TO 140
C  THERE ARE TWO MINIMA BETWEEN Z AND W.  ARBITRARILY PICK THE INTERVAL
C  BETWEEN Y AND W (WHICH INCLUDES P)
270   DO 280 I=1,N
280   Z(I)=Y(I)
      FZ=FY
      MIN=2
      GO TO 140
C  BRACKET ON THE MIN IS SUFFICIENTLY SMALL
290   GO TO (300,320), MIN
C  R IS THE POINT INSIDE THE BRACKET
300   DO 310 I=1,N
310   Y(I)=R(I)
      FY=FR
      GO TO 340
C  P IS THE POINT INSIDE THE BRACKET
320   DO 330  I=1,N
330   Y(I)=P(I)
      FY=FP
340   CONTINUE
    DO 345 I=1,N
345 IF(X(1).NE.Y(1)) GO TO 346
    GO TO 350
346 IF(FY.GE.FX) GO TO 370
```

```
      IF(IPRINT.NE.1) RETURN
      IF (NTOL.NE.0) PRINT 3000,NTOL
      IF(NTRIES.NE.0) PRINT 3100
3000  FORMAT(1X,*TOLERANCE REDUCED *,I1,* TIME(S)*)
3100  FORMAT(1X,*SECOND TRY.*)
      RETURN
C**TAKE CARE OF PATHALOGICAL CONDITONS
C  AT THE PRESENT TOLERANCE LEVEL NO POINT CAN BE FOUND WHICH
C  IS BETTER THAN THE ENTERING POINT.  REDUCE TOL BY A FACTOR OF 100.
350   IF(NTOL.EQ.5) GO TO 360
      NTOL=NTOL+1
      TOL=TOL/100.
      GO TO 146
C  PRINT MESSAGE AND RETURN
360   IF(IPRINT.NE.1) GO TO 376
      IF(NTRIES.NE.0) GO TO 375
      PRINT 2000,TOL
2000  FORMAT(1X,*THE TOLERANCE HAS BEEN REDUCED 5 TIMES TO A CURRENT VAL
     AUE OF*,E15.8,*.*,/,
     B1X,  *A POINT BETTER THAN THE ENTERING POINT CANNOT BE FOUND AT TH
     CIS LEVEL OF TOLERANCE.  THE ENTERING POINT IS BEING RETURNED.*)
      GO TO 376
C** FY.GT.FX, FIND A BRACKET EXCLUDING THE VALLEY CONTAINING Y.
370   IF(NTRIES.EQ.0) GO TO 380
      IF(NTOL.LT.5) GO TO 350
375   PRINT 2100
      PRINT 3000,NTOL
2100  FORMAT(1X,*A POINT WAS FOUND SUCH THAT FY WAS GREATER THAN FX.  A
     BSECOND ATTEMPT TO FIND A POINT WITH A FUNCTION VALUE LESS THAN FX
     CFAILED.*)
376   IF(S(1).NE.-GX(1) .OR.(FY.LT.FX)) RETURN
      PRINT 2200
2200  FORMAT(* SEARCH FAILED ON A GRADIENT STEP.  JOB TERMINATED*)
      PRINT 2300, ITER,NFUNCT,NDRV,FY,(Y(I),I=1,N)
2300  FORMAT(1X,3I7,E16.8,(5E16.8))
      STOP
C  LOOK FOR A BRACKET NEAR X ON THE SIDE OPPOSITE FROM Y.
380   NTRIES=1
      DO 390 I=1,N
      Z(I)=X(I)
      SS(I)=(X(I)-Y(I))/20.
390   W(I)=X(I)+SS(I)
      FZ=FX
      CALL FUN(W,FW)
      IF(FW-FZ) 30,400,450
C  FZ=FW, CHECK MIDPOINT
400   DO 410 I=1,N
410   P(I)=(Z(I)+W(I))/2.
      CALL FUN(P,FP)
      IF(FP-FZ) 420,320,430
C FZ.GT.FP AND FW.GT.FP.  W AND Z FORM A BRACKET
420   MIN=2
      GO TO 140
C  FP.GT.FZ, P IS A BRACKET WITH THE MINIMUM BETWEEN P AND Y
430   DO 440 I=1,N
440   W(I)=P(I)
      FW=FP
C  FW.GT.FZ, W IS A BRACKET WITH THE MINIMUM BETWEEN W AND Y
C  CHECK MIDPOINT OF Y AND W
450   DO 460 I=1,N
      Z(I)=Y(I)
460   P(I)=(Z(I)+W(I))/2.
      FZ=FY
470   CALL FUN(P,FP)
      IF(FP.LE.FZ) GO TO 490
C  TRY AGAIN
      DO 480 I=1,N
      Z(I)=P(I)
```

```
480   P(I)=(W(I)+Z(I))/2.
      FZ=FP
      GO TO 470
C  P IS IN A VALLEY DIFFERENT FROM THE ONE CONTAINING Y.
C  CHECK WHETHER P AND W FORM A BRACKET
490   DO 500 I=1,N
500   R(I)=(P(I)+W(I))/2.
      CALL FUN(R,FR)
      IF(FR.GE.FW) GO TO 560
      IF(FR.GE.FP) GO TO 520
C  P AND W FORM A BRACKET
505   DO 510 I=1,N
510   Z(I)=P(I)
      FZ=FP
      MIN=1
      GO TO 140
C  FR.LT.FW, FR.GE.FP.  HENCE LOOK FOR A BRACKETING VALUE BETWEEN P AND Z.
520   DO 530 I=1,N
      R(I)=P(I)
530   P(I)=(P(I)+Z(I))/2.
      FR=FP
540   CALL FUN(P,FP)
      IF(FP.LE.FZ) GO TO 490
C  FP.GT.FZ.  APPARENTLY Z IS IN THE SAME VALLEY WITH Y.
      DO 550 I=1,N
      Z(I)=P(I)
550   P(I)=(R(I)+Z(I))/2.
      FZ=FP
      GO TO 540
C  FR.GE.FW
560   IF(FR.LT.FP) GO TO 505
C  FR.GE.FP, R AND W FORM A BRACKET
      DO 570 I=1,N
570   Z(I)=R(I)
      FZ=FR
      GO TO 146
      END
```

B.2 INSTRUCTIONS FOR THE OPTIMIZATION METHOD OF POWELL

A separate subroutine MINI has been prepared that carries out the Powell algorithm for unconstrained optimization without the use of derivatives. Note that DER is not used and that INDIC must be set to 2. Special convergence instructions will be found in the comment cards in MINI. Place ICONVG = 1 if one pass through the Powell algorithm is sufficient; place ICONVG = 2 if the final solution is to be perturbed, a new solution sought, and an extrapolation between the two solutions carried out. A special subroutine TEST must accompany MINI.

Other than the above special precautions, subroutine MINI for Powell is completely compatible with Program EXEC and should be used with it. Program EXEC has been previously discussed.

```
      SUBROUTINE MINI
C   POWELL METHOD OF DIRECT SEARCH
C   SUBROUTINE TEST MUST BE PROVIDED FOR CONVERGENCE TESTING
      COMMON /ONE/ X(10),Y(10),S(10),FX,FY
      COMMON/TWO/ DIRECT(10,10),DUM(10),BEFORE(10),FIRST(10)
      COMMON /THREE/ N,NFUNCT,NDRV,ITER,INDIC,IPRINT
      DIMENSION  W(10),SECND(10)
      EQUIVALENCE   (W,SECND)
C *** N = THE NUMBER OF VARIABLES.
C     ICONVG = THE FINAL CONVERGENCE TEST DESIRED.
C            = 1, TERMINATE AS SOON AS TESTING IS SATISFIED.
C            = 2, AS SOON AS THE TESTING CRITERIA ARE SATISFIED INCREASE
C                 ALL THE VARIABLES BY 10*ACC AND SOLVE PROBLEM AGAIN.
C     THEN PERFORM A LINE SEARCH BETWEEN THE SOLUTIONS IF DIFFERENT
C     SOLUTIONS ARE DEEMED TO BE FOUND.
C     STEP = THE INITIAL STEP SIZE.
C     ACC = THE REQUIRED ACCURACY IN THE FUNCTION AND VECTOR VALUES.
C     INSERT IPRINT= 1 FOR COMPLETE PRINT OUT OR IPRINT = 2 FINAL
C    1ANSWER ONLY
      ACC=0.00001
      STEP=1.0
C   INDIC MUST BE SET TO 2
      INDIC=2
      ICONVG=1
      ITER=0
      NTRY=1
      N1=N-1
      STEPA=STEP
C *** SET UP THE INITIAL DIRECTION MATRIX (USING UNIT VECTORS).
      DO 2  I=1,N
      DO 1  J=1,N
    1 DIRECT(J,I)=0.
    2 DIRECT(I,I)=1.
C *** EVALUATED THE FUNCTION AT THE INITIAL VARIABLE VALUES.
  100 CALL FUN(X,FX)
      PRINT 2000, ITER,NFUNCT,FX,(X(I),I=1,N)
2000  FORMAT(1X,2I7,E16.8,(5E16.8))
      GO TO 301
C *** SAVE THE FINAL FUNCTION VALUE (F1) AND THE FINAL VARIABLE VALUES
C     (BEFORE) FROM THE PREVIOUS CYCLE.
    3 ITER=ITER+1
      IF(IPRINT.EQ.1) PRINT 2000, ITER,NFUNCT,FX,(X(I),I=1,N)
  301 F1=FX
      DO 4  I=1,N
    4 BEFORE(I)=X(I)
      SUM=0.
C     AT THE END OF THE CYCLE, SUM WILL CONTAIN THE MAXIMUM CHANGE IN
C     THE FUNCTION VALUE FOR ANY SEARCH DIRECTION, AND ISAVE INDICATES
C     THE DIRECTION VECTOR TO WHICH IT CORRESPONDS.
      DO 9  I=1,N
C     S CONTAINS THE INITIAL STEP SIZES IN THE I-TH DIRECTION.
      DO 5  J=1,N
    5 S(J)=DIRECT(J,I)*STEP
C     FIND THE MINIMUM IN THE I-TH DIRECTION, AND THE CHANGE IN FUNCTION
C     VALUE.
      CALL SEARCH
      A=FX-FY
      IF(A-SUM) 7,7,6
    6 ISAVE=I
      SUM=A
C     TRANSFER THE NEW FUNCTION AND VARIABLE VALUES TO FX AND X.
    7 DO 8  J=1,N
    8 X(J)=Y(J)
    9 FX=FY
C *** NOW INVESTIGATE WHETHER A NEW SEARCH DIRECTION SHOULD BE INCORPOR-
```

```
C     ATED INSTEAD OF THE ISAVE DIRECTION.
      F2=FX
      DO 10  I=1,N
   10 W(I)=2.0*X(I)-BEFORE(I)
      CALL FUN(W,F3)
      A=F3-F1
      IF(A) 11,19,19
   11 A=2.0*(F1-2.0*F2+F3)*((F1-F2-SUM)/A)**2
      IF(A-SUM) 12,19,19
C *** A NEW SEARCH DIRECTION IS REQUIRED. FIRST REMOVE ROW ISAVE.
   12 IF(ISAVE-N) 13,15,15
   13 DO 14  I=ISAVE,N1
      II=I+1
      DO 14  J=1,N
   14 DIRECT(J,I)=DIRECT(J,II)
C     SET THE N-TH DIRECTION VECTOR EQUAL TO THE NORMALISED DIFFERENCE
C     BETWEEN THE INITIAL AND FINAL VARIABLE VALUES FOR LAST CYCLE.
   15 A=0.
      DO 16  J=1,N
      DIRECT(J,N)=X(J)-BEFORE(J)
   16 A=DIRECT(J,N)**2+A
      A=1.0/SQRT(A)
      DO 17  J=1,N
      DIRECT(J,N)=DIRECT(J,N)*A
   17 S(J)=DIRECT(J,N)*STEP
      CALL SEARCH
      FX=FY
      DO 18  I=1,N
   18 X(I)=Y(I)
C *** TEST FOR CONVERGENCE.
   19 CALL TEST(F1,FX,BEFORE,X,FLAG,N,ACC)
      IF(FLAG) 22,22,20
C *** CONVERGENCE NOT YET ACHEIVED. COMPUTE A NEW STEP SIZE AND
C     GO BACK TO 3.
   20 IF(F1-FX)121,120,120
  121 STEP=-0.4*SQRT(ABS(F1-FX))
      GO TO 123
  120 STEP=0.4*SQRT(F1-FX)
  123 IF(STEPA-STEP) 21,3,3
   21 STEP=STEPA
      GO TO 3
C *** CONVERGENCE ACHEIVED. IF ICONVG=2, INCREASE ALL VARIABLES BY
C     10*ACC AND GO BACK TO 3.
   22 GO TO (23,24),ICONVG
   23 RETURN
   24 GO TO (25,27),NTRY
   25 NTRY=2
      DO 26  I=1,N
      FIRST(I)=X(I)
   26 X(I)=X(I)+ACC*10.
      FFIRST=FX
      GO TO 100
C *** CONVERGENCE ATTAINED USING TWO DIFFERENT STARTING POINTS. CONSTRUC
C     UNIT VECTOR BETWEEN SOLUTIONS AND SEARCH DIRECTION FOR A MINIMUM.
   27 FSECND=FX
      A=0.
      DO 28  I=1,N
      SECND(I)=X(I)
      S(I)=FIRST(I)-SECND(I)
   28 A=A+S(I)**2
      IF(A) 23,23,29
   29 A=STEP/SQRT(A)
      DO 30  I=1,N
   30 S(I)=S(I)*A
      CALL SEARCH
C *** TEST IF NEW POINT IS SUFFICIENTLY CLOSE TO EITHER OF THE TWO
C     SOLUTIONS. IF SO RETURN.
      CALL TEST(FFIRST,FY,FIRST,Y,FLAG,N,ACC)
```

```
      IF(FLAG) 32,32,31
   31 CALL TEST(FSECND,FY,SECND,Y,FLAG,N,ACC)
      IF(FLAG) 32,32,34
   32 DO 33  I=1,N
   33 X(I)=Y(I)
      FX=FY
      RETURN
C *** FINAL SOLUTION NOT ACCURATE ENOUGH.  REPLACE THE FIRST DIRECTION
C     VECTOR BY INTER-SOLUTION VECTOR (NORMALISED) AND RECYCLE
   34 A=A/STEP
      DO 35  I=1,N
      DIRECT(I,1)=(FIRST(I)-SECND(I))*A
   35 FIRST(I)=SECND(I)
      GO TO 3
      END

      SUBROUTINE TEST(FI,FF,RI,RF,FLAG,N,ACC)
C   THIS SUBROUTINE IS PECULIAR TO THE POWELL METHOD OF DIRECT SEARCH
      DIMENSION  RI(10),RF(10)
      FLAG=+2.
      IF(ABS(FI)-ACC) 2,2,1
    1 IF(ABS((FI-FF)/FI)-ACC) 3,3,7
    2 IF(ABS(FI-FF)-ACC) 3,3,7
    3 DO 6  I=1,N
      IF(ABS(RI(I))-ACC) 5,5,4
    4 IF(ABS((RI(I)-RF(I))/RI(I))-ACC) 6,6,7
    5 IF(ABS(RI(I)-RF(I))-ACC) 6,6,7
    6 CONTINUE
      FLAG=-2.
    7 RETURN
      END
```

B.3 OPTIMIZATION METHOD OF NELDER AND MEAD: INSTRUCTIONS TO INTRODUCE DATA INTO THE DECK

The present function in the program deck is Wood's function. The card (SUM(IN) = $f(x)$), the third last card in the deck, must be changed for each different function. Allowance has been made for a 50-dimension problem, that is, X(1) to X(50).

The data cards to be provided by the user are as follows:

Card 1: Punch NX, the number of variables in the objective function in format I5 in columns 1 through 5 right-justified, and STEP, the step size in format (F10.5) in columns 6 through 16. In the absence of other information select

$$\text{STEP} = \min\left\{\frac{0.2}{n}\sum_{i=1}^{n} d_i, \quad d_1, d_2, \ldots, d_n\right\}$$

where n is the number of independent variables and d_i is the possible region for search for the variable x_i.

Card 2: Punch the initial guess for each variable in format F10.5. Cards 2 and 3 can be repeated changing the step size and initial variables as desired, but after the last card of type 2 must come:

Card m: Blank card.

```
      PROGRAM SIMPLEX(INPUT,OUTPUT)
C     NX IS THE NUMBER OF INDEPENDENT VARIABLES.
C     STEP IS THE INITIAL STEP SIZE.
C     X(I) IS THE ARRAY OF INITIAL GUESSES.
C     DATA CARDS ARE AS FOLLOWS.
C     CARD NO.           PARAMETERS           FORMAT          COLUMNS
C        1                 NX                   I5            1 THRU 5
C        1                 STEP                 F10.5         6 THRU 15
C        2                 X(I)                 F10.5         1 THRU 10
C     CARD 3 IS BLANK.
C     TO OPTIMIZE THE OBJECTIVE FUNCTION FOR ANOTHER SET OF PARAMETERS
C     REPEAT CARDS 1 AND 2 ONLY.
C     FOR PROPER PRINTOUT OF DESIRED X(I) ARRAY, FORMAT STATEMENTS 103
C     AND 101 MUST BE REVISED ACCORDINGLY.
      DIMENSION X1(50,50), X(50), SUM(50)
      COMMON/1/ X,X1,NX,STEP,K1,SUM,IN
    1 FORMAT(I5,F10.5)
  100 READ1, NX,STEP
      IF(NX) 998,999,998
  998 READ 2, (X(I),I=1,NX)
    2 FORMAT(10F10.5)
      ALFA=1.0
      BETA=0.5
      GAMA=2.0
      DIFER = 0.
      XNX = NX
      IN = 1
      CALL SUMR
       PRINT 102,SUM(1),(X(I),I=1,NX)
      PRINT 1002,STEP
      CALL SECOND(TIME)
      PRINT 105,TIME
  105 FORMAT(/50X,11HTIME IS NOW,F10.3,8H SECONDS/)
      PRINT 103
  103 FORMAT(4X,14HFUNCTION VALUE,15X,3HX1=,20X,3HX2=,20X,3HX3=,20X,3HX4
     1=,16X,12HFUNC. CHANGE)
  102 FORMAT(1H1,12X,23HFUNCTION STARTING VALUE,F10.5,/,*THE X ARRAY IS*
     1,/,5X,10(E11.4,2X))
 1002 FORMAT(12X,*STEP=*,F6.2)
      K1 = NX + 1
      K2 = NX + 2
      K3 = NX + 3
      K4 = NX + 4
      CALL START
   25 DO 3 I = 1, K1
      DO 4 J = 1, NX
    4 X(J) = X1(I  ,J)
      IN = I
      CALL SUMR
    3 CONTINUE
C  SELECT LARGEST VALUE OF SUM(I) IN SIMPLEX
   28 SUMH = SUM(1)
      INDEX = 1
      DO 7 I = 2, K1
      IF(SUM(I).LE.SUMH) GO TO 7
      SUMH = SUM(I)
      INDEX = I
    7 CONTINUE
```

```
C   SELECT MINIMUM VALUE OF SUM(I) IN SIMPLEX
      SUML = SUM(1)
      KOUNT = 1
      DO 8 I = 2, K1
      IF(SUML.LE.SUM(I)) GO TO 8
      SUML = SUM(I)
      KOUNT = I
    8 CONTINUE
C   FIND CENTROID OF POINTS WITH I DIFFERENT THAN INDEX
      DO 9 J = 1, NX
      SUM2 = 0.
      DO 10 I = 1, K1
   10 SUM2 = SUM2 + X1(I,J)
      X1(K2,J) =1./XNX*(SUM2 - X1(INDEX,J))
C   FIND REFLECTION OF HIGH POINT THROUGH CENTROID
      X1(K3,J) = (1. + ALFA)*X1(K2,J) - ALFA*X1(INDEX,J)
    9 X(J) = X1(K3,J)
      IN = K3
      CALL SUMR
      IF(SUM(K3).LT.SUML) GO TO 11
C    SELECT SECOND LARGEST VALUE IN SIMPLEX
      IF(INDEX.EQ.1) GO TO 38
      SUMS = SUM(1)
      GO TO 39
   38 SUMS = SUM(2)
   39 DO 12 I = 1, K1
      IF((INDEX - I).EQ.0) GO TO 12
      IF(SUM(I).LE.SUMS) GO TO 12
      SUMS = SUM(I)
   12 CONTINUE
      IF(SUM(K3).GT.SUMS) GO TO 13
      GO TO 14
C   FORM EXPANSION OF NEW MINIMUM IF REFLECTION HAS PRODUCED ONE MINIMUM
   11 DO 15 J = 1, NX
      X1(K4,J) = (1  - GAMA)*X1(K2,J) + GAMA*X1(K3,J)
   15 X(J) = X1(K4,J)
      IN = K4
      CALL SUMR
      IF(SUM(K4).LT.SUML) GO TO 16
      GO TO 14
   13 IF(SUM(K3).GT.SUMH) GO TO 17
      DO 18 J = 1, NX
   18 X1(INDEX,J) = X1(K3,J)
   17 DO 19 J = 1, NX
      X1(K4,J) = BETA*X1(INDEX,J) + (1. - BETA)*X1(K2,J)
   19 X(J) = X1(K4,J)
      IN = K4
      CALL SUMR
      IF(SUMH.GT.SUM(K4)) GO TO 16
C   REDUCE SIMPLEX BY HALF IF REFLECTION HAPPENS TO PRODUCE A LARGER VAL
C   LUE THAN THE MAXIMUM
      DO 20 J = 1, NX
      DO 20 I = 1, K1
   20 X1(I,J) = 0.5*(X1(I,J) + X1(KOUNT,J))
      DO 29 I = 1, K1
      DO 30 J = 1, NX
   30 X(J) = X1(I,J)
      IN = I
      CALL SUMR
   29 CONTINUE
      GO TO 26
   16 DO 21 J = 1, NX
      X1(INDEX,J) = X1(K4,J)
   21 X(J) = X1(INDEX,J)
      IN = INDEX
      CALL SUMR
      GO TO 26
   14 DO 22 J = 1, NX
```

```
      X1(INDEX,J) = X1(K3,J)
   22 X(J) = X1(INDEX,J)
      IN = INDEX
      CALL SUMR
   26 DO 23 J = 1, NX
   23 X(J) = X1(K2,J)
      IN = K2
      CALL SUMR
      DIFER = 0.
      DO 24 I = 1, K1
   24 DIFER = DIFER + (SUM(I) - SUM(K2))**2
      DIFER =1./XNX*SQRT(DIFER)
      PRINT 101, SUML, (X1(KOUNT,J), J= 1,NX), DIFER
  101 FORMAT(2(2X,E16.6),3(7X,E16.6),12X,E16.6)
      IF( DIFER.GE.0.0000001) GO TO 28
      CALL SECOND(TIME)
      PRINT 105,TIME
      GO TO 100
  999 CONTINUE
      END
      SUBROUTINE START
      DIMENSION A(50,50), X1(50,50), X(50), SUM(50)
      COMMON/1/ X,X1,NX,STEP,K1,SUM,IN
      VN = NX
      STEP1 = STEP/(VN*SQRT(2.))*(SQRT(VN + 1.) + VN - 1.)
      STEP2= STEP/(VN*SQRT(2.))*(SQRT(VN + 1.) - 1.)
      DO 1 J = 1, NX
    1 A(1,J) = 0.
      DO 2 I = 2, K1
      DO 2 J = 1, NX
      A(I,J) = STEP2
      L = I - 1
      A(I,L) = STEP1
    2 CONTINUE
      DO 3 I = 1, K1
      DO 3 J = 1, NX
    3 X1(I,J) = X(J) + A(I,J)
      RETURN
      END
      SUBROUTINE SUMR
      COMMON/1/ X,X1,NX,STEP,K1,SUM,IN
      DIMENSION X1(50,50), X(50), SUM(50)
      SUM(IN)=(X(1)+10.*X(2))**2+5.*(X(3)-X(4))**2+(X(2)-2.*X(3))**4+
     110.*(X(1)-X(4))**4
      RETURN
      END
```

```
    4   0.5
3.0          -1.0          0.0          1.0
```

B.4 PROGRAM FLEXIPLEX (THE FLEXIBLE TOLERANCE METHOD)

1. *Purpose*

Flexiplex solves the general nonlinear programming problem

$$\begin{aligned} &\text{Minimize:} && y = f(\mathbf{x}) \quad \mathbf{x} \in E^n \\ &\text{Subject to:} && h_i(\mathbf{x}) = 0 \quad i = 1, \ldots, m \\ & && g_i(\mathbf{x}) \geq 0 \quad i = m+1, \ldots, p \end{aligned} \tag{B.4-1}$$

where $f(\mathbf{x})$ is the objective function to be minimized (or maximized), $\mathbf{x} = (x_1, x_2, \ldots, x_n)^T$ is a column vector whose elements are the n variables of the problem in the n-dimensional space, $h_i(\mathbf{x})$, $i = 1, \ldots, m$, are the equality constraints, and $g_i(\mathbf{x}) \geq 0$, $i = m + 1, \ldots, p$, are the inequality constraints. The expressions $f(\mathbf{x})$, $h_i(\mathbf{x})$, $g_i(\mathbf{x})$ may be linear and/or nonlinear functions. Both m and/or $(p - m)$ may be equal to zero. Thus, for the case of $m = 0$ and $(p - m) = 0$, the optimization of $f(\mathbf{x})$ is unconstrained.[1]

2. *Introduction of the Problem into Program Flexiplex*

The objective function and the constraints of problem (B.4–1) are introduced into the computer by means of SUBROUTINE PROBLEM (INQ). The parameter INQ identifies the objective function and the respective set of constraints. INQ = 1 corresponds to the equality constraints; INQ = 2, the inequality constraints; and INQ = 3, the objective function. Throughout the entire program each individual equality constraint, inequality constraint, and the objective function are identified by the subscripted variable $R(I)$, I $= 1, \ldots, m, m + 1, \ldots, p, p + 1$.

SUBROUTINE PROBLEM (INQ) is organized as follows:

1. After the comment card "Equality Constraints" and statement 1, place the equality constraints, if any, in the form

$$R(1) = h_1(\mathbf{x})$$
$$\cdots\cdots\cdots\cdots$$
$$R(m) = h_m(\mathbf{x})$$

2. After the comment card "Inequality Constraints" and statement 2, place the inequality constraints as

$$R(m + 1) = g_{m+1}(\mathbf{x})$$
$$\cdots\cdots\cdots\cdots\cdots$$
$$R(p) = g_p(\mathbf{x})$$

3. After the comment card "Objective Function" and statement 3, put the objective function as

$$R(p + 1) = f(\mathbf{x})$$

If the problem statement does not contain equalities ($m = 0$), do not place any statement following statement 1, and $R(m + 1)$ becomes $R(1)$.

[1]The details of the technique used to solve problem (B.4–1) can be found in D. A. Paviani, A new method for the solution of the general nonlinear programming problem, Ph.D. dissertation, The University of Texas, Austin, Tex., May, 1969.

Similarly, if there are equalities but no inequalities, omit any statement following statement 2, and $R(p + 1)$ becomes $R(m + 1)$. In the case of an unconstrained problem, $R(p + 1) = R(1)$.

For example, the problem

$$\text{Minimize:} \quad f(\mathbf{x}) = 1000 - x_1^2 - 2x_2^2 - x_3^2 - x_1x_2$$

$$\text{Subject to:} \quad h_1(\mathbf{x}): \; x_1^2 + x_2^2 + x_3^2 - 25 = 0$$

$$h_2(\mathbf{x}): \; 8x_1 + 14x_2 + 7x_3 - 56 = 0$$

$$g_i(\mathbf{x}): \; x_i \geq 0, \qquad i = 1, \ldots, 3$$

should be introduced into subroutine PROBLEM (INQ) as follows:

```
C  EQUALITY CONSTRAINTS

   1  CONTINUE
      R(1) = X(1)**2 + X(2)**2 + X(3)**2 - 25.
      R(2) = 8.*X(1) + 14.*X(2) + 7.*X(3) - 56.
      Go to 5

C  INEQUALITY CONSTRAINTS

   2  CONTINUE
      R(3) = X(1)
      R(4) = X(2)
      R(5) = X(3)
      Go to 5

C  OBJECTIVE FUNCTION

   3  CONTINUE
      R(6) = 1000. - X(1)**2 - 2.*X(2)**2 - X(3)**2 - X(1)*X(2)

   5  Return
```

---

3. *Introduction of Data*

First Data Card

This card is a header card to identify the problem being solved. Any alphanumeric statement can be placed in columns 1 through 80.

Second Data Card

This card contains the parameters of the problem as follows:

NX = total number of variables (dependent + independent) in format I5, right-justified.

NC = total number of equality constraints (m) in format I5, right-justified.

NIC = total number of inequality constraints ($p = m$) in format I5, right-justified. Note that upper and lower bounds on the **x** vector are also counted as inequalities.

SIZE = t, the size of the flexible polyhedron during the initiating phase of the search (use format F10.5). The explanation of how one should choose the value for SIZE is given below.

CONVER = ε, an arbitrarily chosen positive small number used to terminate the search; ε is also known as the limit of convergence and usually is chosen to be 10^{-5} or 10^{-6}.

The recommended value for SIZE is as follows. When upper and lower bounds on **x** are known select:

1. SIZE $\approx$ 20 percent of the difference between an upper and a lower bound on **x** if the expected range of variation of the x's along each coordinate is about the same.
2. If the expected range of variation of the x's along each coordinate is different, make SIZE $\approx$ to the smallest difference between the respective upper and lower bounds for any x.

Examples

(1)	(2)
$-11 \le x_1 \le 98.7$	$0 \le x_1 \le 400$
$-10 \le x_2 \le 100.1$	$0 \le x_2 \le 1000$
$-9.5 \le x_3 \le 101$	$340 \le x_3 \le 420$
$-10.2 \le x_4 \le 99.5$	$340 \le x_4 \le 420$
$-9.8 \le x_5 \le 100$	$-1000 \le x_5 \le 1000$
	$0 \le x_6 \le 0.5236$
SIZE $\approx 0.2*110 = 22.$	SIZE $\approx 1.$

Third and Following Data Cards

If data for the problem, such as constants, coefficients, values for $f(\mathbf{x})$, etc., are to be read in, they should be punched in the third and succeeding cards. Use as many cards as necessary and any convenient format. These data are read into the main Program Flexi and transferred to the subroutine which evaluates the functions and expressions of the optimization problem

{SUBROUTINE PROBLEM (INQ)} by means of suitable common statements. The FORMAT, COMMON, and READ statements for specific data are to be provided by the user.

Place READ statements for data (constants, coefficients, etc.) that will be retained for all subsequent calculations at the beginning of the main program following the comment card "Permanent Data for the Problem . . . ." (If no such data are required to be read in, then the user should remove any read or print statements following this comment card [and before statement 10]. Then the cards immediately following the second data card will read in the initial guesses for the variables of the problem, that is, $x_i^{(0)}$, $i = 1, \ldots, \text{NX}$.) The initial guesses for $\mathbf{x}^{(0)}$ are placed after the last data card described above (e.g., after the second card if no coefficients or constants are to be read in). The initial guesses $\mathbf{x}^{(0)}$ should be punched in format 8F10.5.

The program can handle more than one set of initial guesses. That is, after finding the solution for the first set of initial guesses, the main program is guided to read in an additional set of initial guesses, and the problem is solved once more. After one solution is completed, control in the program is transferred to statement 10 in order to read in the next $\mathbf{x}^{(0)}$ and to solve the problem once more. If it is desired to change the data for the problem (new coefficients or new constants), the read statements with the appropriate common and format statements should be placed after statement 10. The program is terminated when the "End of File" card is encountered.

```
      PROGRAM FLEXI ( INPUT, OUTPUT, TAPE10 = INPUT )
C
C
C     * * * * * * P R O G R A M   F L E X I P L E X * * * * * *
C
C
C
C     NX       TOTAL NUMBER OF INDEPENDENT VARIABLES
C     NC       TOTAL NUMBER OF EQUALITY CONSTRAINTS
C     NIC      TOTAL NUMBER OF INEQUALITY CONSTRAINTS
C     SIZE     EDGE LENGHT OF THE INITIAL POLYHEDRON
C     CONVER   CONVERGENCE CRITERION FOR TERMINATION OF THE SEARCH
C     ALFA     THE REFLECTION COEFFICIENT
C     BETA     THE CONTRACTION COEFFICIENT
C     GAMA     THE EXPANSION COEFFICIENT
C     X(I)     THE ASSUMED VECTOR TO INITIATE THE SEARCH
C     FDIFER   THE TOLERANCE CRITERION FOR CONSTRAINT VIOLATION
C     ICONT    A COUNTER TO RECORD STAGE COMPUTATIONS
C     NCONT    A COUNTER TO PRINT INFORMATION EVERY (NX+1) STAGE
C     LOW      AN INDEX TO IDENTIFY INFORMATION RELATED TO THE LOWEST
C              VALUE OF OBJ. FUNCTION IN MOST RECENT POLYHEDRON
C     LHIGH    AN INDEX TO IDENTIFY INFORMATION RELATED TO LARGEST VALUE
C              OF OBJ. FUNCTION IN MOST RECENT POLYHEDRON
C     LSEC     AN INDEX TO IDENTIFY INFORMATION RELATED TO THE SECOND
C     LARGEST VALUE OF OBJ. FUNCTION IN MOST RECENT POLYHEDRON
C
```

```
C                          ***************                         0300
C                                                                  310
      DIMENSION X(50),X1(50,50),X2(50,50),R(100),SUM(50),F(50),SR(50),  0320
     1 ROLD(100), H(50)                                           0330
      COMMON/1/NX,NC,NIC,STEP,ALFA,BETA,GAMA,IN,INF,FDIFER,SEQL,K1,K2,  0340
     1K3,K4,K5,K6,K7,K8,K9,X,X1,X2,R,SUM,F,SR,ROLD,SCALE,FOLD    0350
      COMMON/2/LFEAS,L5,L6,L7,L8,L9,R1A,R2A,R3A                   0360
C     PROBLEM IDENTIFICATION HEADER IS READ IN AFTER THIS CARD   0370
      READ 759                                                   400
C     PARAMETERS FOR THE PROBLEM ARE READ IN AFTER THIS CARD     0410
      READ 1, NX,NC,NIC,SIZE,CONVER                              0420
      ALFA = 1.                                                  0430
      BETA = 0.5                                                 440
      GAMA = 2.                                                  0450
C     PERMANENT DATA FOR THE PROBLEM SHOULD BE READ IN AFTER THIS CARD  0460
   10 CALL SECOND(TIME)                                          0510
C     TEMPORARY DATA FOR THE PROBLEM, SUCH AS VARIABLE COEFFICIENTS OR  0520
C     NEW PARAMETERS SHOULD BE READ IN AFTER THIS CARD           0530
      STEP = SIZE                                                540
C     THE ASSUMED INITIAL VECTOR IS READ IN AFTER THIS CARD      0550
      READ 2 , (X(I), I = 1, NX)                                 0560
      IF(EOF,10)9999,11                                          0570
   11 PRINT 106                                                  0580
      PRINT 759                                                  0590
      PRINT 756, NX,NC,NIC,SIZE,CONVER,TIME                      0600
      K1 = NX + 1                                                0610
      K2 = NX + 2                                                0620
      K3 = NX + 3                                                0630
      K4 = NX + 4                                                0640
      K5 = NX + 5                                                0650
      K6 = NC + NIC                                              0660
      K7 = NC + 1                                                0670
      K8 = NC + NIC                                              0680
      K9 = K8 + 1                                                0690
      N = NX - NC                                                0700
      N1 = N + 1                                                 0710
      IF(N1.GE.3) GO TO 50                                       0720
      N1 = 3                                                     0730
      N = 2                                                      0740
   50 N2 = N + 2                                                 0750
      N3 = N + 3                                                 0760
      N4 = N + 4                                                 0770
      N5 = N + 5                                                 0780
      N6 = N + 6                                                 0800
      N7 = N + 7                                                 0810
      N8 = N + 8                                                 0820
      XN = N                                                     0830
      XNX = NX                                                   0840
      XN1 = N1                                                   0850
      R1A = 0.5*(SQRT(5.) - 1.)                                  0860
      R2A = R1A*R1A                                              0870
      R3A = R2A*R1A                                              0880
      L5 = NX + 5                                                0890
      L6 = NX + 6                                                0900
      L7 = NX + 7                                                0910
      L8 = NX + 8                                                0920
      L9 = NX + 9                                                0930
      ICONT = 1                                                  0940
      NCONT = 1                                                  0950
      PRINT 115                                                  0960
      PRINT 116, (X(J), J = 1, NX)                               0970
      FDIFER = 2.*(NC + 1)*STEP                                  0980
      FOLD = FDIFER                                              0990
      IN = N1                                                    1000
      CALL SUMR                                                  1010
      SR(N1) = SQRT(SEQL)                                        1020
      PRINT 763, FDIFER, SR(N1)                                  1030
```

```
      IF(SR(N1).LT.FDIFER) GO TO 341                                1040
      CALL WRITEX                                                   1041
      PRINT 757                                                     1050
      INF = N1                                                      1060
      STEP = 0.05*FDIFER                                            1061
      CALL FEASBL                                                   1070
      PRINT 764                                                     1080
      PRINT 116, (X2(INF,J),J = 1, NX)                              1090
      PRINT 765, SR(INF)                                            1100
      IF(FOLD.LT.1.0E-09) GO TO 80                                  1110
  341 PRINT 35                                                      1120
      PRINT 758, ICONT, FDIFER                                      1130
      CALL WRITEX                                                   1140
      FTER = R(K9)                                                  1150
C     COMPUTE CENTROID OF ALL VERTICES OF INITIAL POLYHEDRON        1160
  237 STEP1 = STEP*(SQRT(XNX + 1.) + XNX - 1.)/(XNX*SQRT(2.))       1170
      STEP2 = STEP*(SQRT(XNX + 1.) - 1.)/(XNX*SQRT(2.))             1180
      ETA = (STEP1 + (XNX - 1.)*STEP2)/(XNX + 1.)                   1190
      DO 4 J = 1, NX                                                1200
      X(J) = X(J) - ETA                                             1210
    4 CONTINUE                                                      1220
      CALL START                                                    1230
      DO 9 I = 1, N1                                                1240
      DO 9 J = 1, NX                                                1250
      X2(I,J) = X1(I,J)                                             1260
    9 CONTINUE                                                      1270
      DO 5 I = 1, N1                                                1280
      IN = I                                                        1290
      DO 6 J = 1,NX                                                 1300
    6 X(J) = X2(I,J)                                                1310
      CALL SUMR                                                     1320
      SR(I) = SQRT(SEQL)                                            1330
      IF(SR(I).LT.FDIFER) GO TO 8                                   1340
      CALL FEASBL                                                   1350
      IF(FOLD.LT.1.0E-09) GO TO 80                                  1360
    8 CALL PROBLEM(3)                                               1370
      F(I) = R(K9)                                                  1380
    5 CONTINUE                                                      1390
 1000 STEP = 0.05*FDIFER                                            1400
      ICONT = ICONT + 1                                             1410
C  SELECT LARGEST VALUE OF OBJECTIVE FUNCTION FROM POLYHEDRON VERTICES  1420
      FH = F(1)                                                     1430
      LHIGH = 1                                                     1440
      DO 16 I = 2, N1                                               1450
      IF(F(I).LT.FH) GO TO 16                                       1460
      FH = F(I)                                                     1470
      LHIGH = I                                                     1480
   16 CONTINUE                                                      1490
C   SELECT MINIMUM VALUE OF OBJECTIVE FUMCTION FROM POLYHEDRON VERTICES 1500
   41 FL = F(1)                                                     1510
      LOW = 1                                                       1520
      DO 17 I = 2, N1                                               1530
      IF(FL.LT.F(I)) GO TO 17                                       1540
      FL = F(I)                                                     1550
      LOW = I                                                       1560
   17 CONTINUE                                                      1570
      DO 86 J = 1, NX                                               1580
   86 X(J) = X2(LOW,J)                                              1590
      IN = LOW                                                      1600
      CALL SUMR                                                     1610
      SR(LOW) = SQRT(SEQL)                                          1620
      IF(SR(LOW).LT.FDIFER) GO TO 87                                1630
      INF = LOW                                                     1640
      CALL FEASBL                                                   1650
      IF(FOLD.LT.1.0E-09) GO TO 80                                  1660
      CALL PROBLEM(3)                                               1670
      F(LOW) = R(K9)                                                1680
      GO TO 41                                                      1690
```

```
    87 CONTINUE                                                       1700
C      FIND CENTROID OF POINTS WITH I DIFFERENT THAN LHIGH           1710
       DO 19 J = 1, NX                                               1720
       SUM2 = 0.                                                     1730
       DO 20 I = 1, N1                                               1740
    20 SUM2 = SUM2 + X2(I,J)                                         1750
    19 X2(N2,J) = 1./XN*(SUM2-X2(LHIGH,J))                           1760

       SUM2 = 0.                                                     1770
       DO 36 I = 1, N1                                               1780
       DO 36 J = 1, NX                                               1790
       SUM2 = SUM2 + (X2(I,J) - X2(N2,J))**2                         1800
    36 CONTINUE                                                      1810
       FDIFER = (NC + 1)/XN1*SQRT(SUM2)                              1820
       IF(FDIFER.LT.FOLD) GO TO 98                                   1830
       FDIFER = FOLD                                                 1840
       GO TO 198                                                     1850
    98 FOLD = FDIFER                                                 1860
   198 CONTINUE                                                      1870
       FTER = F(LOW)                                                 1880
   137 NCONT = NCONT + 1                                             1890
       IF(NCONT.LT.4*N1) GO TO 37                                    1900
       IF(ICONT.LT.1500) GO TO 337                                   1901
       FOLD = 0.5*FOLD                                               1902
   337 NCONT = 0                                                     1910
       PRINT 35                                                      1920
       PRINT 758, ICONT, FDIFER                                      1930
       CALL WRITEX                                                   1940
    37 IF(FDIFER.LT.CONVER) GO TO 81                                 1950
C  SELECT SECOND LARGEST VALUE OF OBJECTIVE FUNCTION                 1960
       IF(LHIGH.EQ.1) GO TO 43                                       1970
       FS = F(1)                                                     1980
       LSEC = 1                                                      1990
       GO TO 44                                                      2000
    43 FS = F(2)                                                     2010
       LSEC = 2                                                      2020
    44 DO 18 I = 1, N1                                               2030
       IF(LHIGH.EQ.I) GO TO 18                                       2040
       IF(F(I).LT.FS) GO TO 18                                       2050
       FS = F(I)                                                     2060
       LSEC = I                                                      2070
    18 CONTINUE                                                      2080
C      REFLECT HIGH POINT THROUGH CENTROID                           2090
       DO 61 J = 1, NX                                               2100
       X2(N3,J) = X2(N2,J) + ALFA*(X2(N2,J) - X2(LHIGH,J))           2110
    61 X(J) = X2(N3,J)                                               2120
       IN = N3                                                       2130
       CALL SUMR                                                     2140
       SR(N3) = SQRT(SEQL)                                           2150
    89 IF(SR(N3).LT.FDIFER) GO TO 82                                 2160
       INF = N3                                                      2170
       CALL FEASBL                                                   2180
       IF(FOLD.LT.1.0E-09) GO TO 80                                  2190
    82 CALL PROBLEM(3)                                               2200
       F(N3) = R(K9)                                                 2210
       IF(F(N3).LT.F(LOW)) GO TO 84                                  2220
       IF(F(N3).LT.F(LSEC)) GO TO 92                                 2230
       GO TO 60                                                      2240
    92 DO 93 J = 1, NX                                               2250
    93 X2(LHIGH,J) = X2(N3,J)                                        2260
       SR(LHIGH) = SR(N3)                                            2270
       F(LHIGH) = F(N3)                                              2280
       GO TO 1000                                                    2290
C    EXPAND VECTOR OF SEARCH ALONG DIRECTION THROUGH CENTROID AND    2300
C      REFLECTED VECTOR                                              2310
    84 DO 23 J = 1, NX                                               2320
       X2(N4,J) = X2(N3,J) + GAMA*(X2( N3,J) - X2(N2,J))             2330
    23 X(J) = X2(N4,J)                                               2340
       IN = N4                                                       2350
```

```
      CALL SUMR                                                    2360
      SR(N4) = SQRT(SEQL)                                          2370
      IF(SR(N4).LT.FDIFER) GO TO 25                               2380
      INF = N4                                                     2390
      CALL FEASBL                                                  2400
      IF(FOLD.LT.1.0E-09) GO TO 80                                2410
   25 CALL PROBLEM(3)                                              2420
      F(N4) = R(K9)                                                2430
      IF(F(LOW).LT.F(N4)) GO TO 92                                2440
      DO 26 J = 1, NX                                              2450
   26 X2(LHIGH,J) = X2(N4,J)                                       2460
      F(LHIGH) = F(N4)                                             2470
      SR(LHIGH) = SR(N4)                                           2480
      GO TO 1000                                                   2490
   60 IF(F(N3).GT.F(LHIGH)) GO TO 64                               2500
      DO 65 J = 1, NX                                              2510
   65 X2(LHIGH,J) = X2(N3,J)                                       2520
   64 DO 66 J = 1, NX                                              2530
      X2(N4,J) = BETA*X2(LHIGH,J) + (1. - BETA)*X2(N2,J)          2540
   66 X(J) = X2(N4,J)                                              2550
      IN = N4                                                      2560
      CALL SUMR                                                    2570
      SR(N4) = SQRT(SEQL)                                          2580
      IF(SR(N4).LT.FDIFER) GO TO 67                               2590
      INF = N4                                                     2600
      CALL FEASBL                                                  2610
      IF(FOLD.LT.1.0E-09) GO TO 80                                2620
   67 CALL PROBLEM(3)                                              2630
      F(N4) = R(K9)                                                2640
      IF(F(LHIGH).GT.F(N4)) GO TO 68                               2650
      DO 69 J = 1, NX                                              2660
      DO 69 I = 1, N1                                              2670
   69 X2(I,J) = 0.5*(X2(I,J) + X2(LOW,J))                         2680
      DO 70 I = 1, N1                                              2690
      DO 71 J = 1, NX                                              2700
   71 X(J) = X2(I,J)                                               2710
      IN = I                                                       2720
      CALL SUMR                                                    2730
      SR(I) = SQRT(SEQL)                                           2740
      IF(SR(I).LT.FDIFER) GO TO 72                                2750
      INF = I                                                      2760
      CALL FEASBL                                                  2770
      IF(FOLD.LT.1.0E-09) GO TO 80                                2780
   72 CALL PROBLEM(3)                                              2790
   70 F(I) = R(K9)                                                 2800
      GO TO 1000                                                   2820
   68 DO 73 J = 1, NX                                              2830
   73 X2(LHIGH,J) = X2(N4,J)                                       2840
      SR(LHIGH) = SR(N4)                                           2850
      F(LHIGH) = F(N4)                                             2860
      GO TO 1000                                                   2870
   81 PRINT 760,ICONT, FDIFER                                      2880
      CALL WRITEX                                                  2890
      CALL SECOND(TIME)                                            2900
      PRINT 755, TIME                                              2810
      PRINT 761                                                    2910
      GO TO 10                                                     2920
   80 PRINT 760, ICONT, FDIFER                                     2930
      CALL WRITEX                                                  2931
      PRINT 762                                                    2940
      GO TO 10                                                     2941
    1 FORMAT(3I5,F10.5,E10.3)                                      2950
    2 FORMAT(8F10.5)                                               2960
   35 FORMAT(/,40X,48H * * * * * * * * * * * * * * * * * * * * * * * * )  2970
  106 FORMAT(1H1,//)                                               2980
  115 FORMAT(//, 41H THE STARTING VECTOR SELECTED BY USER IS )     2990
  116 FORMAT(8E16.6)                                               3000
  755 FORMAT(//, 35H THE COMPUTATION TIME IN SECONDS = E12.5)      3010
```

```
      756 FORMAT(//,10X,40H NUMBER OF INDEPENDENT VARIABLES        I5,/,10X     3020
     1,40H NUMBER OF EQUALITY CONSTRAINTS          I5,/,10X,40H NUMBER O        3030
     2F INEQUALITY CONSTRAINTS        I5,/,10X,40H SIZE OF INITIAL POLY          3040
     3HEDRON           E12.5,/,10X,40H THE DESIRED CONVERGENCE IS               3050
     4          E12.5,/,10X,40H THE COMPUTATION TIME IN SECONDS                 3060
     5E12.5)                                                                    3070
      757 FORMAT(//,71H THE INITIAL X VECTOR DOES NOT SATISFY THE INITIAL TO     3080
     1LERANCE CRITERION )                                                       3090
      758 FORMAT( /,10X,27H STAGE CALCULATION NUMBER = I5, 20X, 27H THE TOLE     3100
     2RANCE CRITERION = E14.6)                                                  3110
      759 FORMAT(80H                                                            3120
     1                                       )                                  3130
      760 FORMAT(//, 39H TOTAL NUMBER OF STAGES CALCULATIONS = I5, 10X, 25H      3140
     1THE CONVERGENCE LIMIT = E14.6)                                            3150
      761 FORMAT(//,50X,25H THESE ARE FINAL ANSWERS )                           3160
      762 FORMAT(//,50X,29H THESE ARE NOT FINAL ANSWERS )                       3170
      763 FORMAT(//,10X,40H THE INITIAL TOLERANCE CRITERION IS      E12.5,/,     3180
     110X,40H THE SUM OF VIOLATED CONSTRAINTS IS        E12.5)                  3190
      764 FORMAT(//,70H THE VECTOR FOUND BY PROGRAM WHICH SATISFIES THE INIT     3200
     1IAL TOLERANCE IS )                                                        3210
      765 FORMAT(/, 31H SUM OF VIOLATED CONSTRAINTS = E17.7)                     3220
     9999 STOP                                                                  3230
          END                                                                  3240
          SUBROUTINE FEASBL                                                    3250
C                                                                              3260
C*****SUBROUTINE FEASBL MINIMIZES THE SUM OF THE SQUARE VALUES OF THE          3270
C     VIOLATED CONSTRAINTS.  IT IS CALLED EVERY TIME THE COMBINED VALUE        3280
C     OF THE VIOLATED CONSTRAINTS EXCEEDS THE THE VALUE OF THE TOLERANCE       3290
C     CRITERION FOR THE CURRENT STAGE                                          3300
C                                                                              3310
      DIMENSION X(50),X1(50,50),X2(50,50),R(100),SUM(50),F(50),SR(50),         3320
     1ROLD(100), R1(100), R2(100),R3(100), FLG(10), H(50)                      3330
  100 FORMAT(8E16.6)                                                           3340
      COMMON/1/NX,NC,NIC,STEP,DUM1,DUM2,DUM3,IN,INF,FDIFER,SEQL,K1,K2,          3350
     1K3,K4,K5,K6,K7,K8,K9,X,X1,X2,R,SUM,F,SR,ROLD,SCALE,FOLD                   3360
      COMMON/2/LFEAS,L5,L6,L7,L8,L9,R1A,R2A,R3A                                 3370
      ALFA = 1.                                                                3380
      BETA = 0.5                                                               3390
      GAMA = 2.                                                                3400
      XNX = NX                                                                 3410
      ICONT = 0                                                                3420
      LCHEK = 0                                                                3430
      ICHEK = 0                                                                3431
   25 CALL START                                                              3440
      DO 3 I = 1, K1                                                           3450
      DO 4 J = 1, NX                                                           3460
    4 X(J) = X1(I ,J)                                                          3470
      IN = I                                                                   3480
      CALL SUMR                                                                3490
    3 CONTINUE                                                                 3500
C SELECT LARGEST VALUE OF SUM(I) IN SIMPLEX                                    3510
   28 SUMH = SUM(1)                                                            3520
      INDEX = 1                                                               3530
      DO 7 I = 2, K1                                                           3540
      IF(SUM(I).LE.SUMH) GO TO 7                                               3550
      SUMH = SUM(I)                                                            3560
      INDEX = I                                                                3570
    7 CONTINUE                                                                 3580
C SELECT MINIMUM VALUE OF SUM(I) IN SIMPLEX                                    3590
      SUML = SUM(1)                                                            3600
      KOUNT = 1                                                               3610
      DO 8 I = 2, K1                                                           3620
      IF(SUML.LE.SUM(I)) GO TO 8                                               3630
      SUML = SUM(I)                                                            3640
      KOUNT = I                                                                3650
    8 CONTINUE                                                                 3660
C FIND CENTROID OF POINTS WITH I DIFFERENT THAN INDEX                          3670
      DO 9 J = 1, NX                                                           3680
```

```
      SUM2 = 0.                                              3690
      DO 10 I = 1, K1                                        3700
   10 SUM2 = SUM2 + X1(I,J)                                  3710
      X1(K2,J) =1./XNX*(SUM2 - X1(INDEX,J))                  3720
C  FIND REFLECTION OF HIGH POINT THROUGH CENTROID            3730
      X1(K3,J) = 2.*X1(K2,J) - X1(INDEX,J)                   3740
    9 X(J) = X1(K3,J)                                        3750
      IN = K3                                                3760
      CALL SUMR                                              3770
      IF(SUM(K3).LT.SUML) GO TO 11                           3780
C   SELECT SECOND LARGEST VALUE IN SIMPLEX                   3790
      IF(INDEX.EQ.1) GO TO 38                                3800
      SUMS = SUM(1)                                          3810
      GO TO 39                                               3820
   38 SUMS = SUM(2)                                          3830
   39 DO 12 I = 1, K1                                        3840
      IF((INDEX - I).EQ.0) GO TO 12                          3850
      IF(SUM(I).LE.SUMS) GO TO 12                            3860
      SUMS = SUM(I)                                          3870
   12 CONTINUE                                               3880
      IF(SUM(K3).GT.SUMS) GO TO 13                           3890
      GO TO 14                                               3900
C  FORM EXPANSION OF NEW MINIMUM IF REFLECTION HAS PRODUCED ONE MINIMUM   3910
   11 DO 15 J = 1, NX                                        3920
      X1(K4,J) =  X1(K2,J) + 2.*(X1(K3,J) - X1(K2,J))        3930
   15 X(J) = X1(K4,J)                                        3940
      IN = K4                                                3950
      CALL SUMR                                              3960
      IF(SUM(K4).LT.SUML) GO TO 16                           3970
      GO TO 14                                               3980
   13 IF(SUM(K3).GT.SUMH) GO TO 17                           3990
      DO 18 J = 1, NX                                        4000
   18 X1(INDEX,J) = X1(K3,J)                                 4010
   17 DO 19 J = 1, NX                                        4020
      X1(K4,J) = 0.5*X1(INDEX,J) + 0.5*X1(K2,J)              4030
   19 X(J) = X1(K4,J)                                        4040
      IN = K4                                                4050
      CALL SUMR                                              4060
      IF(SUMH.GT.SUM(K4)) GO TO 6                            4070
C  REDUCE SIMPLEX BY HALF IF REFLECTION HAPPENS TO PRODUCE A LARGER VAL   4080
C  LUE THAN THE MAXIMUM                                      4090
      DO 20 J = 1, NX                                        4100
      DO 20 I = 1, K1                                        4110
   20 X1(I,J) = 0.5*(X1(I,J) + X1(KOUNT,J))                  4120
      DO 29 I = 1, K1                                        4130
      DO 30 J = 1, NX                                        4140
   30 X(J) = X1(I,J)                                         4150
      IN = I                                                 4160
      CALL SUMR                                              4170
   29 CONTINUE                                               4180
    5 SUML = SUM(1)                                          4190
      KOUNT = 1                                              4200
      DO 23 I = 2, K1                                        4210
      IF(SUML.LT.SUM(I)) GO TO 23                            4220
      SUML = SUM(I)                                          4230
      KOUNT = I                                              4240
   23 CONTINUE                                               4250
      SR(INF) = SQRT(SUM(KOUNT))                             4260
      DO 27 J = 1, NX                                        4270
   27 X(J) = X1(KOUNT,J)                                     4280
      GO TO 26                                               4290
    6 DO 31 J = 1, NX                                        4300
   31 X1(INDEX,J) = X1(K4,J)                                 4310
      SUM(INDEX) = SUM(K4)                                   4320
      GO TO 5                                                4330
   16 DO 21 J = 1, NX                                        4340
      X1(INDEX,J) = X1(K4,J)                                 4350
   21 X(J) = X1(INDEX,J)                                     4360
```

```
        SUM(INDEX) = SUM(K4)                                            4370
        SR(INF) = SQRT(SUM(K4))                                         4380
        GO TO 26                                                        4390
     14 DO 22 J = 1, NX                                                 4400
        X1(INDEX,J) = X1(K3,J)                                          4410
     22 X(J) = X1(INDEX,J)                                              4420
        SUM(INDEX) = SUM(K3)                                            4430
        SR(INF) = SQRT(SUM(K3))                                         4440
     26 ICONT = ICONT + 1                                               4450
        DO 36 J = 1,NX                                                  4460
     36 X2(INF,J) = X(J)                                                4470
        IF(ICONT.LT.2*K1) GO TO 50                                      4480
        ICONT = 0                                                       4490
        DO 24 J = 1, NX                                                 4500
     24 X(J) = X1(K2,J)                                                 4510
        IN = K2                                                         4520
        CALL SUMR                                                       4530
        DIFER = 0.                                                      4540
        DO 57 I = 1, K1                                                 4550
     57 DIFER = DIFER + (SUM(I) - SUM(K2))**2                           4560
        DIFER = 1./(K7*XNX)*SQRT(DIFER)                                 4570
        IF(DIFER.GT.1.0E-14) GO TO 50                                   4580
C       IF FLEXIBLE SIMPLEX METHOD FAILED TO SATISFY THE CONSTRAINTS WITHIN  4590
C       THE TOLERANCE CRITERION FOR THE CURRENT STAGE,  THE SEARCH IS   4600
C       PERTURBED FROM THE POSITION WHERE THE X VECTOR IS STUCK AND THEN 4610
C       FEASBL IS REPEATED ONCE MORE FROM THE BEGINNING                 4620
     51 IN = K1                                                         4630
        STEP = 20.*FDIFER                                               4640
        CALL SUMR                                                       4650
        SR(INF) = SQRT(SEQL)                                            4660
        DO 52 J = 1, NX                                                 4670
     52 X1(K1,J) = X(J)                                                 4680
        DO 53 J = 1, NX                                                 4690
        FACTOR = 1.                                                     4700
        X(J) = X1(K1,J) + FACTOR*STEP                                   4710
        X1(L9,J) = X(J)                                                 4720
        IN = L9                                                         4730
        CALL SUMR                                                       4740
        X(J) = X1(K1,J) - FACTOR*STEP                                   4750
        X1(L5,J) = X(J)                                                 4760
        IN = L5                                                         4770
        CALL SUMR                                                       4780
     56 IF(SUM(L9).LT.SUM(K1)) GO TO 54                                 4790
        IF(SUM(L5).LT.SUM(K1)) GO TO 55                                 4800
        GO TO 97                                                        4810
     54 X1(L5,J) = X1(K1,J)                                             4820
        SUM(L5) = SUM(K1)                                               4830
        X1(K1,J) = X1(L9,J)                                             4840
        SUM(K1) = SUM(L9)                                               4850
        FACTOR = FACTOR + 1.                                            4860
        X(J) = X1(K1,J) + FACTOR*STEP                                   4870
        IN = L9                                                         4880
        CALL SUMR                                                       4890
        GO TO 56                                                        4900
     55 X1(L9,J) = X1(K1,J)                                             4910
        SUM(L9) = SUM(K1)                                               4920
        X1(K1,J) = X1(L5,J)                                             4930
        SUM(K1) = SUM(L5)                                               4940
        FACTOR = FACTOR + 1.                                            4950
        X(J) = X1(K1,J) - FACTOR*STEP                                   4960
        IN = L5                                                         4970
        CALL SUMR                                                       4980
        GO TO 56                                                        4990
C       ONE DIMENSIONAL SEARCH BY GOLDEN SECTION ALONG EACH COORDINATE  5000
     97 H(J) = X1(L9,J) - X1(L5,J)                                      5010
        X1(L6,J) = X1(L5,J) + H(J)*R1A                                  5020
        X(J) = X1(L6,J)                                                 5030
        IN = L6                                                         5040
```

```
      CALL SUMR                                                    5050
      X1(L7,J) = X1(L5,J) + H(J)*R2A                               5060
      X(J) = X1(L7,J)                                              5070
      IN = L7                                                      5080
      CALL SUMR                                                    5090
      IF(SUM(L6).GT.SUM(L7)) GO TO 68                              5100
      X1(L8,J) = X1(L5,J) + (1. - R3A)*H(J)                        5110
      X1(L5,J) = X1(L7,J)                                          5120
      X(J) = X1(L8,J)                                              5130
      IN = L8                                                      5140
      CALL SUMR                                                    5150
      IF(SUM(L8).GT.SUM(L6)) GO TO 76                              5160
      X1(L5,J) = X1(L6,J)                                          5170
      SUM(L5) = SUM(L6)                                            5180
      GO TO 75                                                     5190
   76 X1(L9,J) = X1(L8,J)                                          5200
      SUM(L9) = SUM(L8)                                            5210
      GO TO 75                                                     5220
   68 X1(L9,J) = X1(L6,J)                                          5230
      X1(L8,J) = X1(L5,J) + R3A*H(J)                               5240
      X(J) = X1(L8,J)                                              5250
      IN = L8                                                      5260
      CALL SUMR                                                    5270
      STEP = SIZE                                                   540
      SUM(L9) = SUM(L6)                                            5280
      IF(SUM(L7).GT.SUM(L8)) GO TO 71                              5290
      X1(L5,J) = X1(L8,J)                                          5300
      SUM(L5) = SUM(L8)                                            5310
      GO TO 75                                                     5320
   71 X1(L9,J) = X1(L7,J)                                          5330
      SUM(L9) = SUM(L7)                                            5340
   75 IF(ABS(X1(L9,J) - X1(L5,J)).GT.0.01*FDIFER) GO TO 97        5350
      X1(K1,J) = X1(L7,J)                                          5360
      X(J) = X1(L7,J)                                              5370
      SUM(K1) = SUM(L5)                                            5380
      SR(INF) = SQRT(SUM(K1))                                      5390
      IF(SR(INF).LT.FDIFER) GO TO 760                              5400
   53 CONTINUE                                                     5410
      ICHEK = ICHEK + 1                                            5420
      STEP = FDIFER                                                5430
      IF(ICHEK.LE.2) GO TO 25                                      5440
      FOLD = 1.0E-12                                               5450
      PRINT 853                                                    5460
      PRINT 850                                                    5470
      PRINT 851, (X(J),J=1,NX)                                     5480
      PRINT 852, FDIFER, SR(INF)                                   5490
      GO TO 46                                                     5500
  760 DO 761 J = 1, NX                                             5510
      X2(INF,J) = X1(K1,J)                                         5520
  761 X(J) = X1(K1,J)                                              5530
   50 IF(SR(INF).GT.FDIFER) GO TO 28                               5540
C  MODIFIED LAGRANGE INTERPOLATION FOR TIGHT INEQUALITIES          5550
      IF(SR(INF).GT.0.) GO TO 35                                   5560
      CALL PROBLEM(3)                                              5570
      FINT = R(K9)                                                 5580
      DO 139 J = 1, NX                                             5590
  139 X(J) = X2(INF,J)                                             5600
      CALL PROBLEM(2)                                              5610
      DO 40 J = K7,K8                                              5620
   40 R1(J) = R(J)                                                 5630
      DO 41 J = 1, NX                                              5640
   41 X(J) = X1(KOUNT,J)                                           5650
      CALL PROBLEM(2)                                              5660
      DO 42 J = K7,K8                                              5670
   42 R3(J) = R(J)                                                 5680
      DO 43 J = 1, NX                                              5690
      H(J) = X1(KOUNT,J) - X2(INF,J)                               5700
   43 X(J) = X2(INF,J) + 0.5*H(J)                                  5710
```

```
      CALL PROBLEM(2)                                                 5720
      FLG(1) = 0.                                                     5730
      FLG(2) = 0.                                                     5740
      FLG(3) = 0.                                                     5750
      DO 44 J = K7,K8                                                 5760
      IF(R3(J).GE.0.) GO TO 44                                        5770
      FLG(1) = FLG(1) + R1(J)*R1(J)                                   5780
      FLG(2) = FLG(2) + R(J)*R(J)                                     5790
      FLG(3) = FLG(3) + R3(J)*R3(J)                                   5800
   44 CONTINUE                                                        5810
      SR(INF) = SQRT(FLG(1))                                          5820
      IF(SR(INF).LT.FDIFER) GO TO 35                                  5830
      ALFA1 = FLG(1) - 2.*FLG(2) + FLG(3)                             5840
      BETA1 = 3.*FLG(1) - 4.*FLG(2) + FLG(3)                          5850
      RATIO = BETA1/(4.*ALFA1)                                        5860
      DO 45 J = 1, NX                                                 5870
   45 X(J) = X2(INF,J) + H(J)*RATIO                                   5880
      IN = INF                                                        5890
      CALL SUMR                                                       5900
      SR(INF) = SQRT(SEQL)                                            5910
      IF(SR(INF).LT.FDIFER) GO TO 465                                 5920
      DO 49 I = 1, 20                                                 5930
      DO 48 J = 1, NX                                                 5940
   48 X(J) = X(J) - 0.05*H(J)                                         5950
      CALL SUMR                                                       5960
      SR(INF) = SQRT(SEQL)                                            5970
      IF(SR(INF).LT.FDIFER) GO TO 465                                 5980
   49 CONTINUE                                                        5990
  465 CALL PROBLEM(3)                                                 6000
      IF(FINT.GT.R(K9)) GO TO 46                                      6010
      SR(INF) = 0.                                                    6020
      GO TO 35                                                        6030
   46 DO 47 J = 1, NX                                                 6040
   47 X2(INF,J) = X(J)                                                6050
   35 CONTINUE                                                        6060
      DO 335 J = 1, NX                                                6070
  335 X(J) = X2(INF,J)                                                6080
  850 FORMAT(//108H IT IS NOT POSSIBLE TO SATISFY THE VIOLATED CONSTRAIN 6090
     1T SET FROM THIS VECTOR. THE SEARCH WILL BE TERMINATED. /68H PLEASE 6100
     2 CHOOSE A NEW STARTING VECTOR AND REPEAT SOLUTION AGAIN       ) 6110
  851 FORMAT(//,63H THE VECTOR FOR WHICH THE CONSTRAINTS COULD NOT BE SA 6120
     1TISFIED IS /,(8E16.6))                                         6130
  852 FORMAT(//,27H THE TOLERANCE CRITERION = E14.6,20X, 49H THE SQUARE 6140
     1ROOT OF THE CONSTRAINTS SQUARED IS = E16.6)                    6150
  853 FORMAT(//,81H * * * * * * SUBROUTINE  FEASBL  FAILS TO FIND A FEAS 6160
     1IBLE POINT * * * * * * * * )                                   6170
      RETURN                                                          6180
      END                                                            6190
      SUBROUTINE START                                                6200
      DIMENSION A(50,50)                                              6210
      DIMENSION X(50),X1(50,50),X2(50,50),R(100),SUM(50),F(50),SR(50), 6220
     1 ROLD(100)                                                     6230
      COMMON/1/NX,NC,NIC,STEP,ALFA,BETA,GAMA,IN,INF,FDIFER,SEQL,K1,K2, 6240
     1K3,K4,K5,K6,K7,K8,K9,X,X1,X2,R,SUM,F,SR,ROLD,SCALE,FOLD         6250
      COMMON/2/LFEAS,L5,L6,L7,L8,L9,R1A,R2A,R3A                       6260
      VN = NX                                                         6270
      STEP1 = STEP/(VN*SQRT(2.))*(SQRT(VN + 1.) + VN - 1.)            6280
      STEP2= STEP/(VN*SQRT(2.))*(SQRT(VN + 1.) - 1.)                  6290
      DO 1 J = 1, NX                                                  6300
    1 A(1,J) = 0.                                                     6310
      DO 2 I = 2, K1                                                  6320
      DO 4 J = 1, NX                                                  6330
    4 A(I,J) = STEP2                                                  6340
      L = I - 1                                                       6350
      A(I,L) = STEP1                                                  6360
    2 CONTINUE                                                        6370
      DO 3 I = 1, K1                                                  6380
      DO 3 J = 1, NX                                                  6390
```

```
   3 X1(I,J) = X(J) + A(I,J)                                      6400
     RETURN                                                       6410
     END                                                          6420
     SUBROUTINE WRITEX                                            6430
     DIMENSION X(50),X1(50,50),X2(50,50),R(100),SUM(50),F(50),SR(50),  6440
   1 ROLD(100)                                                    6450
     COMMON/1/NX,NC,NIC,STEP,ALFA,BETA,GAMA,IN,INF,FDIFER,SEQL,K1,K2,  6460
   1K3,K4,K5,K6,K7,K8,K9,X,X1,X2,R,SUM,F,SR,ROLD,SCALE,FOLD       6470
     COMMON/2/LFEAS,L5,L6,L7,L8,L9,R1A,R2A,R3A                    6480
     CALL PROBLEM(3)                                              6490
     PRINT 1, R(K9)                                               6500
   1 FORMAT(/, 28H OBJECTIVE FUNCTION VALUE = E17.7)              6510
     PRINT 2, (X(J), J = 1, NX)                                   6520
   2 FORMAT(/, 29H THE INDEPENDENT VECTORS ARE /(6E17.7)          6530
     IF(NC.EQ.0) GO TO 6                                          6540
     CALL PROBLEM(1)                                              6550
     PRINT 3, (R(J), J = 1, NC)                                   6560
   3 FORMAT(/, 36H THE EQUALITY CONSTRAINT VALUES ARE /(6E17.7)   6570
   6 IF(NIC.EQ.0) GO TO 5                                         6580
     CALL PROBLEM(2)                                              6590
     PRINT 4 , (R(J), J = K7,K6)                                  6600
   4 FORMAT(/, 34H THE INEQUALITY CONSTRAINT VALUES /(6E17.7)     6610
   5 RETURN                                                       6620
     END                                                          6630
     SUBROUTINE SUMR                                              6640
C                                                                 6650
C*****THIS SUBROUTINE COMPUTES THE SUM OF THE SQUARE VALUES OF THE  6660
C     VIOLATED CONSTRAINTS IN ORDER TO BE COMPARED WITH THE TOLERANCE  6670
C     CRITERION                                                   6680
C                                                                 6690
     DIMENSION X(50),X1(50,50),X2(50,50),R(100),SUM(50),F(50),SR(50),  6700
   1 ROLD(100)                                                    6710
     COMMON/1/NX,NC,NIC,STEP,ALFA,BETA,GAMA,IN,INF,FDIFER,SEQL,K1,K2,  6720
   1K3,K4,K5,K6,K7,K8,K9,X,X1,X2,R,SUM,F,SR,ROLD,SCALE,FOLD       6730
     COMMON/2/LFEAS,L5,L6,L7,L8,L9,R1A,R2A,R3A                    6740
     SUM(IN) = 0.                                                 6750
     CALL PROBLEM(2)                                              6760
     SEQL = 0.                                                    6770
     IF(NIC.EQ.0) GO TO 4                                         6780
     DO 1 J = K7, K8                                              6790
     IF(R(J).GE.0.) GO TO 1                                       6800
     SEQL = SEQL + R(J)*R(J)                                      6810
   1 CONTINUE                                                     6820
   4 IF(NC.EQ.0) GO TO 3                                          6830
     CALL PROBLEM(1)                                              6840
     DO 2 J = 1, NC                                               6850
   2 SEQL = SEQL + R(J)*R(J)                                      6860
   3 SUM(IN) = SEQL                                               6870
   5 RETURN                                                       6880
     END                                                          6890
```

appendix c

Matrices

Matrix algebra is widely used whenever large numbers of linearly combined variables must be handled. Familiarity with some of the notation, methods, limits, and applications of matrix theory is essential to the understanding of how to solve important classes of linear problems and how to simplify complex notation. Matrix operations are particularly adaptable to manipulation at high speeds on digital computers; hence, whoever uses these techniques is relieved of an immense amount of tedious repetitive detail. We summarize here some of the important properties of and operations on matrices.

C.1 DEFINITIONS AND NOTATION

A *matrix* is an array of elements

$$\mathbf{a} = \begin{bmatrix} a_{11} & a_{12} & \cdots & a_{1n} \\ a_{21} & a_{22} & \cdots & a_{2n} \\ \cdots & \cdots & \cdots & \cdots \\ a_{m1} & a_{m2} & \cdots & a_{mn} \end{bmatrix}$$

in a definite order. The first subscript designates the row, and the second subscript designates the column.

A *square matrix* is one in which the number of rows and the number of columns are equal. For example, an $n \times n$ matrix with $n = 3$ is

$$\mathbf{a} = \begin{bmatrix} 1 & 2 & 3 \\ 2 & 3 & 4 \\ 3 & 4 & 5 \end{bmatrix} \qquad \text{a } 3 \times 3 \text{ matrix}$$

A *rectangular matrix* has m rows and n columns. A *scalar* is a 1×1 matrix.

For two matrices to be equal, each and every element in the corresponding position in the two matrices must be equal.

A matrix consisting of a single column is called a *column vector*, and a matrix consisting of a single row is a *row vector*:

$$\begin{bmatrix} 1 \\ 2 \\ 3 \\ 4 \end{bmatrix} \quad \text{column vector} \qquad [1 \quad 2 \quad 3 \quad 4] \quad \text{row vector}$$

A *diagonal matrix* is a square matrix in which only the elements of the principal diagonal are nonzero.

In the *identity matrix* (given the special notation $\mathbf{I}$), the elements on the main diagonal are 1 and the rest of the elements are 0:

$$\mathbf{I} = \begin{bmatrix} 1 & 0 & 0 \\ 0 & 1 & 0 \\ 0 & 0 & 1 \end{bmatrix} \qquad \text{a } 3 \times 3 \text{ identity matrix}$$

A matrix with all elements equal to zero is a *null*, or *zero, matrix* designated by $\mathbf{0}$.

The determinant of a matrix $\mathbf{a}$ will be designated by det $(\mathbf{a})$. If det $(\mathbf{a}) \neq 0$, then $\mathbf{a}$ is called a *nonsingular matrix*; if det $(\mathbf{a})$ is zero, then $\mathbf{a}$ is called a *singular matrix*.

The *transpose of a matrix* is obtained by interchange of rows and columns:

$$\mathbf{a}^T = \begin{bmatrix} a_{11} & a_{21} & \cdots & a_{m1} \\ a_{12} & a_{22} & \cdots & a_{m2} \\ \cdots & \cdots & \cdots & \cdots \\ a_{1n} & a_{2n} & \cdots & a_{mn} \end{bmatrix}$$

For example, if

$$\mathbf{a} = \begin{bmatrix} 2 & 0 & -1 \\ 1 & 1 & 4 \end{bmatrix}$$

then
$$\mathbf{a}^T = \begin{bmatrix} 2 & 1 \\ 0 & 1 \\ -1 & 4 \end{bmatrix}$$

A *symmetric matrix* is one in which $\mathbf{a} = \mathbf{a}^T$:

$$\mathbf{a} = \begin{bmatrix} 0 & 1 & 2 \\ 1 & 2 & 3 \\ 2 & 3 & 4 \end{bmatrix} \qquad \mathbf{a}^T = \begin{bmatrix} 0 & 1 & 2 \\ 1 & 2 & 3 \\ 2 & 3 & 4 \end{bmatrix}$$

C.2 MATRIX OPERATIONS

Addition of matrices: The sum of two matrices, $\mathbf{a} + \mathbf{b} = \mathbf{c}$, all $m \times n$ in size, is obtained by adding the elements in the corresponding positions of **a** and **b**. Note that the sum of matrices of different dimensions is not defined.

$$\mathbf{c} = \mathbf{a} + \mathbf{b} = \begin{bmatrix} 2 & 0 \\ 6 & 3 \end{bmatrix} + \begin{bmatrix} 1 & -2 \\ 3 & 2 \end{bmatrix} = \begin{bmatrix} 3 & -2 \\ 9 & 5 \end{bmatrix}$$

Multiplication of a matrix by a scalar: When a matrix is multiplied by a scalar, the result is a matrix in which each element of the original matrix is multiplied by the given scalar. Let $\alpha = 3$ and

$$\mathbf{a} = \begin{bmatrix} 3 & 4 & 1 \\ 2 & 6 & 2 \\ 1 & 0 & 1 \end{bmatrix}$$

Then

$$\alpha\mathbf{a} = \begin{bmatrix} (3 \times 3)(3 \times 4)(3 \times 1) \\ (3 \times 2)(3 \times 6)(3 \times 2) \\ (3 \times 1)(3 \times 0)(3 \times 1) \end{bmatrix} = \begin{bmatrix} 9 & 12 & 3 \\ 6 & 18 & 6 \\ 3 & 0 & 3 \end{bmatrix}$$

To sum up the operations described so far we can write

$$\mathbf{a} + (\mathbf{b} + \mathbf{c}) = (\mathbf{a} + \mathbf{b}) + \mathbf{c}$$

$$\mathbf{a} + \mathbf{b} = \mathbf{b} + \mathbf{a}$$

$$\mathbf{a} + \mathbf{0} = \mathbf{a}$$

$$\alpha(\mathbf{a} + \mathbf{b}) = \alpha\mathbf{a} + \alpha\mathbf{b}$$

Multiplication of a matrix by a matrix: To multiply two matrices together, **ab**, they must be *conformable*; that is, the number of columns of the first matrix **a** must equal the number of rows of the second matrix **b** (**a** is the *premultiplier* and **b** the *postmultiplier*). Notice that **ab** does not equal **ba** except in unusual cases. To multiply the two matrices **a** and **b** together, take the first element in the first row of **a** and multiply it into the first element of the first column of **b**. Take the second element of the first row of **a** and multiply it into the second element of the first column of **b**. Continue until each element of the first row of **a** has been multiplied into the corresponding element of the first column of **b**, and then sum the products. This sum forms the new element c_{11} of $\mathbf{ab} = \mathbf{c}$:

$$c_{11} = \sum_{j=1}^{n} a_{1j} b_{j1}$$

Next, multiply in a similar fashion the first row of **a** into the second column of **b**, and sum the products; this becomes c_{12}. Repeat until the first row of **a** has been multiplied into each column of **b**. This completes the first row of the product **c**. Then repeat the entire process by using the second row of **a**; multiply it into the first, second, etc., columns of **b** to form the second row of the product **c**. The sequence of steps is continued until all rows of **a** have been accounted for. We now illustrate the method for two 3×3 matrices.

$$\mathbf{a} = \begin{bmatrix} 1 & 0 & 2 \\ 2 & 1 & 1 \\ 0 & 1 & 2 \end{bmatrix} \qquad \mathbf{b} = \begin{bmatrix} 0 & 1 & 3 \\ 2 & 1 & 0 \\ 3 & 2 & 1 \end{bmatrix}$$

$$\mathbf{ab} = \begin{matrix} (0 + 0 + 6)(1 + 0 + 4)(3 + 0 + 2) \\ (0 + 2 + 3)(2 + 1 + 2)(6 + 0 + 1) \\ (0 + 2 + 6)(0 + 1 + 4)(0 + 0 + 2) \end{matrix}$$

$$= \begin{bmatrix} 6 & 5 & 7 \\ 5 & 5 & 7 \\ 8 & 5 & 2 \end{bmatrix}$$

Now that multiplication of matrices has been described, we can exàmine some additional characteristics of matrices.

Transpose of a product of two matrices: The transpose of a product of two matrices is the product of the transpose of each of the individual matrices arranged in the reverse order:

$$(\mathbf{ab})^T = \mathbf{b}^T \mathbf{a}^T$$

For example, let

$$\mathbf{a} = \begin{bmatrix} 3 & 4 \\ 1 & 5 \end{bmatrix} \qquad \mathbf{b} = \begin{bmatrix} 0 & 2 \\ 4 & 3 \end{bmatrix}$$

$$\mathbf{ab} = \begin{bmatrix} 16 & 18 \\ 20 & 17 \end{bmatrix} \qquad (\mathbf{ab})^T = \begin{bmatrix} 16 & 20 \\ 18 & 17 \end{bmatrix} = \begin{bmatrix} 0 & 4 \\ 2 & 3 \end{bmatrix}\begin{bmatrix} 3 & 1 \\ 4 & 5 \end{bmatrix}$$
$$= \begin{bmatrix} 16 & 20 \\ 18 & 17 \end{bmatrix}$$

Inverse of a matrix: By analogy with the reciprocal of a scalar, if $\mathbf{a}$ is a nonsingular square matrix, then a unique matrix $\mathbf{a}^{-1}$ exists, having the property that

$$\mathbf{aa}^{-1} = \mathbf{I} \qquad \text{and} \qquad \mathbf{a}^{-1}\mathbf{a} = \mathbf{I}$$

There are various methods of determining the elements of the matrix $\mathbf{a}^{-1}$ from the elements of the matrix $\mathbf{a}$; consult a text on numerical analysis. If $\mathbf{a}^T = \mathbf{a}^{-1}$, $\mathbf{a}$ is said to be *orthogonal.*

The product of the matrix $\mathbf{a}$ *and its transpose* $\mathbf{a}^T$ *is symmetric.* Let

$$\mathbf{b} = \mathbf{aa}^T$$

Then
$$\mathbf{b}^T = (\mathbf{aa}^T)^T = (\mathbf{a}^T)^T\mathbf{a}^T = \mathbf{aa}^T$$

The inverse of the transpose of a nonsingular square matrix $\mathbf{a}$ *is equal to the transpose of the inverse of* $\mathbf{a}$*:*

$$(\mathbf{a}^T)^{-1} = (\mathbf{a}^{-1})^T$$

Normalization: The *norm* of a real vector is defined as

$$\text{Norm} = (\mathbf{x}^T\mathbf{x})^{\frac{1}{2}} = \sqrt{\sum_{i=1}^{n} x_i^2}$$

Normalization of a vector $\mathbf{x}$ is the process of dividing every component of $\mathbf{x}$ by the length of the vector (to yield a unit vector). For example,

$$\mathbf{x} = [1, 2, -3, 0]$$
$$\text{Norm } \mathbf{x} = \sqrt{1^2 + 2^2 + (-3)^2 + 0^2} = \sqrt{14}$$
$$\hat{\mathbf{x}} = \left[\frac{1}{\sqrt{14}}, \frac{2}{\sqrt{14}}, \frac{-3}{\sqrt{14}}, 0\right]^T$$

C.3 POSITIVE DEFINITE MATRICES

Associated with each quadratic form

$$f(\mathbf{x}) = \sum_{\substack{i=j \\ j=i}}^{n} a_{ij}x_ix_j = \mathbf{x}^T\mathbf{ax}$$

is the real symmetric square matrix **a**. **a** is termed positive semidefinite if $f(\mathbf{x}) \geq 0$ and (strictly) positive definite if $f(\mathbf{x}) > 0$ for all $\mathbf{x} \neq 0$. Also associated with each quadratic form are an infinite number of other square matrices, $\mathbf{b}_n$, that are *not* symmetric:

$$f(\mathbf{x}) = \mathbf{x}^T\mathbf{a}\mathbf{x} = \mathbf{x}^T\mathbf{b}_n\mathbf{x}$$

The well-known necessary and sufficient conditions for positive definiteness, such that all the principal minors and the determinant of **a** are positive, or that all the eigenvalues of **a** are positive, apply only to the matrix **a** and not to $\mathbf{b}_n$. A real nonsymmetric matrix may have positive eigenvalues and positive principal minors and yet not be positive definite.

For example, consider

$$f(\mathbf{x}) = x^2 + 3x + 2 = [1 \quad x]\begin{bmatrix} 2 & 3 \\ 0 & 1 \end{bmatrix}\begin{bmatrix} 1 \\ x \end{bmatrix} = \mathbf{x}^T\mathbf{b}\mathbf{x}$$

where
$$\mathbf{x} = \begin{bmatrix} 1 \\ x \end{bmatrix} \qquad \mathbf{b} = \begin{bmatrix} 2 & 3 \\ 0 & 1 \end{bmatrix}$$

The eigenvalues of **b** are 2 and 1, the det $(\mathbf{b}) = 2$, and the first minor of **b** is 2, yet $f(\mathbf{x})$ is negative in the range $-2 < x < -1$. On the other hand, if $f(\mathbf{x})$ is expressed in terms of the symmetric matrix **a**,

$$f(\mathbf{x}) = x^2 + 3x + 2 = [1 \quad x]\begin{bmatrix} 2 & \frac{3}{2} \\ \frac{3}{2} & 1 \end{bmatrix}\begin{bmatrix} 1 \\ x \end{bmatrix} = \mathbf{x}^T\mathbf{a}\mathbf{x}$$

the eigenvalues of **a** are $\lambda = \frac{3}{2} + \sqrt{10}/2$ and $\lambda = \frac{3}{2} - \sqrt{10}/2$ (negative), and the determinant of **a** is negative, in agreement with the conditions for a *symmetric* matrix.

appendix d

Standard timing program

```
      PROGRAM STDR (OUTPUT)
      DIMENSION A(40,40),C(40),NA(41),NB(41)
    1 NDIM = 40
      N = 40
      NN = 10
      T = 0.0000001
      DO 50 L = 1, NN
      DO 25 I = 1, N
      DO 25 J = 1, N
      A(I,J) = 1.
      IF(I-J) 25,20,25
   20 A(I,J) = I + J
   25 CONTINUE
      CALL MATINV(A,NA,NB,N,NDIM,T)
   50 CONTINUE
      PRINT 100, ((A(I,J),J = 1, N),I = 1, N)
  100 FORMAT(/,(10F13.5))
      END
      SUBROUTINE MATINV(A,IROW,ICOL,N,NDIM,SMLST)
      DIMENSION A(1),IROW(1),ICOL(1)
      NP1 = N + 1
      DO 5 I = 1, N
      ICOL(I) = I
    5 IROW(I) = I
      DO 75 ITER = 1, N
      MAXR = ITER
```

```
      MAXO = 1
      TEMP = A(MAXR)
      IF(TEMP)300,301,301
  300 TEMP = -TEMP
  301 CONTINUE
      LIMITO = NP1 - ITER
      DO 15 I = ITER,N
      DO 15 J = 1, LIMITO
      IJ = (J-1)*NDIM + I
      ABSA = A(IJ)
      IF(ABSA)302,303,303
  302 ABSA = - ABSA
  303 IF(TEMP-ABSA)10,15,15
   10 MAXR = I
      MAXO = J
      TEMP = A(IJ)
      IF(TEMP)304,305,305
  304 TEMP = -TEMP
  305 CONTINUE
   15 CONTINUE
      IF(TEMP-SMLST) 20,20,25
   20 IROW(NP1) = ITER
      RETURN
   25 IF(MAXR-ITER) 30,40,30
   30 DO 35 J = 1, N
      MAXRJ = (J-1)*NDIM + MAXR
      ITJ = (J-1)*NDIM + ITER
      TEMP = A(MAXRJ)
      A(MAXRJ) = A(ITJ)
   35 A(ITJ) = TEMP
      ITEMP= IROW(MAXR)
      IROW(MAXR) = IROW(ITER)
      IROW(ITER) = ITEMP
   40 IF(MAXO - 1) 45,55,45
   45 DO 50 I = 1, N
      IMAXO = (MAXO-1)*NDIM + 1
      TEMP = A(I)
      A(I) = A(IMAXO)
   50 A(IMAXO) = TEMP
      ITEMP = ICOL(MAXO)
      ICOL(MAXO) = ICOL(1)
      ICOL(1) = ITEMP
   55 TEMP = A(ITER)
      ITEMP = ICOL(1)
      DO 60 J = 2, N
      ITJM1 = (J-2)*NDIM + ITER
      ITJ = (J-1)*NDIM + ITER
      A(ITJM1) = A(ITJ)/TEMP
   60 ICOL(J-1) = ICOL(J)
      ITN = (N-1)*NDIM + ITER
      A(ITN) = 1.0/TEMP
      ICOL(N) = ITEMP
      DO 75 I = 1, N
      IF(I-ITER) 65,75,65
   65 TEMP = A(I)
      DO 70 J = 2, N
      IJM1 = (J-2)*NDIM + I
      IJ = (J-1)*NDIM+I
      ITJM1 = (J-2)*NDIM+ITER
      A(IJM1) = A(IJ) - A(ITJM1)*TEMP
   70 CONTINUE
      IN = (N-1)*NDIM + I
      ITN = (N-1)*NDIM + ITER
      A(IN) = -(TEMP*A(ITN))
   75 CONTINUE
      DO 100 I = 1, N
      DO 80 J = 1, N
      IF(IROW(J) - I) 80,85,80
```

```
 80 CONTINUE
 85 IF(I-J)90,100,90
 90 DO 95 L = 1, N
    LI = (I-1)*NDIM + L
    LJ = (J-1)*NDIM + L
    TEMP = A(LI)
    A(LI) = A(LJ)
 95 A(LJ) = TEMP
    IROW(J) = IROW(I)
100 CONTINUE
    DO 125 I = 1, N
    DO 105 J = 1, N
    IF(ICOL(J)-I) 105.110,105
110 IF(I-J)115,125,115
115 DO 120 L = 1, N
    IL = (L - 1)*NDIM + I
    JL = (L - 1)*NDIM + J
    TEMP = A(IL)
    A(IL) = A(JL)
120 A(JL) = TEMP
    ICOL(J) = ICOL(I)
    GO TO 125
105 CONTINUE
125 CONTINUE
    IROW(NP1) = 0
    RETURN
    END
```

appendix e

Notation

a	constants or coefficients (distinguished by subscripts)
a_{ij}	elements of the matrix $\mathbf{a}$ (or $\mathbf{A}$)
$\mathbf{a}$	a matrix of coefficients
$\mathbf{a}_j$	column vector of $\mathbf{A}^T$
$\mathscr{A}^{(s)}$	the numerical value of Eq. (8.3–7)
$\mathbf{A}$	a constant matrix consisting of elements a_{ij}
$\mathbf{A}_i$	vectors associated with Rosenbrock's method
$\mathbf{A}^{(k)}$	matrix associated with Eq. (3.4–5)
$\mathbf{A}_\ell$	matrix of coefficients of a constraint set of size ℓ
b	constants or coefficients (distinguished by subscripts)
$\tilde{b}$	eigenvalue (distinguished by subscripts)
$\mathbf{b}$	a column vector of coefficients
$\mathbf{b}_j$	jth row of $\mathbf{B}_m$
$\mathbf{B}_i$	matrices defined in connection with Eq. (4.3–2)
$\mathbf{B}^{(k)}$	matrix associated with Eq. (3.4–5)
$\mathbf{B}_m$	a matrix of coefficients of inequality constraints
c	constants or coefficients (distinguished by subscripts)

c_i	a constant
c_{ii}	diagonal element of the matrix $\mathbf{C}$
$\mathbf{c}$	a column vector of constant coefficients
$\mathbf{C}$	diagonal matrix defined in connection with Eq. (3.2–8)
d	total derivative symbol; also elements of $\mathbf{D}$ matrix
d_i	normal random variable
d_k	defined in connection with Eq. (6.5–10)
D_i	direction cosine
$\mathbf{D}$	the matrix for building a regular polyhedron in E^n
$\mathbf{D}_i$	a column vector of $\mathbf{D}$
$\mathbf{e}_i$	an eigenvector associated with α_i
E	efficiency in unidimensional search
$E(k)$	relative gain in the objective function during one stage of the optimization
E^n	n-dimensional euclidean space
$E_{j,i}$	linearity error in POP
$E(\mathbf{x},\mathbf{u},\mathbf{w})$	dual of the P function
$f(\mathbf{x})$	the objective function; the value of the objective function at $\mathbf{x}$
$f(\mathbf{x}^*)$	the optimal value of $f(\mathbf{x})$
$F(\mathbf{x})$	an argument of $f(\mathbf{x})$
F_n	Fibonacci number
$F(\mathbf{x}^{(k)},d)$	parameter in the Goldstein-Price algorithm
$g(\mathbf{x})$	inequality constraint (distinguished by subscripts)
$\Delta\mathbf{g}^{(i)}$	$[\nabla f(\mathbf{x}^{(i+1)}) - \nabla f(\mathbf{x}^{(i)})]$
$G(g_i(\mathbf{x}))$	the functional of the inequality constraints
$\mathbf{G}^{(i)}$	$[\Delta\mathbf{g}^{(0)} \quad \Delta\mathbf{g}^{(1)} \quad \ldots \quad \Delta\mathbf{g}^{(i-1)}]$
$h_{ii},\tilde{h}_{ii}$	diagonal element of the matrix $\mathbf{H}(\mathbf{x})$ or $(\tilde{\mathbf{H}}(\mathbf{x}))$
$\mathbf{h}$	vector of equality constraints
$h(\mathbf{x})$	equality constraint (distinguished by subscripts)
$\mathbf{H},\mathbf{H}(\mathbf{x})$	the hessian matrix of the objective function
$\tilde{\mathbf{H}},\tilde{\mathbf{H}}(\mathbf{x}),\tilde{\mathbf{H}}^*(\mathbf{x})$	approximate to or estimate of the hessian matrix of the objective function
$H(h_i(\mathbf{x}))$	a functional of the equality constraints
$\mathbf{I}$	the identity matrix
$\mathbf{I}_j$	jth column of the identity matrix $\mathbf{I}$
$\mathbf{J}$	jacobian matrix
K	a large constant
K'	set of indices that can be added to the basis
L	Lagrange function

L_i	lower bound on x_i
m	total number of equality constraints
$m_j^{(k)}$	defined in connection with Eq. (6.1–3)
$\mathbf{M}_\ell^{(k)}$	estimate at stage k of $(\mathbf{A}_\ell \boldsymbol{\eta}^{(k)} \mathbf{A}_\ell^T)^{-1}$
$\mathscr{M}$	linear manifold
n	total number of variables
N	norm
p	total number of equality and inequality constraints
$\hat{p}$	total number of inequality constraints not satisfied at an exterior point
p^*	total number of inequality constraints
$p_j^{(k)}$	defined in connection with Eq. (6.3–1)
$P(\mathbf{x}^{(k)}, \rho^{(k)})$	penalty function (generalized augmented function) at stage k with a weight $\rho^{(k)}$
$P(\mathbf{x}^{(k)}, r^{(k)})$	penalty function (generalized augmented function) at stage k with a weight $r^{(k)}$
$P(\mathbf{x})$	the generalized augmented function; the penalty function
$\mathbf{P}_\ell^{(k)}$	a projection matrix at stage k; subscript designates associated number of constraints
$\hat{\mathbf{P}}_\ell^{(k)}$	a projection matrix; subscript denotes associated number of constraints
q	a constant
$q_j^{(k)}$	defined in connection with Eq. (6.3–1)
$q(\mathbf{x})$	a quadratic objective function or its approximate
$\mathbf{Q}$	a positive definite square matrix
r	$n - m$, the number of degrees of freedom; also the weighting factor in penalty function methods
$\mathbf{r}(\mathbf{x}^{(k)})$	a return vector given by Eq. (6.3–17)
$\mathbf{r}_i$	diagonal matrix of random numbers
R	the set of feasible points in E^n
$R(\mathbf{x})$	$\sum_{i=1}^{p} \frac{1}{g_i(\mathbf{x})}$
$\mathbf{R}$	a symmetric matrix used in Pearson's algorithms
s	distance
$\mathbf{s}$	a column vector indicating direction of search
$\hat{\mathbf{s}}$	a unit column vector to indicate direction of search
S^*	a set of feasible points
$\mathbf{S}^{(k)}$	vector of scale factors
t	distance between two vertices; also the size of the initial polyhedron in the flexible tolerance method

$T(\mathbf{x})$	a functional of equality and inequality constraints
u_i	slack variable for inequality i
u_j	lagrangian multiplier associated with inequality constraint j
u_j^*	Lagrange multiplier at the extremum
$\mathbf{u}$	vector of lagrangian multipliers
$\mathbf{u}_\ell^{(k)}$	vector of Lagrange multipliers associated with ℓ active constraints at stage k
$\mathbf{U}$	unitary matrix
$\mathscr{U}_i$	Heaviside operator (either 0 or 1)
U_i	upper bound on x_i
v_j	slack variable for inequality j
$\mathbf{v}$	any general column vector
w_i	artificial variable for equation i
w_j	lagrangian multiplier associated with equality constraint
w_j^*	Lagrange multiplier at the extremum
$\mathbf{W}$	a positive definite symmetric matrix
x	a general independent variable
x_i	components of $\mathbf{x}$
x_i^*	components of $\mathbf{x}^*$
x_{ij}	the jth component of the ith vector in E^n
$\tilde{x}_i^*$	approximate to the minimum x_i^*
$\mathbf{x}$	column vector of independent variables; vector of variables
$\mathbf{x}^*$	$\mathbf{x}$ at the optimum solution of the programming problem
$\mathbf{x}_h$	vertex with highest value of objective function
$\mathbf{x}_i$	the ith vector or vertex in the minimization of $f(\mathbf{x})$
$\mathbf{x}_\ell$	vertex with lowest value of objective function
$\hat{\mathbf{x}}_i$	the ith vector in the minimization of $T(\mathbf{x})$
$\tilde{\mathbf{x}}^*$	approximate minimum $\mathbf{x}$
X_i	a general scalar, polynomial, or vector
$\mathbf{X}^{(i)}$	$[\Delta\mathbf{x}^{(0)} \quad \Delta\mathbf{x}^{(1)} \quad \ldots \quad \Delta\mathbf{x}^{(i-1)}]^T$
y	a variable; also the objective function
$y_i^{(k)}$	computed independent variable in a unidimensional search
$\mathbf{y}$	arbitrary column vector
z_j	an element of the reduced gradient
$\mathbf{z}$	arbitrary column vector; also the reduced gradient; also history vector used in connection with Eq. (4.5–1)

$Z(\mathbf{x})$	$\sum_{i=1}^{\hat{p}} g_i^2(\mathbf{x})$, the sum of the squares of the violated constraints at an exterior point

Greek letters and symbols

α	an expansion factor in Rosenbrock's method; also a constant; also the reflection coefficient in the Nelder and Mead method
α_i	an eigenvalue
α_k	a coefficient
β	the contraction coefficient in the Nelder and Mead method; also a constant in Eq. (3.2–11); also a reduction factor in Rosenbrock's method
γ	the expansion coefficient in the method of Nelder and Mead; also a constant of small value; a constant
$\boldsymbol{\gamma}$	defined in connection with Eq. (6.3–8)
$\boldsymbol{\Gamma}$	defined in Sec. 6.5–4
δ	the parameter in the Goldstein-Price algorithm
$\boldsymbol{\delta}_i$	unit vector in the x_i direction
$\delta_j^{(k)}$	a constant; a parameter
$\delta(\mathbf{x})$	an argument for which $f(\mathbf{x})$ is not defined for certain $\mathbf{x}$ in E^n
∂	partial-derivative symbol
Δ	change in a variable or vector, as Δx
$\boldsymbol{\Delta}^{(k)}$	bracketing interval for unidimensional search
$\boldsymbol{\nabla}_x$	the gradient containing only the elements composed of the partial derivatives with respect to the elements of the vector $\mathbf{x}$
$\boldsymbol{\nabla}\phi(\mathbf{x})$	a vector to denote the gradient of $\phi(\mathbf{x})$
$\boldsymbol{\nabla}^2\phi(\mathbf{x})$	the hessian matrix of $\phi(\mathbf{x})$
ε	an arbitrary small positive number
η	the weighting factor of the lagrangian
$\boldsymbol{\eta}^{(k)}, \boldsymbol{\eta}(\mathbf{x}^{(k)})$	the direction matrix on stage k
$\boldsymbol{\eta}_\ell^{(k)}$	the direction matrix with ℓ binding constraints on stage k
θ	a constant between 0 and 1; also an angle
$\theta^{(k)}$	a parameter in the Goldstein-Price algorithm; defined in Eq. (8.1–2)
λ, λ^*	a parameter that determines the distance of movement in the direction of search

$\lambda^{(k)}, \lambda^{*(k)}$	the step length to minimize $f(\mathbf{x})$ in the direction of search (sometimes identified with subscripts)
λ_j	a counter in NLP
Λ_i	search direction defined in connection with Eq. (4.3–1)
μ_i	scale factor
$v^{(j)}$	a coefficient in Eq. (3.3–4)
v_0	the value of the upper bound of the dual in SUMT
ξ	adjustable constant used in POP; also, a small number
π_k	plane tangent to the contour of the objective function at $\mathbf{x}^{(k)}$
$\mathbf{\Pi}$	scaled approximate hessian matrix
$\tilde{\mathbf{\Pi}}$	approximation to $\mathbf{\Pi}$ but with positive eigenvalues
ρ	the weighting factor in the augmented (penalty) function
ρ_j	a parameter that counts oscillations in NLP
$\boldsymbol{\tau}$	unit coordinate vector with respect to the basis $\hat{\mathbf{A}}$
τ_j	element of $\boldsymbol{\tau}$
$\mathbf{\Upsilon}^{(k)}$	approximate to the hessian matrix of the objective function
ϕ	random angle (uniformly distributed)
$\phi(\mathbf{x})$	a convex function; also a general function
$\boldsymbol{\phi}$	a column vector defined in connection with Eq. (6.3–17)
$\Phi^{(k)}$	the tolerance criterion for constraint violation in the flexible-tolerance method
$\varphi(\mathbf{x}^{(k)})$	direction in the Goldstein-Price algorithm
$\varphi(\mathbf{x})$	a function of $\mathbf{x}$
ω_i	weighting factor
Ω_r	rth row of the matrix $(\partial\mathbf{h}/\partial\mathbf{x}_1)^{-1}$

Superscripts

a,b,c,m	denote points in the unidimensional search
k	denotes stages in the minimization of $f(\mathbf{x})$
s	denotes stages in the minimization of $T(\mathbf{x})$
T	the transpose of a vector
( )	encloses stage number

Special subscripts

h	the ith vertex in E^n with the largest value of $f(\mathbf{x})$
ℓ	the set of constraints that are binding
$\mathscr{M}$	projection of a vector on a manifold $\mathscr{M}$

Overlays

$\tilde{}$	approximate or transformed
$\hat{}$	unit; also potential vector
$'$	used to differentiate one constant or variable from another

Other signs

$\| \ \|$	the magnitude of a vector; the norm, i.e., the square root of the sum of the squares of the elements of the vector
$\| \ \|$	the absolute value of a scalar
$\{ \ \}$	set
$\|$	given that
$\in$	an element of
Π	product operator
$(\ )$	encloses argument of function

Indexes

Name Index

Subject Index